PEARSON

ALWAYS LEARNING

Randal E. Bryant • David R. O'Hallaron

Computer Systems
A Programmer's Perspective

Third Custom Edition for Stanford University
CS 107 Computer Organization and Systems

Taken from:
Computer Systems: A Programmer's Perspective,
Third Edition
by Randal E. Bryant and David R. O'Hallaron

Cover Art: Courtesy of Photodisc, Stockbyte/Getty Images.

Taken from:

Computer Systems: A Programmer's Perspective, Third Edition
by Randal E. Bryant and David R. O'Hallaron
Copyright © 2016, 2011, and 2003 by Pearson Education, Inc.
New York, NY 10013

This special edition published in cooperation with Pearson Learning Solutions.

Pearson Learning Solutions, 330 Hudson Street, New York, New York 10013
A Pearson Education Company
www.pearsoned.com

Printed in the United States of America

1 2 3 4 5 6 7 8 9 10 V092 16 15

000200010272026344

EF

ISBN 10: 1-323-31142-4
ISBN 13: 978-1-323-31142-4

To the students and instructors of the 15-213
course at Carnegie Mellon University, for inspiring
us to develop and refine the material for this book.

MasteringEngineering®

For *Computer Systems: A Programmer's Perspective,* Third Edition

---

Mastering is Pearson's proven online Tutorial Homework program, newly available with the third edition of *Computer Systems: A Programmer's Perspective*. The Mastering platform allows you to integrate dynamic homework—with many problems taken directly from the Bryant/O'Hallaron textbook—with automatic grading. Mastering allows you to easily track the performance of your entire class on an assignment-by-assignment basis, or view the detailed work of an individual student.

For more information or a demonstration of the course, visit www.MasteringEngineering.com or contact your local Pearson representative.

Contents

3

Machine-Level Representation of Programs   163

5

Optimizing Program Performance   495

6

The Memory Hierarchy   579

Part II   Running Programs on a System

7

Linking   669

9

Virtual Memory   801

A

Error Handling   1041

Preface

This book (known as CS:APP) is for computer scientists, computer engineers, and others who want to be able to write better programs by learning what is going on "under the hood" of a computer system.

Our aim is to explain the enduring concepts underlying all computer systems, and to show you the concrete ways that these ideas affect the correctness, performance, and utility of your application programs. Many systems books are written from a *builder's perspective*, describing how to implement the hardware or the systems software, including the operating system, compiler, and network interface. This book is written from a *programmer's perspective*, describing how application programmers can use their knowledge of a system to write better programs. Of course, learning what a system is supposed to do provides a good first step in learning how to build one, so this book also serves as a valuable introduction to those who go on to implement systems hardware and software. Most systems books also tend to focus on just one aspect of the system, for example, the hardware architecture, the operating system, the compiler, or the network. This book spans all of these aspects, with the unifying theme of a programmer's perspective.

If you study and learn the concepts in this book, you will be on your way to becoming the rare *power programmer* who knows how things work and how to fix them when they break. You will be able to write programs that make better use of the capabilities provided by the operating system and systems software, that operate correctly across a wide range of operating conditions and run-time parameters, that run faster, and that avoid the flaws that make programs vulnerable to cyberattack. You will be prepared to delve deeper into advanced topics such as compilers, computer architecture, operating systems, embedded systems, networking, and cybersecurity.

Assumptions about the Reader's Background

This book focuses on systems that execute x86-64 machine code. x86-64 is the latest in an evolutionary path followed by Intel and its competitors that started with the 8086 microprocessor in 1978. Due to the naming conventions used by Intel for its microprocessor line, this class of microprocessors is referred to colloquially as "x86." As semiconductor technology has evolved to allow more transistors to be integrated onto a single chip, these processors have progressed greatly in their computing power and their memory capacity. As part of this progression, they have gone from operating on 16-bit words, to 32-bit words with the introduction of IA32 processors, and most recently to 64-bit words with x86-64.

We consider how these machines execute C programs on Linux. Linux is one of a number of operating systems having their heritage in the Unix operating system developed originally by Bell Laboratories. Other members of this class

New to C?   Advice on the C programming language

To help readers whose background in C programming is weak (or nonexistent), we have also included these special notes to highlight features that are especially important in C. We assume you are familiar with C++ or Java.

of operating systems include Solaris, FreeBSD, and MacOS X. In recent years, these operating systems have maintained a high level of compatibility through the efforts of the Posix and Standard Unix Specification standardization efforts. Thus, the material in this book applies almost directly to these "Unix-like" operating systems.

The text contains numerous programming examples that have been compiled and run on Linux systems. We assume that you have access to such a machine, and are able to log in and do simple things such as listing files and changing directories. If your computer runs Microsoft Windows, we recommend that you install one of the many different virtual machine environments (such as VirtualBox or VMWare) that allow programs written for one operating system (the guest OS) to run under another (the host OS).

We also assume that you have some familiarity with C or C++. If your only prior experience is with Java, the transition will require more effort on your part, but we will help you. Java and C share similar syntax and control statements. However, there are aspects of C (particularly pointers, explicit dynamic memory allocation, and formatted I/O) that do not exist in Java. Fortunately, C is a small language, and it is clearly and beautifully described in the classic "K&R" text by Brian Kernighan and Dennis Ritchie [61]. Regardless of your programming background, consider K&R an essential part of your personal systems library. If your prior experience is with an interpreted language, such as Python, Ruby, or Perl, you will definitely want to devote some time to learning C before you attempt to use this book.

Several of the early chapters in the book explore the interactions between C programs and their machine-language counterparts. The machine-language examples were all generated by the GNU GCC compiler running on x86-64 processors. We do not assume any prior experience with hardware, machine language, or assembly-language programming.

How to Read the Book

Learning how computer systems work from a programmer's perspective is great fun, mainly because you can do it actively. Whenever you learn something new, you can try it out right away and see the result firsthand. In fact, we believe that the only way to learn systems is to *do* systems, either working concrete problems or writing and running programs on real systems.

This theme pervades the entire book. When a new concept is introduced, it is followed in the text by one or more *practice problems* that you should work

code/intro/hello.c

```
1   #include <stdio.h>
2
3   int main()
4   {
5       printf("hello, world\n");
6       return 0;
7   }
```

code/intro/hello.c

Figure 1   A typical code example.

immediately to test your understanding. Solutions to the practice problems are at the end of each chapter. As you read, try to solve each problem on your own and then check the solution to make sure you are on the right track. Each chapter is followed by a set of *homework problems* of varying difficulty. Your instructor has the solutions to the homework problems in an instructor's manual. For each homework problem, we show a rating of the amount of effort we feel it will require:

◆ Should require just a few minutes. Little or no programming required.

◆◆ Might require up to 20 minutes. Often involves writing and testing some code. (Many of these are derived from problems we have given on exams.)

◆◆◆ Requires a significant effort, perhaps 1–2 hours. Generally involves writing and testing a significant amount of code.

◆◆◆◆ A lab assignment, requiring up to 10 hours of effort.

Each code example in the text was formatted directly, without any manual intervention, from a C program compiled with GCC and tested on a Linux system. Of course, your system may have a different version of GCC, or a different compiler altogether, so your compiler might generate different machine code; but the overall behavior should be the same. All of the source code is available from the CS:APP Web page ("CS:APP" being our shorthand for the book's title) at csapp .cs.cmu.edu. In the text, the filenames of the source programs are documented in horizontal bars that surround the formatted code. For example, the program in Figure 1 can be found in the file hello.c in directory code/intro/. We encourage you to try running the example programs on your system as you encounter them.

To avoid having a book that is overwhelming, both in bulk and in content, we have created a number of *Web asides* containing material that supplements the main presentation of the book. These asides are referenced within the book with a notation of the form CHAP:TOP, where CHAP is a short encoding of the chapter subject, and TOP is a short code for the topic that is covered. For example, Web Aside DATA:BOOL contains supplementary material on Boolean algebra for the presentation on data representations in Chapter 2, while Web Aside ARCH:VLOG contains material describing processor designs using the Verilog hardware description language, supplementing the presentation of processor design in Chapter 4. All of these Web asides are available from the CS:APP Web page.

Book Overview

The CS:APP book consists of 12 chapters designed to capture the core ideas in computer systems. Here is an overview.

Chapter 1: A Tour of Computer Systems. This chapter introduces the major ideas and themes in computer systems by tracing the life cycle of a simple "hello, world" program.

Chapter 2: Representing and Manipulating Information. We cover computer arithmetic, emphasizing the properties of unsigned and two's-complement number representations that affect programmers. We consider how numbers are represented and therefore what range of values can be encoded for a given word size. We consider the effect of casting between signed and unsigned numbers. We cover the mathematical properties of arithmetic operations. Novice programmers are often surprised to learn that the (two's-complement) sum or product of two positive numbers can be negative. On the other hand, two's-complement arithmetic satisfies many of the algebraic properties of integer arithmetic, and hence a compiler can safely transform multiplication by a constant into a sequence of shifts and adds. We use the bit-level operations of C to demonstrate the principles and applications of Boolean algebra. We cover the IEEE floating-point format in terms of how it represents values and the mathematical properties of floating-point operations.

Having a solid understanding of computer arithmetic is critical to writing reliable programs. For example, programmers and compilers cannot replace the expression $(x<y)$ with $(x-y < 0)$, due to the possibility of overflow. They cannot even replace it with the expression $(-y < -x)$, due to the asymmetric range of negative and positive numbers in the two's-complement representation. Arithmetic overflow is a common source of programming errors and security vulnerabilities, yet few other books cover the properties of computer arithmetic from a programmer's perspective.

Chapter 3: Machine-Level Representation of Programs. We teach you how to read the x86-64 machine code generated by a C compiler. We cover the basic instruction patterns generated for different control constructs, such as conditionals, loops, and `switch` statements. We cover the implementation of procedures, including stack allocation, register usage conventions, and parameter passing. We cover the way different data structures such as structures, unions, and arrays are allocated and accessed. We cover the instructions that implement both integer and floating-point arithmetic. We also use the machine-level view of programs as a way to understand common code security vulnerabilities, such as buffer overflow, and steps that the pro-

Aside   What is an aside?

You will encounter asides of this form throughout the text. Asides are parenthetical remarks that give you some additional insight into the current topic. Asides serve a number of purposes. Some are little history lessons. For example, where did C, Linux, and the Internet come from? Other asides are meant to clarify ideas that students often find confusing. For example, what is the difference between a cache line, set, and block? Other asides give real-world examples, such as how a floating-point error crashed a French rocket or the geometric and operational parameters of a commercial disk drive. Finally, some asides are just fun stuff. For example, what is a "hoinky"?

grammer, the compiler, and the operating system can take to reduce these threats. Learning the concepts in this chapter helps you become a better programmer, because you will understand how programs are represented on a machine. One certain benefit is that you will develop a thorough and concrete understanding of pointers.

Chapter 4: Processor Architecture. This chapter covers basic combinational and sequential logic elements, and then shows how these elements can be combined in a datapath that executes a simplified subset of the x86-64 instruction set called "Y86-64." We begin with the design of a single-cycle datapath. This design is conceptually very simple, but it would not be very fast. We then introduce *pipelining*, where the different steps required to process an instruction are implemented as separate stages. At any given time, each stage can work on a different instruction. Our five-stage processor pipeline is much more realistic. The control logic for the processor designs is described using a simple hardware description language called HCL. Hardware designs written in HCL can be compiled and linked into simulators provided with the textbook, and they can be used to generate Verilog descriptions suitable for synthesis into working hardware.

Chapter 5: Optimizing Program Performance. This chapter introduces a number of techniques for improving code performance, with the idea being that programmers learn to write their C code in such a way that a compiler can then generate efficient machine code. We start with transformations that reduce the work to be done by a program and hence should be standard practice when writing any program for any machine. We then progress to transformations that enhance the degree of instruction-level parallelism in the generated machine code, thereby improving their performance on modern "superscalar" processors. To motivate these transformations, we introduce a simple operational model of how modern out-of-order processors work, and show how to measure the potential performance of a program in terms of the critical paths through a graphical representation of a program. You will be surprised how much you can speed up a program by simple transformations of the C code.

Chapter 6: The Memory Hierarchy. The memory system is one of the most visible parts of a computer system to application programmers. To this point, you have relied on a conceptual model of the memory system as a linear array with uniform access times. In practice, a memory system is a hierarchy of storage devices with different capacities, costs, and access times. We cover the different types of RAM and ROM memories and the geometry and organization of magnetic-disk and solid state drives. We describe how these storage devices are arranged in a hierarchy. We show how this hierarchy is made possible by locality of reference. We make these ideas concrete by introducing a unique view of a memory system as a "memory mountain" with ridges of temporal locality and slopes of spatial locality. Finally, we show you how to improve the performance of application programs by improving their temporal and spatial locality.

Chapter 7: Linking. This chapter covers both static and dynamic linking, including the ideas of relocatable and executable object files, symbol resolution, re-location, static libraries, shared object libraries, position-independent code, and library interpositioning. Linking is not covered in most systems texts, but we cover it for two reasons. First, some of the most confusing errors that programmers can encounter are related to glitches during linking, especially for large software packages. Second, the object files produced by linkers are tied to concepts such as loading, virtual memory, and memory mapping.

Chapter 8: Exceptional Control Flow. In this part of the presentation, we step beyond the single-program model by introducing the general concept of exceptional control flow (i.e., changes in control flow that are outside the normal branches and procedure calls). We cover examples of exceptional control flow that exist at all levels of the system, from low-level hardware exceptions and interrupts, to context switches between concurrent processes, to abrupt changes in control flow caused by the receipt of Linux signals, to the nonlocal jumps in C that break the stack discipline.

This is the part of the book where we introduce the fundamental idea of a *process*, an abstraction of an executing program. You will learn how processes work and how they can be created and manipulated from application programs. We show how application programmers can make use of multiple processes via Linux system calls. When you finish this chapter, you will be able to write a simple Linux shell with job control. It is also your first introduction to the nondeterministic behavior that arises with concurrent program execution.

Chapter 9: Virtual Memory. Our presentation of the virtual memory system seeks to give some understanding of how it works and its characteristics. We want you to know how it is that the different simultaneous processes can each use an identical range of addresses, sharing some pages but having individual copies of others. We also cover issues involved in managing and manip-ulating virtual memory. In particular, we cover the operation of storage allocators such as the standard-library malloc and free operations. Covering this material serves several purposes. It reinforces the concept that the virtual memory space is just an array of bytes that the program can subdivide into different storage units. It helps you understand the effects of programs containing memory referencing errors such as storage leaks and invalid pointer references. Finally, many application programmers write their own storage allocators optimized toward the needs and characteristics of the application. This chapter, more than any other, demonstrates the benefit of covering both the hardware and the software aspects of computer systems in a unified way. Traditional computer architecture and operating systems texts present only part of the virtual memory story.

Chapter 10: System-Level I/O. We cover the basic concepts of Unix I/O such as files and descriptors. We describe how files are shared, how I/O redirection works, and how to access file metadata. We also develop a robust buffered I/O package that deals correctly with a curious behavior known as *short counts*, where the library function reads only part of the input data. We cover the C standard I/O library and its relationship to Linux I/O, focusing on limitations of standard I/O that make it unsuitable for network programming. In general, the topics covered in this chapter are building blocks for the next two chapters on network and concurrent programming.

Chapter 11: Network Programming. Networks are interesting I/O devices to program, tying together many of the ideas that we study earlier in the text, such as processes, signals, byte ordering, memory mapping, and dynamic storage allocation. Network programs also provide a compelling context for concurrency, which is the topic of the next chapter. This chapter is a thin slice through network programming that gets you to the point where you can write a simple Web server. We cover the client-server model that underlies all network applications. We present a programmer's view of the Internet and show how to write Internet clients and servers using the sockets interface. Finally, we introduce HTTP and develop a simple iterative Web server.

Chapter 12: Concurrent Programming. This chapter introduces concurrent programming using Internet server design as the running motivational example. We compare and contrast the three basic mechanisms for writing concurrent programs—processes, I/O multiplexing, and threads—and show how to use them to build concurrent Internet servers. We cover basic principles of synchronization using P and V semaphore operations, thread safety and reentrancy, race conditions, and deadlocks. Writing concurrent code is essential for most server applications. We also describe the use of thread-level programming to express parallelism in an application program, enabling faster execution on multi-core processors. Getting all of the cores working on a single computational problem requires a careful coordination of the concurrent threads, both for correctness and to achieve high performance.

New to This Edition

The first edition of this book was published with a copyright of 2003, while the second had a copyright of 2011. Considering the rapid evolution of computer technology, the book content has held up surprisingly well. Intel x86 machines running C programs under Linux (and related operating systems) has proved to be a combination that continues to encompass many systems today. However, changes in hardware technology, compilers, program library interfaces, and the experience of many instructors teaching the material have prompted a substantial revision.

The biggest overall change from the second edition is that we have switched our presentation from one based on a mix of IA32 and x86-64 to one based exclusively on x86-64. This shift in focus affected the contents of many of the chapters. Here is a summary of the significant changes.

Chapter 1: A Tour of Computer Systems We have moved the discussion of Amdahl's Law from Chapter 5 into this chapter.

Chapter 2: Representing and Manipulating Information. A consistent bit of feedback from readers and reviewers is that some of the material in this chapter can be a bit overwhelming. So we have tried to make the material more accessible by clarifying the points at which we delve into a more mathematical style of presentation. This enables readers to first skim over mathematical details to get a high-level overview and then return for a more thorough reading.

Chapter 3: Machine-Level Representation of Programs. We have converted from the earlier presentation based on a mix of IA32 and x86-64 to one based entirely on x86-64. We have also updated for the style of code generated by more recent versions of GCC. The result is a substantial rewriting, including changing the order in which some of the concepts are presented. We also have included, for the first time, a presentation of the machine-level support for programs operating on floating-point data. We have created a Web aside describing IA32 machine code for legacy reasons.

Chapter 4: Processor Architecture. We have revised the earlier processor design, based on a 32-bit architecture, to one that supports 64-bit words and operations.

Chapter 5: Optimizing Program Performance. We have updated the material to reflect the performance capabilities of recent generations of x86-64 processors. With the introduction of more functional units and more sophisticated control logic, the model of program performance we developed based on a data-flow representation of programs has become a more reliable predictor of performance than it was before.

Chapter 6: The Memory Hierarchy. We have updated the material to reflect more recent technology.

Chapter 7: Linking. We have rewritten this chapter for x86-64, expanded the discussion of using the GOT and PLT to create position-independent code, and added a new section on a powerful linking technique known as *library interpositioning.*

Chapter 8: Exceptional Control Flow. We have added a more rigorous treatment of signal handlers, including async-signal-safe functions, specific guidelines for writing signal handlers, and using `sigsuspend` to wait for handlers.

Chapter 9: Virtual Memory. This chapter has changed only slightly.

Chapter 10: System-Level I/O. We have added a new section on files and the file hierarchy, but otherwise, this chapter has changed only slightly.

Chapter 11: Network Programming. We have introduced techniques for protocol-independent and thread-safe network programming using the modern `getaddrinfo` and `getnameinfo` functions, which replace the obsolete and non-reentrant `gethostbyname` and `gethostbyaddr` functions.

Chapter 12: Concurrent Programming. We have increased our coverage of using thread-level parallelism to make programs run faster on multi-core machines.

In addition, we have added and revised a number of practice and homework problems throughout the text.

Origins of the Book

This book stems from an introductory course that we developed at Carnegie Mellon University in the fall of 1998, called 15-213: Introduction to Computer Systems (ICS) [14]. The ICS course has been taught every semester since then. Over 400 students take the course each semester. The students range from sophomores to graduate students in a wide variety of majors. It is a required core course for all undergraduates in the CS and ECE departments at Carnegie Mellon, and it has become a prerequisite for most upper-level systems courses in CS and ECE.

The idea with ICS was to introduce students to computers in a different way. Few of our students would have the opportunity to build a computer system. On the other hand, most students, including all computer scientists and computer engineers, would be required to use and program computers on a daily basis. So we decided to teach about systems from the point of view of the programmer, using the following filter: we would cover a topic only if it affected the performance, correctness, or utility of user-level C programs.

For example, topics such as hardware adder and bus designs were out. Topics such as machine language were in; but instead of focusing on how to write assembly language by hand, we would look at how a C compiler translates C constructs into machine code, including pointers, loops, procedure calls, and switch statements. Further, we would take a broader and more holistic view of the system as both hardware and systems software, covering such topics as linking, loading, processes, signals, performance optimization, virtual memory, I/O, and network and concurrent programming.

This approach allowed us to teach the ICS course in a way that is practical, concrete, hands-on, and exciting for the students. The response from our students and faculty colleagues was immediate and overwhelmingly positive, and we realized that others outside of CMU might benefit from using our approach. Hence this book, which we developed from the ICS lecture notes, and which we have now revised to reflect changes in technology and in how computer systems are implemented.

Via the multiple editions and multiple translations of this book, ICS and many variants have become part of the computer science and computer engineering curricula at hundreds of colleges and universities worldwide.

For Instructors: Courses Based on the Book

Instructors can use the CS:APP book to teach a number of different types of systems courses. Five categories of these courses are illustrated in Figure 2. The particular course depends on curriculum requirements, personal taste, and the backgrounds and abilities of the students. From left to right in the figure, the courses are characterized by an increasing emphasis on the programmer's perspective of a system. Here is a brief description.

ORG. A computer organization course with traditional topics covered in an untraditional style. Traditional topics such as logic design, processor architecture, assembly language, and memory systems are covered. However, there is more emphasis on the impact for the programmer. For example, data representations are related back to the data types and operations of C programs, and the presentation on assembly code is based on machine code generated by a C compiler rather than handwritten assembly code.

ORG+. The ORG course with additional emphasis on the impact of hardware on the performance of application programs. Compared to ORG, students learn more about code optimization and about improving the memory performance of their C programs.

ICS. The baseline ICS course, designed to produce enlightened programmers who understand the impact of the hardware, operating system, and compilation system on the performance and correctness of their application programs. A significant difference from ORG+ is that low-level processor architecture is not covered. Instead, programmers work with a higher-level model of a modern out-of-order processor. The ICS course fits nicely into a 10-week quarter, and can also be stretched to a 15-week semester if covered at a more leisurely pace.

ICS+. The baseline ICS course with additional coverage of systems programming topics such as system-level I/O, network programming, and concurrent programming. This is the semester-long Carnegie Mellon course, which covers every chapter in CS:APP except low-level processor architecture.

Chapter	Topic	ORG	ORG+	ICS	ICS+	SP
				Course		
1	Tour of systems	•	•	•	•	•
2	Data representation	•	•	•	•	$\odot$ (d)
3	Machine language	•	•	•	•	•
4	Processor architecture	•	•			
5	Code optimization		•	•	•	
6	Memory hierarchy	$\odot$ (a)	•	•	•	$\odot$ (a)
7	Linking			$\odot$ (c)	$\odot$ (c)	•
8	Exceptional control flow			•	•	•
9	Virtual memory	$\odot$ (b)	•	•	•	•
10	System-level I/O				•	•
11	Network programming				•	•
12	Concurrent programming				•	•

Figure 2   Five systems courses based on the CS:APP book. ICS+ is the 15-213 course from Carnegie Mellon. Notes: The $\odot$ symbol denotes partial coverage of a chapter, as follows: (a) hardware only; (b) no dynamic storage allocation; (c) no dynamic linking; (d) no floating point.

SP. A systems programming course. This course is similar to ICS+, but it drops floating point and performance optimization, and it places more emphasis on systems programming, including process control, dynamic linking, system-level I/O, network programming, and concurrent programming. Instructors might want to supplement from other sources for advanced topics such as daemons, terminal control, and Unix IPC.

The main message of Figure 2 is that the CS:APP book gives a lot of options to students and instructors. If you want your students to be exposed to lower-level processor architecture, then that option is available via the ORG and ORG+ courses. On the other hand, if you want to switch from your current computer organization course to an ICS or ICS+ course, but are wary of making such a drastic change all at once, then you can move toward ICS incrementally. You can start with ORG, which teaches the traditional topics in a nontraditional way. Once you are comfortable with that material, then you can move to ORG+, and eventually to ICS. If students have no experience in C (e.g., they have only programmed in Java), you could spend several weeks on C and then cover the material of ORG or ICS.

Finally, we note that the ORG+ and SP courses would make a nice two-term sequence (either quarters or semesters). Or you might consider offering ICS+ as one term of ICS and one term of SP.

For Instructors: Classroom-Tested Laboratory Exercises

The ICS+ course at Carnegie Mellon receives very high evaluations from students. Median scores of 5.0/5.0 and means of 4.6/5.0 are typical for the student course evaluations. Students cite the fun, exciting, and relevant laboratory exercises as the primary reason. The labs are available from the CS:APP Web page. Here are examples of the labs that are provided with the book.

Data Lab. This lab requires students to implement simple logical and arithmetic functions, but using a highly restricted subset of C. For example, they must compute the absolute value of a number using only bit-level operations. This lab helps students understand the bit-level representations of C data types and the bit-level behavior of the operations on data.

Binary Bomb Lab. A *binary bomb* is a program provided to students as an object-code file. When run, it prompts the user to type in six different strings. If any of these are incorrect, the bomb "explodes," printing an error message and logging the event on a grading server. Students must "defuse" their own unique bombs by disassembling and reverse engineering the programs to determine what the six strings should be. The lab teaches students to understand assembly language and also forces them to learn how to use a debugger.

Buffer Overflow Lab. Students are required to modify the run-time behavior of a binary executable by exploiting a buffer overflow vulnerability. This lab teaches the students about the stack discipline and about the danger of writing code that is vulnerable to buffer overflow attacks.

Architecture Lab. Several of the homework problems of Chapter 4 can be combined into a lab assignment, where students modify the HCL description of a processor to add new instructions, change the branch prediction policy, or add or remove bypassing paths and register ports. The resulting processors can be simulated and run through automated tests that will detect most of the possible bugs. This lab lets students experience the exciting parts of processor design without requiring a complete background in logic design and hardware description languages.

Performance Lab. Students must optimize the performance of an application kernel function such as convolution or matrix transposition. This lab provides a very clear demonstration of the properties of cache memories and gives students experience with low-level program optimization.

Cache Lab. In this alternative to the performance lab, students write a general-purpose cache simulator, and then optimize a small matrix transpose kernel to minimize the number of misses on a simulated cache. We use the Valgrind tool to generate real address traces for the matrix transpose kernel.

Shell Lab. Students implement their own Unix shell program with job control, including the Ctrl+C and Ctrl+Z keystrokes and the fg, bg, and jobs commands. This is the student's first introduction to concurrency, and it gives them a clear idea of Unix process control, signals, and signal handling.

Malloc Lab. Students implement their own versions of `malloc`, `free`, and (optionally) `realloc`. This lab gives students a clear understanding of data layout and organization, and requires them to evaluate different trade-offs between space and time efficiency.

Proxy Lab. Students implement a concurrent Web proxy that sits between their browsers and the rest of the World Wide Web. This lab exposes the students to such topics as Web clients and servers, and ties together many of the concepts from the course, such as byte ordering, file I/O, process control, signals, signal handling, memory mapping, sockets, and concurrency. Students like being able to see their programs in action with real Web browsers and Web servers.

The CS:APP instructor's manual has a detailed discussion of the labs, as well as directions for downloading the support software.

Acknowledgments for the Third Edition

It is a pleasure to acknowledge and thank those who have helped us produce this third edition of the CS:APP text.

We would like to thank our Carnegie Mellon colleagues who have taught the ICS course over the years and who have provided so much insightful feedback and encouragement: Guy Blelloch, Roger Dannenberg, David Eckhardt, Franz Franchetti, Greg Ganger, Seth Goldstein, Khaled Harras, Greg Kesden, Bruce Maggs, Todd Mowry, Andreas Nowatzyk, Frank Pfenning, Markus Pueschel, and Anthony Rowe. David Winters was very helpful in installing and configuring the reference Linux box.

Jason Fritts (St. Louis University) and Cindy Norris (Appalachian State) provided us with detailed and thoughtful reviews of the second edition. Yili Gong (Wuhan University) wrote the Chinese translation, maintained the errata page for the Chinese version, and contributed many bug reports. Godmar Back (Virginia Tech) helped us improve the text significantly by introducing us to the notions of async-signal safety and protocol-independent network programming.

Many thanks to our eagle-eyed readers who reported bugs in the second edition: Rami Ammari, Paul Anagnostopoulos, Lucas Bärenfänger, Godmar Back, Ji Bin, Sharbel Bousemaan, Richard Callahan, Seth Chaiken, Cheng Chen, Libo Chen, Tao Du, Pascal Garcia, Yili Gong, Ronald Greenberg, Dorukhan Gülöz, Dong Han, Dominik Helm, Ronald Jones, Mustafa Kazdagli, Gordon Kindlmann, Sankar Krishnan, Kanak Kshetri, Junlin Lu, Qiangqiang Luo, Sebastian Luy, Lei Ma, Ashwin Nanjappa, Gregoire Paradis, Jonas Pfenninger, Karl Pichotta, David Ramsey, Kaustabh Roy, David Selvaraj, Sankar Shanmugam, Dominique Smulkowska, Dag Sørbø, Michael Spear, Yu Tanaka, Steven Tricanowicz, Scott Wright, Waiki Wright, Han Xu, Zhengshan Yan, Firo Yang, Shuang Yang, John Ye, Taketo Yoshida, Yan Zhu, and Michael Zink.

Thanks also to our readers who have contributed to the labs, including Godmar Back (Virginia Tech), Taymon Beal (Worcester Polytechnic Institute), Aran Clauson (Western Washington University), Cary Gray (Wheaton College), Paul Haiduk (West Texas A&M University), Len Hamey (Macquarie University), Eddie Kohler (Harvard), Hugh Lauer (Worcester Polytechnic Institute), Robert Marmorstein (Longwood University), and James Riely (DePaul University).

Once again, Paul Anagnostopoulos of Windfall Software did a masterful job of typesetting the book and leading the production process. Many thanks to Paul and his stellar team: Richard Camp (copyediting), Jennifer McClain (proofreading), Laurel Muller (art production), and Ted Laux (indexing). Paul even spotted a bug in our description of the origins of the acronym BSS that had persisted undetected since the first edition!

Finally, we would like to thank our friends at Prentice Hall. Marcia Horton and our editor, Matt Goldstein, have been unflagging in their support and encouragement, and we are deeply grateful to them.

Acknowledgments from the Second Edition

We are deeply grateful to the many people who have helped us produce this second edition of the CS:APP text.

First and foremost, we would like to recognize our colleagues who have taught the ICS course at Carnegie Mellon for their insightful feedback and encouragement: Guy Blelloch, Roger Dannenberg, David Eckhardt, Greg Ganger, Seth Goldstein, Greg Kesden, Bruce Maggs, Todd Mowry, Andreas Nowatzyk, Frank Pfenning, and Markus Pueschel.

Thanks also to our sharp-eyed readers who contributed reports to the errata page for the first edition: Daniel Amelang, Rui Baptista, Quarup Barreirinhas, Michael Bombyk, Jörg Brauer, Jordan Brough, Yixin Cao, James Caroll, Rui Carvalho, Hyoung-Kee Choi, Al Davis, Grant Davis, Christian Dufour, Mao Fan, Tim Freeman, Inge Frick, Max Gebhardt, Jeff Goldblat, Thomas Gross, Anita Gupta, John Hampton, Hiep Hong, Greg Israelsen, Ronald Jones, Haudy Kazemi, Brian Kell, Constantine Kousoulis, Sacha Krakowiak, Arun Krishnaswamy, Martin Kulas, Michael Li, Zeyang Li, Ricky Liu, Mario Lo Conte, Dirk Maas, Devon Macey, Carl Marcinik, Will Marrero, Simone Martins, Tao Men, Mark Morrissey, Venkata Naidu, Bhas Nalabothula, Thomas Niemann, Eric Peskin, David Po, Anne Rogers, John Ross, Michael Scott, Seiki, Ray Shih, Darren Shultz, Erik Silkensen, Suryanto, Emil Tarazi, Nawanan Theera-Ampornpunt, Joe Trdinich, Michael Trigoboff, James Troup, Martin Vopatek, Alan West, Betsy Wolff, Tim Wong, James Woodruff, Scott Wright, Jackie Xiao, Guanpeng Xu, Qing Xu, Caren Yang, Yin Yongsheng, Wang Yuanxuan, Steven Zhang, and Day Zhong. Special thanks to Inge Frick, who identified a subtle deep copy bug in our lock-and-copy example, and to Ricky Liu for his amazing proofreading skills.

Our Intel Labs colleagues Andrew Chien and Limor Fix were exceptionally supportive throughout the writing of the text. Steve Schlosser graciously provided some disk drive characterizations. Casey Helfrich and Michael Ryan installed and maintained our new Core i7 box. Michael Kozuch, Babu Pillai, and Jason Campbell provided valuable insight on memory system performance, multi-core systems, and the power wall. Phil Gibbons and Shimin Chen shared their considerable expertise on solid state disk designs.

We have been able to call on the talents of many, including Wen-Mei Hwu, Markus Pueschel, and Jiri Simsa, to provide both detailed comments and high-level advice. James Hoe helped us create a Verilog version of the Y86 processor and did all of the work needed to synthesize working hardware.

Many thanks to our colleagues who provided reviews of the draft manuscript: James Archibald (Brigham Young University), Richard Carver (George Mason University), Mirela Damian (Villanova University), Peter Dinda (Northwestern University), John Fiore (Temple University), Jason Fritts (St. Louis University), John Greiner (Rice University), Brian Harvey (University of California, Berkeley), Don Heller (Penn State University), Wei Chung Hsu (University of Minnesota), Michelle Hugue (University of Maryland), Jeremy Johnson (Drexel University), Geoff Kuenning (Harvey Mudd College), Ricky Liu, Sam Madden (MIT), Fred Martin (University of Massachusetts, Lowell), Abraham Matta (Boston University), Markus Pueschel (Carnegie Mellon University), Norman Ramsey (Tufts University), Glenn Reinmann (UCLA), Michela Taufer (University of Delaware), and Craig Zilles (UIUC).

Paul Anagnostopoulos of Windfall Software did an outstanding job of typesetting the book and leading the production team. Many thanks to Paul and his superb team: Rick Camp (copyeditor), Joe Snowden (compositor), MaryEllen N. Oliver (proofreader), Laurel Muller (artist), and Ted Laux (indexer).

Finally, we would like to thank our friends at Prentice Hall. Marcia Horton has always been there for us. Our editor, Matt Goldstein, provided stellar leadership from beginning to end. We are profoundly grateful for their help, encouragement, and insights.

Acknowledgments from the First Edition

We are deeply indebted to many friends and colleagues for their thoughtful criticisms and encouragement. A special thanks to our 15-213 students, whose infectious energy and enthusiasm spurred us on. Nick Carter and Vinny Furia generously provided their malloc package.

Guy Blelloch, Greg Kesden, Bruce Maggs, and Todd Mowry taught the course over multiple semesters, gave us encouragement, and helped improve the course material. Herb Derby provided early spiritual guidance and encouragement. Allan Fisher, Garth Gibson, Thomas Gross, Satya, Peter Steenkiste, and Hui Zhang encouraged us to develop the course from the start. A suggestion from Garth early on got the whole ball rolling, and this was picked up and refined with the help of a group led by Allan Fisher. Mark Stehlik and Peter Lee have been very supportive about building this material into the undergraduate curriculum. Greg Kesden provided helpful feedback on the impact of ICS on the OS course. Greg Ganger and Jiri Schindler graciously provided some disk drive characterizations and answered our questions on modern disks. Tom Stricker showed us the memory mountain. James Hoe provided useful ideas and feedback on how to present processor architecture.

A special group of students—Khalil Amiri, Angela Demke Brown, Chris Colohan, Jason Crawford, Peter Dinda, Julio Lopez, Bruce Lowekamp, Jeff Pierce, Sanjay Rao, Balaji Sarpeshkar, Blake Scholl, Sanjit Seshia, Greg Steffan, Tiankai Tu, Kip Walker, and Yinglian Xie—were instrumental in helping us develop the content of the course. In particular, Chris Colohan established a fun (and funny) tone that persists to this day, and invented the legendary "binary bomb" that has proven to be a great tool for teaching machine code and debugging concepts.

Chris Bauer, Alan Cox, Peter Dinda, Sandhya Dwarkadas, John Greiner, Don Heller, Bruce Jacob, Barry Johnson, Bruce Lowekamp, Greg Morrisett, Brian Noble, Bobbie Othmer, Bill Pugh, Michael Scott, Mark Smotherman, Greg Steffan, and Bob Wier took time that they did not have to read and advise us on early drafts of the book. A very special thanks to Al Davis (University of Utah), Peter Dinda (Northwestern University), John Greiner (Rice University), Wei Hsu (University of Minnesota), Bruce Lowekamp (College of William & Mary), Bobbie Othmer (University of Minnesota), Michael Scott (University of Rochester), and Bob Wier (Rocky Mountain College) for class testing the beta version. A special thanks to their students as well!

We would also like to thank our colleagues at Prentice Hall. Marcia Horton, Eric Frank, and Harold Stone have been unflagging in their support and vision. Harold also helped us present an accurate historical perspective on RISC and CISC processor architectures. Jerry Ralya provided sharp insights and taught us a lot about good writing.

Finally, we would like to acknowledge the great technical writers Brian Kernighan and the late W. Richard Stevens, for showing us that technical books can be beautiful.

Thank you all.

Randy Bryant
Dave O'Hallaron
Pittsburgh, Pennsylvania

About the Authors

Randal E. Bryant received his bachelor's degree from the University of Michigan in 1973 and then attended graduate school at the Massachusetts Institute of Technology, receiving his PhD degree in computer science in 1981. He spent three years as an assistant professor at the California Institute of Technology, and has been on the faculty at Carnegie Mellon since 1984. For five of those years he served as head of the Computer Science Department, and for ten of them he served as Dean of the School of Computer Science. He is currently a university professor of computer science. He also holds a courtesy appointment with the Department of Electrical and Computer Engineering.

Professor Bryant has taught courses in computer systems at both the undergraduate and graduate level for around 40 years. Over many years of teaching computer architecture courses, he began shifting the focus from how computers are designed to how programmers can write more efficient and reliable programs if they understand the system better. Together with Professor O'Hallaron, he developed the course 15-213, Introduction to Computer Systems, at Carnegie Mellon that is the basis for this book. He has also taught courses in algorithms, programming, computer networking, distributed systems, and VLSI design.

Most of Professor Bryant's research concerns the design of software tools to help software and hardware designers verify the correctness of their systems. These include several types of simulators, as well as formal verification tools that prove the correctness of a design using mathematical methods. He has published over 150 technical papers. His research results are used by major computer manufacturers, including Intel, IBM, Fujitsu, and Microsoft. He has won several major awards for his research. These include two inventor recognition awards and a technical achievement award from the Semiconductor Research Corporation, the Kanellakis Theory and Practice Award from the Association for Computer Machinery (ACM), and the W. R. G. Baker Award, the Emmanuel Piore Award, the Phil Kaufman Award, and the A. Richard Newton Award from the Institute of Electrical and Electronics Engineers (IEEE). He is a fellow of both the ACM and the IEEE and a member of both the US National Academy of Engineering and the American Academy of Arts and Sciences.

David R. O'Hallaron is a professor of computer science and electrical and computer engineering at Carnegie Mellon University. He received his PhD from the University of Virginia. He served as the director of Intel Labs, Pittsburgh, from 2007 to 2010.

He has taught computer systems courses at the undergraduate and graduate levels for 20 years on such topics as computer architecture, introductory computer systems, parallel processor design, and Internet services. Together with Professor Bryant, he developed the course at Carnegie Mellon that led to this book. In 2004, he was awarded the Herbert Simon Award for Teaching Excellence by the CMU School of Computer Science, an award for which the winner is chosen based on a poll of the students.

Professor O'Hallaron works in the area of computer systems, with specific interests in software systems for scientific computing, data-intensive computing, and virtualization. The best-known example of his work is the Quake project, an endeavor involving a group of computer scientists, civil engineers, and seismologists who have developed the ability to predict the motion of the ground during strong earthquakes. In 2003, Professor O'Hallaron and the other members of the Quake team won the Gordon Bell Prize, the top international prize in high-performance computing. His current work focuses on the notion of autograding, that is, programs that evaluate the quality of other programs.

1

A Tour of Computer Systems

A *computer system* consists of hardware and systems software that work together to run application programs. Specific implementations of systems change over time, but the underlying concepts do not. All computer systems have similar hardware and software components that perform similar functions. This book is written for programmers who want to get better at their craft by understanding how these components work and how they affect the correctness and performance of their programs.

You are poised for an exciting journey. If you dedicate yourself to learning the concepts in this book, then you will be on your way to becoming a rare "power programmer," enlightened by an understanding of the underlying computer system and its impact on your application programs.

You are going to learn practical skills such as how to avoid strange numerical errors caused by the way that computers represent numbers. You will learn how to optimize your C code by using clever tricks that exploit the designs of modern processors and memory systems. You will learn how the compiler implements procedure calls and how to use this knowledge to avoid the security holes from buffer overflow vulnerabilities that plague network and Internet software. You will learn how to recognize and avoid the nasty errors during linking that confound the average programmer. You will learn how to write your own Unix shell, your own dynamic storage allocation package, and even your own Web server. You will learn the promises and pitfalls of concurrency, a topic of increasing importance as multiple processor cores are integrated onto single chips.

In their classic text on the C programming language [61], Kernighan and Ritchie introduce readers to C using the `hello` program shown in Figure 1.1. Although `hello` is a very simple program, every major part of the system must work in concert in order for it to run to completion. In a sense, the goal of this book is to help you understand what happens and why when you run `hello` on your system.

We begin our study of systems by tracing the lifetime of the `hello` program, from the time it is created by a programmer, until it runs on a system, prints its simple message, and terminates. As we follow the lifetime of the program, we will briefly introduce the key concepts, terminology, and components that come into play. Later chapters will expand on these ideas.

─── *code/intro/hello.c*

```
1   #include <stdio.h>
2
3   int main()
4   {
5       printf("hello, world\n");
6       return 0;
7   }
```

─── *code/intro/hello.c*

Figure 1.1   The `hello` program. (Source: [60])

#	i	n	c	l	u	d	e	*SP*	<	s	t	d	i	o	.
35	105	110	99	108	117	100	101	32	60	115	116	100	105	111	46
h	>	\n	\n	i	n	t	*SP*	m	a	i	n	(	)	\n	{
104	62	10	10	105	110	116	32	109	97	105	110	40	41	10	123
\n	*SP*	*SP*	*SP*	*SP*	p	r	i	n	t	f	(	"	h	e	l
10	32	32	32	32	112	114	105	110	116	102	40	34	104	101	108
l	o	,	*SP*	w	o	r	l	d	\	n	"	)	;	\n	*SP*
108	111	44	32	119	111	114	108	100	92	110	34	41	59	10	32
SP	*SP*	*SP*	r	e	t	u	r	n	*SP*	0	;	\n	}	\n	
32	32	32	114	101	116	117	114	110	32	48	59	10	125	10	

Figure 1.2   The ASCII text representation of hello.c.

1.1   Information Is Bits + Context

Our hello program begins life as a *source program* (or *source file*) that the programmer creates with an editor and saves in a text file called hello.c. The source program is a sequence of bits, each with a value of 0 or 1, organized in 8-bit chunks called *bytes*. Each byte represents some text character in the program.

Most computer systems represent text characters using the ASCII standard that represents each character with a unique byte-size integer value.[1] For example, Figure 1.2 shows the ASCII representation of the hello.c program.

The hello.c program is stored in a file as a sequence of bytes. Each byte has an integer value that corresponds to some character. For example, the first byte has the integer value 35, which corresponds to the character '#'. The second byte has the integer value 105, which corresponds to the character 'i', and so on. Notice that each text line is terminated by the invisible *newline* character '\n', which is represented by the integer value 10. Files such as hello.c that consist exclusively of ASCII characters are known as *text files*. All other files are known as *binary files*.

The representation of hello.c illustrates a fundamental idea: All information in a system—including disk files, programs stored in memory, user data stored in memory, and data transferred across a network—is represented as a bunch of bits. The only thing that distinguishes different data objects is the context in which we view them. For example, in different contexts, the same sequence of bytes might represent an integer, floating-point number, character string, or machine instruction.

As programmers, we need to understand machine representations of numbers because they are not the same as integers and real numbers. They are finite

---

1. Other encoding methods are used to represent text in non-English languages. See the aside on page 50 for a discussion on this.

Aside   Origins of the C programming language

C was developed from 1969 to 1973 by Dennis Ritchie of Bell Laboratories. The American National Standards Institute (ANSI) ratified the ANSI C standard in 1989, and this standardization later became the responsibility of the International Standards Organization (ISO). The standards define the C language and a set of library functions known as the *C standard library*. Kernighan and Ritchie describe ANSI C in their classic book, which is known affectionately as "K&R" [61]. In Ritchie's words [92], C is "quirky, flawed, and an enormous success." So why the success?

- *C was closely tied with the Unix operating system.* C was developed from the beginning as the system programming language for Unix. Most of the Unix kernel (the core part of the operating system), and all of its supporting tools and libraries, were written in C. As Unix became popular in universities in the late 1970s and early 1980s, many people were exposed to C and found that they liked it. Since Unix was written almost entirely in C, it could be easily ported to new machines, which created an even wider audience for both C and Unix.

- *C is a small, simple language.* The design was controlled by a single person, rather than a committee, and the result was a clean, consistent design with little baggage. The K&R book describes the complete language and standard library, with numerous examples and exercises, in only 261 pages. The simplicity of C made it relatively easy to learn and to port to different computers.

- *C was designed for a practical purpose.* C was designed to implement the Unix operating system. Later, other people found that they could write the programs they wanted, without the language getting in the way.

C is the language of choice for system-level programming, and there is a huge installed base of application-level programs as well. However, it is not perfect for all programmers and all situations. C pointers are a common source of confusion and programming errors. C also lacks explicit support for useful abstractions such as classes, objects, and exceptions. Newer languages such as C++ and Java address these issues for application-level programs.

approximations that can behave in unexpected ways. This fundamental idea is explored in detail in Chapter 2.

1.2   Programs Are Translated by Other Programs into Different Forms

The `hello` program begins life as a high-level C program because it can be read and understood by human beings in that form. However, in order to run `hello.c` on the system, the individual C statements must be translated by other programs into a sequence of low-level *machine-language* instructions. These instructions are then packaged in a form called an *executable object program* and stored as a binary disk file. Object programs are also referred to as *executable object files*.

On a Unix system, the translation from source file to object file is performed by a *compiler driver:*

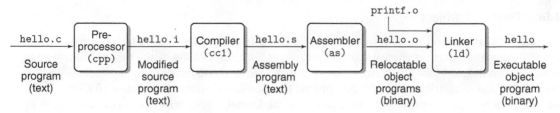

Figure 1.3   The compilation system.

linux> *gcc -o hello hello.c*

Here, the GCC compiler driver reads the source file hello.c and translates it into an executable object file hello. The translation is performed in the sequence of four phases shown in Figure 1.3. The programs that perform the four phases (*preprocessor*, *compiler*, *assembler*, and *linker*) are known collectively as the *compilation system*.

- *Preprocessing phase.* The preprocessor (cpp) modifies the original C program according to directives that begin with the '#' character. For example, the #include <stdio.h> command in line 1 of hello.c tells the preprocessor to read the contents of the system header file stdio.h and insert it directly into the program text. The result is another C program, typically with the .i suffix.

- *Compilation phase.* The compiler (cc1) translates the text file hello.i into the text file hello.s, which contains an *assembly-language program*. This program includes the following definition of function main:

```
1   main:
2       subq    $8, %rsp
3       movl    $.LC0, %edi
4       call    puts
5       movl    $0, %eax
6       addq    $8, %rsp
7       ret
```

Each of lines 2–7 in this definition describes one low-level machine-language instruction in a textual form. Assembly language is useful because it provides a common output language for different compilers for different high-level languages. For example, C compilers and Fortran compilers both generate output files in the same assembly language.

- *Assembly phase.* Next, the assembler (as) translates hello.s into machine-language instructions, packages them in a form known as a *relocatable object program*, and stores the result in the object file hello.o. This file is a binary file containing 17 bytes to encode the instructions for function main. If we were to view hello.o with a text editor, it would appear to be gibberish.

Aside The GNU project

Gcc is one of many useful tools developed by the GNU (short for GNU's Not Unix) project. The GNU project is a tax-exempt charity started by Richard Stallman in 1984, with the ambitious goal of developing a complete Unix-like system whose source code is unencumbered by restrictions on how it can be modified or distributed. The GNU project has developed an environment with all the major components of a Unix operating system, except for the kernel, which was developed separately by the Linux project. The GNU environment includes the EMACS editor, GCC compiler, GDB debugger, assembler, linker, utilities for manipulating binaries, and other components. The GCC compiler has grown to support many different languages, with the ability to generate code for many different machines. Supported languages include C, C++, Fortran, Java, Pascal, Objective-C, and Ada.

The GNU project is a remarkable achievement, and yet it is often overlooked. The modern open-source movement (commonly associated with Linux) owes its intellectual origins to the GNU project's notion of *free software* ("free" as in "free speech," not "free beer"). Further, Linux owes much of its popularity to the GNU tools, which provide the environment for the Linux kernel.

- *Linking phase.* Notice that our `hello` program calls the `printf` function, which is part of the *standard C library* provided by every C compiler. The `printf` function resides in a separate precompiled object file called `printf.o`, which must somehow be merged with our `hello.o` program. The linker (`ld`) handles this merging. The result is the `hello` file, which is an executable object file (or simply *executable*) that is ready to be loaded into memory and executed by the system.

1.3 It Pays to Understand How Compilation Systems Work

For simple programs such as `hello.c`, we can rely on the compilation system to produce correct and efficient machine code. However, there are some important reasons why programmers need to understand how compilation systems work:

- *Optimizing program performance.* Modern compilers are sophisticated tools that usually produce good code. As programmers, we do not need to know the inner workings of the compiler in order to write efficient code. However, in order to make good coding decisions in our C programs, we do need a basic understanding of machine-level code and how the compiler translates different C statements into machine code. For example, is a `switch` statement always more efficient than a sequence of `if-else` statements? How much overhead is incurred by a function call? Is a `while` loop more efficient than a `for` loop? Are pointer references more efficient than array indexes? Why does our loop run so much faster if we sum into a local variable instead of an argument that is passed by reference? How can a function run faster when we simply rearrange the parentheses in an arithmetic expression?

In Chapter 3, we introduce x86-64, the machine language of recent generations of Linux, Macintosh, and Windows computers. We describe how compilers translate different C constructs into this language. In Chapter 5, you will learn how to tune the performance of your C programs by making simple transformations to the C code that help the compiler do its job better. In Chapter 6, you will learn about the hierarchical nature of the memory system, how C compilers store data arrays in memory, and how your C programs can exploit this knowledge to run more efficiently.

• *Understanding link-time errors.* In our experience, some of the most perplexing programming errors are related to the operation of the linker, especially when you are trying to build large software systems. For example, what does it mean when the linker reports that it cannot resolve a reference? What is the difference between a static variable and a global variable? What happens if you define two global variables in different C files with the same name? What is the difference between a static library and a dynamic library? Why does it matter what order we list libraries on the command line? And scariest of all, why do some linker-related errors not appear until run time? You will learn the answers to these kinds of questions in Chapter 7.

• *Avoiding security holes.* For many years, *buffer overflow vulnerabilities* have accounted for many of the security holes in network and Internet servers. These vulnerabilities exist because too few programmers understand the need to carefully restrict the quantity and forms of data they accept from untrusted sources. A first step in learning secure programming is to understand the consequences of the way data and control information are stored on the program stack. We cover the stack discipline and buffer overflow vulnerabilities in Chapter 3 as part of our study of assembly language. We will also learn about methods that can be used by the programmer, compiler, and operating system to reduce the threat of attack.

1.4   Processors Read and Interpret Instructions Stored in Memory

At this point, our `hello.c` source program has been translated by the compilation system into an executable object file called `hello` that is stored on disk. To run the executable file on a Unix system, we type its name to an application program known as a *shell:*

```
linux> ./hello
hello, world
linux>
```

The shell is a command-line interpreter that prints a prompt, waits for you to type a command line, and then performs the command. If the first word of the command line does not correspond to a built-in shell command, then the shell

Figure 1.4
Hardware organization of a typical system. CPU: central processing unit, ALU: arithmetic/logic unit, PC: program counter, USB: Universal Serial Bus.

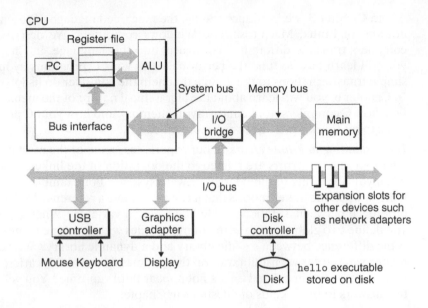

assumes that it is the name of an executable file that it should load and run. So in this case, the shell loads and runs the `hello` program and then waits for it to terminate. The `hello` program prints its message to the screen and then terminates. The shell then prints a prompt and waits for the next input command line.

1.4.1 Hardware Organization of a System

To understand what happens to our `hello` program when we run it, we need to understand the hardware organization of a typical system, which is shown in Figure 1.4. This particular picture is modeled after the family of recent Intel systems, but all systems have a similar look and feel. Don't worry about the complexity of this figure just now. We will get to its various details in stages throughout the course of the book.

Buses

Running throughout the system is a collection of electrical conduits called *buses* that carry bytes of information back and forth between the components. Buses are typically designed to transfer fixed-size chunks of bytes known as *words*. The number of bytes in a word (the *word size*) is a fundamental system parameter that varies across systems. Most machines today have word sizes of either 4 bytes (32 bits) or 8 bytes (64 bits). In this book, we do not assume any fixed definition of word size. Instead, we will specify what we mean by a "word" in any context that requires this to be defined.

I/O Devices

Input/output (I/O) devices are the system's connection to the external world. Our example system has four I/O devices: a keyboard and mouse for user input, a display for user output, and a disk drive (or simply disk) for long-term storage of data and programs. Initially, the executable `hello` program resides on the disk.

Each I/O device is connected to the I/O bus by either a *controller* or an *adapter*. The distinction between the two is mainly one of packaging. Controllers are chip sets in the device itself or on the system's main printed circuit board (often called the *motherboard*). An adapter is a card that plugs into a slot on the motherboard. Regardless, the purpose of each is to transfer information back and forth between the I/O bus and an I/O device.

Chapter 6 has more to say about how I/O devices such as disks work. In Chapter 10, you will learn how to use the Unix I/O interface to access devices from your application programs. We focus on the especially interesting class of devices known as networks, but the techniques generalize to other kinds of devices as well.

Main Memory

The *main memory* is a temporary storage device that holds both a program and the data it manipulates while the processor is executing the program. Physically, main memory consists of a collection of *dynamic random access memory* (DRAM) chips. Logically, memory is organized as a linear array of bytes, each with its own unique address (array index) starting at zero. In general, each of the machine instructions that constitute a program can consist of a variable number of bytes. The sizes of data items that correspond to C program variables vary according to type. For example, on an x86-64 machine running Linux, data of type `short` require 2 bytes, types `int` and `float` 4 bytes, and types `long` and `double` 8 bytes.

Chapter 6 has more to say about how memory technologies such as DRAM chips work, and how they are combined to form main memory.

Processor

The *central processing unit* (CPU), or simply *processor*, is the engine that interprets (or *executes*) instructions stored in main memory. At its core is a word-size storage device (or *register*) called the *program counter* (PC). At any point in time, the PC points at (contains the address of) some machine-language instruction in main memory.[2]

From the time that power is applied to the system until the time that the power is shut off, a processor repeatedly executes the instruction pointed at by the program counter and updates the program counter to point to the next instruction. A processor *appears* to operate according to a very simple instruction execution model, defined by its *instruction set architecture*. In this model, instructions execute

---

2. PC is also a commonly used acronym for "personal computer." However, the distinction between the two should be clear from the context.

in strict sequence, and executing a single instruction involves performing a series of steps. The processor reads the instruction from memory pointed at by the program counter (PC), interprets the bits in the instruction, performs some simple operation dictated by the instruction, and then updates the PC to point to the next instruction, which may or may not be contiguous in memory to the instruction that was just executed.

There are only a few of these simple operations, and they revolve around main memory, the *register file*, and the *arithmetic/logic unit* (ALU). The register file is a small storage device that consists of a collection of word-size registers, each with its own unique name. The ALU computes new data and address values. Here are some examples of the simple operations that the CPU might carry out at the request of an instruction:

- *Load:* Copy a byte or a word from main memory into a register, overwriting the previous contents of the register.
- *Store:* Copy a byte or a word from a register to a location in main memory, overwriting the previous contents of that location.
- *Operate:* Copy the contents of two registers to the ALU, perform an arithmetic operation on the two words, and store the result in a register, overwriting the previous contents of that register.
- *Jump:* Extract a word from the instruction itself and copy that word into the program counter (PC), overwriting the previous value of the PC.

We say that a processor appears to be a simple implementation of its instruction set architecture, but in fact modern processors use far more complex mechanisms to speed up program execution. Thus, we can distinguish the processor's instruction set architecture, describing the effect of each machine-code instruction, from its *microarchitecture*, describing how the processor is actually implemented. When we study machine code in Chapter 3, we will consider the abstraction provided by the machine's instruction set architecture. Chapter 4 has more to say about how processors are actually implemented. Chapter 5 describes a model of how modern processors work that enables predicting and optimizing the performance of machine-language programs.

1.4.2 Running the `hello` Program

Given this simple view of a system's hardware organization and operation, we can begin to understand what happens when we run our example program. We must omit a lot of details here that will be filled in later, but for now we will be content with the big picture.

Initially, the shell program is executing its instructions, waiting for us to type a command. As we type the characters `./hello` at the keyboard, the shell program reads each one into a register and then stores it in memory, as shown in Figure 1.5.

When we hit the `enter` key on the keyboard, the shell knows that we have finished typing the command. The shell then loads the executable `hello` file by executing a sequence of instructions that copies the code and data in the `hello`

Figure 1.5
Reading the hello
command from the
keyboard.

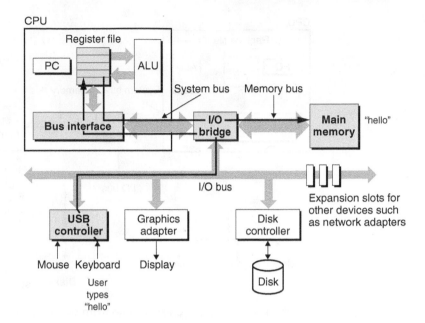

Figure 1.5
Reading the hello
command from the
keyboard.

object file from disk to main memory. The data includes the string of characters
hello, world\n that will eventually be printed out.

Using a technique known as *direct memory access* (DMA, discussed in Chapter 6), the data travel directly from disk to main memory, without passing through
the processor. This step is shown in Figure 1.6.

Once the code and data in the hello object file are loaded into memory,
the processor begins executing the machine-language instructions in the hello
program's main routine. These instructions copy the bytes in the hello, world\n
string from memory to the register file, and from there to the display device, where
they are displayed on the screen. This step is shown in Figure 1.7.

1.5 Caches Matter

An important lesson from this simple example is that a system spends a lot of
time moving information from one place to another. The machine instructions in
the hello program are originally stored on disk. When the program is loaded,
they are copied to main memory. As the processor runs the program, instructions are copied from main memory into the processor. Similarly, the data string
hello,world\n, originally on disk, is copied to main memory and then copied
from main memory to the display device. From a programmer's perspective, much
of this copying is overhead that slows down the "real work" of the program. Thus,
a major goal for system designers is to make these copy operations run as fast as
possible.

Because of physical laws, larger storage devices are slower than smaller storage devices. And faster devices are more expensive to build than their slower

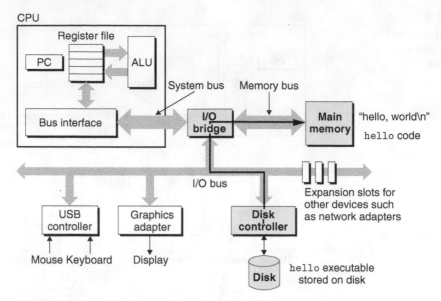

Figure 1.6 Loading the executable from disk into main memory.

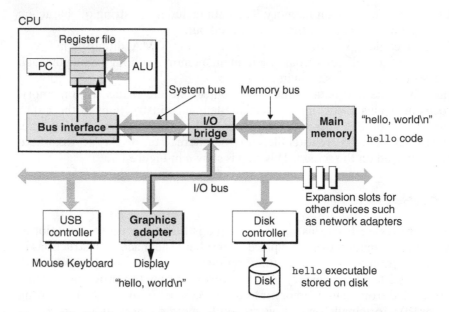

Figure 1.7 Writing the output string from memory to the display.

Figure 1.8
Cache memories.

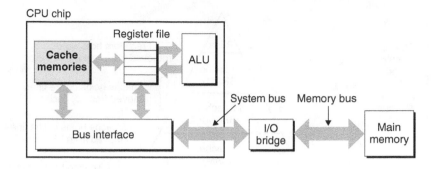

counterparts. For example, the disk drive on a typical system might be 1,000 times larger than the main memory, but it might take the processor 10,000,000 times longer to read a word from disk than from memory.

Similarly, a typical register file stores only a few hundred bytes of information, as opposed to billions of bytes in the main memory. However, the processor can read data from the register file almost 100 times faster than from memory. Even more troublesome, as semiconductor technology progresses over the years, this *processor–memory gap* continues to increase. It is easier and cheaper to make processors run faster than it is to make main memory run faster.

To deal with the processor–memory gap, system designers include smaller, faster storage devices called *cache memories* (or simply caches) that serve as temporary staging areas for information that the processor is likely to need in the near future. Figure 1.8 shows the cache memories in a typical system. An *L1 cache* on the processor chip holds tens of thousands of bytes and can be accessed nearly as fast as the register file. A larger *L2 cache* with hundreds of thousands to millions of bytes is connected to the processor by a special bus. It might take 5 times longer for the processor to access the L2 cache than the L1 cache, but this is still 5 to 10 times faster than accessing the main memory. The L1 and L2 caches are implemented with a hardware technology known as *static random access memory* (SRAM). Newer and more powerful systems even have three levels of cache: L1, L2, and L3. The idea behind caching is that a system can get the effect of both a very large memory and a very fast one by exploiting *locality*, the tendency for programs to access data and code in localized regions. By setting up caches to hold data that are likely to be accessed often, we can perform most memory operations using the fast caches.

One of the most important lessons in this book is that application programmers who are aware of cache memories can exploit them to improve the performance of their programs by an order of magnitude. You will learn more about these important devices and how to exploit them in Chapter 6.

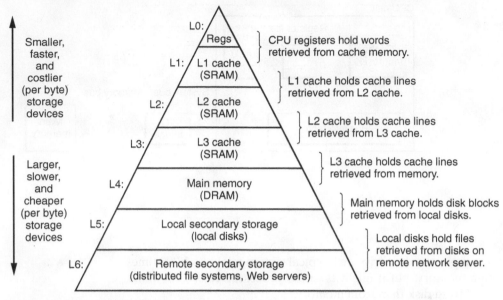

Figure 1.9   An example of a memory hierarchy.

1.6   Storage Devices Form a Hierarchy

This notion of inserting a smaller, faster storage device (e.g., cache memory) between the processor and a larger, slower device (e.g., main memory) turns out to be a general idea. In fact, the storage devices in every computer system are organized as a *memory hierarchy* similar to Figure 1.9. As we move from the top of the hierarchy to the bottom, the devices become slower, larger, and less costly per byte. The register file occupies the top level in the hierarchy, which is known as level 0 or L0. We show three levels of caching L1 to L3, occupying memory hierarchy levels 1 to 3. Main memory occupies level 4, and so on.

The main idea of a memory hierarchy is that storage at one level serves as a cache for storage at the next lower level. Thus, the register file is a cache for the L1 cache. Caches L1 and L2 are caches for L2 and L3, respectively. The L3 cache is a cache for the main memory, which is a cache for the disk. On some networked systems with distributed file systems, the local disk serves as a cache for data stored on the disks of other systems.

Just as programmers can exploit knowledge of the different caches to improve performance, programmers can exploit their understanding of the entire memory hierarchy. Chapter 6 will have much more to say about this.

1.7   The Operating System Manages the Hardware

Back to our hello example. When the shell loaded and ran the hello program, and when the hello program printed its message, neither program accessed the

Figure 1.10
Layered view of a computer system.

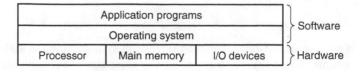

Figure 1.11
Abstractions provided by an operating system.

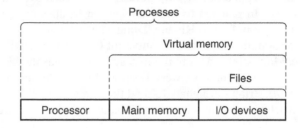

keyboard, display, disk, or main memory directly. Rather, they relied on the services provided by the *operating system*. We can think of the operating system as a layer of software interposed between the application program and the hardware, as shown in Figure 1.10. All attempts by an application program to manipulate the hardware must go through the operating system.

The operating system has two primary purposes: (1) to protect the hardware from misuse by runaway applications and (2) to provide applications with simple and uniform mechanisms for manipulating complicated and often wildly different low-level hardware devices. The operating system achieves both goals via the fundamental abstractions shown in Figure 1.11: *processes*, *virtual memory*, and *files*. As this figure suggests, files are abstractions for I/O devices, virtual memory is an abstraction for both the main memory and disk I/O devices, and processes are abstractions for the processor, main memory, and I/O devices. We will discuss each in turn.

1.7.1   Processes

When a program such as `hello` runs on a modern system, the operating system provides the illusion that the program is the only one running on the system. The program appears to have exclusive use of both the processor, main memory, and I/O devices. The processor appears to execute the instructions in the program, one after the other, without interruption. And the code and data of the program appear to be the only objects in the system's memory. These illusions are provided by the notion of a process, one of the most important and successful ideas in computer science.

A *process* is the operating system's abstraction for a running program. Multiple processes can run concurrently on the same system, and each process appears to have exclusive use of the hardware. By *concurrently*, we mean that the instructions of one process are interleaved with the instructions of another process. In most systems, there are more processes to run than there are CPUs to run them.

Aside Unix, Posix, and the Standard Unix Specification

The 1960s was an era of huge, complex operating systems, such as IBM's OS/360 and Honeywell's Multics systems. While OS/360 was one of the most successful software projects in history, Multics dragged on for years and never achieved wide-scale use. Bell Laboratories was an original partner in the Multics project but dropped out in 1969 because of concern over the complexity of the project and the lack of progress. In reaction to their unpleasant Multics experience, a group of Bell Labs researchers—Ken Thompson, Dennis Ritchie, Doug McIlroy, and Joe Ossanna—began work in 1969 on a simpler operating system for a Digital Equipment Corporation PDP-7 computer, written entirely in machine language. Many of the ideas in the new system, such as the hierarchical file system and the notion of a shell as a user-level process, were borrowed from Multics but implemented in a smaller, simpler package. In 1970, Brian Kernighan dubbed the new system "Unix" as a pun on the complexity of "Multics." The kernel was rewritten in C in 1973, and Unix was announced to the outside world in 1974 [93].

Because Bell Labs made the source code available to schools with generous terms, Unix developed a large following at universities. The most influential work was done at the University of California at Berkeley in the late 1970s and early 1980s, with Berkeley researchers adding virtual memory and the Internet protocols in a series of releases called Unix 4.xBSD (Berkeley Software Distribution). Concurrently, Bell Labs was releasing their own versions, which became known as System V Unix. Versions from other vendors, such as the Sun Microsystems Solaris system, were derived from these original BSD and System V versions.

Trouble arose in the mid 1980s as Unix vendors tried to differentiate themselves by adding new and often incompatible features. To combat this trend, IEEE (Institute for Electrical and Electronics Engineers) sponsored an effort to standardize Unix, later dubbed "Posix" by Richard Stallman. The result was a family of standards, known as the Posix standards, that cover such issues as the C language interface for Unix system calls, shell programs and utilities, threads, and network programming. More recently, a separate standardization effort, known as the "Standard Unix Specification," has joined forces with Posix to create a single, unified standard for Unix systems. As a result of these standardization efforts, the differences between Unix versions have largely disappeared.

Traditional systems could only execute one program at a time, while newer *multicore* processors can execute several programs simultaneously. In either case, a single CPU can appear to execute multiple processes concurrently by having the processor switch among them. The operating system performs this interleaving with a mechanism known as *context switching*. To simplify the rest of this discussion, we consider only a *uniprocessor system* containing a single CPU. We will return to the discussion of *multiprocessor* systems in Section 1.9.2.

The operating system keeps track of all the state information that the process needs in order to run. This state, which is known as the *context*, includes information such as the current values of the PC, the register file, and the contents of main memory. At any point in time, a uniprocessor system can only execute the code for a single process. When the operating system decides to transfer control from the current process to some new process, it performs a *context switch* by saving the context of the current process, restoring the context of the new process, and

Figure 1.12
Process context switching.

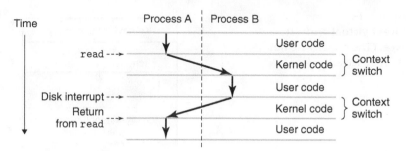

then passing control to the new process. The new process picks up exactly where it left off. Figure 1.12 shows the basic idea for our example `hello` scenario.

There are two concurrent processes in our example scenario: the shell process and the `hello` process. Initially, the shell process is running alone, waiting for input on the command line. When we ask it to run the `hello` program, the shell carries out our request by invoking a special function known as a *system call* that passes control to the operating system. The operating system saves the shell's context, creates a new `hello` process and its context, and then passes control to the new `hello` process. After `hello` terminates, the operating system restores the context of the shell process and passes control back to it, where it waits for the next command-line input.

As Figure 1.12 indicates, the transition from one process to another is managed by the operating system *kernel*. The kernel is the portion of the operating system code that is always resident in memory. When an application program requires some action by the operating system, such as to read or write a file, it executes a special *system call* instruction, transferring control to the kernel. The kernel then performs the requested operation and returns back to the application program. Note that the kernel is not a separate process. Instead, it is a collection of code and data structures that the system uses to manage all the processes.

Implementing the process abstraction requires close cooperation between both the low-level hardware and the operating system software. We will explore how this works, and how applications can create and control their own processes, in Chapter 8.

1.7.2   Threads

Although we normally think of a process as having a single control flow, in modern systems a process can actually consist of multiple execution units, called *threads*, each running in the context of the process and sharing the same code and global data. Threads are an increasingly important programming model because of the requirement for concurrency in network servers, because it is easier to share data between multiple threads than between multiple processes, and because threads are typically more efficient than processes. Multi-threading is also one way to make programs run faster when multiple processors are available, as we will discuss in

Figure 1.13
Process virtual address space. (The regions are not drawn to scale.)

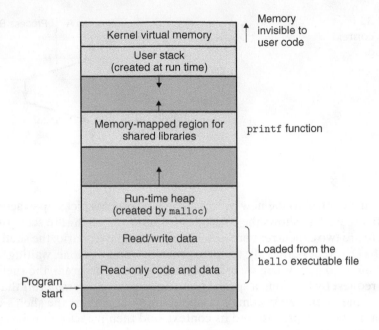

Section 1.9.2. You will learn the basic concepts of concurrency, including how to write threaded programs, in Chapter 12.

1.7.3   Virtual Memory

Virtual memory is an abstraction that provides each process with the illusion that it has exclusive use of the main memory. Each process has the same uniform view of memory, which is known as its *virtual address space*. The virtual address space for Linux processes is shown in Figure 1.13. (Other Unix systems use a similar layout.) In Linux, the topmost region of the address space is reserved for code and data in the operating system that is common to all processes. The lower region of the address space holds the code and data defined by the user's process. Note that addresses in the figure increase from the bottom to the top.

The virtual address space seen by each process consists of a number of well-defined areas, each with a specific purpose. You will learn more about these areas later in the book, but it will be helpful to look briefly at each, starting with the lowest addresses and working our way up:

- *Program code and data.* Code begins at the same fixed address for all processes, followed by data locations that correspond to global C variables. The code and data areas are initialized directly from the contents of an executable object file—in our case, the `hello` executable. You will learn more about this part of the address space when we study linking and loading in Chapter 7.
- *Heap.* The code and data areas are followed immediately by the run-time *heap*. Unlike the code and data areas, which are fixed in size once the process begins

running, the heap expands and contracts dynamically at run time as a result of calls to C standard library routines such as `malloc` and `free`. We will study heaps in detail when we learn about managing virtual memory in Chapter 9.

- *Shared libraries.* Near the middle of the address space is an area that holds the code and data for *shared libraries* such as the C standard library and the math library. The notion of a shared library is a powerful but somewhat difficult concept. You will learn how they work when we study dynamic linking in Chapter 7.

- *Stack.* At the top of the user's virtual address space is the *user stack* that the compiler uses to implement function calls. Like the heap, the user stack expands and contracts dynamically during the execution of the program. In particular, each time we call a function, the stack grows. Each time we return from a function, it contracts. You will learn how the compiler uses the stack in Chapter 3.

- *Kernel virtual memory.* The top region of the address space is reserved for the kernel. Application programs are not allowed to read or write the contents of this area or to directly call functions defined in the kernel code. Instead, they must invoke the kernel to perform these operations.

For virtual memory to work, a sophisticated interaction is required between the hardware and the operating system software, including a hardware translation of every address generated by the processor. The basic idea is to store the contents of a process's virtual memory on disk and then use the main memory as a cache for the disk. Chapter 9 explains how this works and why it is so important to the operation of modern systems.

1.7.4 Files

A *file* is a sequence of bytes, nothing more and nothing less. Every I/O device, including disks, keyboards, displays, and even networks, is modeled as a file. All input and output in the system is performed by reading and writing files, using a small set of system calls known as *Unix I/O.*

This simple and elegant notion of a file is nonetheless very powerful because it provides applications with a uniform view of all the varied I/O devices that might be contained in the system. For example, application programmers who manipulate the contents of a disk file are blissfully unaware of the specific disk technology. Further, the same program will run on different systems that use different disk technologies. You will learn about Unix I/O in Chapter 10.

1.8 Systems Communicate with Other Systems Using Networks

Up to this point in our tour of systems, we have treated a system as an isolated collection of hardware and software. In practice, modern systems are often linked to other systems by networks. From the point of view of an individual system, the

Aside The Linux project

In August 1991, a Finnish graduate student named Linus Torvalds modestly announced a new Unix-like operating system kernel:

```
From: torvalds@klaava.Helsinki.FI (Linus Benedict Torvalds)
Newsgroups: comp.os.minix
Subject: What would you like to see most in minix?
Summary: small poll for my new operating system
Date: 25 Aug 91 20:57:08 GMT

Hello everybody out there using minix -
I'm doing a (free) operating system (just a hobby, won't be big and
professional like gnu) for 386(486) AT clones. This has been brewing
since April, and is starting to get ready. I'd like any feedback on
things people like/dislike in minix, as my OS resembles it somewhat
(same physical layout of the file-system (due to practical reasons)
among other things).

I've currently ported bash(1.08) and gcc(1.40), and things seem to work.
This implies that I'll get something practical within a few months, and
I'd like to know what features most people would want. Any suggestions
are welcome, but I won't promise I'll implement them :-)

Linus (torvalds@kruuna.helsinki.fi)
```

As Torvalds indicates, his starting point for creating Linux was Minix, an operating system developed by Andrew S. Tanenbaum for educational purposes [113].

The rest, as they say, is history. Linux has evolved into a technical and cultural phenomenon. By combining forces with the GNU project, the Linux project has developed a complete, Posix-compliant version of the Unix operating system, including the kernel and all of the supporting infrastructure. Linux is available on a wide array of computers, from handheld devices to mainframe computers. A group at IBM has even ported Linux to a wristwatch!

network can be viewed as just another I/O device, as shown in Figure 1.14. When the system copies a sequence of bytes from main memory to the network adapter, the data flow across the network to another machine, instead of, say, to a local disk drive. Similarly, the system can read data sent from other machines and copy these data to its main memory.

With the advent of global networks such as the Internet, copying information from one machine to another has become one of the most important uses of computer systems. For example, applications such as email, instant messaging, the World Wide Web, FTP, and telnet are all based on the ability to copy information over a network.

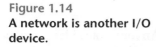

Figure 1.14
A network is another I/O device.

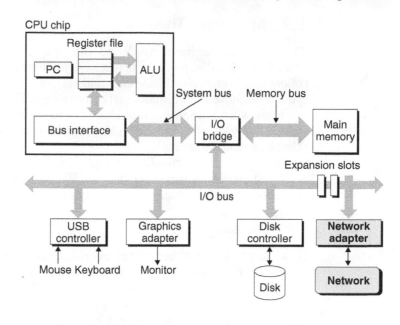

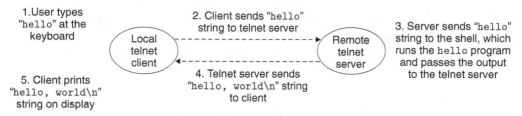

1.User types "hello" at the keyboard

2. Client sends "hello" string to telnet server

3. Server sends "hello" string to the shell, which runs the hello program and passes the output to the telnet server

5. Client prints "hello, world\n" string on display

4. Telnet server sends "hello, world\n" string to client

Figure 1.15   Using telnet to run hello remotely over a network.

Returning to our hello example, we could use the familiar telnet application to run hello on a remote machine. Suppose we use a telnet *client* running on our local machine to connect to a telnet *server* on a remote machine. After we log in to the remote machine and run a shell, the remote shell is waiting to receive an input command. From this point, running the hello program remotely involves the five basic steps shown in Figure 1.15.

After we type in the hello string to the telnet client and hit the enter key, the client sends the string to the telnet server. After the telnet server receives the string from the network, it passes it along to the remote shell program. Next, the remote shell runs the hello program and passes the output line back to the telnet server. Finally, the telnet server forwards the output string across the network to the telnet client, which prints the output string on our local terminal.

This type of exchange between clients and servers is typical of all network applications. In Chapter 11 you will learn how to build network applications and apply this knowledge to build a simple Web server.

1.9   Important Themes

This concludes our initial whirlwind tour of systems. An important idea to take away from this discussion is that a system is more than just hardware. It is a collection of intertwined hardware and systems software that must cooperate in order to achieve the ultimate goal of running application programs. The rest of this book will fill in some details about the hardware and the software, and it will show how, by knowing these details, you can write programs that are faster, more reliable, and more secure.

To close out this chapter, we highlight several important concepts that cut across all aspects of computer systems. We will discuss the importance of these concepts at multiple places within the book.

1.9.1   Amdahl's Law

Gene Amdahl, one of the early pioneers in computing, made a simple but insightful observation about the effectiveness of improving the performance of one part of a system. This observation has come to be known as *Amdahl's law*. The main idea is that when we speed up one part of a system, the effect on the overall system performance depends on both how significant this part was and how much it sped up. Consider a system in which executing some application requires time T_{old}. Suppose some part of the system requires a fraction α of this time, and that we improve its performance by a factor of k. That is, the component originally required time αT_{old}, and it now requires time $(\alpha T_{old})/k$. The overall execution time would thus be

$$T_{new} = (1 - \alpha)T_{old} + (\alpha T_{old})/k$$
$$= T_{old}[(1 - \alpha) + \alpha/k]$$

From this, we can compute the speedup $S = T_{old}/T_{new}$ as

$$S = \frac{1}{(1 - \alpha) + \alpha/k} \tag{1.1}$$

As an example, consider the case where a part of the system that initially consumed 60% of the time ($\alpha = 0.6$) is sped up by a factor of 3 ($k = 3$). Then we get a speedup of $1/[0.4 + 0.6/3] = 1.67\times$. Even though we made a substantial improvement to a major part of the system, our net speedup was significantly less than the speedup for the one part. This is the major insight of Amdahl's law—to significantly speed up the entire system, we must improve the speed of a very large fraction of the overall system.

Practice Problem 1.1 (solution page 28)

Suppose you work as a truck driver, and you have been hired to carry a load of potatoes from Boise, Idaho, to Minneapolis, Minnesota, a total distance of 2,500 kilometers. You estimate you can average 100 km/hr driving within the speed limits, requiring a total of 25 hours for the trip.

Aside   Expressing relative performance

The best way to express a performance improvement is as a ratio of the form T_{old}/T_{new}, where T_{old} is the time required for the original version and T_{new} is the time required by the modified version. This will be a number greater than 1.0 if any real improvement occurred. We use the suffix '$\times$' to indicate such a ratio, where the factor "2.2$\times$" is expressed verbally as "2.2 times."

The more traditional way of expressing relative change as a percentage works well when the change is small, but its definition is ambiguous. Should it be $100 \cdot (T_{old} - T_{new})/T_{new}$, or possibly $100 \cdot (T_{old} - T_{new})/T_{old}$, or something else? In addition, it is less instructive for large changes. Saying that "performance improved by 120%" is more difficult to comprehend than simply saying that the performance improved by 2.2$\times$.

A. You hear on the news that Montana has just abolished its speed limit, which constitutes 1,500 km of the trip. Your truck can travel at 150 km/hr. What will be your speedup for the trip?

B. You can buy a new turbocharger for your truck at www.fasttrucks.com. They stock a variety of models, but the faster you want to go, the more it will cost. How fast must you travel through Montana to get an overall speedup for your trip of 1.67$\times$?

Practice Problem 1.2 (solution page 28)

The marketing department at your company has promised your customers that the next software release will show a 2$\times$ performance improvement. You have been assigned the task of delivering on that promise. You have determined that only 80% of the system can be improved. How much (i.e., what value of k) would you need to improve this part to meet the overall performance target?

One interesting special case of Amdahl's law is to consider the effect of setting k to ∞. That is, we are able to take some part of the system and speed it up to the point at which it takes a negligible amount of time. We then get

$$S_\infty = \frac{1}{(1 - \alpha)} \tag{1.2}$$

So, for example, if we can speed up 60% of the system to the point where it requires close to no time, our net speedup will still only be $1/0.4 = 2.5\times$.

Amdahl's law describes a general principle for improving any process. In addition to its application to speeding up computer systems, it can guide a company trying to reduce the cost of manufacturing razor blades, or a student trying to improve his or her grade point average. Perhaps it is most meaningful in the world of computers, where we routinely improve performance by factors of 2 or more. Such high factors can only be achieved by optimizing large parts of a system.

1.9.2 Concurrency and Parallelism

Throughout the history of digital computers, two demands have been constant forces in driving improvements: we want them to do more, and we want them to run faster. Both of these factors improve when the processor does more things at once. We use the term *concurrency* to refer to the general concept of a system with multiple, simultaneous activities, and the term *parallelism* to refer to the use of concurrency to make a system run faster. Parallelism can be exploited at multiple levels of abstraction in a computer system. We highlight three levels here, working from the highest to the lowest level in the system hierarchy.

Thread-Level Concurrency

Building on the process abstraction, we are able to devise systems where multiple programs execute at the same time, leading to *concurrency*. With threads, we can even have multiple control flows executing within a single process. Support for concurrent execution has been found in computer systems since the advent of time-sharing in the early 1960s. Traditionally, this concurrent execution was only *simulated*, by having a single computer rapidly switch among its executing processes, much as a juggler keeps multiple balls flying through the air. This form of concurrency allows multiple users to interact with a system at the same time, such as when many people want to get pages from a single Web server. It also allows a single user to engage in multiple tasks concurrently, such as having a Web browser in one window, a word processor in another, and streaming music playing at the same time. Until recently, most actual computing was done by a single processor, even if that processor had to switch among multiple tasks. This configuration is known as a *uniprocessor system*.

When we construct a system consisting of multiple processors all under the control of a single operating system kernel, we have a *multiprocessor system*. Such systems have been available for large-scale computing since the 1980s, but they have more recently become commonplace with the advent of *multi-core* processors and *hyperthreading*. Figure 1.16 shows a taxonomy of these different processor types.

Multi-core processors have several CPUs (referred to as "cores") integrated onto a single integrated-circuit chip. Figure 1.17 illustrates the organization of a

Figure 1.16
Categorizing different processor configurations. Multiprocessors are becoming prevalent with the advent of multi-core processors and hyperthreading.

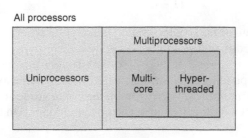

Figure 1.17
Multi-core processor organization. Four processor cores are integrated onto a single chip.

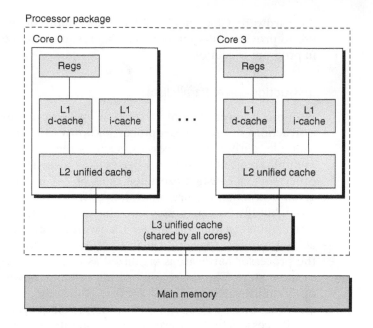

typical multi-core processor, where the chip has four CPU cores, each with its own L1 and L2 caches, and with each L1 cache split into two parts—one to hold recently fetched instructions and one to hold data. The cores share higher levels of cache as well as the interface to main memory. Industry experts predict that they will be able to have dozens, and ultimately hundreds, of cores on a single chip.

Hyperthreading, sometimes called *simultaneous multi-threading*, is a technique that allows a single CPU to execute multiple flows of control. It involves having multiple copies of some of the CPU hardware, such as program counters and register files, while having only single copies of other parts of the hardware, such as the units that perform floating-point arithmetic. Whereas a conventional processor requires around 20,000 clock cycles to shift between different threads, a hyperthreaded processor decides which of its threads to execute on a cycle-by-cycle basis. It enables the CPU to take better advantage of its processing resources. For example, if one thread must wait for some data to be loaded into a cache, the CPU can proceed with the execution of a different thread. As an example, the Intel Core i7 processor can have each core executing two threads, and so a four-core system can actually execute eight threads in parallel.

The use of multiprocessing can improve system performance in two ways. First, it reduces the need to simulate concurrency when performing multiple tasks. As mentioned, even a personal computer being used by a single person is expected to perform many activities concurrently. Second, it can run a single application program faster, but only if that program is expressed in terms of multiple threads that can effectively execute in parallel. Thus, although the principles of concurrency have been formulated and studied for over 50 years, the advent of multi-core and hyperthreaded systems has greatly increased the desire to find ways to write application programs that can exploit the thread-level parallelism available with the hardware. Chapter 12 will look much more deeply into concurrency and its use to provide a sharing of processing resources and to enable more parallelism in program execution.

Instruction-Level Parallelism

At a much lower level of abstraction, modern processors can execute multiple instructions at one time, a property known as *instruction-level parallelism*. For example, early microprocessors, such as the 1978-vintage Intel 8086, required multiple (typically 3–10) clock cycles to execute a single instruction. More recent processors can sustain execution rates of 2–4 instructions per clock cycle. Any given instruction requires much longer from start to finish, perhaps 20 cycles or more, but the processor uses a number of clever tricks to process as many as 100 instructions at a time. In Chapter 4, we will explore the use of *pipelining*, where the actions required to execute an instruction are partitioned into different steps and the processor hardware is organized as a series of stages, each performing one of these steps. The stages can operate in parallel, working on different parts of different instructions. We will see that a fairly simple hardware design can sustain an execution rate close to 1 instruction per clock cycle.

Processors that can sustain execution rates faster than 1 instruction per cycle are known as *superscalar* processors. Most modern processors support superscalar operation. In Chapter 5, we will describe a high-level model of such processors. We will see that application programmers can use this model to understand the performance of their programs. They can then write programs such that the generated code achieves higher degrees of instruction-level parallelism and therefore runs faster.

Single-Instruction, Multiple-Data (SIMD) Parallelism

At the lowest level, many modern processors have special hardware that allows a single instruction to cause multiple operations to be performed in parallel, a mode known as *single-instruction, multiple-data* (SIMD) parallelism. For example, recent generations of Intel and AMD processors have instructions that can add 8 pairs of single-precision floating-point numbers (C data type `float`) in parallel.

These SIMD instructions are provided mostly to speed up applications that process image, sound, and video data. Although some compilers attempt to automatically extract SIMD parallelism from C programs, a more reliable method is to write programs using special *vector* data types supported in compilers such as GCC. We describe this style of programming in Web Aside OPT:SIMD, as a supplement to the more general presentation on program optimization found in Chapter 5.

1.9.3 The Importance of Abstractions in Computer Systems

The use of *abstractions* is one of the most important concepts in computer science. For example, one aspect of good programming practice is to formulate a simple application program interface (API) for a set of functions that allow programmers to use the code without having to delve into its inner workings. Different program-

Figure 1.18
Some abstractions provided by a computer system. A major theme in computer systems is to provide abstract representations at different levels to hide the complexity of the actual implementations.

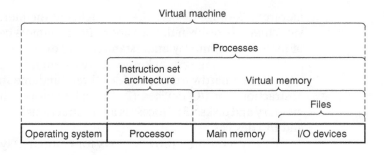

ming languages provide different forms and levels of support for abstraction, such as Java class declarations and C function prototypes.

We have already been introduced to several of the abstractions seen in computer systems, as indicated in Figure 1.18. On the processor side, the *instruction set architecture* provides an abstraction of the actual processor hardware. With this abstraction, a machine-code program behaves as if it were executed on a processor that performs just one instruction at a time. The underlying hardware is far more elaborate, executing multiple instructions in parallel, but always in a way that is consistent with the simple, sequential model. By keeping the same execution model, different processor implementations can execute the same machine code while offering a range of cost and performance.

On the operating system side, we have introduced three abstractions: *files* as an abstraction of I/O devices, *virtual memory* as an abstraction of program memory, and *processes* as an abstraction of a running program. To these abstractions we add a new one: the *virtual machine*, providing an abstraction of the entire computer, including the operating system, the processor, and the programs. The idea of a virtual machine was introduced by IBM in the 1960s, but it has become more prominent recently as a way to manage computers that must be able to run programs designed for multiple operating systems (such as Microsoft Windows, Mac OS X, and Linux) or different versions of the same operating system.

We will return to these abstractions in subsequent sections of the book.

1.10   Summary

A computer system consists of hardware and systems software that cooperate to run application programs. Information inside the computer is represented as groups of bits that are interpreted in different ways, depending on the context. Programs are translated by other programs into different forms, beginning as ASCII text and then translated by compilers and linkers into binary executable files.

Processors read and interpret binary instructions that are stored in main memory. Since computers spend most of their time copying data between memory, I/O devices, and the CPU registers, the storage devices in a system are arranged in a hierarchy, with the CPU registers at the top, followed by multiple levels of hardware cache memories, DRAM main memory, and disk storage. Storage devices that are higher in the hierarchy are faster and more costly per bit than those lower in the hierarchy. Storage devices that are higher in the hierarchy serve as caches for devices that are lower in the hierarchy. Programmers can optimize the performance of their C programs by understanding and exploiting the memory hierarchy.

The operating system kernel serves as an intermediary between the application and the hardware. It provides three fundamental abstractions: (1) Files are abstractions for I/O devices. (2) Virtual memory is an abstraction for both main memory and disks. (3) Processes are abstractions for the processor, main memory, and I/O devices.

Finally, networks provide ways for computer systems to communicate with one another. From the viewpoint of a particular system, the network is just another I/O device.

Bibliographic Notes

Ritchie has written interesting firsthand accounts of the early days of C and Unix [91, 92]. Ritchie and Thompson presented the first published account of Unix [93]. Silberschatz, Galvin, and Gagne [102] provide a comprehensive history of the different flavors of Unix. The GNU (www.gnu.org) and Linux (www.linux .org) Web pages have loads of current and historical information. The Posix standards are available online at (www.unix.org).

Solutions to Practice Problems

Solution to Problem 1.1 (page 22)

This problem illustrates that Amdahl's law applies to more than just computer systems.

A. In terms of Equation 1.1, we have $\alpha = 0.6$ and $k = 1.5$. More directly, traveling the 1,500 kilometers through Montana will require 10 hours, and the rest of the trip also requires 10 hours. This will give a speedup of $25/(10 + 10) = 1.25\times$.

B. In terms of Equation 1.1, we have $\alpha = 0.6$, and we require $S = 1.67$, from which we can solve for k. More directly, to speed up the trip by $1.67\times$, we must decrease the overall time to 15 hours. The parts outside of Montana will still require 10 hours, so we must drive through Montana in 5 hours. This requires traveling at 300 km/hr, which is pretty fast for a truck!

Solution to Problem 1.2 (page 23)

Amdahl's law is best understood by working through some examples. This one requires you to look at Equation 1.1 from an unusual perspective.

This problem is a simple application of the equation. You are given $S = 2$ and $\alpha = 0.8$, and you must then solve for k:

$$2 = \frac{1}{(1 - 0.8) + 0.8/k}$$

$$0.4 + 1.6/k = 1.0$$

$$k = 2.67$$

Part I

Program Structure and Execution

Our exploration of computer systems starts by studying the computer itself, comprising a processor and a memory subsystem. At the core, we require ways to represent basic data types, such as approximations to integer and real arithmetic. From there, we can consider how machine-level instructions manipulate data and how a compiler translates C programs into these instructions. Next, we study several methods of implementing a processor to gain a better understanding of how hardware resources are used to execute instructions. Once we understand compilers and machine-level code, we can examine how to maximize program performance by writing C programs that, when compiled, achieve the maximum possible performance. We conclude with the design of the memory subsystem, one of the most complex components of a modern computer system.

This part of the book will give you a deep understanding of how application programs are represented and executed. You will gain skills that help you write programs that are secure, reliable, and make the best use of the computing resources.

CHAPTER

2

Representing and Manipulating Information

Modern computers store and process information represented as two-valued signals. These lowly binary digits, or *bits*, form the basis of the digital revolution. The familiar decimal, or base-10, representation has been in use for over 1,000 years, having been developed in India, improved by Arab mathematicians in the 12th century, and brought to the West in the 13th century by the Italian mathematician Leonardo Pisano (ca. 1170 to ca. 1250), better known as Fibonacci. Using decimal notation is natural for 10-fingered humans, but binary values work better when building machines that store and process information. Two-valued signals can readily be represented, stored, and transmitted—for example, as the presence or absence of a hole in a punched card, as a high or low voltage on a wire, or as a magnetic domain oriented clockwise or counterclockwise. The electronic circuitry for storing and performing computations on two-valued signals is very simple and reliable, enabling manufacturers to integrate millions, or even billions, of such circuits on a single silicon chip.

In isolation, a single bit is not very useful. When we group bits together and apply some *interpretation* that gives meaning to the different possible bit patterns, however, we can represent the elements of any finite set. For example, using a binary number system, we can use groups of bits to encode nonnegative numbers. By using a standard character code, we can encode the letters and symbols in a document. We cover both of these encodings in this chapter, as well as encodings to represent negative numbers and to approximate real numbers.

We consider the three most important representations of numbers. *Unsigned* encodings are based on traditional binary notation, representing numbers greater than or equal to 0. *Two's-complement* encodings are the most common way to represent *signed* integers, that is, numbers that may be either positive or negative. *Floating-point* encodings are a base-2 version of scientific notation for representing real numbers. Computers implement arithmetic operations, such as addition and multiplication, with these different representations, similar to the corresponding operations on integers and real numbers.

Computer representations use a limited number of bits to encode a number, and hence some operations can *overflow* when the results are too large to be represented. This can lead to some surprising results. For example, on most of today's computers (those using a 32-bit representation for data type int), computing the expression

```
200 * 300 * 400 * 500
```

yields −884,901,888. This runs counter to the properties of integer arithmetic—computing the product of a set of positive numbers has yielded a negative result.

On the other hand, integer computer arithmetic satisfies many of the familiar properties of true integer arithmetic. For example, multiplication is associative and commutative, so that computing any of the following C expressions yields −884,901,888:

```
(500  *   400) * (300 * 200)
((500 *   400) * 300) * 200
((200 *   500) * 300) * 400
400   * (200 * (300 * 500))
```

The computer might not generate the expected result, but at least it is consistent!

Floating-point arithmetic has altogether different mathematical properties. The product of a set of positive numbers will always be positive, although overflow will yield the special value $+\infty$. Floating-point arithmetic is not associative due to the finite precision of the representation. For example, the C expression (3.14+1e20)-1e20 will evaluate to 0.0 on most machines, while 3.14+(1e20-1e20) will evaluate to 3.14. The different mathematical properties of integer versus floating-point arithmetic stem from the difference in how they handle the finiteness of their representations—integer representations can encode a comparatively small range of values, but do so precisely, while floating-point representations can encode a wide range of values, but only approximately.

By studying the actual number representations, we can understand the ranges of values that can be represented and the properties of the different arithmetic operations. This understanding is critical to writing programs that work correctly over the full range of numeric values and that are portable across different combinations of machine, operating system, and compiler. As we will describe, a number of computer security vulnerabilities have arisen due to some of the subtleties of computer arithmetic. Whereas in an earlier era program bugs would only inconvenience people when they happened to be triggered, there are now legions of hackers who try to exploit any bug they can find to obtain unauthorized access to other people's systems. This puts a higher level of obligation on programmers to understand how their programs work and how they can be made to behave in undesirable ways.

Computers use several different binary representations to encode numeric values. You will need to be familiar with these representations as you progress into machine-level programming in Chapter 3. We describe these encodings in this chapter and show you how to reason about number representations.

We derive several ways to perform arithmetic operations by directly manipulating the bit-level representations of numbers. Understanding these techniques will be important for understanding the machine-level code generated by compilers in their attempt to optimize the performance of arithmetic expression evaluation.

Our treatment of this material is based on a core set of mathematical principles. We start with the basic definitions of the encodings and then derive such properties as the range of representable numbers, their bit-level representations, and the properties of the arithmetic operations. We believe it is important for you to examine the material from this abstract viewpoint, because programmers need to have a clear understanding of how computer arithmetic relates to the more familiar integer and real arithmetic.

The C++ programming language is built upon C, using the exact same numeric representations and operations. Everything said in this chapter about C also holds for C++. The Java language definition, on the other hand, created a new set of standards for numeric representations and operations. Whereas the C standards are designed to allow a wide range of implementations, the Java standard is quite specific on the formats and encodings of data. We highlight the representations and operations supported by Java at several places in the chapter.

Aside How to read this chapter

In this chapter, we examine the fundamental properties of how numbers and other forms of data are represented on a computer and the properties of the operations that computers perform on these data. This requires us to delve into the language of mathematics, writing formulas and equations and showing derivations of important properties.

To help you navigate this exposition, we have structured the presentation to first state a property as a *principle* in mathematical notation. We then illustrate this principle with examples and an informal discussion. We recommend that you go back and forth between the statement of the principle and the examples and discussion until you have a solid intuition for what is being said and what is important about the property. For more complex properties, we also provide a *derivation*, structured much like a mathematical proof. You should try to understand these derivations eventually, but you could skip over them on first reading.

We also encourage you to work on the practice problems as you proceed through the presentation. The practice problems engage you in *active learning*, helping you put thoughts into action. With these as background, you will find it much easier to go back and follow the derivations. Be assured, as well, that the mathematical skills required to understand this material are within reach of someone with a good grasp of high school algebra.

2.1 Information Storage

Rather than accessing individual bits in memory, most computers use blocks of 8 bits, or *bytes*, as the smallest addressable unit of memory. A machine-level program views memory as a very large array of bytes, referred to as *virtual memory*. Every byte of memory is identified by a unique number, known as its *address*, and the set of all possible addresses is known as the *virtual address space*. As indicated by its name, this virtual address space is just a conceptual image presented to the machine-level program. The actual implementation (presented in Chapter 9) uses a combination of dynamic random access memory (DRAM), flash memory, disk storage, special hardware, and operating system software to provide the program with what appears to be a monolithic byte array.

In subsequent chapters, we will cover how the compiler and run-time system partitions this memory space into more manageable units to store the different *program objects*, that is, program data, instructions, and control information. Various mechanisms are used to allocate and manage the storage for different parts of the program. This management is all performed within the virtual address space. For example, the value of a pointer in C—whether it points to an integer, a structure, or some other program object—is the virtual address of the first byte of some block of storage. The C compiler also associates *type* information with each pointer, so that it can generate different machine-level code to access the value stored at the location designated by the pointer depending on the type of that value. Although the C compiler maintains this type information, the actual machine-level program it generates has no information about data types. It simply treats each program object as a block of bytes and the program itself as a sequence of bytes.

Aside   The evolution of the C programming language

As was described in an aside on page 4, the C programming language was first developed by Dennis Ritchie of Bell Laboratories for use with the Unix operating system (also developed at Bell Labs). At the time, most system programs, such as operating systems, had to be written largely in assembly code in order to have access to the low-level representations of different data types. For example, it was not feasible to write a memory allocator, such as is provided by the `malloc` library function, in other high-level languages of that era.

The original Bell Labs version of C was documented in the first edition of the book by Brian Kernighan and Dennis Ritchie [60]. Over time, C has evolved through the efforts of several standardization groups. The first major revision of the original Bell Labs C led to the ANSI C standard in 1989, by a group working under the auspices of the American National Standards Institute. ANSI C was a major departure from Bell Labs C, especially in the way functions are declared. ANSI C is described in the second edition of Kernighan and Ritchie's book [61], which is still considered one of the best references on C.

The International Standards Organization took over responsibility for standardizing the C language, adopting a version that was substantially the same as ANSI C in 1990 and hence is referred to as "ISO C90."

This same organization sponsored an updating of the language in 1999, yielding "ISO C99." Among other things, this version introduced some new data types and provided support for text strings requiring characters not found in the English language. A more recent standard was approved in 2011, and hence is named "ISO C11," again adding more data types and features. Most of these recent additions have been *backward compatible*, meaning that programs written according to the earlier standard (at least as far back as ISO C90) will have the same behavior when compiled according to the newer standards.

The GNU Compiler Collection (GCC) can compile programs according to the conventions of several different versions of the C language, based on different command-line options, as shown in Figure 2.1. For example, to compile program `prog.c` according to ISO C11, we could give the command line

```
linux> gcc -std=c11 prog.c
```

The options `-ansi` and `-std=c89` have identical effect—the code is compiled according to the ANSI or ISO C90 standard. (C90 is sometimes referred to as "C89," since its standardization effort began in 1989.) The option `-std=c99` causes the compiler to follow the ISO C99 convention.

As of the writing of this book, when no option is specified, the program will be compiled according to a version of C based on ISO C90, but including some features of C99, some of C11, some of C++, and others specific to GCC. The GNU project is developing a version that combines ISO C11, plus other features, that can be specified with the command-line option `-std=gnu11`. (Currently, this implementation is incomplete.) This will become the default version.

C version	GCC command-line option
GNU 89	*none*, `-std=gnu89`
ANSI, ISO C90	`-ansi`, `-std=c89`
ISO C99	`-std=c99`
ISO C11	`-std=c11`

Figure 2.1   **Specifying different versions of C to GCC.**

New to C? The role of pointers in C

Pointers are a central feature of C. They provide the mechanism for referencing elements of data structures, including arrays. Just like a variable, a pointer has two aspects: its *value* and its *type*. The value indicates the location of some object, while its type indicates what kind of object (e.g., integer or floating-point number) is stored at that location.

Truly understanding pointers requires examining their representation and implementation at the machine level. This will be a major focus in Chapter 3, culminating in an in-depth presentation in Section 3.10.1.

2.1.1 Hexadecimal Notation

A single byte consists of 8 bits. In binary notation, its value ranges from 00000000_2 to 11111111_2. When viewed as a decimal integer, its value ranges from 0_{10} to 255_{10}. Neither notation is very convenient for describing bit patterns. Binary notation is too verbose, while with decimal notation it is tedious to convert to and from bit patterns. Instead, we write bit patterns as base-16, or *hexadecimal* numbers. Hexadecimal (or simply "hex") uses digits '0' through '9' along with characters 'A' through 'F' to represent 16 possible values. Figure 2.2 shows the decimal and binary values associated with the 16 hexadecimal digits. Written in hexadecimal, the value of a single byte can range from 00_{16} to FF_{16}.

In C, numeric constants starting with 0x or 0X are interpreted as being in hexadecimal. The characters 'A' through 'F' may be written in either upper- or lowercase. For example, we could write the number $FA1D37B_{16}$ as 0xFA1D37B, as 0xfa1d37b, or even mixing upper- and lowercase (e.g., 0xFa1D37b). We will use the C notation for representing hexadecimal values in this book.

A common task in working with machine-level programs is to manually convert between decimal, binary, and hexadecimal representations of bit patterns. Converting between binary and hexadecimal is straightforward, since it can be performed one hexadecimal digit at a time. Digits can be converted by referring to a chart such as that shown in Figure 2.2. One simple trick for doing the conversion in your head is to memorize the decimal equivalents of hex digits A, C, and F.

Hex digit	0	1	2	3	4	5	6	7
Decimal value	0	1	2	3	4	5	6	7
Binary value	0000	0001	0010	0011	0100	0101	0110	0111
Hex digit	8	9	A	B	C	D	E	F
Decimal value	8	9	10	11	12	13	14	15
Binary value	1000	1001	1010	1011	1100	1101	1110	1111

Figure 2.2 **Hexadecimal notation.** Each hex digit encodes one of 16 values.

The hex values B, D, and E can be translated to decimal by computing their values relative to the first three.

For example, suppose you are given the number 0x173A4C. You can convert this to binary format by expanding each hexadecimal digit, as follows:

Hexadecimal	1	7	3	A	4	C
Binary	0001	0111	0011	1010	0100	1100

This gives the binary representation 000101110011101001001100.

Conversely, given a binary number 1111001010110110110011, you convert it to hexadecimal by first splitting it into groups of 4 bits each. Note, however, that if the total number of bits is not a multiple of 4, you should make the *leftmost* group be the one with fewer than 4 bits, effectively padding the number with leading zeros. Then you translate each group of bits into the corresponding hexadecimal digit:

Binary	11	1100	1010	1101	1011	0011
Hexadecimal	3	C	A	D	B	3

Practice Problem 2.1 (solution page 143)

Perform the following number conversions:

A. 0x39A7F8 to binary

B. binary 1100100101111011 to hexadecimal

C. 0xD5E4C to binary

D. binary 1001101110011110110101 to hexadecimal

When a value x is a power of 2, that is, $x = 2^n$ for some nonnegative integer n, we can readily write x in hexadecimal form by remembering that the binary representation of x is simply 1 followed by n zeros. The hexadecimal digit 0 represents 4 binary zeros. So, for n written in the form $i + 4j$, where $0 \leq i \leq 3$, we can write x with a leading hex digit of 1 ($i = 0$), 2 ($i = 1$), 4 ($i = 2$), or 8 ($i = 3$), followed by j hexadecimal 0s. As an example, for $x = 2,048 = 2^{11}$, we have $n = 11 = 3 + 4 \cdot 2$, giving hexadecimal representation 0x800.

Practice Problem 2.2 (solution page 143)

Fill in the blank entries in the following table, giving the decimal and hexadecimal representations of different powers of 2:

n	2^n (decimal)	2^n (hexadecimal)
9	512	0x200
19	_____	_____
_____	16,384	_____
_____	_____	0x10000
17	_____	_____
_____	32	_____
_____	_____	0x80

Converting between decimal and hexadecimal representations requires using multiplication or division to handle the general case. To convert a decimal number x to hexadecimal, we can repeatedly divide x by 16, giving a quotient q and a remainder r, such that $x = q \cdot 16 + r$. We then use the hexadecimal digit representing r as the least significant digit and generate the remaining digits by repeating the process on q. As an example, consider the conversion of decimal 314,156:

$$314{,}156 = 19{,}634 \cdot 16 + 12 \quad \text{(C)}$$
$$19{,}634 = 1{,}227 \cdot 16 + 2 \quad \text{(2)}$$
$$1{,}227 = 76 \cdot 16 + 11 \quad \text{(B)}$$
$$76 = 4 \cdot 16 + 12 \quad \text{(C)}$$
$$4 = 0 \cdot 16 + 4 \quad \text{(4)}$$

From this we can read off the hexadecimal representation as 0x4CB2C.

Conversely, to convert a hexadecimal number to decimal, we can multiply each of the hexadecimal digits by the appropriate power of 16. For example, given the number 0x7AF, we compute its decimal equivalent as $7 \cdot 16^2 + 10 \cdot 16 + 15 = 7 \cdot 256 + 10 \cdot 16 + 15 = 1{,}792 + 160 + 15 = 1{,}967$.

Practice Problem 2.3 (solution page 144)

A single byte can be represented by 2 hexadecimal digits. Fill in the missing entries in the following table, giving the decimal, binary, and hexadecimal values of different byte patterns:

Decimal	Binary	Hexadecimal
0	0000 0000	0x00
167	_____	_____
62	_____	_____
188	_____	_____
_____	0011 0111	_____
_____	1000 1000	_____
_____	1111 0011	_____

Aside   Converting between decimal and hexadecimal

For converting larger values between decimal and hexadecimal, it is best to let a computer or calculator do the work. There are numerous tools that can do this. One simple way is to use any of the standard search engines, with queries such as

>   Convert 0xabcd to decimal

or

>   123 in hex

Decimal	Binary	Hexadecimal
_____	_____	0x52
_____	_____	0xAC
_____	_____	0xE7

Practice Problem 2.4 (solution page 144)

Without converting the numbers to decimal or binary, try to solve the following arithmetic problems, giving the answers in hexadecimal. *Hint:* Just modify the methods you use for performing decimal addition and subtraction to use base 16.

A. 0x503c + 0x8 = _____

B. 0x503c − 0x40 = _____

C. 0x503c + 64 = _____

D. 0x50ea − 0x503c = _____

2.1.2   Data Sizes

Every computer has a *word size*, indicating the nominal size of pointer data. Since a virtual address is encoded by such a word, the most important system parameter determined by the word size is the maximum size of the virtual address space. That is, for a machine with a w-bit word size, the virtual addresses can range from 0 to $2^w - 1$, giving the program access to at most 2^w bytes.

In recent years, there has been a widespread shift from machines with 32-bit word sizes to those with word sizes of 64 bits. This occurred first for high-end machines designed for large-scale scientific and database applications, followed by desktop and laptop machines, and most recently for the processors found in smartphones. A 32-bit word size limits the virtual address space to 4 gigabytes (written 4 GB), that is, just over 4×10^9 bytes. Scaling up to a 64-bit word size leads to a virtual address space of 16 *exabytes*, or around 1.84×10^{19} bytes.

Most 64-bit machines can also run programs compiled for use on 32-bit machines, a form of backward compatibility. So, for example, when a program prog.c is compiled with the directive

```
linux> gcc -m32 prog.c
```

then this program will run correctly on either a 32-bit or a 64-bit machine. On the other hand, a program compiled with the directive

```
linux> gcc -m64 prog.c
```

will only run on a 64-bit machine. We will therefore refer to programs as being either "32-bit programs" or "64-bit programs," since the distinction lies in how a program is compiled, rather than the type of machine on which it runs.

Computers and compilers support multiple data formats using different ways to encode data, such as integers and floating point, as well as different lengths. For example, many machines have instructions for manipulating single bytes, as well as integers represented as 2-, 4-, and 8-byte quantities. They also support floating-point numbers represented as 4- and 8-byte quantities.

The C language supports multiple data formats for both integer and floating-point data. Figure 2.3 shows the number of bytes typically allocated for different C data types. (We discuss the relation between what is guaranteed by the C standard versus what is typical in Section 2.2.) The exact numbers of bytes for some data types depends on how the program is compiled. We show sizes for typical 32-bit and 64-bit programs. Integer data can be either *signed*, able to represent negative, zero, and positive values, or *unsigned*, only allowing nonnegative values. Data type char represents a single byte. Although the name char derives from the fact that it is used to store a single character in a text string, it can also be used to store integer values. Data types short, int, and long are intended to provide a range of

C declaration		Bytes	
Signed	Unsigned	32-bit	64-bit
[signed] char	unsigned char	1	1
short	unsigned short	2	2
int	unsigned	4	4
long	unsigned long	4	8
int32_t	uint32_t	4	4
int64_t	uint64_t	8	8
char *		4	8
float		4	4
double		8	8

Figure 2.3 **Typical sizes (in bytes) of basic C data types.** The number of bytes allocated varies with how the program is compiled. This chart shows the values typical of 32-bit and 64-bit programs.

sizes. Even when compiled for 64-bit systems, data type int is usually just 4 bytes. Data type long commonly has 4 bytes in 32-bit programs and 8 bytes in 64-bit programs.

To avoid the vagaries of relying on "typical" sizes and different compiler settings, ISO C99 introduced a class of data types where the data sizes are fixed regardless of compiler and machine settings. Among these are data types int32_t and int64_t, having exactly 4 and 8 bytes, respectively. Using fixed-size integer types is the best way for programmers to have close control over data representations.

Most of the data types encode signed values, unless prefixed by the keyword unsigned or using the specific unsigned declaration for fixed-size data types. The exception to this is data type char. Although most compilers and machines treat these as signed data, the C standard does not guarantee this. Instead, as indicated by the square brackets, the programmer should use the declaration signed char to guarantee a 1-byte signed value. In many contexts, however, the program's behavior is insensitive to whether data type char is signed or unsigned.

The C language allows a variety of ways to order the keywords and to include or omit optional keywords. As examples, all of the following declarations have identical meaning:

```
unsigned long
unsigned long int
long unsigned
long unsigned int
```

We will consistently use the forms found in Figure 2.3.

Figure 2.3 also shows that a pointer (e.g., a variable declared as being of type char *) uses the full word size of the program. Most machines also support two different floating-point formats: single precision, declared in C as float, and double precision, declared in C as double. These formats use 4 and 8 bytes, respectively.

Programmers should strive to make their programs portable across different machines and compilers. One aspect of portability is to make the program insensitive to the exact sizes of the different data types. The C standards set lower bounds on the numeric ranges of the different data types, as will be covered later, but there are no upper bounds (except with the fixed-size types). With 32-bit machines and 32-bit programs being the dominant combination from around 1980 until around 2010, many programs have been written assuming the allocations listed for 32-bit programs in Figure 2.3. With the transition to 64-bit machines, many hidden word size dependencies have arisen as bugs in migrating these programs to new machines. For example, many programmers historically assumed that an object declared as type int could be used to store a pointer. This works fine for most 32-bit programs, but it leads to problems for 64-bit programs.

2.1.3   Addressing and Byte Ordering

For program objects that span multiple bytes, we must establish two conventions: what the address of the object will be, and how we will order the bytes in memory. In virtually all machines, a multi-byte object is stored as a contiguous sequence of bytes, with the address of the object given by the smallest address of the bytes used. For example, suppose a variable x of type int has address 0x100; that is, the value of the address expression &x is 0x100. Then (assuming data type int has a 32-bit representation) the 4 bytes of x would be stored in memory locations 0x100, 0x101, 0x102, and 0x103.

For ordering the bytes representing an object, there are two common conventions. Consider a w-bit integer having a bit representation $[x_{w-1}, x_{w-2}, \ldots, x_1, x_0]$, where x_{w-1} is the most significant bit and x_0 is the least. Assuming w is a multiple of 8, these bits can be grouped as bytes, with the most significant byte having bits $[x_{w-1}, x_{w-2}, \ldots, x_{w-8}]$, the least significant byte having bits $[x_7, x_6, \ldots, x_0]$, and the other bytes having bits from the middle. Some machines choose to store the object in memory ordered from least significant byte to most, while other machines store them from most to least. The former convention—where the least significant byte comes first—is referred to as *little endian*. The latter convention—where the most significant byte comes first—is referred to as *big endian*.

Suppose the variable x of type int and at address 0x100 has a hexadecimal value of 0x01234567. The ordering of the bytes within the address range 0x100 through 0x103 depends on the type of machine:

Big endian

	0x100	0x101	0x102	0x103	
...	01	23	45	67	...

Little endian

	0x100	0x101	0x102	0x103	
...	67	45	23	01	...

Note that in the word 0x01234567 the high-order byte has hexadecimal value 0x01, while the low-order byte has value 0x67.

Most Intel-compatible machines operate exclusively in little-endian mode. On the other hand, most machines from IBM and Oracle (arising from their acquisi-

Aside Origin of "endian"

Here is how Jonathan Swift, writing in 1726, described the history of the controversy between big and little endians:

> . . . Lilliput and Blefuscu . . . have, as I was going to tell you, been engaged in a most obstinate war for six-and-thirty moons past. It began upon the following occasion. It is allowed on all hands, that the primitive way of breaking eggs, before we eat them, was upon the larger end; but his present majesty's grandfather, while he was a boy, going to eat an egg, and breaking it according to the ancient practice, happened to cut one of his fingers. Whereupon the emperor his father published an edict, commanding all his subjects, upon great penalties, to break the smaller end of their eggs. The people so highly resented this law, that our histories tell us, there have been six rebellions raised on that account; wherein one emperor lost his life, and another his crown. These civil commotions were constantly fomented by the monarchs of Blefuscu; and when they were quelled, the exiles always fled for refuge to that empire. It is computed that eleven thousand persons have at several times suffered death, rather than submit to break their eggs at the smaller end. Many hundred large volumes have been published upon this controversy: but the books of the Big-endians have been long forbidden, and the whole party rendered incapable by law of holding employments. (Jonathan Swift. Gulliver's Travels, Benjamin Motte, 1726.)

In his day, Swift was satirizing the continued conflicts between England (Lilliput) and France (Blefuscu). Danny Cohen, an early pioneer in networking protocols, first applied these terms to refer to byte ordering [24], and the terminology has been widely adopted.

tion of Sun Microsystems in 2010) operate in big-endian mode. Note that we said "most." The conventions do not split precisely along corporate boundaries. For example, both IBM and Oracle manufacture machines that use Intel-compatible processors and hence are little endian. Many recent microprocessor chips are *bi-endian*, meaning that they can be configured to operate as either little- or big-endian machines. In practice, however, byte ordering becomes fixed once a particular operating system is chosen. For example, ARM microprocessors, used in many cell phones, have hardware that can operate in either little- or big-endian mode, but the two most common operating systems for these chips—Android (from Google) and IOS (from Apple)—operate only in little-endian mode.

People get surprisingly emotional about which byte ordering is the proper one. In fact, the terms "little endian" and "big endian" come from the book *Gulliver's Travels* by Jonathan Swift, where two warring factions could not agree as to how a soft-boiled egg should be opened—by the little end or by the big. Just like the egg issue, there is no technological reason to choose one byte ordering convention over the other, and hence the arguments degenerate into bickering about sociopolitical issues. As long as one of the conventions is selected and adhered to consistently, the choice is arbitrary.

For most application programmers, the byte orderings used by their machines are totally invisible; programs compiled for either class of machine give identical results. At times, however, byte ordering becomes an issue. The first is when binary data are communicated over a network between different machines. A common problem is for data produced by a little-endian machine to be sent to a big-endian machine, or vice versa, leading to the bytes within the words being in reverse order for the receiving program. To avoid such problems, code written for networking applications must follow established conventions for byte ordering to make sure the sending machine converts its internal representation to the network standard, while the receiving machine converts the network standard to its internal representation. We will see examples of these conversions in Chapter 11.

A second case where byte ordering becomes important is when looking at the byte sequences representing integer data. This occurs often when inspecting machine-level programs. As an example, the following line occurs in a file that gives a text representation of the machine-level code for an Intel x86-64 processor:

```
4004d3:   01 05 43 0b 20 00        add     %eax,0x200b43(%rip)
```

This line was generated by a *disassembler*, a tool that determines the instruction sequence represented by an executable program file. We will learn more about disassemblers and how to interpret lines such as this in Chapter 3. For now, we simply note that this line states that the hexadecimal byte sequence 01 05 43 0b 20 00 is the byte-level representation of an instruction that adds a word of data to the value stored at an address computed by adding 0x200b43 to the current value of the *program counter*, the address of the next instruction to be executed. If we take the final 4 bytes of the sequence 43 0b 20 00 and write them in reverse order, we have 00 20 0b 43. Dropping the leading 0, we have the value 0x200b43, the numeric value written on the right. Having bytes appear in reverse order is a common occurrence when reading machine-level program representations generated for little-endian machines such as this one. The natural way to write a byte sequence is to have the lowest-numbered byte on the left and the highest on the right, but this is contrary to the normal way of writing numbers with the most significant digit on the left and the least on the right.

A third case where byte ordering becomes visible is when programs are written that circumvent the normal type system. In the C language, this can be done using a *cast* or a *union* to allow an object to be referenced according to a different data type from which it was created. Such coding tricks are strongly discouraged for most application programming, but they can be quite useful and even necessary for system-level programming.

Figure 2.4 shows C code that uses casting to access and print the byte representations of different program objects. We use typedef to define data type byte_pointer as a pointer to an object of type unsigned char. Such a byte pointer references a sequence of bytes where each byte is considered to be a nonnegative integer. The first routine show_bytes is given the address of a sequence of bytes, indicated by a byte pointer, and a byte count. The byte count is specified as having data type size_t, the preferred data type for expressing the sizes of data structures. It prints the individual bytes in hexadecimal. The C formatting directive %.2x indicates that an integer should be printed in hexadecimal with at least 2 digits.

```
1    #include <stdio.h>
2
3    typedef unsigned char *byte_pointer;
4
5    void show_bytes(byte_pointer start, size_t len) {
6        int i;
7        for (i = 0; i < len; i++)
8            printf(" %.2x", start[i]);
9        printf("\n");
10   }
11
12   void show_int(int x) {
13       show_bytes((byte_pointer) &x, sizeof(int));
14   }
15
16   void show_float(float x) {
17       show_bytes((byte_pointer) &x, sizeof(float));
18   }
19
20   void show_pointer(void *x) {
21       show_bytes((byte_pointer) &x, sizeof(void *));
22   }
```

Figure 2.4 Code to print the byte representation of program objects. This code uses casting to circumvent the type system. Similar functions are easily defined for other data types.

Procedures show_int, show_float, and show_pointer demonstrate how to use procedure show_bytes to print the byte representations of C program objects of type int, float, and void *, respectively. Observe that they simply pass show_ bytes a pointer &x to their argument x, casting the pointer to be of type unsigned char *. This cast indicates to the compiler that the program should consider the pointer to be to a sequence of bytes rather than to an object of the original data type. This pointer will then be to the lowest byte address occupied by the object.

These procedures use the C sizeof operator to determine the number of bytes used by the object. In general, the expression sizeof(T) returns the number of bytes required to store an object of type T. Using sizeof rather than a fixed value is one step toward writing code that is portable across different machine types.

We ran the code shown in Figure 2.5 on several different machines, giving the results shown in Figure 2.6. The following machines were used:

Linux 32   Intel IA32 processor running Linux.

Windows   Intel IA32 processor running Windows.

Sun   Sun Microsystems SPARC processor running Solaris. (These machines are now produced by Oracle.)

Linux 64   Intel x86-64 processor running Linux.

code/data/show-bytes.c

```
1   void test_show_bytes(int val) {
2       int ival = val;
3       float fval = (float) ival;
4       int *pval = &ival;
5       show_int(ival);
6       show_float(fval);
7       show_pointer(pval);
8   }
```

code/data/show-bytes.c

Figure 2.5 Byte representation examples. This code prints the byte representations of sample data objects.

Machine	Value	Type	Bytes (hex)
Linux 32	12,345	int	39 30 00 00
Windows	12,345	int	39 30 00 00
Sun	12,345	int	00 00 30 39
Linux 64	12,345	int	39 30 00 00
Linux 32	12,345.0	float	00 e4 40 46
Windows	12,345.0	float	00 e4 40 46
Sun	12,345.0	float	46 40 e4 00
Linux 64	12,345.0	float	00 e4 40 46
Linux 32	&ival	int *	e4 f9 ff bf
Windows	&ival	int *	b4 cc 22 00
Sun	&ival	int *	ef ff fa 0c
Linux 64	&ival	int *	b8 11 e5 ff ff 7f 00 00

Figure 2.6 Byte representations of different data values. Results for int and float are identical, except for byte ordering. Pointer values are machine dependent.

Our argument 12,345 has hexadecimal representation 0x00003039. For the int data, we get identical results for all machines, except for the byte ordering. In particular, we can see that the least significant byte value of 0x39 is printed first for Linux 32, Windows, and Linux 64, indicating little-endian machines, and last for Sun, indicating a big-endian machine. Similarly, the bytes of the float data are identical, except for the byte ordering. On the other hand, the pointer values are completely different. The different machine/operating system configurations use different conventions for storage allocation. One feature to note is that the Linux 32, Windows, and Sun machines use 4-byte addresses, while the Linux 64 machine uses 8-byte addresses.

New to C?   Naming data types with `typedef`

The `typedef` declaration in C provides a way of giving a name to a data type. This can be a great help in improving code readability, since deeply nested type declarations can be difficult to decipher.

The syntax for `typedef` is exactly like that of declaring a variable, except that it uses a type name rather than a variable name. Thus, the declaration of `byte_pointer` in Figure 2.4 has the same form as the declaration of a variable of type `unsigned char *`.

For example, the declaration

```
typedef int *int_pointer;
int_pointer ip;
```

defines type `int_pointer` to be a pointer to an `int`, and declares a variable `ip` of this type. Alternatively, we could declare this variable directly as

```
int *ip;
```

New to C?   Formatted printing with `printf`

The `printf` function (along with its cousins `fprintf` and `sprintf`) provides a way to print information with considerable control over the formatting details. The first argument is a *format string*, while any remaining arguments are values to be printed. Within the format string, each character sequence starting with '%' indicates how to format the next argument. Typical examples include `%d` to print a decimal integer, `%f` to print a floating-point number, and `%c` to print a character having the character code given by the argument.

Specifying the formatting of fixed-size data types, such as `int_32t`, is a bit more involved, as is described in the aside on page 67.

Observe that although the floating-point and the integer data both encode the numeric value 12,345, they have very different byte patterns: 0x00003039 for the integer and 0x4640E400 for floating point. In general, these two formats use different encoding schemes. If we expand these hexadecimal patterns into binary form and shift them appropriately, we find a sequence of 13 matching bits, indicated by a sequence of asterisks, as follows:

```
    0    0    0    0    3    0    3    9
00000000000000000011000000111001
                  *************
              4    6    4    0    E    4    0    0
            01000110010000001110010000000000
```

This is not coincidental. We will return to this example when we study floating-point formats.

New to C? Pointers and arrays

In function show_bytes (Figure 2.4), we see the close connection between pointers and arrays, as will be discussed in detail in Section 3.8. We see that this function has an argument start of type byte_pointer (which has been defined to be a pointer to unsigned char), but we see the array reference start[i] on line 8. In C, we can dereference a pointer with array notation, and we can reference array elements with pointer notation. In this example, the reference start[i] indicates that we want to read the byte that is i positions beyond the location pointed to by start.

New to C? Pointer creation and dereferencing

In lines 13, 17, and 21 of Figure 2.4 we see uses of two operations that give C (and therefore C++) its distinctive character. The C "address of" operator '&' creates a pointer. On all three lines, the expression &x creates a pointer to the location holding the object indicated by variable x. The type of this pointer depends on the type of x, and hence these three pointers are of type int *, float *, and void **, respectively. (Data type void * is a special kind of pointer with no associated type information.)

The cast operator converts from one data type to another. Thus, the cast (byte_pointer) &x indicates that whatever type the pointer &x had before, the program will now reference a pointer to data of type unsigned char. The casts shown here do not change the actual pointer; they simply direct the compiler to refer to the data being pointed to according to the new data type.

Aside Generating an ASCII table

You can display a table showing the ASCII character code by executing the command man ascii.

Practice Problem 2.5 (solution page 144)

Consider the following three calls to show_bytes:

```
int val = 0x87654321;
byte_pointer valp = (byte_pointer) &val;
show_bytes(valp, 1); /* A. */
show_bytes(valp, 2); /* B. */
show_bytes(valp, 3); /* C. */
```

Indicate the values that will be printed by each call on a little-endian machine and on a big-endian machine:

A. Little endian: _____   Big endian: _____

B. Little endian: _____   Big endian: _____

C. Little endian: _____   Big endian: _____

Practice Problem 2.6 (solution page 145)

Using show_int and show_float, we determine that the integer 3510593 has hexadecimal representation 0x00359141, while the floating-point number 3510593.0 has hexadecimal representation 0x4A564504.

   A. Write the binary representations of these two hexadecimal values.

   B. Shift these two strings relative to one another to maximize the number of matching bits. How many bits match?

   C. What parts of the strings do not match?

2.1.4   Representing Strings

A string in C is encoded by an array of characters terminated by the null (having value 0) character. Each character is represented by some standard encoding, with the most common being the ASCII character code. Thus, if we run our routine show_bytes with arguments "12345" and 6 (to include the terminating character), we get the result 31 32 33 34 35 00. Observe that the ASCII code for decimal digit x happens to be 0x3x, and that the terminating byte has the hex representation 0x00. This same result would be obtained on any system using ASCII as its character code, independent of the byte ordering and word size conventions. As a consequence, text data are more platform independent than binary data.

Practice Problem 2.7 (solution page 145)

What would be printed as a result of the following call to show_bytes?

```
const char *s = "abcdef";
show_bytes((byte_pointer) s, strlen(s));
```

Note that letters 'a' through 'z' have ASCII codes 0x61 through 0x7A.

2.1.5   Representing Code

Consider the following C function:

```
1    int sum(int x, int y) {
2        return x + y;
3    }
```

   When compiled on our sample machines, we generate machine code having the following byte representations:

Linux 32   55 89 e5 8b 45 0c 03 45 08 c9 c3
Windows   55 89 e5 8b 45 0c 03 45 08 5d c3
Sun   81 c3 e0 08 90 02 00 09
Linux 64   55 48 89 e5 89 7d fc 89 75 f8 03 45 fc c9 c3

Aside The Unicode standard for text encoding

 The ASCII character set is suitable for encoding English-language documents, but it does not have much in the way of special characters, such as the French 'ç'. It is wholly unsuited for encoding documents in languages such as Greek, Russian, and Chinese. Over the years, a variety of methods have been developed to encode text for different languages. The Unicode Consortium has devised the most comprehensive and widely accepted standard for encoding text. The current Unicode standard (version 7.0) has a repertoire of over 100,000 characters supporting a wide range of languages, including the ancient languages of Egypt and Babylon. To their credit, the Unicode Technical Committee rejected a proposal to include a standard writing for Klingon, a fictional civilization from the television series *Star Trek*.

 The base encoding, known as the "Universal Character Set" of Unicode, uses a 32-bit representation of characters. This would seem to require every string of text to consist of 4 bytes per character. However, alternative codings are possible where common characters require just 1 or 2 bytes, while less common ones require more. In particular, the UTF-8 representation encodes each character as a sequence of bytes, such that the standard ASCII characters use the same single-byte encodings as they have in ASCII, implying that all ASCII byte sequences have the same meaning in UTF-8 as they do in ASCII.

 The Java programming language uses Unicode in its representations of strings. Program libraries are also available for C to support Unicode.

Here we find that the instruction codings are different. Different machine types use different and incompatible instructions and encodings. Even identical processors running different operating systems have differences in their coding conventions and hence are not binary compatible. Binary code is seldom portable across different combinations of machine and operating system.

A fundamental concept of computer systems is that a program, from the perspective of the machine, is simply a sequence of bytes. The machine has no information about the original source program, except perhaps some auxiliary tables maintained to aid in debugging. We will see this more clearly when we study machine-level programming in Chapter 3.

2.1.6 Introduction to Boolean Algebra

Since binary values are at the core of how computers encode, store, and manipulate information, a rich body of mathematical knowledge has evolved around the study of the values 0 and 1. This started with the work of George Boole (1815–1864) around 1850 and thus is known as *Boolean algebra*. Boole observed that by encoding logic values TRUE and FALSE as binary values 1 and 0, he could formulate an algebra that captures the basic principles of logical reasoning.

The simplest Boolean algebra is defined over the two-element set {0, 1}. Figure 2.7 defines several operations in this algebra. Our symbols for representing these operations are chosen to match those used by the C bit-level operations,

~	
0	1
1	0

&	0	1
0	0	0
1	0	1

|	0	1
0	0	1
1	1	1

^	0	1
0	0	1
1	1	0

Figure 2.7 Operations of Boolean algebra. Binary values 1 and 0 encode logic values TRUE and FALSE, while operations ~, &, |, and ^ encode logical operations NOT, AND, OR, and EXCLUSIVE-OR, respectively.

as will be discussed later. The Boolean operation ~ corresponds to the logical operation NOT, denoted by the symbol $\neg$. That is, we say that $\neg P$ is true when P is not true, and vice versa. Correspondingly, ~p equals 1 when p equals 0, and vice versa. Boolean operation & corresponds to the logical operation AND, denoted by the symbol $\wedge$. We say that $P \wedge Q$ holds when both P is true and Q is true. Correspondingly, p & q equals 1 only when $p = 1$ and $q = 1$. Boolean operation | corresponds to the logical operation OR, denoted by the symbol $\vee$. We say that $P \vee Q$ holds when either P is true or Q is true. Correspondingly, $p \mid q$ equals 1 when either $p = 1$ or $q = 1$. Boolean operation ^ corresponds to the logical operation EXCLUSIVE-OR, denoted by the symbol $\oplus$. We say that $P \oplus Q$ holds when either P is true or Q is true, but not both. Correspondingly, p ^ q equals 1 when either $p = 1$ and $q = 0$, or $p = 0$ and $q = 1$.

Claude Shannon (1916–2001), who later founded the field of information theory, first made the connection between Boolean algebra and digital logic. In his 1937 master's thesis, he showed that Boolean algebra could be applied to the design and analysis of networks of electromechanical relays. Although computer technology has advanced considerably since, Boolean algebra still plays a central role in the design and analysis of digital systems.

We can extend the four Boolean operations to also operate on *bit vectors*, strings of zeros and ones of some fixed length w. We define the operations over bit vectors according to their applications to the matching elements of the arguments. Let a and b denote the bit vectors $[a_{w-1}, a_{w-2}, \ldots, a_0]$ and $[b_{w-1}, b_{w-2}, \ldots, b_0]$, respectively. We define a & b to also be a bit vector of length w, where the ith element equals a_i & b_i, for $0 \leq i < w$. The operations |, ^, and ~ are extended to bit vectors in a similar fashion.

As examples, consider the case where $w = 4$, and with arguments $a = [0110]$ and $b = [1100]$. Then the four operations a & b, $a \mid b$, a ^ b, and ~b yield

```
    0110          0110          0110
&   1100      |   1100      ^   1100      ~   1100
   ─────         ─────         ─────         ─────
    0100          1110          1010          0011
```

Practice Problem 2.8 (solution page 145)

Fill in the following table showing the results of evaluating Boolean operations on bit vectors.

Web Aside DATA:BOOL   More on Boolean algebra and Boolean rings

The Boolean operations |, &, and ~ operating on bit vectors of length w form a *Boolean algebra*, for any integer $w > 0$. The simplest is the case where $w = 1$ and there are just two elements, but for the more general case there are 2^w bit vectors of length w. Boolean algebra has many of the same properties as arithmetic over integers. For example, just as multiplication distributes over addition, written $a \cdot (b + c) = (a \cdot b) + (a \cdot c)$, Boolean operation & distributes over |, written $a \, \& \, (b \mid c) = (a \, \& \, b) \mid (a \, \& \, c)$. In addition, however, Boolean operation | distributes over &, and so we can write $a \mid (b \, \& \, c) = (a \mid b) \, \& \, (a \mid c)$, whereas we cannot say that $a + (b \cdot c) = (a + b) \cdot (a + c)$ holds for all integers.

When we consider operations ^, &, and ~ operating on bit vectors of length w, we get a different mathematical form, known as a *Boolean ring*. Boolean rings have many properties in common with integer arithmetic. For example, one property of integer arithmetic is that every value x has an *additive inverse* $-x$, such that $x + -x = 0$. A similar property holds for Boolean rings, where ^ is the "addition" operation, but in this case each element is its own additive inverse. That is, $a \, \hat{} \, a = 0$ for any value a, where we use 0 here to represent a bit vector of all zeros. We can see this holds for single bits, since $0 \, \hat{} \, 0 = 1 \, \hat{} \, 1 = 0$, and it extends to bit vectors as well. This property holds even when we rearrange terms and combine them in a different order, and so $(a \, \hat{} \, b) \, \hat{} \, a = b$. This property leads to some interesting results and clever tricks, as we will explore in Problem 2.10.

Operation	Result
a	[01101001]
b	[01010101]
~a	_____
~b	_____
$a \, \& \, b$	_____
$a \mid b$	_____
$a \, \hat{} \, b$	_____

One useful application of bit vectors is to represent finite sets. We can encode any subset $A \subseteq \{0, 1, \ldots, w - 1\}$ with a bit vector $[a_{w-1}, \ldots, a_1, a_0]$, where $a_i = 1$ if and only if $i \in A$. For example, recalling that we write a_{w-1} on the left and a_0 on the right, bit vector $a = [01101001]$ encodes the set $A = \{0, 3, 5, 6\}$, while bit vector $b = [01010101]$ encodes the set $B = \{0, 2, 4, 6\}$. With this way of encoding sets, Boolean operations | and & correspond to set union and intersection, respectively, and ~ corresponds to set complement. Continuing our earlier example, the operation $a \, \& \, b$ yields bit vector [01000001], while $A \cap B = \{0, 6\}$.

We will see the encoding of sets by bit vectors in a number of practical applications. For example, in Chapter 8, we will see that there are a number of different *signals* that can interrupt the execution of a program. We can selectively enable or disable different signals by specifying a bit-vector mask, where a 1 in bit position i indicates that signal i is enabled and a 0 indicates that it is disabled. Thus, the mask represents the set of enabled signals.

Practice Problem 2.9 (solution page 146)

Computers generate color pictures on a video screen or liquid crystal display by mixing three different colors of light: red, green, and blue. Imagine a simple scheme, with three different lights, each of which can be turned on or off, projecting onto a glass screen:

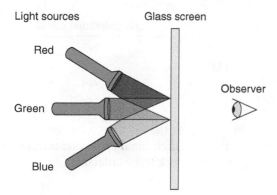

We can then create eight different colors based on the absence (0) or presence (1) of light sources R, G, and B:

R	G	B	Color
0	0	0	Black
0	0	1	Blue
0	1	0	Green
0	1	1	Cyan
1	0	0	Red
1	0	1	Magenta
1	1	0	Yellow
1	1	1	White

Each of these colors can be represented as a bit vector of length 3, and we can apply Boolean operations to them.

A. The complement of a color is formed by turning off the lights that are on and turning on the lights that are off. What would be the complement of each of the eight colors listed above?

B. Describe the effect of applying Boolean operations on the following colors:

    Blue | Green   = _____
    Yellow & Cyan = _____
    Red ^ Magenta = _____

2.1.7 Bit-Level Operations in C

One useful feature of C is that it supports bitwise Boolean operations. In fact, the symbols we have used for the Boolean operations are exactly those used by C: | for OR, & for AND, ~ for NOT, and ^ for EXCLUSIVE-OR. These can be applied to any "integral" data type, including all of those listed in Figure 2.3. Here are some examples of expression evaluation for data type char:

C expression	Binary expression	Binary result	Hexadecimal result
~0x41	~[0100 0001]	[1011 1110]	0xBE
~0x00	~[0000 0000]	[1111 1111]	0xFF
0x69 & 0x55	[0110 1001] & [0101 0101]	[0100 0001]	0x41
0x69 | 0x55	[0110 1001] | [0101 0101]	[0111 1101]	0x7D

As our examples show, the best way to determine the effect of a bit-level expression is to expand the hexadecimal arguments to their binary representations, perform the operations in binary, and then convert back to hexadecimal.

Practice Problem 2.10 (solution page 146)

As an application of the property that $a \wedge a = 0$ for any bit vector a, consider the following program:

```
1    void inplace_swap(int *x, int *y) {
2        *y = *x ^ *y;   /* Step 1 */
3        *x = *x ^ *y;   /* Step 2 */
4        *y = *x ^ *y;   /* Step 3 */
5    }
```

As the name implies, we claim that the effect of this procedure is to swap the values stored at the locations denoted by pointer variables x and y. Note that unlike the usual technique for swapping two values, we do not need a third location to temporarily store one value while we are moving the other. There is no performance advantage to this way of swapping; it is merely an intellectual amusement.

Starting with values a and b in the locations pointed to by x and y, respectively, fill in the table that follows, giving the values stored at the two locations after each step of the procedure. Use the properties of ^ to show that the desired effect is achieved. Recall that every element is its own additive inverse (that is, $a \wedge a = 0$).

Step	*x	*y
Initially	a	b
Step 1	_____	_____
Step 2	_____	_____
Step 3	_____	_____

Practice Problem 2.11 (solution page 146)

Armed with the function `inplace_swap` from Problem 2.10, you decide to write code that will reverse the elements of an array by swapping elements from opposite ends of the array, working toward the middle.

You arrive at the following function:

```
1   void reverse_array(int a[], int cnt) {
2       int first, last;
3       for (first = 0, last = cnt-1;
4            first <= last;
5            first++,last--)
6           inplace_swap(&a[first], &a[last]);
7   }
```

When you apply your function to an array containing elements 1, 2, 3, and 4, you find the array now has, as expected, elements 4, 3, 2, and 1. When you try it on an array with elements 1, 2, 3, 4, and 5, however, you are surprised to see that the array now has elements 5, 4, 0, 2, and 1. In fact, you discover that the code always works correctly on arrays of even length, but it sets the middle element to 0 whenever the array has odd length.

A. For an array of odd length $cnt = 2k + 1$, what are the values of variables `first` and `last` in the final iteration of function `reverse_array`?

B. Why does this call to function `inplace_swap` set the array element to 0?

C. What simple modification to the code for `reverse_array` would eliminate this problem?

One common use of bit-level operations is to implement *masking* operations, where a mask is a bit pattern that indicates a selected set of bits within a word. As an example, the mask 0xFF (having ones for the least significant 8 bits) indicates the low-order byte of a word. The bit-level operation x & 0xFF yields a value consisting of the least significant byte of x, but with all other bytes set to 0. For example, with x = 0x89ABCDEF, the expression would yield 0x000000EF. The expression ~0 will yield a mask of all ones, regardless of the size of the data representation. The same mask can be written 0xFFFFFFFF when data type int is 32 bits, but it would not be as portable.

Practice Problem 2.12 (solution page 146)

Write C expressions, in terms of variable x, for the following values. Your code should work for any word size $w \geq 8$. For reference, we show the result of evaluating the expressions for x = 0x87654321, with $w = 32$.

A. The least significant byte of x, with all other bits set to 0. [0x00000021]

B. All but the least significant byte of x complemented, with the least significant byte left unchanged. [0x789ABC21]

C. The least significant byte set to all ones, and all other bytes of x left unchanged. [0x876543FF]

Practice Problem 2.13 (solution page 147)

The Digital Equipment VAX computer was a very popular machine from the late 1970s until the late 1980s. Rather than instructions for Boolean operations AND and OR, it had instructions bis (bit set) and bic (bit clear). Both instructions take a data word x and a mask word m. They generate a result z consisting of the bits of x modified according to the bits of m. With bis, the modification involves setting z to 1 at each bit position where m is 1. With bic, the modification involves setting z to 0 at each bit position where m is 1.

To see how these operations relate to the C bit-level operations, assume we have functions bis and bic implementing the bit set and bit clear operations, and that we want to use these to implement functions computing bitwise operations | and ^, without using any other C operations. Fill in the missing code below. *Hint:* Write C expressions for the operations bis and bic.

```
/* Declarations of functions implementing operations bis and bic */
int bis(int x, int m);
int bic(int x, int m);

/* Compute x|y using only calls to functions bis and bic */
int bool_or(int x, int y) {
    int result = _____;
    return result;
}

/* Compute x^y using only calls to functions bis and bic */
int bool_xor(int x, int y) {
    int result = _____;
    return result;
}
```

2.1.8 Logical Operations in C

C also provides a set of *logical* operators ||, &&, and !, which correspond to the OR, AND, and NOT operations of logic. These can easily be confused with the bit-level operations, but their behavior is quite different. The logical operations treat any nonzero argument as representing TRUE and argument 0 as representing FALSE. They return either 1 or 0, indicating a result of either TRUE or FALSE, respectively. Here are some examples of expression evaluation:

Expression	Result
!0x41	0x00
!0x00	0x01
!!0x41	0x01
0x69 && 0x55	0x01
0x69 || 0x55	0x01

Observe that a bitwise operation will have behavior matching that of its logical counterpart only in the special case in which the arguments are restricted to 0 or 1.

A second important distinction between the logical operators '&&' and '||' versus their bit-level counterparts '&' and '|' is that the logical operators do not evaluate their second argument if the result of the expression can be determined by evaluating the first argument. Thus, for example, the expression a && 5/a will never cause a division by zero, and the expression p && *p++ will never cause the dereferencing of a null pointer.

Practice Problem 2.14 (solution page 147)

Suppose that x and y have byte values 0x66 and 0x39, respectively. Fill in the following table indicating the byte values of the different C expressions:

Expression	Value	Expression	Value
x & y	_____	x && y	_____
x | y	_____	x || y	_____
~x | ~y	_____	!x || !y	_____
x & !y	_____	x && ~y	_____

Practice Problem 2.15 (solution page 148)

Using only bit-level and logical operations, write a C expression that is equivalent to x == y. In other words, it will return 1 when x and y are equal and 0 otherwise.

2.1.9 Shift Operations in C

C also provides a set of *shift* operations for shifting bit patterns to the left and to the right. For an operand x having bit representation $[x_{w-1}, x_{w-2}, \ldots, x_0]$, the C expression x << k yields a value with bit representation $[x_{w-k-1}, x_{w-k-2}, \ldots, x_0, 0, \ldots, 0]$. That is, x is shifted k bits to the left, dropping off the k most significant bits and filling the right end with k zeros. The shift amount should be a value between 0 and $w - 1$. Shift operations associate from left to right, so x << j << k is equivalent to (x << j) << k.

There is a corresponding right shift operation, written in C as x >> k, but it has a slightly subtle behavior. Generally, machines support two forms of right shift:

Logical. A logical right shift fills the left end with k zeros, giving a result $[0, \ldots, 0, x_{w-1}, x_{w-2}, \ldots x_k]$.

Arithmetic. An arithmetic right shift fills the left end with k repetitions of the most significant bit, giving a result $[x_{w-1}, \ldots, x_{w-1}, x_{w-1}, x_{w-2}, \ldots x_k]$. This convention might seem peculiar, but as we will see, it is useful for operating on signed integer data.

As examples, the following table shows the effect of applying the different shift operations to two different values of an 8-bit argument x:

Operation	Value 1	Value 2
Argument x	[01100011]	[10010101]
x << 4	[0011*0000*]	[0101*0000*]
x >> 4 (logical)	[*0000*0110]	[*0000*1001]
x >> 4 (arithmetic)	[*0000*0110]	[*1111*1001]

The italicized digits indicate the values that fill the right (left shift) or left (right shift) ends. Observe that all but one entry involves filling with zeros. The exception is the case of shifting [10010101] right arithmetically. Since its most significant bit is 1, this will be used as the fill value.

The C standards do not precisely define which type of right shift should be used with signed numbers—either arithmetic or logical shifts may be used. This unfortunately means that any code assuming one form or the other will potentially encounter portability problems. In practice, however, almost all compiler/machine combinations use arithmetic right shifts for signed data, and many programmers assume this to be the case. For unsigned data, on the other hand, right shifts must be logical.

In contrast to C, Java has a precise definition of how right shifts should be performed. The expression x >> k shifts x arithmetically by k positions, while x >>> k shifts it logically.

Practice Problem 2.16 (solution page 148)

Fill in the table below showing the effects of the different shift operations on single-byte quantities. The best way to think about shift operations is to work with binary representations. Convert the initial values to binary, perform the shifts, and then convert back to hexadecimal. Each of the answers should be 8 binary digits or 2 hexadecimal digits.

x		x << 3		Logical x >> 2		Arithmetic x >> 2	
Hex	Binary	Binary	Hex	Binary	Hex	Binary	Hex
0xC3	___	___	___	___	___	___	___
0x75	___	___	___	___	___	___	___
0x87	___	___	___	___	___	___	___
0x66	___	___	___	___	___	___	___

Aside   Shifting by k, for large values of k

For a data type consisting of w bits, what should be the effect of shifting by some value $k \geq w$? For example, what should be the effect of computing the following expressions, assuming data type `int` has $w = 32$:

```
int      lval = 0xFEDCBA98  << 32;
int      aval = 0xFEDCBA98  >> 36;
unsigned uval = 0xFEDCBA98u >> 40;
```

The C standards carefully avoid stating what should be done in such a case. On many machines, the shift instructions consider only the lower $\log_2 w$ bits of the shift amount when shifting a w-bit value, and so the shift amount is computed as $k \bmod w$. For example, with $w = 32$, the above three shifts would be computed as if they were by amounts 0, 4, and 8, respectively, giving results

```
lval    0xFEDCBA98
aval    0xFFEDCBA9
uval    0x00FEDCBA
```

This behavior is not guaranteed for C programs, however, and so shift amounts should be kept less than the word size.

Java, on the other hand, specifically requires that shift amounts should be computed in the modular fashion we have shown.

Aside   Operator precedence issues with shift operations

It might be tempting to write the expression `1<<2 + 3<<4`, intending it to mean `(1<<2) + (3<<4)`. However, in C the former expression is equivalent to `1 << (2+3) << 4`, since addition (and subtraction) have higher precedence than shifts. The left-to-right associativity rule then causes this to be parenthesized as `(1 << (2+3)) << 4`, giving value 512, rather than the intended 52.

Getting the precedence wrong in C expressions is a common source of program errors, and often these are difficult to spot by inspection. When in doubt, put in parentheses!

2.2 Integer Representations

In this section, we describe two different ways bits can be used to encode integers—one that can only represent nonnegative numbers, and one that can represent negative, zero, and positive numbers. We will see later that they are strongly related both in their mathematical properties and their machine-level implementations. We also investigate the effect of expanding or shrinking an encoded integer to fit a representation with a different length.

Figure 2.8 lists the mathematical terminology we introduce to precisely define and characterize how computers encode and operate on integer data. This

Symbol	Type	Meaning	Page
$B2T_w$	Function	Binary to two's complement	64
$B2U_w$	Function	Binary to unsigned	62
$U2B_w$	Function	Unsigned to binary	64
$U2T_w$	Function	Unsigned to two's complement	71
$T2B_w$	Function	Two's complement to binary	65
$T2U_w$	Function	Two's complement to unsigned	71
$TMin_w$	Constant	Minimum two's-complement value	65
$TMax_w$	Constant	Maximum two's-complement value	65
$UMax_w$	Constant	Maximum unsigned value	63
$+_w^t$	Operation	Two's-complement addition	90
$+_w^u$	Operation	Unsigned addition	85
$*_w^t$	Operation	Two's-complement multiplication	97
$*_w^u$	Operation	Unsigned multiplication	96
$-_w^t$	Operation	Two's-complement negation	95
$-_w^u$	Operation	Unsigned negation	89

Figure 2.8 Terminology for integer data and arithmetic operations. The subscript w denotes the number of bits in the data representation. The "Page" column indicates the page on which the term is defined.

terminology will be introduced over the course of the presentation. The figure is included here as a reference.

2.2.1 Integral Data Types

C supports a variety of *integral* data types—ones that represent finite ranges of integers. These are shown in Figures 2.9 and 2.10, along with the ranges of values they can have for "typical" 32- and 64-bit programs. Each type can specify a size with keyword char, short, long, as well as an indication of whether the represented numbers are all nonnegative (declared as unsigned), or possibly negative (the default.) As we saw in Figure 2.3, the number of bytes allocated for the different sizes varies according to whether the program is compiled for 32 or 64 bits. Based on the byte allocations, the different sizes allow different ranges of values to be represented. The only machine-dependent range indicated is for size designator long. Most 64-bit programs use an 8-byte representation, giving a much wider range of values than the 4-byte representation used with 32-bit programs.

One important feature to note in Figures 2.9 and 2.10 is that the ranges are not symmetric—the range of negative numbers extends one further than the range of positive numbers. We will see why this happens when we consider how negative numbers are represented.

C data type	Minimum	Maximum
[signed] char	−128	127
unsigned char	0	255
short	−32,768	32,767
unsigned short	0	65,535
int	−2,147,483,648	2,147,483,647
unsigned	0	4,294,967,295
long	−2,147,483,648	2,147,483,647
unsigned long	0	4,294,967,295
int32_t	−2,147,483,648	2,147,483,647
uint32_t	0	4,294,967,295
int64_t	−9,223,372,036,854,775,808	9,223,372,036,854,775,807
uint64_t	0	18,446,744,073,709,551,615

Figure 2.9   Typical ranges for C integral data types for 32-bit programs.

C data type	Minimum	Maximum
[signed] char	−128	127
unsigned char	0	255
short	−32,768	32,767
unsigned short	0	65,535
int	−2,147,483,648	2,147,483,647
unsigned	0	4,294,967,295
long	−9,223,372,036,854,775,808	9,223,372,036,854,775,807
unsigned long	0	18,446,744,073,709,551,615
int32_t	−2,147,483,648	2,147,483,647
uint32_t	0	4,294,967,295
int64_t	−9,223,372,036,854,775,808	9,223,372,036,854,775,807
uint64_t	0	18,446,744,073,709,551,615

Figure 2.10   Typical ranges for C integral data types for 64-bit programs.

The C standards define minimum ranges of values that each data type must be able to represent. As shown in Figure 2.11, their ranges are the same or smaller than the typical implementations shown in Figures 2.9 and 2.10. In particular, with the exception of the fixed-size data types, we see that they require only a

C data type	Minimum	Maximum
[signed] char	−127	127
unsigned char	0	255
short	−32,767	32,767
unsigned short	0	65,535
int	−32,767	32,767
unsigned	0	65,535
long	−2,147,483,647	2,147,483,647
unsigned long	0	4,294,967,295
int32_t	−2,147,483,648	2,147,483,647
uint32_t	0	4,294,967,295
int64_t	−9,223,372,036,854,775,808	9,223,372,036,854,775,807
uint64_t	0	18,446,744,073,709,551,615

Figure 2.11   Guaranteed ranges for C integral data types. The C standards require that the data types have at least these ranges of values.

symmetric range of positive and negative numbers. We also see that data type `int` could be implemented with 2-byte numbers, although this is mostly a throwback to the days of 16-bit machines. We also see that size `long` can be implemented with 4-byte numbers, and it typically is for 32-bit programs. The fixed-size data types guarantee that the ranges of values will be exactly those given by the typical numbers of Figure 2.9, including the asymmetry between negative and positive.

2.2.2   Unsigned Encodings

Let us consider an integer data type of w bits. We write a bit vector as either $\vec{x}$, to denote the entire vector, or as $[x_{w-1}, x_{w-2}, \ldots, x_0]$ to denote the individual bits within the vector. Treating $\vec{x}$ as a number written in binary notation, we obtain the *unsigned* interpretation of $\vec{x}$. In this encoding, each bit x_i has value 0 or 1, with the latter case indicating that value 2^i should be included as part of the numeric value. We can express this interpretation as a function $B2U_w$ (for "binary to unsigned," length w):

Figure 2.12

Unsigned number examples for $w = 4$. When bit i in the binary representation has value 1, it contributes 2^i to the value.

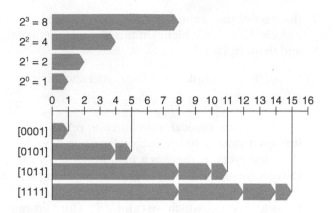

PRINCIPLE: Definition of unsigned encoding

For vector $\vec{x} = [x_{w-1}, x_{w-2}, \ldots, x_0]$:

$$B2U_w(\vec{x}) \doteq \sum_{i=0}^{w-1} x_i 2^i \qquad (2.1)$$

■

In this equation, the notation $\doteq$ means that the left-hand side is defined to be equal to the right-hand side. The function $B2U_w$ maps strings of zeros and ones of length w to nonnegative integers. As examples, Figure 2.12 shows the mapping, given by $B2U$, from bit vectors to integers for the following cases:

$$
\begin{aligned}
B2U_4([0001]) &= 0 \cdot 2^3 + 0 \cdot 2^2 + 0 \cdot 2^1 + 1 \cdot 2^0 &= 0+0+0+1 &= 1 \\
B2U_4([0101]) &= 0 \cdot 2^3 + 1 \cdot 2^2 + 0 \cdot 2^1 + 1 \cdot 2^0 &= 0+4+0+1 &= 5 \\
B2U_4([1011]) &= 1 \cdot 2^3 + 0 \cdot 2^2 + 1 \cdot 2^1 + 1 \cdot 2^0 &= 8+0+2+1 &= 11 \\
B2U_4([1111]) &= 1 \cdot 2^3 + 1 \cdot 2^2 + 1 \cdot 2^1 + 1 \cdot 2^0 &= 8+4+2+1 &= 15
\end{aligned}
$$

$$(2.2)$$

In the figure, we represent each bit position i by a rightward-pointing blue bar of length 2^i. The numeric value associated with a bit vector then equals the sum of the lengths of the bars for which the corresponding bit values are 1.

Let us consider the range of values that can be represented using w bits. The least value is given by bit vector $[00 \cdots 0]$ having integer value 0, and the greatest value is given by bit vector $[11 \cdots 1]$ having integer value $UMax_w \doteq \sum_{i=0}^{w-1} 2^i = 2^w - 1$. Using the 4-bit case as an example, we have $UMax_4 = B2U_4([1111]) = 2^4 - 1 = 15$. Thus, the function $B2U_w$ can be defined as a mapping $B2U_w : \{0, 1\}^w \rightarrow \{0, \ldots, UMax_w\}$.

The unsigned binary representation has the important property that every number between 0 and $2^w - 1$ has a unique encoding as a w-bit value. For example, there is only one representation of decimal value 11 as an unsigned 4-bit number—namely, [1011]. We highlight this as a mathematical principle, which we first state and then explain.

PRINCIPLE: Uniqueness of unsigned encoding

Function $B2U_w$ is a bijection. ∎

The mathematical term *bijection* refers to a function f that goes two ways: it maps a value x to a value y where $y = f(x)$, but it can also operate in reverse, since for every y, there is a unique value x such that $f(x) = y$. This is given by the *inverse* function f^{-1}, where, for our example, $x = f^{-1}(y)$. The function $B2U_w$ maps each bit vector of length w to a unique number between 0 and $2^w - 1$, and it has an inverse, which we call $U2B_w$ (for "unsigned to binary"), that maps each number in the range 0 to $2^w - 1$ to a unique pattern of w bits.

2.2.3 Two's-Complement Encodings

For many applications, we wish to represent negative values as well. The most common computer representation of signed numbers is known as *two's-complement* form. This is defined by interpreting the most significant bit of the word to have negative weight. We express this interpretation as a function $B2T_w$ (for "binary to two's complement" length w):

PRINCIPLE: Definition of two's-complement encoding

For vector $\vec{x} = [x_{w-1}, x_{w-2}, \ldots, x_0]$:

$$B2T_w(\vec{x}) \doteq -x_{w-1}2^{w-1} + \sum_{i=0}^{w-2} x_i 2^i \tag{2.3}$$

∎

The most significant bit x_{w-1} is also called the *sign bit*. Its "weight" is -2^{w-1}, the negation of its weight in an unsigned representation. When the sign bit is set to 1, the represented value is negative, and when set to 0, the value is nonnegative. As examples, Figure 2.13 shows the mapping, given by $B2T$, from bit vectors to integers for the following cases:

$$
\begin{aligned}
B2T_4([0001]) &= -0 \cdot 2^3 + 0 \cdot 2^2 + 0 \cdot 2^1 + 1 \cdot 2^0 &= 0 + 0 + 0 + 1 &= 1 \\
B2T_4([0101]) &= -0 \cdot 2^3 + 1 \cdot 2^2 + 0 \cdot 2^1 + 1 \cdot 2^0 &= 0 + 4 + 0 + 1 &= 5 \\
B2T_4([1011]) &= -1 \cdot 2^3 + 0 \cdot 2^2 + 1 \cdot 2^1 + 1 \cdot 2^0 &= -8 + 0 + 2 + 1 &= -5 \\
B2T_4([1111]) &= -1 \cdot 2^3 + 1 \cdot 2^2 + 1 \cdot 2^1 + 1 \cdot 2^0 &= -8 + 4 + 2 + 1 &= -1
\end{aligned}
$$

$$\tag{2.4}$$

In the figure, we indicate that the sign bit has negative weight by showing it as a leftward-pointing gray bar. The numeric value associated with a bit vector is then given by the combination of the possible leftward-pointing gray bar and the rightward-pointing blue bars.

Figure 2.13
**Two's-complement
number examples for**
$w = 4$. Bit 3 serves as a
sign bit; when set to 1, it
contributes $-2^3 = -8$ to
the value. This weighting
is shown as a leftward-
pointing gray bar.

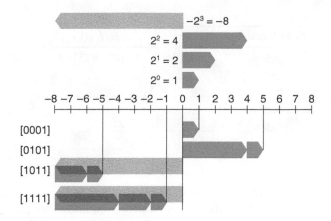

We see that the bit patterns are identical for Figures 2.12 and 2.13 (as well as for Equations 2.2 and 2.4), but the values differ when the most significant bit is 1, since in one case it has weight $+8$, and in the other case it has weight -8.

Let us consider the range of values that can be represented as a w-bit two's-complement number. The least representable value is given by bit vector $[10 \cdots 0]$ (set the bit with negative weight but clear all others), having integer value $TMin_w \doteq -2^{w-1}$. The greatest value is given by bit vector $[01 \cdots 1]$ (clear the bit with negative weight but set all others), having integer value $TMax_w \doteq \sum_{i=0}^{w-2} 2^i = 2^{w-1} - 1$. Using the 4-bit case as an example, we have $TMin_4 = B2T_4([1000]) = -2^3 = -8$ and $TMax_4 = B2T_4([0111]) = 2^2 + 2^1 + 2^0 = 4 + 2 + 1 = 7$.

We can see that $B2T_w$ is a mapping of bit patterns of length w to numbers between $TMin_w$ and $TMax_w$, written as $B2T_w : \{0, 1\}^w \rightarrow \{TMin_w, \ldots, TMax_w\}$. As we saw with the unsigned representation, every number within the representable range has a unique encoding as a w-bit two's-complement number. This leads to a principle for two's-complement numbers similar to that for unsigned numbers:

PRINCIPLE: Uniqueness of two's-complement encoding

Function $B2T_w$ is a bijection.   ■

We define function $T2B_w$ (for "two's complement to binary") to be the inverse of $B2T_w$. That is, for a number x, such that $TMin_w \leq x \leq TMax_w$, $T2B_w(x)$ is the (unique) w-bit pattern that encodes x.

Practice Problem 2.17 (solution page 148)

Assuming $w = 4$, we can assign a numeric value to each possible hexadecimal digit, assuming either an unsigned or a two's-complement interpretation. Fill in the following table according to these interpretations by writing out the nonzero powers of 2 in the summations shown in Equations 2.1 and 2.3:

$\vec{x}$ Hexadecimal	Binary	$B2U_4(\vec{x})$	$B2T_4(\vec{x})$
0xE	[1110]	$2^3 + 2^2 + 2^1 = 14$	$-2^3 + 2^2 + 2^1 = -2$
0x0	_____	_____	_____
0x5	_____	_____	_____
0x8	_____	_____	_____
0xD	_____	_____	_____
0xF	_____	_____	_____

Figure 2.14 shows the bit patterns and numeric values for several important numbers for different word sizes. The first three give the ranges of representable integers in terms of the values of $UMax_w$, $TMin_w$, and $TMax_w$. We will refer to these three special values often in the ensuing discussion. We will drop the subscript w and refer to the values $UMax$, $TMin$, and $TMax$ when w can be inferred from context or is not central to the discussion.

A few points are worth highlighting about these numbers. First, as observed in Figures 2.9 and 2.10, the two's-complement range is asymmetric: $|TMin| = |TMax| + 1$; that is, there is no positive counterpart to $TMin$. As we shall see, this leads to some peculiar properties of two's-complement arithmetic and can be the source of subtle program bugs. This asymmetry arises because half the bit patterns (those with the sign bit set to 1) represent negative numbers, while half (those with the sign bit set to 0) represent nonnegative numbers. Since 0 is nonnegative, this means that it can represent one less positive number than negative. Second, the maximum unsigned value is just over twice the maximum two's-complement value: $UMax = 2TMax + 1$. All of the bit patterns that denote negative numbers in two's-complement notation become positive values in an unsigned representation.

Value	Word size w			
	8	16	32	64
$UMax_w$	0xFF	0xFFFF	0xFFFFFFFF	0xFFFFFFFFFFFFFFFF
	255	65,535	4,294,967,295	18,446,744,073,709,551,615
$TMin_w$	0x80	0x8000	0x80000000	0x8000000000000000
	−128	−32,768	−2,147,483,648	−9,223,372,036,854,775,808
$TMax_w$	0x7F	0x7FFF	0x7FFFFFFF	0x7FFFFFFFFFFFFFFF
	127	32,767	2,147,483,647	9,223,372,036,854,775,807
−1	0xFF	0xFFFF	0xFFFFFFFF	0xFFFFFFFFFFFFFFFF
0	0x00	0x0000	0x00000000	0x0000000000000000

Figure 2.14 **Important numbers.** Both numeric values and hexadecimal representations are shown.

Aside   More on fixed-size integer types

For some programs, it is essential that data types be encoded using representations with specific sizes. For example, when writing programs to enable a machine to communicate over the Internet according to a standard protocol, it is important to have data types compatible with those specified by the protocol. We have seen that some C data types, especially long, have different ranges on different machines, and in fact the C standards only specify the minimum ranges for any data type, not the exact ranges. Although we can choose data types that will be compatible with standard representations on most machines, there is no guarantee of portability.

We have already encountered the 32- and 64-bit versions of fixed-size integer types (Figure 2.3); they are part of a larger class of data types. The ISO C99 standard introduces this class of integer types in the file stdint.h. This file defines a set of data types with declarations of the form int$N$_t and uint$N$_t, specifying N-bit signed and unsigned integers, for different values of N. The exact values of N are implementation dependent, but most compilers allow values of 8, 16, 32, and 64. Thus, we can unambiguously declare an unsigned 16-bit variable by giving it type uint16_t, and a signed variable of 32 bits as int32_t.

Along with these data types are a set of macros defining the minimum and maximum values for each value of N. These have names of the form INTN_MIN, INTN_MAX, and UINTN_MAX.

Formatted printing with fixed-width types requires use of macros that expand into format strings in a system-dependent manner. So, for example, the values of variables x and y of type int32_t and uint64_t can be printed by the following call to printf:

```
printf("x = %" PRId32 ", y = %" PRIu64 "\n", x, y);
```

When compiled as a 64-bit program, macro PRId32 expands to the string "d", while PRIu64 expands to the pair of strings "l" "u". When the C preprocessor encounters a sequence of string constants separated only by spaces (or other whitespace characters), it concatenates them together. Thus, the above call to printf becomes

```
printf("x = %d, y = %lu\n", x, y);
```

Using the macros ensures that a correct format string will be generated regardless of how the code is compiled.

Figure 2.14 also shows the representations of constants -1 and 0. Note that -1 has the same bit representation as *UMax*—a string of all ones. Numeric value 0 is represented as a string of all zeros in both representations.

The C standards do not require signed integers to be represented in two's-complement form, but nearly all machines do so. Programmers who are concerned with maximizing portability across all possible machines should not assume any particular range of representable values, beyond the ranges indicated in Figure 2.11, nor should they assume any particular representation of signed numbers. On the other hand, many programs are written assuming a two's-complement representation of signed numbers, and the "typical" ranges shown in Figures 2.9 and 2.10, and these programs are portable across a broad range of machines and compilers. The file <limits.h> in the C library defines a set of constants

Aside Alternative representations of signed numbers

There are two other standard representations for signed numbers:

Ones' complement. This is the same as two's complement, except that the most significant bit has weight $-(2^{w-1} - 1)$ rather than -2^{w-1}:

$$B2O_w(\vec{x}) \doteq -x_{w-1}(2^{w-1} - 1) + \sum_{i=0}^{w-2} x_i 2^i$$

Sign magnitude. The most significant bit is a sign bit that determines whether the remaining bits should be given negative or positive weight:

$$B2S_w(\vec{x}) \doteq (-1)^{x_{w-1}} \cdot \left(\sum_{i=0}^{w-2} x_i 2^i \right)$$

Both of these representations have the curious property that there are two different encodings of the number 0. For both representations, $[00 \cdots 0]$ is interpreted as $+0$. The value -0 can be represented in sign-magnitude form as $[10 \cdots 0]$ and in ones' complement as $[11 \cdots 1]$. Although machines based on ones'-complement representations were built in the past, almost all modern machines use two's complement. We will see that sign-magnitude encoding is used with floating-point numbers.

Note the different position of apostrophes: *two's* complement versus *ones'* complement. The term "two's complement" arises from the fact that for nonnegative x we compute a w-bit representation of $-x$ as $2^w - x$ (a single two.) The term "ones' complement" comes from the property that we can compute $-x$ in this notation as $[111 \cdots 1] - x$ (multiple ones).

delimiting the ranges of the different integer data types for the particular machine on which the compiler is running. For example, it defines constants INT_MAX, INT_MIN, and UINT_MAX describing the ranges of signed and unsigned integers. For a two's-complement machine in which data type int has w bits, these constants correspond to the values of $TMax_w$, $TMin_w$, and $UMax_w$.

The Java standard is quite specific about integer data type ranges and representations. It requires a two's-complement representation with the exact ranges shown for the 64-bit case (Figure 2.10). In Java, the single-byte data type is called byte instead of char. These detailed requirements are intended to enable Java programs to behave identically regardless of the machines or operating systems running them.

To get a better understanding of the two's-complement representation, consider the following code example:

```
1    short x = 12345;
2    short mx = -x;
3
4    show_bytes((byte_pointer) &x, sizeof(short));
5    show_bytes((byte_pointer) &mx, sizeof(short));
```

Weight	12,345		−12,345		53,191	
	Bit	Value	Bit	Value	Bit	Value
1	1	1	1	1	1	1
2	0	0	1	2	1	2
4	0	0	1	4	1	4
8	1	8	0	0	0	0
16	1	16	0	0	0	0
32	1	32	0	0	0	0
64	0	0	1	64	1	64
128	0	0	1	128	1	128
256	0	0	1	256	1	256
512	0	0	1	512	1	512
1,024	0	0	1	1,024	1	1,024
2,048	0	0	1	2,048	1	2,048
4,096	1	4,096	0	0	0	0
8,192	1	8,192	0	0	0	0
16,384	0	0	1	16,384	1	16,384
±32,768	0	0	1	−32,768	1	32,768
Total		12,345		−12,345		53,191

Figure 2.15   Two's-complement representations of 12,345 and −12,345, and unsigned representation of 53,191. Note that the latter two have identical bit representations.

When run on a big-endian machine, this code prints 30 39 and cf c7, indicating that x has hexadecimal representation 0x3039, while mx has hexadecimal representation 0xCFC7. Expanding these into binary, we get bit patterns [0011000000111001] for x and [1100111111000111] for mx. As Figure 2.15 shows, Equation 2.3 yields values 12,345 and −12,345 for these two bit patterns.

Practice Problem 2.18 (solution page 149)

In Chapter 3, we will look at listings generated by a *disassembler*, a program that converts an executable program file back to a more readable ASCII form. These files contain many hexadecimal numbers, typically representing values in two's-complement form. Being able to recognize these numbers and understand their significance (for example, whether they are negative or positive) is an important skill.

For the lines labeled A–I (on the right) in the following listing, convert the hexadecimal values (in 32-bit two's-complement form) shown to the right of the instruction names (sub, mov, and add) into their decimal equivalents:

```
4004d0:    48 81 ec e0 02 00 00        sub     $0x2e0,%rsp                     A.
4004d7:    48 8b 44 24 a8              mov     -0x58(%rsp),%rax                B.
4004dc:    48 03 47 28                 add     0x28(%rdi),%rax                 C.
4004e0:    48 89 44 24 d0              mov     %rax,-0x30(%rsp)                D.
4004e5:    48 8b 44 24 78              mov     0x78(%rsp),%rax                 E.
4004ea:    48 89 87 88 00 00 00        mov     %rax,0x88(%rdi)                 F.
4004f1:    48 8b 84 24 f8 01 00        mov     0x1f8(%rsp),%rax                G.
4004f8:    00
4004f9:    48 03 44 24 08              add     0x8(%rsp),%rax
4004fe:    48 89 84 24 c0 00 00        mov     %rax,0xc0(%rsp)                 H.
400505:    00
400506:    48 8b 44 d4 b8              mov     -0x48(%rsp,%rdx,8),%rax         I.
```

2.2.4   Conversions between Signed and Unsigned

C allows casting between different numeric data types. For example, suppose variable x is declared as int and u as unsigned. The expression (unsigned) x converts the value of x to an unsigned value, and (int) u converts the value of u to a signed integer. What should be the effect of casting signed value to unsigned, or vice versa? From a mathematical perspective, one can imagine several different conventions. Clearly, we want to preserve any value that can be represented in both forms. On the other hand, converting a negative value to unsigned might yield zero. Converting an unsigned value that is too large to be represented in two's-complement form might yield *TMax*. For most implementations of C, however, the answer to this question is based on a bit-level perspective, rather than on a numeric one.

For example, consider the following code:

```
1        short   int   v  = -12345;
2        unsigned short uv = (unsigned short) v;
3        printf("v = %d, uv = %u\n", v, uv);
```

When run on a two's-complement machine, it generates the following output:

```
v = -12345, uv = 53191
```

What we see here is that the effect of casting is to keep the bit values identical but change how these bits are interpreted. We saw in Figure 2.15 that the 16-bit two's-complement representation of −12,345 is identical to the 16-bit unsigned representation of 53,191. Casting from short to unsigned short changed the numeric value, but not the bit representation.

Similarly, consider the following code:

```
1        unsigned u = 4294967295u;    /* UMax */
2        int      tu = (int) u;
```

```
3        printf("u = %u, tu = %d\n", u, tu);
```

When run on a two's-complement machine, it generates the following output:

```
u = 4294967295, tu = -1
```

We can see from Figure 2.14 that, for a 32-bit word size, the bit patterns representing 4,294,967,295 ($UMax_{32}$) in unsigned form and -1 in two's-complement form are identical. In casting from $\texttt{unsigned}$ to $\texttt{int}$, the underlying bit representation stays the same.

This is a general rule for how most C implementations handle conversions between signed and unsigned numbers with the same word size—the numeric values might change, but the bit patterns do not. Let us capture this idea in a more mathematical form. We defined functions $U2B_w$ and $T2B_w$ that map numbers to their bit representations in either unsigned or two's-complement form. That is, given an integer x in the range $0 \leq x < UMax_w$, the function $U2B_w(x)$ gives the unique w-bit unsigned representation of x. Similarly, when x is in the range $TMin_w \leq x \leq TMax_w$, the function $T2B_w(x)$ gives the unique w-bit two's-complement representation of x.

Now define the function $T2U_w$ as $T2U_w(x) \doteq B2U_w(T2B_w(x))$. This function takes a number between $TMin_w$ and $TMax_w$ and yields a number between 0 and $UMax_w$, where the two numbers have identical bit representations, except that the argument has a two's-complement representation while the result is unsigned. Similarly, for x between 0 and $UMax_w$, the function $U2T_w$, defined as $U2T_w(x) \doteq B2T_w(U2B_w(x))$, yields the number having the same two's-complement representation as the unsigned representation of x.

Pursuing our earlier examples, we see from Figure 2.15 that $T2U_{16}(-12,345) = 53,191$, and that $U2T_{16}(53,191) = -12,345$. That is, the 16-bit pattern written in hexadecimal as $\texttt{0xCFC7}$ is both the two's-complement representation of $-12,345$ and the unsigned representation of $53,191$. Note also that $12,345 + 53,191 = 65,536 = 2^{16}$. This property generalizes to a relationship between the two numeric values (two's complement and unsigned) represented by a given bit pattern. Similarly, from Figure 2.14, we see that $T2U_{32}(-1) = 4,294,967,295$, and $U2T_{32}(4,294,967,295) = -1$. That is, $UMax$ has the same bit representation in unsigned form as does -1 in two's-complement form. We can also see the relationship between these two numbers: $1 + UMax_w = 2^w$.

We see, then, that function $T2U$ describes the conversion of a two's-complement number to its unsigned counterpart, while $U2T$ converts in the opposite direction. These describe the effect of casting between these data types in most C implementations.

Practice Problem 2.19 (solution page 149)

Using the table you filled in when solving Problem 2.17, fill in the following table describing the function $T2U_4$:

x	$T2U_4(x)$
-8	_____
-3	_____
-2	_____
-1	_____
0	_____
5	_____

The relationship we have seen, via several examples, between the two's-complement and unsigned values for a given bit pattern can be expressed as a property of the function $T2U$:

PRINCIPLE: Conversion from two's complement to unsigned

For x such that $TMin_w \leq x \leq TMax_w$:

$$T2U_w(x) = \begin{cases} x + 2^w, & x < 0 \\ x, & x \geq 0 \end{cases} \tag{2.5}$$

∎

For example, we saw that $T2U_{16}(-12{,}345) = -12{,}345 + 2^{16} = 53{,}191$, and also that $T2U_w(-1) = -1 + 2^w = UMax_w$.

This property can be derived by comparing Equations 2.1 and 2.3.

DERIVATION: Conversion from two's complement to unsigned

Comparing Equations 2.1 and 2.3, we can see that for bit pattern $\vec{x}$, if we compute the difference $B2U_w(\vec{x}) - B2T_w(\vec{x})$, the weighted sums for bits from 0 to $w-2$ will cancel each other, leaving a value $B2U_w(\vec{x}) - B2T_w(\vec{x}) = x_{w-1}(2^{w-1} - -2^{w-1}) = x_{w-1}2^w$. This gives a relationship $B2U_w(\vec{x}) = B2T_w(\vec{x}) + x_{w-1}2^w$. We therefore have

$$B2U_w(T2B_w(x)) = T2U_w(x) = x + x_{w-1}2^w \tag{2.6}$$

In a two's-complement representation of x, bit x_{w-1} determines whether or not x is negative, giving the two cases of Equation 2.5. ∎

As examples, Figure 2.16 compares how functions $B2U$ and $B2T$ assign values to bit patterns for $w = 4$. For the two's-complement case, the most significant bit serves as the sign bit, which we diagram as a leftward-pointing gray bar. For the unsigned case, this bit has positive weight, which we show as a rightward-pointing black bar. In going from two's complement to unsigned, the most significant bit changes its weight from -8 to $+8$. As a consequence, the values that are negative in a two's-complement representation increase by $2^4 = 16$ with an unsigned representation. Thus, -5 becomes $+11$, and -1 becomes $+15$.

Figure 2.16
Comparing unsigned and two's-complement representations for $w = 4$. The weight of the most significant bit is -8 for two's complement and $+8$ for unsigned, yielding a net difference of 16.

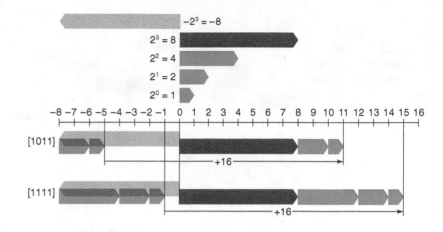

Figure 2.17
Conversion from two's complement to unsigned. Function $T2U$ converts negative numbers to large positive numbers.

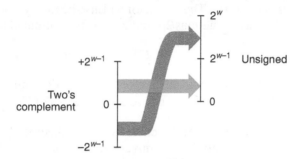

Figure 2.17 illustrates the general behavior of function $T2U$. As it shows, when mapping a signed number to its unsigned counterpart, negative numbers are converted to large positive numbers, while nonnegative numbers remain unchanged.

Practice Problem 2.20 (solution page 149)

Explain how Equation 2.5 applies to the entries in the table you generated when solving Problem 2.19.

Going in the other direction, we can state the relationship between an unsigned number u and its signed counterpart $U2T_w(u)$:

PRINCIPLE: Unsigned to two's-complement conversion

For u such that $0 \leq u \leq UMax_w$:

$$U2T_w(u) = \begin{cases} u, & u \leq TMax_w \\ u - 2^w, & u > TMax_w \end{cases} \qquad (2.7)$$

∎

Figure 2.18

Conversion from unsigned to two's complement. Function $U2T$ converts numbers greater than $2^{w-1} - 1$ to negative values.

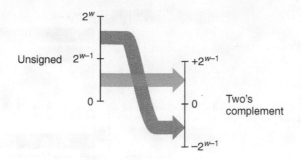

This principle can be justified as follows:

DERIVATION: Unsigned to two's-complement conversion

Let $\vec{u} = U2B_w(u)$. This bit vector will also be the two's-complement representation of $U2T_w(u)$. Equations 2.1 and 2.3 can be combined to give

$$U2T_w(u) = -u_{w-1}2^w + u \qquad (2.8)$$

In the unsigned representation of u, bit u_{w-1} determines whether or not u is greater than $TMax_w = 2^{w-1} - 1$, giving the two cases of Equation 2.7. ∎

The behavior of function $U2T$ is illustrated in Figure 2.18. For small ($\leq TMax_w$) numbers, the conversion from unsigned to signed preserves the numeric value. Large ($> TMax_w$) numbers are converted to negative values.

To summarize, we considered the effects of converting in both directions between unsigned and two's-complement representations. For values x in the range $0 \leq x \leq TMax_w$, we have $T2U_w(x) = x$ and $U2T_w(x) = x$. That is, numbers in this range have identical unsigned and two's-complement representations. For values outside of this range, the conversions either add or subtract 2^w. For example, we have $T2U_w(-1) = -1 + 2^w = UMax_w$—the negative number closest to zero maps to the largest unsigned number. At the other extreme, one can see that $T2U_w(TMin_w) = -2^{w-1} + 2^w = 2^{w-1} = TMax_w + 1$—the most negative number maps to an unsigned number just outside the range of positive two's-complement numbers. Using the example of Figure 2.15, we can see that $T2U_{16}(-12{,}345) = 65{,}536 + -12{,}345 = 53{,}191$.

2.2.5 Signed versus Unsigned in C

As indicated in Figures 2.9 and 2.10, C supports both signed and unsigned arithmetic for all of its integer data types. Although the C standard does not specify a particular representation of signed numbers, almost all machines use two's complement. Generally, most numbers are signed by default. For example, when declaring a constant such as 12345 or 0x1A2B, the value is considered signed. Adding character 'U' or 'u' as a suffix creates an unsigned constant; for example, 12345U or 0x1A2Bu.

C allows conversion between unsigned and signed. Although the C standard does not specify precisely how this conversion should be made, most systems follow the rule that the underlying bit representation does not change. This rule has the effect of applying the function $U2T_w$ when converting from unsigned to signed, and $T2U_w$ when converting from signed to unsigned, where w is the number of bits for the data type.

Conversions can happen due to explicit casting, such as in the following code:

```
1    int tx, ty;
2    unsigned ux, uy;
3
4    tx = (int) ux;
5    uy = (unsigned) ty;
```

Alternatively, they can happen implicitly when an expression of one type is assigned to a variable of another, as in the following code:

```
1    int tx, ty;
2    unsigned ux, uy;
3
4    tx = ux; /* Cast to signed */
5    uy = ty; /* Cast to unsigned */
```

When printing numeric values with `printf`, the directives `%d`, `%u`, and `%x` are used to print a number as a signed decimal, an unsigned decimal, and in hexadecimal format, respectively. Note that `printf` does not make use of any type information, and so it is possible to print a value of type `int` with directive `%u` and a value of type `unsigned` with directive `%d`. For example, consider the following code:

```
1    int x = -1;
2    unsigned u = 2147483648; /* 2 to the 31st */
3
4    printf("x = %u = %d\n", x, x);
5    printf("u = %u = %d\n", u, u);
```

When compiled as a 32-bit program, it prints the following:

```
x = 4294967295 = -1
u = 2147483648 = -2147483648
```

In both cases, `printf` prints the word first as if it represented an unsigned number and second as if it represented a signed number. We can see the conversion routines in action: $T2U_{32}(-1) = UMax_{32} = 2^{32} - 1$ and $U2T_{32}(2^{31}) = 2^{31} - 2^{32} = -2^{31} = TMin_{32}$.

Some possibly nonintuitive behavior arises due to C's handling of expressions containing combinations of signed and unsigned quantities. When an operation is performed where one operand is signed and the other is unsigned, C implicitly casts the signed argument to unsigned and performs the operations

Expression			Type	Evaluation
0	==	0U	Unsigned	1
-1	<	0	Signed	1
-1	<	0U	Unsigned	0 *
2147483647	>	-2147483647-1	Signed	1
2147483647U	>	-2147483647-1	Unsigned	0 *
2147483647	>	(int) 2147483648U	Signed	1 *
-1	>	-2	Signed	1
(unsigned) -1	>	-2	Unsigned	1

Figure 2.19 Effects of C promotion rules. Nonintuitive cases are marked by '*'. When either operand of a comparison is unsigned, the other operand is implicitly cast to unsigned. See Web Aside DATA:TMIN for why we write $TMin_{32}$ as $-2,147,483,647-1$.

assuming the numbers are nonnegative. As we will see, this convention makes little difference for standard arithmetic operations, but it leads to nonintuitive results for relational operators such as < and >. Figure 2.19 shows some sample relational expressions and their resulting evaluations, when data type int has a 32-bit two's-complement representation. Consider the comparison -1 < 0U. Since the second operand is unsigned, the first one is implicitly cast to unsigned, and hence the expression is equivalent to the comparison 4294967295U < 0U (recall that $T2U_w(-1) = UMax_w$), which of course is false. The other cases can be understood by similar analyses.

Practice Problem 2.21 (solution page 149)

Assuming the expressions are evaluated when executing a 32-bit program on a machine that uses two's-complement arithmetic, fill in the following table describing the effect of casting and relational operations, in the style of Figure 2.19:

Expression	Type	Evaluation
-2147483647-1 == 2147483648U	_____	_____
-2147483647-1 < 2147483647	_____	_____
-2147483647-1U < 2147483647	_____	_____
-2147483647-1 < -2147483647	_____	_____
-2147483647-1U < -2147483647	_____	_____

2.2.6 Expanding the Bit Representation of a Number

One common operation is to convert between integers having different word sizes while retaining the same numeric value. Of course, this may not be possible when the destination data type is too small to represent the desired value. Converting from a smaller to a larger data type, however, should always be possible.

Web Aside DATA:TMIN   Writing *TMin* in C

In Figure 2.19 and in Problem 2.21, we carefully wrote the value of $TMin_{32}$ as $-2,147,483,647-1$. Why not simply write it as either $-2,147,483,648$ or 0x80000000? Looking at the C header file limits.h, we see that they use a similar method as we have to write $TMin_{32}$ and $TMax_{32}$:

```
/* Minimum and maximum values a 'signed int' can hold. */
#define INT_MAX    2147483647
#define INT_MIN    (-INT_MAX - 1)
```

Unfortunately, a curious interaction between the asymmetry of the two's-complement representation and the conversion rules of C forces us to write $TMin_{32}$ in this unusual way. Although understanding this issue requires us to delve into one of the murkier corners of the C language standards, it will help us appreciate some of the subtleties of integer data types and representations.

To convert an unsigned number to a larger data type, we can simply add leading zeros to the representation; this operation is known as *zero extension*, expressed by the following principle:

PRINCIPLE: Expansion of an unsigned number by zero extension

Define bit vectors $\vec{u} = [u_{w-1}, u_{w-2}, \ldots, u_0]$ of width w and $\vec{u}' = [0, \ldots, 0, u_{w-1}, u_{w-2}, \ldots, u_0]$ of width w', where $w' > w$. Then $B2U_w(\vec{u}) = B2U_{w'}(\vec{u}')$. ∎

This principle can be seen to follow directly from the definition of the unsigned encoding, given by Equation 2.1.

For converting a two's-complement number to a larger data type, the rule is to perform a *sign extension*, adding copies of the most significant bit to the representation, expressed by the following principle. We show the sign bit x_{w-1} in blue to highlight its role in sign extension.

PRINCIPLE: Expansion of a two's-complement number by sign extension

Define bit vectors $\vec{x} = [x_{w-1}, x_{w-2}, \ldots, x_0]$ of width w and $\vec{x}' = [x_{w-1}, \ldots, x_{w-1}, x_{w-1}, x_{w-2}, \ldots, x_0]$ of width w', where $w' > w$. Then $B2T_w(\vec{x}) = B2T_{w'}(\vec{x}')$. ∎

As an example, consider the following code:

```
1    short sx = -12345;         /* -12345 */
2    unsigned short usx = sx;   /*  53191 */
3    int x = sx;                /* -12345 */
4    unsigned ux = usx;         /*  53191 */
5
6    printf("sx  = %d:\t", sx);
7    show_bytes((byte_pointer) &sx, sizeof(short));
8    printf("usx = %u:\t", usx);
9    show_bytes((byte_pointer) &usx, sizeof(unsigned short));
10   printf("x   = %d:\t", x);
```

```
11      show_bytes((byte_pointer) &x, sizeof(int));
12      printf("ux  = %u:\t", ux);
13      show_bytes((byte_pointer) &ux, sizeof(unsigned));
```

When run as a 32-bit program on a big-endian machine that uses a two's-complement representation, this code prints the output

```
sx  = -12345:  cf c7
usx = 53191:   cf c7
x   = -12345:  ff ff cf c7
ux  = 53191:   00 00 cf c7
```

We see that, although the two's-complement representation of −12,345 and the unsigned representation of 53,191 are identical for a 16-bit word size, they differ for a 32-bit word size. In particular, −12,345 has hexadecimal representation 0xFFFFCFC7, while 53,191 has hexadecimal representation 0x0000CFC7. The former has been sign extended—16 copies of the most significant bit 1, having hexadecimal representation 0xFFFF, have been added as leading bits. The latter has been extended with 16 leading zeros, having hexadecimal representation 0x0000.

As an illustration, Figure 2.20 shows the result of expanding from word size $w = 3$ to $w = 4$ by sign extension. Bit vector [101] represents the value $−4 + 1 = −3$. Applying sign extension gives bit vector [1101] representing the value $−8 + 4 + 1 = −3$. We can see that, for $w = 4$, the combined value of the two most significant bits, $−8 + 4 = −4$, matches the value of the sign bit for $w = 3$. Similarly, bit vectors [111] and [1111] both represent the value −1.

With this as intuition, we can now show that sign extension preserves the value of a two's-complement number.

Figure 2.20
Examples of sign extension from $w = 3$ to $w = 4$. For $w = 4$, the combined weight of the upper 2 bits is $−8 + 4 = −4$, matching that of the sign bit for $w = 3$.

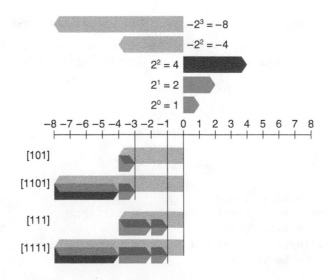

DERIVATION: Expansion of a two's-complement number by sign extension

Let $w' = w + k$. What we want to prove is that

$$B2T_{w+k}([\underbrace{x_{w-1}, \ldots, x_{w-1}}_{k \text{ times}}, x_{w-1}, x_{w-2}, \ldots, x_0]) = B2T_w([x_{w-1}, x_{w-2}, \ldots, x_0])$$

The proof follows by induction on k. That is, if we can prove that sign extending by 1 bit preserves the numeric value, then this property will hold when sign extending by an arbitrary number of bits. Thus, the task reduces to proving that

$$B2T_{w+1}([x_{w-1}, x_{w-1}, x_{w-2}, \ldots, x_0]) = B2T_w([x_{w-1}, x_{w-2}, \ldots, x_0])$$

Expanding the left-hand expression with Equation 2.3 gives the following:

$$B2T_{w+1}([x_{w-1}, x_{w-1}, x_{w-2}, \ldots, x_0]) = -x_{w-1}2^w + \sum_{i=0}^{w-1} x_i 2^i$$

$$= -x_{w-1}2^w + x_{w-1}2^{w-1} + \sum_{i=0}^{w-2} x_i 2^i$$

$$= -x_{w-1}\left(2^w - 2^{w-1}\right) + \sum_{i=0}^{w-2} x_i 2^i$$

$$= -x_{w-1}2^{w-1} + \sum_{i=0}^{w-2} x_i 2^i$$

$$= B2T_w([x_{w-1}, x_{w-2}, \ldots, x_0])$$

The key property we exploit is that $2^w - 2^{w-1} = 2^{w-1}$. Thus, the combined effect of adding a bit of weight -2^w and of converting the bit having weight -2^{w-1} to be one with weight 2^{w-1} is to preserve the original numeric value.   ∎

Practice Problem 2.22 (solution page 150)

Show that each of the following bit vectors is a two's-complement representation of -5 by applying Equation 2.3:

A. [1011]

B. [11011]

C. [111011]

Observe that the second and third bit vectors can be derived from the first by sign extension.

One point worth making is that the relative order of conversion from one data size to another and between unsigned and signed can affect the behavior of a program. Consider the following code:

```
1    short sx = -12345;        /* -12345   */
2    unsigned uy = sx;         /* Mystery! */
3
4    printf("uy   = %u:\t", uy);
5    show_bytes((byte_pointer) &uy, sizeof(unsigned));
```

When run on a big-endian machine, this code causes the following output to be printed:

```
uy = 4294954951:  ff ff cf c7
```

This shows that, when converting from short to unsigned, the program first changes the size and then the type. That is, (unsigned) sx is equivalent to (unsigned) (int) sx, evaluating to 4,294,954,951, not (unsigned) (unsigned short) sx, which evaluates to 53,191. Indeed, this convention is required by the C standards.

Practice Problem 2.23 (solution page 150)

Consider the following C functions:

```
int fun1(unsigned word) {
    return (int) ((word << 24) >> 24);
}

int fun2(unsigned word) {
    return ((int) word << 24) >> 24;
}
```

Assume these are executed as a 32-bit program on a machine that uses two's-complement arithmetic. Assume also that right shifts of signed values are performed arithmetically, while right shifts of unsigned values are performed logically.

A. Fill in the following table showing the effect of these functions for several example arguments. You will find it more convenient to work with a hexadecimal representation. Just remember that hex digits 8 through F have their most significant bits equal to 1.

w	fun1(w)	fun2(w)
0x00000076	_____	_____
0x87654321	_____	_____
0x000000C9	_____	_____
0xEDCBA987	_____	_____

B. Describe in words the useful computation each of these functions performs.

2.2.7   Truncating Numbers

Suppose that, rather than extending a value with extra bits, we reduce the number of bits representing a number. This occurs, for example, in the following code:

```
1      int x = 53191;
2      short sx = (short) x;    /* -12345 */
3      int y = sx;              /* -12345 */
```

Casting x to be short will truncate a 32-bit int to a 16-bit short. As we saw before, this 16-bit pattern is the two's-complement representation of $-12,345$. When casting this back to int, sign extension will set the high-order 16 bits to ones, yielding the 32-bit two's-complement representation of $-12,345$.

When truncating a w-bit number $\vec{x} = [x_{w-1}, x_{w-2}, \ldots, x_0]$ to a k-bit number, we drop the high-order $w - k$ bits, giving a bit vector $\vec{x}' = [x_{k-1}, x_{k-2}, \ldots, x_0]$. Truncating a number can alter its value—a form of overflow. For an unsigned number, we can readily characterize the numeric value that will result.

PRINCIPLE: Truncation of an unsigned number

Let $\vec{x}$ be the bit vector $[x_{w-1}, x_{w-2}, \ldots, x_0]$, and let $\vec{x}'$ be the result of truncating it to k bits: $\vec{x}' = [x_{k-1}, x_{k-2}, \ldots, x_0]$. Let $x = B2U_w(\vec{x})$ and $x' = B2U_k(\vec{x}')$. Then $x' = x \bmod 2^k$. ∎

The intuition behind this principle is simply that all of the bits that were truncated have weights of the form 2^i, where $i \geq k$, and therefore each of these weights reduces to zero under the modulus operation. This is formalized by the following derivation:

DERIVATION: Truncation of an unsigned number

Applying the modulus operation to Equation 2.1 yields

$$B2U_w([x_{w-1}, x_{w-2}, \ldots, x_0]) \bmod 2^k = \left[\sum_{i=0}^{w-1} x_i 2^i\right] \bmod 2^k$$

$$= \left[\sum_{i=0}^{k-1} x_i 2^i\right] \bmod 2^k$$

$$= \sum_{i=0}^{k-1} x_i 2^i$$

$$= B2U_k([x_{k-1}, x_{k-2}, \ldots, x_0])$$

In this derivation, we make use of the property that $2^i \bmod 2^k = 0$ for any $i \geq k$. ∎

A similar property holds for truncating a two's-complement number, except that it then converts the most significant bit into a sign bit:

PRINCIPLE: Truncation of a two's-complement number

Let $\vec{x}$ be the bit vector $[x_{w-1}, x_{w-2}, \ldots, x_0]$, and let $\vec{x}'$ be the result of truncating it to k bits: $\vec{x}' = [x_{k-1}, x_{k-2}, \ldots, x_0]$. Let $x = B2T_w(\vec{x})$ and $x' = B2T_k(\vec{x}')$. Then $x' = U2T_k(x \bmod 2^k)$. ∎

In this formulation, $x \bmod 2^k$ will be a number between 0 and $2^k - 1$. Applying function $U2T_k$ to it will have the effect of converting the most significant bit x_{k-1} from having weight 2^{k-1} to having weight -2^{k-1}. We can see this with the example of converting value $x = 53{,}191$ from int to short. Since $2^{16} = 65{,}536 \geq x$, we have $x \bmod 2^{16} = x$. But when we convert this number to a 16-bit two's-complement number, we get $x' = 53{,}191 - 65{,}536 = -12{,}345$.

DERIVATION: Truncation of a two's-complement number

Using a similar argument to the one we used for truncation of an unsigned number shows that

$$B2T_w([x_{w-1}, x_{w-2}, \ldots, x_0]) \bmod 2^k = B2U_k([x_{k-1}, x_{k-2}, \ldots, x_0])$$

That is, $x \bmod 2^k$ can be represented by an unsigned number having bit-level representation $[x_{k-1}, x_{k-2}, \ldots, x_0]$. Converting this to a two's-complement number gives $x' = U2T_k(x \bmod 2^k)$. ∎

Summarizing, the effect of truncation for unsigned numbers is

$$B2U_k([x_{k-1}, x_{k-2}, \ldots, x_0]) = B2U_w([x_{w-1}, x_{w-2}, \ldots, x_0]) \bmod 2^k \quad (2.9)$$

while the effect for two's-complement numbers is

$$B2T_k([x_{k-1}, x_{k-2}, \ldots, x_0]) = U2T_k(B2U_w([x_{w-1}, x_{w-2}, \ldots, x_0]) \bmod 2^k) \quad (2.10)$$

Practice Problem 2.24 (solution page 150)

Suppose we truncate a 4-bit value (represented by hex digits 0 through F) to a 3-bit value (represented as hex digits 0 through 7.) Fill in the table below showing the effect of this truncation for some cases, in terms of the unsigned and two's-complement interpretations of those bit patterns.

Hex		Unsigned		Two's complement	
Original	Truncated	Original	Truncated	Original	Truncated
0	0	0	_____	0	_____
2	2	2	_____	2	_____
9	1	9	_____	−7	_____
B	3	11	_____	−5	_____
F	7	15	_____	−1	_____

Explain how Equations 2.9 and 2.10 apply to these cases.

2.2.8 Advice on Signed versus Unsigned

As we have seen, the implicit casting of signed to unsigned leads to some non-intuitive behavior. Nonintuitive features often lead to program bugs, and ones involving the nuances of implicit casting can be especially difficult to see. Since the casting takes place without any clear indication in the code, programmers often overlook its effects.

The following two practice problems illustrate some of the subtle errors that can arise due to implicit casting and the unsigned data type.

Practice Problem 2.25 (solution page 151)

Consider the following code that attempts to sum the elements of an array a, where the number of elements is given by parameter `length`:

```
1   /* WARNING: This is buggy code */
2   float sum_elements(float a[], unsigned length) {
3       int i;
4       float result = 0;
5
6       for (i = 0; i <= length-1; i++)
7           result += a[i];
8       return result;
9   }
```

When run with argument `length` equal to 0, this code should return 0.0. Instead, it encounters a memory error. Explain why this happens. Show how this code can be corrected.

Practice Problem 2.26 (solution page 151)

You are given the assignment of writing a function that determines whether one string is longer than another. You decide to make use of the string library function `strlen` having the following declaration:

```
/* Prototype for library function strlen */
size_t strlen(const char *s);
```

Here is your first attempt at the function:

```
/* Determine whether string s is longer than string t */
/* WARNING: This function is buggy */
int strlonger(char *s, char *t) {
    return strlen(s) - strlen(t) > 0;
}
```

When you test this on some sample data, things do not seem to work quite right. You investigate further and determine that, when compiled as a 32-bit program, data type `size_t` is defined (via `typedef`) in header file `stdio.h` to be unsigned.

A. For what cases will this function produce an incorrect result?

B. Explain how this incorrect result comes about.

C. Show how to fix the code so that it will work reliably.

We have seen multiple ways in which the subtle features of unsigned arithmetic, and especially the implicit conversion of signed to unsigned, can lead to errors or vulnerabilities. One way to avoid such bugs is to never use unsigned numbers. In fact, few languages other than C support unsigned integers. Apparently, these other language designers viewed them as more trouble than they are worth. For example, Java supports only signed integers, and it requires that they be implemented with two's-complement arithmetic. The normal right shift operator `>>` is guaranteed to perform an arithmetic shift. The special operator `>>>` is defined to perform a logical right shift.

Unsigned values are very useful when we want to think of words as just collections of bits with no numeric interpretation. This occurs, for example, when packing a word with *flags* describing various Boolean conditions. Addresses are naturally unsigned, so systems programmers find unsigned types to be helpful. Unsigned values are also useful when implementing mathematical packages for modular arithmetic and for multiprecision arithmetic, in which numbers are represented by arrays of words.

2.3 Integer Arithmetic

Many beginning programmers are surprised to find that adding two positive numbers can yield a negative result, and that the comparison x < y can yield a different result than the comparison x−y < 0. These properties are artifacts of the finite nature of computer arithmetic. Understanding the nuances of computer arithmetic can help programmers write more reliable code.

2.3.1 Unsigned Addition

Consider two nonnegative integers x and y, such that $0 \le x, y < 2^w$. Each of these values can be represented by a w-bit unsigned number. If we compute their sum, however, we have a possible range $0 \le x + y \le 2^{w+1} - 2$. Representing this sum could require $w + 1$ bits. For example, Figure 2.21 shows a plot of the function $x + y$ when x and y have 4-bit representations. The arguments (shown on the horizontal axes) range from 0 to 15, but the sum ranges from 0 to 30. The shape of the function is a sloping plane (the function is linear in both dimensions). If we were to maintain the sum as a $(w + 1)$-bit number and add it to another value, we may require $w + 2$ bits, and so on. This continued "word size

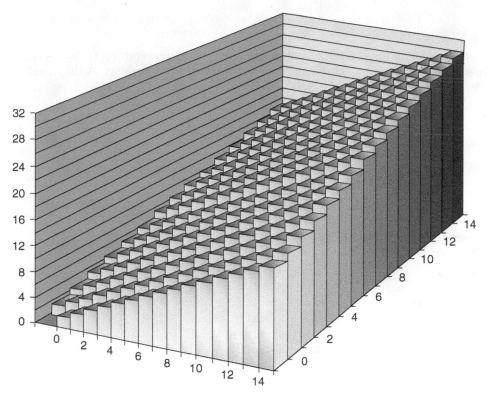

Figure 2.21   Integer addition. With a 4-bit word size, the sum could require 5 bits.

inflation" means we cannot place any bound on the word size required to fully represent the results of arithmetic operations. Some programming languages, such as Lisp, actually support *arbitrary size* arithmetic to allow integers of any size (within the memory limits of the computer, of course.) More commonly, programming languages support fixed-size arithmetic, and hence operations such as "addition" and "multiplication" differ from their counterpart operations over integers.

Let us define the operation $+_w^u$ for arguments x and y, where $0 \le x, y < 2^w$, as the result of truncating the integer sum $x + y$ to be w bits long and then viewing the result as an unsigned number. This can be characterized as a form of modular arithmetic, computing the sum modulo 2^w by simply discarding any bits with weight greater than 2^{w-1} in the bit-level representation of $x + y$. For example, consider a 4-bit number representation with $x = 9$ and $y = 12$, having bit representations [1001] and [1100], respectively. Their sum is 21, having a 5-bit representation [10101]. But if we discard the high-order bit, we get [0101], that is, decimal value 5. This matches the value 21 mod 16 = 5.

Aside Security vulnerability in getpeername

In 2002, programmers involved in the FreeBSD open-source operating systems project realized that their implementation of the getpeername library function had a security vulnerability. A simplified version of their code went something like this:

```
1    /*
2     * Illustration of code vulnerability similar to that found in
3     * FreeBSD's implementation of getpeername()
4     */
5
6    /* Declaration of library function memcpy */
7    void *memcpy(void *dest, void *src, size_t n);
8
9    /* Kernel memory region holding user-accessible data */
10   #define KSIZE 1024
11   char kbuf[KSIZE];
12
13   /* Copy at most maxlen bytes from kernel region to user buffer */
14   int copy_from_kernel(void *user_dest, int maxlen) {
15       /* Byte count len is minimum of buffer size and maxlen */
16       int len = KSIZE < maxlen ? KSIZE : maxlen;
17       memcpy(user_dest, kbuf, len);
18       return len;
19   }
```

In this code, we show the prototype for library function memcpy on line 7, which is designed to copy a specified number of bytes n from one region of memory to another.

The function copy_from_kernel, starting at line 14, is designed to copy some of the data maintained by the operating system kernel to a designated region of memory accessible to the user. Most of the data structures maintained by the kernel should not be readable by a user, since they may contain sensitive information about other users and about other jobs running on the system, but the region shown as kbuf was intended to be one that the user could read. The parameter maxlen is intended to be the length of the buffer allocated by the user and indicated by argument user_dest. The computation at line 16 then makes sure that no more bytes are copied than are available in either the source or the destination buffer.

Suppose, however, that some malicious programmer writes code that calls copy_from_kernel with a negative value of maxlen. Then the minimum computation on line 16 will compute this value for len, which will then be passed as the parameter n to memcpy. Note, however, that parameter n is declared as having data type size_t. This data type is declared (via typedef) in the library file stdio.h. Typically, it is defined to be unsigned for 32-bit programs and unsigned long for 64-bit programs. Since argument n is unsigned, memcpy will treat it as a very large positive number and attempt to copy that many bytes from the kernel region to the user's buffer. Copying that many bytes (at least 2^{31}) will not actually work, because the program will encounter invalid addresses in the process, but the program could read regions of the kernel memory for which it is not authorized.

We can characterize operation $+_w^u$ as follows:

PRINCIPLE: Unsigned addition

For x and y such that $0 \le x, y < 2^w$:

$$x +_w^u y = \begin{cases} x + y, & x + y < 2^w \quad \text{Normal} \\ x + y - 2^w, & 2^w \le x + y < 2^{w+1} \quad \text{Overflow} \end{cases} \quad (2.11)$$

The two cases of Equation 2.11 are illustrated in Figure 2.22, showing the sum $x + y$ on the left mapping to the unsigned w-bit sum $x +_w^u y$ on the right. The normal case preserves the value of $x + y$, while the overflow case has the effect of decrementing this sum by 2^w.

DERIVATION: Unsigned addition

In general, we can see that if $x + y < 2^w$, the leading bit in the $(w + 1)$-bit representation of the sum will equal 0, and hence discarding it will not change the numeric value. On the other hand, if $2^w \le x + y < 2^{w+1}$, the leading bit in the $(w + 1)$-bit representation of the sum will equal 1, and hence discarding it is equivalent to subtracting 2^w from the sum.

An arithmetic operation is said to *overflow* when the full integer result cannot fit within the word size limits of the data type. As Equation 2.11 indicates, overflow

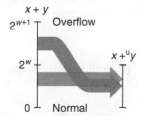

Figure 2.22   Relation between integer addition and unsigned addition. When $x + y$ is greater than $2^w - 1$, the sum overflows.

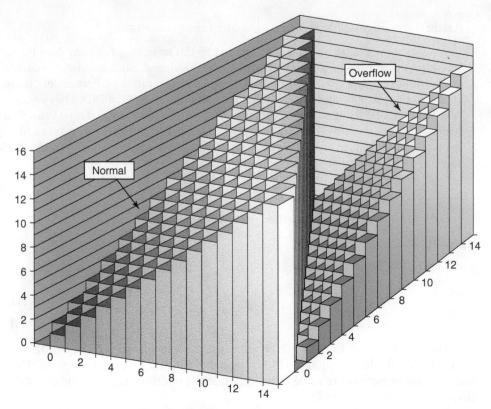

Figure 2.23 Unsigned addition. With a 4-bit word size, addition is performed modulo 16.

occurs when the two operands sum to 2^w or more. Figure 2.23 shows a plot of the unsigned addition function for word size $w = 4$. The sum is computed modulo $2^4 = 16$. When $x + y < 16$, there is no overflow, and $x +_4^u y$ is simply $x + y$. This is shown as the region forming a sloping plane labeled "Normal." When $x + y \geq 16$, the addition overflows, having the effect of decrementing the sum by 16. This is shown as the region forming a sloping plane labeled "Overflow."

When executing C programs, overflows are not signaled as errors. At times, however, we might wish to determine whether or not overflow has occurred.

PRINCIPLE: Detecting overflow of unsigned addition

For x and y in the range $0 \leq x, y \leq UMax_w$, let $s \doteq x +_w^u y$. Then the computation of s overflowed if and only if $s < x$ (or equivalently, $s < y$). ∎

As an illustration, in our earlier example, we saw that $9 +_4^u 12 = 5$. We can see that overflow occurred, since $5 < 9$.

DERIVATION: Detecting overflow of unsigned addition

Observe that $x + y \geq x$, and hence if s did not overflow, we will surely have $s \geq x$. On the other hand, if s did overflow, we have $s = x + y - 2^w$. Given that $y < 2^w$, we have $y - 2^w < 0$, and hence $s = x + (y - 2^w) < x$. ∎

Practice Problem 2.27 (solution page 152)

Write a function with the following prototype:

```
/* Determine whether arguments can be added without overflow */
int uadd_ok(unsigned x, unsigned y);
```

This function should return 1 if arguments x and y can be added without causing overflow.

Modular addition forms a mathematical structure known as an *abelian group*, named after the Norwegian mathematician Niels Henrik Abel (1802–1829). That is, it is commutative (that's where the "abelian" part comes in) and associative; it has an identity element 0, and every element has an additive inverse. Let us consider the set of w-bit unsigned numbers with addition operation $+_w^u$. For every value x, there must be some value $-_w^u x$ such that $-_w^u x +_w^u x = 0$. This additive inverse operation can be characterized as follows:

PRINCIPLE: Unsigned negation

For any number x such that $0 \leq x < 2^w$, its w-bit unsigned negation $-_w^u x$ is given by the following:

$$-_w^u x = \begin{cases} x, & x = 0 \\ 2^w - x, & x > 0 \end{cases} \tag{2.12}$$

∎

This result can be readily derived by case analysis:

DERIVATION: Unsigned negation

When $x = 0$, the additive inverse is clearly 0. For $x > 0$, consider the value $2^w - x$. Observe that this number is in the range $0 < 2^w - x < 2^w$. We can also see that $(x + 2^w - x) \bmod 2^w = 2^w \bmod 2^w = 0$. Hence it is the inverse of x under $+_w^u$. ∎

Practice Problem 2.28 (solution page 152)

We can represent a bit pattern of length $w = 4$ with a single hex digit. For an unsigned interpretation of these digits, use Equation 2.12 to fill in the following table giving the values and the bit representations (in hex) of the unsigned additive inverses of the digits shown.

x		$-_4^u x$	
Hex	Decimal	Decimal	Hex
0			
5			
8			
D			
F			

2.3.2 Two's-Complement Addition

With two's-complement addition, we must decide what to do when the result is either too large (positive) or too small (negative) to represent. Given integer values x and y in the range $-2^{w-1} \leq x, y \leq 2^{w-1} - 1$, their sum is in the range $-2^w \leq x + y \leq 2^w - 2$, potentially requiring $w + 1$ bits to represent exactly. As before, we avoid ever-expanding data sizes by truncating the representation to w bits. The result is not as familiar mathematically as modular addition, however. Let us define $x +_w^t y$ to be the result of truncating the integer sum $x + y$ to be w bits long and then viewing the result as a two's-complement number.

PRINCIPLE: Two's-complement addition

For integer values x and y in the range $-2^{w-1} \leq x, y \leq 2^{w-1} - 1$:

$$x +_w^t y = \begin{cases} x + y - 2^w, & 2^{w-1} \leq x + y & \text{Positive overflow} \\ x + y, & -2^{w-1} \leq x + y < 2^{w-1} & \text{Normal} \\ x + y + 2^w, & x + y < -2^{w-1} & \text{Negative overflow} \end{cases} \quad (2.13)$$

This principle is illustrated in Figure 2.24, where the sum $x + y$ is shown on the left, having a value in the range $-2^w \leq x + y \leq 2^w - 2$, and the result of truncating the sum to a w-bit two's-complement number is shown on the right. (The labels "Case 1" to "Case 4" in this figure are for the case analysis of the formal derivation of the principle.) When the sum $x + y$ exceeds $TMax_w$ (case 4), we say that *positive overflow* has occurred. In this case, the effect of truncation is to subtract 2^w from the sum. When the sum $x + y$ is less than $TMin_w$ (case 1), we say that *negative overflow* has occurred. In this case, the effect of truncation is to add 2^w to the sum.

The w-bit two's-complement sum of two numbers has the exact same bit-level representation as the unsigned sum. In fact, most computers use the same machine instruction to perform either unsigned or signed addition.

DERIVATION: Two's-complement addition

Since two's-complement addition has the exact same bit-level representation as unsigned addition, we can characterize the operation $+_w^t$ as one of converting its arguments to unsigned, performing unsigned addition, and then converting back to two's complement:

Figure 2.24

Relation between integer and two's-complement addition. When $x + y$ is less than -2^{w-1}, there is a negative overflow. When it is greater than or equal to 2^{w-1}, there is a positive overflow.

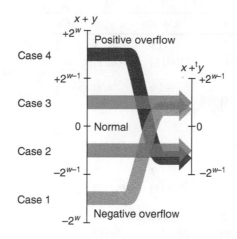

$$x +_w^t y = U2T_w(T2U_w(x) +_w^u T2U_w(y)) \tag{2.14}$$

By Equation 2.6, we can write $T2U_w(x)$ as $x_{w-1}2^w + x$ and $T2U_w(y)$ as $y_{w-1}2^w + y$. Using the property that $+_w^u$ is simply addition modulo 2^w, along with the properties of modular addition, we then have

$$
\begin{aligned}
x +_w^t y &= U2T_w(T2U_w(x) +_w^u T2U_w(y)) \\
&= U2T_w[(x_{w-1}2^w + x + y_{w-1}2^w + y) \bmod 2^w] \\
&= U2T_w[(x + y) \bmod 2^w]
\end{aligned}
$$

The terms $x_{w-1}2^w$ and $y_{w-1}2^w$ drop out since they equal 0 modulo 2^w.

To better understand this quantity, let us define z as the integer sum $z \doteq x + y$, z' as $z' \doteq z \bmod 2^w$, and z'' as $z'' \doteq U2T_w(z')$. The value z'' is equal to $x +_w^t y$. We can divide the analysis into four cases as illustrated in Figure 2.24:

1. $-2^w \le z < -2^{w-1}$. Then we will have $z' = z + 2^w$. This gives $0 \le z' < -2^{w-1} + 2^w = 2^{w-1}$. Examining Equation 2.7, we see that z' is in the range such that $z'' = z'$. This is the case of negative overflow. We have added two negative numbers x and y (that's the only way we can have $z < -2^{w-1}$) and obtained a nonnegative result $z'' = x + y + 2^w$.

2. $-2^{w-1} \le z < 0$. Then we will again have $z' = z + 2^w$, giving $-2^{w-1} + 2^w = 2^{w-1} \le z' < 2^w$. Examining Equation 2.7, we see that z' is in such a range that $z'' = z' - 2^w$, and therefore $z'' = z' - 2^w = z + 2^w - 2^w = z$. That is, our two's-complement sum z'' equals the integer sum $x + y$.

3. $0 \le z < 2^{w-1}$. Then we will have $z' = z$, giving $0 \le z' < 2^{w-1}$, and hence $z'' = z' = z$. Again, the two's-complement sum z'' equals the integer sum $x + y$.

4. $2^{w-1} \le z < 2^w$. We will again have $z' = z$, giving $2^{w-1} \le z' < 2^w$. But in this range we have $z'' = z' - 2^w$, giving $z'' = x + y - 2^w$. This is the case of positive overflow. We have added two positive numbers x and y (that's the only way we can have $z \ge 2^{w-1}$) and obtained a negative result $z'' = x + y - 2^w$. ■

x	y	$x + y$	$x +_4^t y$	Case
-8	-5	-13	3	1
[1000]	[1011]	[10011]	[0011]	
-8	-8	-16	0	1
[1000]	[1000]	[10000]	[0000]	
-8	5	-3	-3	2
[1000]	[0101]	[11101]	[1101]	
2	5	7	7	3
[0010]	[0101]	[00111]	[0111]	
5	5	10	-6	4
[0101]	[0101]	[01010]	[1010]	

Figure 2.25 Two's-complement addition examples. The bit-level representation of the 4-bit two's-complement sum can be obtained by performing binary addition of the operands and truncating the result to 4 bits.

As illustrations of two's-complement addition, Figure 2.25 shows some examples when $w = 4$. Each example is labeled by the case to which it corresponds in the derivation of Equation 2.13. Note that $2^4 = 16$, and hence negative overflow yields a result 16 more than the integer sum, and positive overflow yields a result 16 less. We include bit-level representations of the operands and the result. Observe that the result can be obtained by performing binary addition of the operands and truncating the result to 4 bits.

Figure 2.26 illustrates two's-complement addition for word size $w = 4$. The operands range between -8 and 7. When $x + y < -8$, two's-complement addition has a negative overflow, causing the sum to be incremented by 16. When $-8 \leq x + y < 8$, the addition yields $x + y$. When $x + y \geq 8$, the addition has a positive overflow, causing the sum to be decremented by 16. Each of these three ranges forms a sloping plane in the figure.

Equation 2.13 also lets us identify the cases where overflow has occurred:

PRINCIPLE: Detecting overflow in two's-complement addition

For x and y in the range $TMin_w \leq x, y \leq TMax_w$, let $s \doteq x +_w^t y$. Then the computation of s has had positive overflow if and only if $x > 0$ and $y > 0$ but $s \leq 0$. The computation has had negative overflow if and only if $x < 0$ and $y < 0$ but $s \geq 0$. ∎

Figure 2.25 shows several illustrations of this principle for $w = 4$. The first entry shows a case of negative overflow, where two negative numbers sum to a positive one. The final entry shows a case of positive overflow, where two positive numbers sum to a negative one.

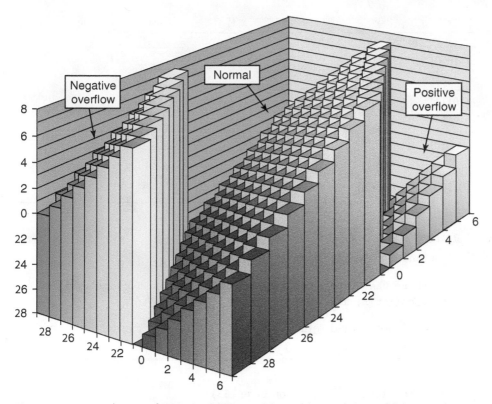

Figure 2.26   Two's-complement addition. With a 4-bit word size, addition can have a negative overflow when $x + y < -8$ and a positive overflow when $x + y \geq 8$.

DERIVATION: Detecting overflow of two's-complement addition

Let us first do the analysis for positive overflow. If both $x > 0$ and $y > 0$ but $s \leq 0$, then clearly positive overflow has occurred. Conversely, positive overflow requires (1) that $x > 0$ and $y > 0$ (otherwise, $x + y < TMax_w$) and (2) that $s \leq 0$ (from Equation 2.13). A similar set of arguments holds for negative overflow.   ∎

Practice Problem 2.29 (solution page 152)

Fill in the following table in the style of Figure 2.25. Give the integer values of the 5-bit arguments, the values of both their integer and two's-complement sums, the bit-level representation of the two's-complement sum, and the case from the derivation of Equation 2.13.

x	y	$x + y$	$x +_5^t y$	Case
[10100]	[10001]			

x	y	$x + y$	$x +_5^t y$	Case
[11000]	[11000]			
[10111]	[01000]			
[00010]	[00101]			
[01100]	[00100]			

Practice Problem 2.30 (solution page 153)

Write a function with the following prototype:

```
/* Determine whether arguments can be added without overflow */
int tadd_ok(int x, int y);
```

This function should return 1 if arguments x and y can be added without causing overflow.

Practice Problem 2.31 (solution page 153)

Your coworker gets impatient with your analysis of the overflow conditions for two's-complement addition and presents you with the following implementation of tadd_ok:

```
/* Determine whether arguments can be added without overflow */
/* WARNING: This code is buggy. */
int tadd_ok(int x, int y) {
    int sum = x+y;
    return (sum-x == y) && (sum-y == x);
}
```

You look at the code and laugh. Explain why.

Practice Problem 2.32 (solution page 153)

You are assigned the task of writing code for a function tsub_ok, with arguments x and y, that will return 1 if computing x-y does not cause overflow. Having just written the code for Problem 2.30, you write the following:

```
/* Determine whether arguments can be subtracted without overflow */
/* WARNING: This code is buggy. */
int tsub_ok(int x, int y) {
```

```
        return tadd_ok(x, -y);
}
```

For what values of x and y will this function give incorrect results? Writing a correct version of this function is left as an exercise (Problem 2.74).

2.3.3   Two's-Complement Negation

We can see that every number x in the range $TMin_w \leq x \leq TMax_w$ has an additive inverse under $+_w^t$, which we denote $-_w^t x$ as follows:

PRINCIPLE: Two's-complement negation

For x in the range $TMin_w \leq x \leq TMax_w$, its two's-complement negation $-_w^t x$ is given by the formula

$$-_w^t x = \begin{cases} TMin_w, & x = TMin_w \\ -x, & x > TMin_w \end{cases} \qquad (2.15)$$

         ■

That is, for w-bit two's-complement addition, $TMin_w$ is its own additive inverse, while any other value x has $-x$ as its additive inverse.

DERIVATION: Two's-complement negation

Observe that $TMin_w + TMin_w = -2^{w-1} + -2^{w-1} = -2^w$. This would cause negative overflow, and hence $TMin_w +_w^t TMin_w = -2^w + 2^w = 0$. For values of x such that $x > TMin_w$, the value $-x$ can also be represented as a w-bit two's-complement number, and their sum will be $-x + x = 0$.   ■

Practice Problem 2.33 (solution page 153)

We can represent a bit pattern of length $w = 4$ with a single hex digit. For a two's-complement interpretation of these digits, fill in the following table to determine the additive inverses of the digits shown:

x		$-_4^t x$	
Hex	Decimal	Decimal	Hex
0			
5			
8			
D			
F			

What do you observe about the bit patterns generated by two's-complement and unsigned (Problem 2.28) negation?

Web Aside DATA:TNEG   Bit-level representation of two's-complement negation

There are several clever ways to determine the two's-complement negation of a value represented at the bit level. The following two techniques are both useful, such as when one encounters the value 0xfffffffa when debugging a program, and they lend insight into the nature of the two's-complement representation.

One technique for performing two's-complement negation at the bit level is to complement the bits and then increment the result. In C, we can state that for any integer value x, computing the expressions -x and ~x + 1 will give identical results.

Here are some examples with a 4-bit word size:

$\vec{x}$		$\sim\vec{x}$		$incr(\sim\vec{x})$	
[0101]	5	[1010]	−6	[1011]	−5
[0111]	7	[1000]	−8	[1001]	−7
[1100]	−4	[0011]	3	[0100]	4
[0000]	0	[1111]	−1	[0000]	0
[1000]	−8	[0111]	7	[1000]	−8

For our earlier example, we know that the complement of 0xf is 0x0 and the complement of 0xa is 0x5, and so 0xfffffffa is the two's-complement representation of −6.

A second way to perform two's-complement negation of a number x is based on splitting the bit vector into two parts. Let k be the position of the rightmost 1, so the bit-level representation of x has the form $[x_{w-1}, x_{w-2}, \ldots, x_{k+1}, 1, 0, \ldots 0]$. (This is possible as long as $x \neq 0$.) The negation is then written in binary form as $[\sim x_{w-1}, \sim x_{w-2}, \ldots \sim x_{k+1}, 1, 0, \ldots, 0]$. That is, we complement each bit to the left of bit position k.

We illustrate this idea with some 4-bit numbers, where we highlight the rightmost pattern 1, 0, . . . , 0 in italics:

x		$-x$	
[1*100*]	−4	[0*100*]	4
[*1000*]	−8	[*1000*]	−8
[010*1*]	5	[101*1*]	−5
[011*1*]	7	[100*1*]	−7

2.3.4   Unsigned Multiplication

Integers x and y in the range $0 \leq x, y \leq 2^w - 1$ can be represented as w-bit unsigned numbers, but their product $x \cdot y$ can range between 0 and $(2^w - 1)^2 = 2^{2w} - 2^{w+1} + 1$. This could require as many as $2w$ bits to represent. Instead, unsigned multiplication in C is defined to yield the w-bit value given by the low-order w bits of the $2w$-bit integer product. Let us denote this value as $x *_w^u y$.

Truncating an unsigned number to w bits is equivalent to computing its value modulo 2^w, giving the following:

PRINCIPLE: Unsigned multiplication

For x and y such that $0 \leq x, y \leq UMax_w$:

$$x *_w^u y = (x \cdot y) \bmod 2^w \tag{2.16}$$

■

2.3.5   Two's-Complement Multiplication

Integers x and y in the range $-2^{w-1} \leq x, y \leq 2^{w-1} - 1$ can be represented as w-bit two's-complement numbers, but their product $x \cdot y$ can range between $-2^{w-1} \cdot (2^{w-1} - 1) = -2^{2w-2} + 2^{w-1}$ and $-2^{w-1} \cdot -2^{w-1} = 2^{2w-2}$. This could require as many as $2w$ bits to represent in two's-complement form. Instead, signed multiplication in C generally is performed by truncating the $2w$-bit product to w bits. We denote this value as $x *_w^t y$. Truncating a two's-complement number to w bits is equivalent to first computing its value modulo 2^w and then converting from unsigned to two's complement, giving the following:

PRINCIPLE: Two's-complement multiplication

For x and y such that $TMin_w \leq x, y \leq TMax_w$:

$$x *_w^t y = U2T_w((x \cdot y) \bmod 2^w) \tag{2.17}$$

■

We claim that the bit-level representation of the product operation is identical for both unsigned and two's-complement multiplication, as stated by the following principle:

PRINCIPLE: Bit-level equivalence of unsigned and two's-complement multiplication

Let $\vec{x}$ and $\vec{y}$ be bit vectors of length w. Define integers x and y as the values represented by these bits in two's-complement form: $x = B2T_w(\vec{x})$ and $y = B2T_w(\vec{y})$. Define nonnegative integers x' and y' as the values represented by these bits in unsigned form: $x' = B2U_w(\vec{x})$ and $y' = B2U_w(\vec{y})$. Then

$$T2B_w(x *_w^t y) = U2B_w(x' *_w^u y')$$

■

As illustrations, Figure 2.27 shows the results of multiplying different 3-bit numbers. For each pair of bit-level operands, we perform both unsigned and two's-complement multiplication, yielding 6-bit products, and then truncate these to 3 bits. The unsigned truncated product always equals $x \cdot y \bmod 8$. The bit-level representations of both truncated products are identical for both unsigned and two's-complement multiplication, even though the full 6-bit representations differ.

Mode	x		y		$x \cdot y$		Truncated $x \cdot y$	
Unsigned	5	[101]	3	[011]	15	[001111]	7	[111]
Two's complement	−3	[101]	3	[011]	−9	[110111]	−1	[111]
Unsigned	4	[100]	7	[111]	28	[011100]	4	[100]
Two's complement	−4	[100]	−1	[111]	4	[000100]	−4	[100]
Unsigned	3	[011]	3	[011]	9	[001001]	1	[001]
Two's complement	3	[011]	3	[011]	9	[001001]	1	[001]

Figure 2.27 Three-bit unsigned and two's-complement multiplication examples.
Although the bit-level representations of the full products may differ, those of the
truncated products are identical.

DERIVATION: Bit-level equivalence of unsigned and two's-complement multiplication

From Equation 2.6, we have $x' = x + x_{w-1}2^w$ and $y' = y + y_{w-1}2^w$. Computing the
product of these values modulo 2^w gives the following:

$$(x' \cdot y') \bmod 2^w = [(x + x_{w-1}2^w) \cdot (y + y_{w-1}2^w)] \bmod 2^w \qquad (2.18)$$

$$= [x \cdot y + (x_{w-1}y + y_{w-1}x)2^w + x_{w-1}y_{w-1}2^{2w}] \bmod 2^w$$

$$= (x \cdot y) \bmod 2^w$$

The terms with weight 2^w and 2^{2w} drop out due to the modulus operator. By Equation 2.17, we have $x *_w^t y = U2T_w((x \cdot y) \bmod 2^w)$. We can apply the operation
$T2U_w$ to both sides to get

$$T2U_w(x *_w^t y) = T2U_w(U2T_w((x \cdot y) \bmod 2^w)) = (x \cdot y) \bmod 2^w$$

Combining this result with Equations 2.16 and 2.18 shows that $T2U_w(x *_w^t y) =
(x' \cdot y') \bmod 2^w = x' *_w^u y'$. We can then apply $U2B_w$ to both sides to get

$$U2B_w(T2U_w(x *_w^t y)) = T2B_w(x *_w^t y) = U2B_w(x' *_w^u y')$$

■

Practice Problem 2.34 (solution page 153)

Fill in the following table showing the results of multiplying different 3-bit numbers, in the style of Figure 2.27:

Mode	x		y		$x \cdot y$		Truncated $x \cdot y$	
Unsigned	____	[100]	____	[101]	____	____	____	____
Two's complement	____	[100]	____	[101]	____	____	____	____
Unsigned	____	[010]	____	[111]	____	____	____	____
Two's complement	____	[010]	____	[111]	____	____	____	____

Mode		x		y	$x \cdot y$	Truncated $x \cdot y$
Unsigned	____	[110]	____	[110]	____ ____	____ ____
Two's complement	____	[110]	____	[110]	____ ____	____ ____

Practice Problem 2.35 (solution page 154)

You are given the assignment to develop code for a function `tmult_ok` that will determine whether two arguments can be multiplied without causing overflow. Here is your solution:

```
/* Determine whether arguments can be multiplied without overflow */
int tmult_ok(int x, int y) {
    int p = x*y;
    /* Either x is zero, or dividing p by x gives y */
    return !x || p/x == y;
}
```

You test this code for a number of values of x and y, and it seems to work properly. Your coworker challenges you, saying, "If I can't use subtraction to test whether addition has overflowed (see Problem 2.31), then how can you use division to test whether multiplication has overflowed?"

Devise a mathematical justification of your approach, along the following lines. First, argue that the case $x = 0$ is handled correctly. Otherwise, consider w-bit numbers x ($x \neq 0$), y, p, and q, where p is the result of performing two's-complement multiplication on x and y, and q is the result of dividing p by x.

1. Show that $x \cdot y$, the integer product of x and y, can be written in the form $x \cdot y = p + t2^w$, where $t \neq 0$ if and only if the computation of p overflows.
2. Show that p can be written in the form $p = x \cdot q + r$, where $|r| < |x|$.
3. Show that $q = y$ if and only if $r = t = 0$.

Practice Problem 2.36 (solution page 154)

For the case where data type `int` has 32 bits, devise a version of `tmult_ok` (Problem 2.35) that uses the 64-bit precision of data type `int64_t`, without using division.

Practice Problem 2.37 (solution page 155)

You are given the task of patching the vulnerability in the XDR code shown in the aside on page 100 for the case where both data types `int` and `size_t` are 32 bits. You decide to eliminate the possibility of the multiplication overflowing by computing the number of bytes to allocate using data type `uint64_t`. You replace

Aside   Security vulnerability in the XDR library

In 2002, it was discovered that code supplied by Sun Microsystems to implement the XDR library, a widely used facility for sharing data structures between programs, had a security vulnerability arising from the fact that multiplication can overflow without any notice being given to the program.

Code similar to that containing the vulnerability is shown below:

```
1   /* Illustration of code vulnerability similar to that found in
2    * Sun's XDR library.
3    */
4   void* copy_elements(void *ele_src[], int ele_cnt, size_t ele_size) {
5       /*
6        * Allocate buffer for ele_cnt objects, each of ele_size bytes
7        * and copy from locations designated by ele_src
8        */
9       void *result = malloc(ele_cnt * ele_size);
10      if (result == NULL)
11          /* malloc failed */
12          return NULL;
13      void *next = result;
14      int i;
15      for (i = 0; i < ele_cnt; i++) {
16          /* Copy object i to destination */
17          memcpy(next, ele_src[i], ele_size);
18          /* Move pointer to next memory region */
19          next += ele_size;
20      }
21      return result;
22  }
```

The function `copy_elements` is designed to copy `ele_cnt` data structures, each consisting of `ele_size` bytes into a buffer allocated by the function on line 9. The number of bytes required is computed as `ele_cnt * ele_size`.

Imagine, however, that a malicious programmer calls this function with `ele_cnt` being 1,048,577 ($2^{20} + 1$) and `ele_size` being 4,096 (2^{12}) with the program compiled for 32 bits. Then the multiplication on line 9 will overflow, causing only 4,096 bytes to be allocated, rather than the 4,294,971,392 bytes required to hold that much data. The loop starting at line 15 will attempt to copy all of those bytes, overrunning the end of the allocated buffer, and therefore corrupting other data structures. This could cause the program to crash or otherwise misbehave.

The Sun code was used by almost every operating system and in such widely used programs as Internet Explorer and the Kerberos authentication system. The Computer Emergency Response Team (CERT), an organization run by the Carnegie Mellon Software Engineering Institute to track security vulnerabilities and breaches, issued advisory "CA-2002-25," and many companies rushed to patch their code. Fortunately, there were no reported security breaches caused by this vulnerability.

A similar vulnerability existed in many implementations of the library function `calloc`. These have since been patched. Unfortunately, many programmers call allocation functions, such as `malloc`, using arithmetic expressions as arguments, without checking these expressions for overflow. Writing a reliable version of `calloc` is left as an exercise (Problem 2.76).

the original call to `malloc` (line 9) as follows:

```
uint64_t asize =
    ele_cnt * (uint64_t) ele_size;
void *result = malloc(asize);
```

Recall that the argument to `malloc` has type `size_t`.

A. Does your code provide any improvement over the original?

B. How would you change the code to eliminate the vulnerability?

2.3.6   Multiplying by Constants

Historically, the integer multiply instruction on many machines was fairly slow, requiring 10 or more clock cycles, whereas other integer operations—such as addition, subtraction, bit-level operations, and shifting—required only 1 clock cycle. Even on the Intel Core i7 Haswell we use as our reference machine, integer multiply requires 3 clock cycles. As a consequence, one important optimization used by compilers is to attempt to replace multiplications by constant factors with combinations of shift and addition operations. We will first consider the case of multiplying by a power of 2, and then we will generalize this to arbitrary constants.

PRINCIPLE: Multiplication by a power of 2

Let x be the unsigned integer represented by bit pattern $[x_{w-1}, x_{w-2}, \ldots, x_0]$. Then for any $k \geq 0$, the $w + k$-bit unsigned representation of $x2^k$ is given by $[x_{w-1}, x_{w-2}, \ldots, x_0, 0, \ldots, 0]$, where k zeros have been added to the right. ∎

So, for example, 11 can be represented for $w = 4$ as [1011]. Shifting this left by $k = 2$ yields the 6-bit vector [101100], which encodes the unsigned number $11 \cdot 4 = 44$.

DERIVATION: Multiplication by a power of 2

This property can be derived using Equation 2.1:

$$B2U_{w+k}([x_{w-1}, x_{w-2}, \ldots, x_0, 0, \ldots, 0]) = \sum_{i=0}^{w-1} x_i 2^{i+k}$$

$$= \left[\sum_{i=0}^{w-1} x_i 2^i \right] \cdot 2^k$$

$$= x2^k$$

∎

When shifting left by k for a fixed word size, the high-order k bits are discarded, yielding

$$[x_{w-k-1}, x_{w-k-2}, \ldots, x_0, 0, \ldots, 0]$$

but this is also the case when performing multiplication on fixed-size words. We can therefore see that shifting a value left is equivalent to performing unsigned multiplication by a power of 2:

PRINCIPLE: Unsigned multiplication by a power of 2

For C variables x and k with unsigned values x and k, such that $0 \leq k < w$, the C expression x << k yields the value $x *_w^u 2^k$. ∎

Since the bit-level operation of fixed-size two's-complement arithmetic is equivalent to that for unsigned arithmetic, we can make a similar statement about the relationship between left shifts and multiplication by a power of 2 for two's-complement arithmetic:

PRINCIPLE: Two's-complement multiplication by a power of 2

For C variables x and k with two's-complement value x and unsigned value k, such that $0 \leq k < w$, the C expression x << k yields the value $x *_w^t 2^k$. ∎

Note that multiplying by a power of 2 can cause overflow with either unsigned or two's-complement arithmetic. Our result shows that even then we will get the same effect by shifting. Returning to our earlier example, we shifted the 4-bit pattern [1011] (numeric value 11) left by two positions to get [101100] (numeric value 44). Truncating this to 4 bits gives [1100] (numeric value 12 = 44 mod 16).

Given that integer multiplication is more costly than shifting and adding, many C compilers try to remove many cases where an integer is being multiplied by a constant with combinations of shifting, adding, and subtracting. For example, suppose a program contains the expression x*14. Recognizing that $14 = 2^3 + 2^2 + 2^1$, the compiler can rewrite the multiplication as (x<<3) + (x<<2) + (x<<1), replacing one multiplication with three shifts and two additions. The two computations will yield the same result, regardless of whether x is unsigned or two's complement, and even if the multiplication would cause an overflow. Even better, the compiler can also use the property $14 = 2^4 - 2^1$ to rewrite the multiplication as (x<<4) - (x<<1), requiring only two shifts and a subtraction.

Practice Problem 2.38 (solution page 155)

As we will see in Chapter 3, the LEA instruction can perform computations of the form (a<<k) + b, where k is either 0, 1, 2, or 3, and b is either 0 or some program value. The compiler often uses this instruction to perform multiplications by constant factors. For example, we can compute 3*a as (a<<1) + a.

Considering cases where b is either 0 or equal to a, and all possible values of k, what multiples of a can be computed with a single LEA instruction?

Generalizing from our example, consider the task of generating code for the expression $x * K$, for some constant K. The compiler can express the binary representation of K as an alternating sequence of zeros and ones:

$$[(0 \ldots 0)\,(1 \ldots 1)\,(0 \ldots 0) \cdots (1 \ldots 1)]$$

For example, 14 can be written as $[(0 \ldots 0)(111)(0)]$. Consider a run of ones from bit position n down to bit position m ($n \geq m$). (For the case of 14, we have $n = 3$ and $m = 1$.) We can compute the effect of these bits on the product using either of two different forms:

Form A: $(x<<n) + (x<<(n-1)) + \cdots + (x<<m)$

Form B: $(x<<(n+1)) - (x<<m)$

By adding together the results for each run, we are able to compute $x * K$ without any multiplications. Of course, the trade-off between using combinations of shifting, adding, and subtracting versus a single multiplication instruction depends on the relative speeds of these instructions, and these can be highly machine dependent. Most compilers only perform this optimization when a small number of shifts, adds, and subtractions suffice.

Practice Problem 2.39 (solution page 156)

How could we modify the expression for form B for the case where bit position n is the most significant bit?

Practice Problem 2.40 (solution page 156)

For each of the following values of K, find ways to express $x * K$ using only the specified number of operations, where we consider both additions and subtractions to have comparable cost. You may need to use some tricks beyond the simple form A and B rules we have considered so far.

K	Shifts	Add/Subs	Expression
6	2	1	_____
31	1	1	_____
−6	2	1	_____
55	2	2	_____

Practice Problem 2.41 (solution page 156)

For a run of ones starting at bit position n down to bit position m ($n \geq m$), we saw that we can generate two forms of code, A and B. How should the compiler decide which form to use?

2.3.7 Dividing by Powers of 2

Integer division on most machines is even slower than integer multiplication—requiring 30 or more clock cycles. Dividing by a power of 2 can also be performed

k	>> k (binary)	Decimal	$12,340/2^k$
0	0011000000110100	12,340	12,340.0
1	0001100000011010	6,170	6,170.0
4	*0000*001100000011	771	771.25
8	*00000000*00110000	48	48.203125

Figure 2.28 Dividing unsigned numbers by powers of 2. The examples illustrate how performing a logical right shift by k has the same effect as dividing by 2^k and then rounding toward zero.

using shift operations, but we use a right shift rather than a left shift. The two different right shifts—logical and arithmetic—serve this purpose for unsigned and two's-complement numbers, respectively.

Integer division always rounds toward zero. To define this precisely, let us introduce some notation. For any real number a, define $\lfloor a \rfloor$ to be the unique integer a' such that $a' \leq a < a' + 1$. As examples, $\lfloor 3.14 \rfloor = 3$, $\lfloor -3.14 \rfloor = -4$, and $\lfloor 3 \rfloor = 3$. Similarly, define $\lceil a \rceil$ to be the unique integer a' such that $a' - 1 < a \leq a'$. As examples, $\lceil 3.14 \rceil = 4$, $\lceil -3.14 \rceil = -3$, and $\lceil 3 \rceil = 3$. For $x \geq 0$ and $y > 0$, integer division should yield $\lfloor x/y \rfloor$, while for $x < 0$ and $y > 0$, it should yield $\lceil x/y \rceil$. That is, it should round down a positive result but round up a negative one.

The case for using shifts with unsigned arithmetic is straightforward, in part because right shifting is guaranteed to be performed logically for unsigned values.

PRINCIPLE: Unsigned division by a power of 2

For C variables x and k with unsigned values x and k, such that $0 \leq k < w$, the C expression x >> k yields the value $\lfloor x/2^k \rfloor$. ∎

As examples, Figure 2.28 shows the effects of performing logical right shifts on a 16-bit representation of 12,340 to perform division by 1, 2, 16, and 256. The zeros shifted in from the left are shown in italics. We also show the result we would obtain if we did these divisions with real arithmetic. These examples show that the result of shifting consistently rounds toward zero, as is the convention for integer division.

DERIVATION: Unsigned division by a power of 2

Let x be the unsigned integer represented by bit pattern $[x_{w-1}, x_{w-2}, \ldots, x_0]$, and let k be in the range $0 \leq k < w$. Let x' be the unsigned number with $w - k$-bit representation $[x_{w-1}, x_{w-2}, \ldots, x_k]$, and let x'' be the unsigned number with k-bit representation $[x_{k-1}, \ldots, x_0]$. We can therefore see that $x = 2^k x' + x''$, and that $0 \leq x'' < 2^k$. It therefore follows that $\lfloor x/2^k \rfloor = x'$.

Performing a logical right shift of bit vector $[x_{w-1}, x_{w-2}, \ldots, x_0]$ by k yields the bit vector

$$[0, \ldots, 0, x_{w-1}, x_{w-2}, \ldots, x_k]$$

k	>> k (binary)	Decimal	$-12{,}340/2^k$
0	1100111111001100	$-12{,}340$	$-12{,}340.0$
1	1110011111100110	$-6{,}170$	$-6{,}170.0$
4	1111110011111100	-772	-771.25
8	1111111111001111	-49	-48.203125

Figure 2.29 Applying arithmetic right shift. The examples illustrate that arithmetic right shift is similar to division by a power of 2, except that it rounds down rather than toward zero.

This bit vector has numeric value x', which we have seen is the value that would result by computing the expression x >> k. ∎

The case for dividing by a power of 2 with two's-complement arithmetic is slightly more complex. First, the shifting should be performed using an *arithmetic* right shift, to ensure that negative values remain negative. Let us investigate what value such a right shift would produce.

PRINCIPLE: Two's-complement division by a power of 2, rounding down

Let C variables x and k have two's-complement value x and unsigned value k, respectively, such that $0 \le k < w$. The C expression x >> k, when the shift is performed arithmetically, yields the value $\lfloor x/2^k \rfloor$. ∎

For $x \ge 0$, variable x has 0 as the most significant bit, and so the effect of an arithmetic shift is the same as for a logical right shift. Thus, an arithmetic right shift by k is the same as division by 2^k for a nonnegative number. As an example of a negative number, Figure 2.29 shows the effect of applying arithmetic right shift to a 16-bit representation of $-12{,}340$ for different shift amounts. For the case when no rounding is required ($k = 1$), the result will be $x/2^k$. When rounding is required, shifting causes the result to be rounded downward. For example, the shifting right by four has the effect of rounding -771.25 down to -772. We will need to adjust our strategy to handle division for negative values of x.

DERIVATION: Two's-complement division by a power of 2, rounding down

Let x be the two's-complement integer represented by bit pattern $[x_{w-1}, x_{w-2}, \ldots, x_0]$, and let k be in the range $0 \le k < w$. Let x' be the two's-complement number represented by the $w - k$ bits $[x_{w-1}, x_{w-2}, \ldots, x_k]$, and let x'' be the *unsigned* number represented by the low-order k bits $[x_{k-1}, \ldots, x_0]$. By a similar analysis as the unsigned case, we have $x = 2^k x' + x''$ and $0 \le x'' < 2^k$, giving $x' = \lfloor x/2^k \rfloor$. Furthermore, observe that shifting bit vector $[x_{w-1}, x_{w-2}, \ldots, x_0]$ right *arithmetically* by k yields the bit vector

$$[x_{w-1}, \ldots, x_{w-1}, x_{w-1}, x_{w-2}, \ldots, x_k]$$

which is the sign extension from $w - k$ bits to w bits of $[x_{w-1}, x_{w-2}, \ldots, x_k]$. Thus, this shifted bit vector is the two's-complement representation of $\lfloor x/2^k \rfloor$. ∎

k	Bias	−12,340 + bias (binary)	>> k (binary)	Decimal	−12,340/2^k
0	0	1100111111001100	1100111111001100	−12,340	−12,340.0
1	1	11001111110011*01*	1110011111100110	−6,170	−6,170.0
4	15	11001111110*11011*	1111110011111101	−771	−771.25
8	255	1101000*011001011*	1111111111010000	−48	−48.203125

Figure 2.30   Dividing two's-complement numbers by powers of 2. By adding a bias before the right shift, the result is rounded toward zero.

We can correct for the improper rounding that occurs when a negative number is shifted right by "biasing" the value before shifting.

PRINCIPLE: Two's-complement division by a power of 2, rounding up

Let C variables x and k have two's-complement value x and unsigned value k, respectively, such that $0 \le k < w$. The C expression (x + (1 << k) − 1) >> k, when the shift is performed arithmetically, yields the value $\lceil x/2^k \rceil$.   ∎

Figure 2.30 demonstrates how adding the appropriate bias before performing the arithmetic right shift causes the result to be correctly rounded. In the third column, we show the result of adding the bias value to −12,340, with the lower k bits (those that will be shifted off to the right) shown in italics. We can see that the bits to the left of these may or may not be incremented. For the case where no rounding is required ($k = 1$), adding the bias only affects bits that are shifted off. For the cases where rounding is required, adding the bias causes the upper bits to be incremented, so that the result will be rounded toward zero.

The biasing technique exploits the property that $\lceil x/y \rceil = \lfloor (x + y − 1)/y \rfloor$ for integers x and y such that $y > 0$. As examples, when $x = −30$ and $y = 4$, we have $x + y − 1 = −27$ and $\lceil −30/4 \rceil = −7 = \lfloor −27/4 \rfloor$. When $x = −32$ and $y = 4$, we have $x + y − 1 = −29$ and $\lceil −32/4 \rceil = −8 = \lfloor −29/4 \rfloor$.

DERIVATION: Two's-complement division by a power of 2, rounding up

To see that $\lceil x/y \rceil = \lfloor (x + y − 1)/y \rfloor$, suppose that $x = qy + r$, where $0 \le r < y$, giving $(x + y − 1)/y = q + (r + y − 1)/y$, and so $\lfloor (x + y − 1)/y \rfloor = q + \lfloor (r + y − 1)/y \rfloor$. The latter term will equal 0 when $r = 0$ and 1 when $r > 0$. That is, by adding a bias of $y − 1$ to x and then rounding the division downward, we will get q when y divides x and $q + 1$ otherwise.

Returning to the case where $y = 2^k$, the C expression x + (1 << k) − 1 yields the value $x + 2^k − 1$. Shifting this right arithmetically by k therefore yields $\lceil x/2^k \rceil$.   ∎

These analyses show that for a two's-complement machine using arithmetic right shifts, the C expression

```
(x<0 ? x+(1<<k)-1 : x) >> k
```

will compute the value $x/2^k$.

Practice Problem 2.42 (solution page 156)

Write a function `div16` that returns the value `x/16` for integer argument x. Your function should not use division, modulus, multiplication, any conditionals (`if` or `?:`), any comparison operators (e.g., <, >, or ==), or any loops. You may assume that data type `int` is 32 bits long and uses a two's-complement representation, and that right shifts are performed arithmetically.

We now see that division by a power of 2 can be implemented using logical or arithmetic right shifts. This is precisely the reason the two types of right shifts are available on most machines. Unfortunately, this approach does not generalize to division by arbitrary constants. Unlike multiplication, we cannot express division by arbitrary constants K in terms of division by powers of 2.

Practice Problem 2.43 (solution page 157)

In the following code, we have omitted the definitions of constants M and N:

```
#define M      /* Mystery number 1 */
#define N      /* Mystery number 2 */
int arith(int x, int y) {
    int result = 0;
    result = x*M + y/N; /* M and N are mystery numbers. */
    return result;
}
```

We compiled this code for particular values of M and N. The compiler optimized the multiplication and division using the methods we have discussed. The following is a translation of the generated machine code back into C:

```
/* Translation of assembly code for arith */
int optarith(int x, int y) {
    int t = x;
    x <<= 5;
    x -= t;
    if (y < 0) y += 7;
    y >>= 3;  /* Arithmetic shift */
    return x+y;
}
```

What are the values of M and N?

2.3.8   Final Thoughts on Integer Arithmetic

As we have seen, the "integer" arithmetic performed by computers is really a form of modular arithmetic. The finite word size used to represent numbers limits the range of possible values, and the resulting operations can overflow. We have also seen that the two's-complement representation provides a clever way to represent both negative and positive values, while using the same bit-level implementations as are used to perform unsigned arithmetic—operations such as addition, subtraction, multiplication, and even division have either identical or very similar bit-level behaviors, whether the operands are in unsigned or two's-complement form.

We have seen that some of the conventions in the C language can yield some surprising results, and these can be sources of bugs that are hard to recognize or understand. We have especially seen that the unsigned data type, while conceptually straightforward, can lead to behaviors that even experienced programmers do not expect. We have also seen that this data type can arise in unexpected ways—for example, when writing integer constants and when invoking library routines.

Practice Problem 2.44 (solution page 157)

Assume data type int is 32 bits long and uses a two's-complement representation for signed values. Right shifts are performed arithmetically for signed values and logically for unsigned values. The variables are declared and initialized as follows:

```
int x = foo();   /* Arbitrary value */
int y = bar();   /* Arbitrary value */

unsigned ux = x;
unsigned uy = y;
```

For each of the following C expressions, either (1) argue that it is true (evaluates to 1) for all values of x and y, or (2) give values of x and y for which it is false (evaluates to 0):

A. (x > 0) || (x-1 < 0)

B. (x & 7) != 7 || (x<<29 < 0)

C. (x * x) >= 0

D. x < 0 || -x <= 0

E. x > 0 || -x >= 0

F. x+y == uy+ux

G. x*~y + uy*ux == -x

2.4 Floating Point

A floating-point representation encodes rational numbers of the form $V = x \times 2^y$. It is useful for performing computations involving very large numbers ($|V| \gg 0$),

> **Aside** The IEEE
>
> The Institute of Electrical and Electronics Engineers (IEEE—pronounced "eye-triple-ee") is a professional society that encompasses all of electronic and computer technology. It publishes journals, sponsors conferences, and sets up committees to define standards on topics ranging from power transmission to software engineering. Another example of an IEEE standard is the 802.11 standard for wireless networking.

numbers very close to 0 ($|V| \ll 1$), and more generally as an approximation to real arithmetic.

Up until the 1980s, every computer manufacturer devised its own conventions for how floating-point numbers were represented and the details of the operations performed on them. In addition, they often did not worry too much about the accuracy of the operations, viewing speed and ease of implementation as being more critical than numerical precision.

All of this changed around 1985 with the advent of IEEE Standard 754, a carefully crafted standard for representing floating-point numbers and the operations performed on them. This effort started in 1976 under Intel's sponsorship with the design of the 8087, a chip that provided floating-point support for the 8086 processor. Intel hired William Kahan, a professor at the University of California, Berkeley, as a consultant to help design a floating-point standard for its future processors. They allowed Kahan to join forces with a committee generating an industry-wide standard under the auspices of the Institute of Electrical and Electronics Engineers (IEEE). The committee ultimately adopted a standard close to the one Kahan had devised for Intel. Nowadays, virtually all computers support what has become known as *IEEE floating point*. This has greatly improved the portability of scientific application programs across different machines.

In this section, we will see how numbers are represented in the IEEE floating-point format. We will also explore issues of *rounding*, when a number cannot be represented exactly in the format and hence must be adjusted upward or downward. We will then explore the mathematical properties of addition, multiplication, and relational operators. Many programmers consider floating point to be at best uninteresting and at worst arcane and incomprehensible. We will see that since the IEEE format is based on a small and consistent set of principles, it is really quite elegant and understandable.

2.4.1 Fractional Binary Numbers

A first step in understanding floating-point numbers is to consider binary numbers having fractional values. Let us first examine the more familiar decimal notation. Decimal notation uses a representation of the form

$$d_m \, d_{m-1} \cdots d_1 \, d_0 \,.\, d_{-1} \, d_{-2} \cdots d_{-n}$$

Figure 2.31
Fractional binary representation. Digits to the left of the binary point have weights of the form 2^i, while those to the right have weights of the form $1/2^i$.

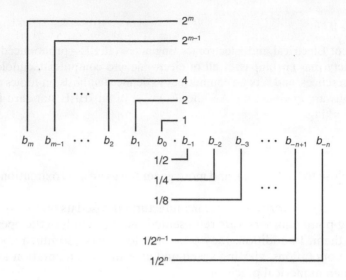

where each decimal digit d_i ranges between 0 and 9. This notation represents a value d defined as

$$d = \sum_{i=-n}^{m} 10^i \times d_i$$

The weighting of the digits is defined relative to the decimal point symbol ('.'), meaning that digits to the left are weighted by nonnegative powers of 10, giving integral values, while digits to the right are weighted by negative powers of 10, giving fractional values. For example, 12.34_{10} represents the number $1 \times 10^1 + 2 \times 10^0 + 3 \times 10^{-1} + 4 \times 10^{-2} = 12\frac{34}{100}$.

By analogy, consider a notation of the form

$$b_m\, b_{m-1} \cdots b_1\, b_0 \,.\, b_{-1}\, b_{-2} \cdots b_{-n+1}\, b_{-n}$$

where each binary digit, or bit, b_i ranges between 0 and 1, as is illustrated in Figure 2.31. This notation represents a number b defined as

$$b = \sum_{i=-n}^{m} 2^i \times b_i \tag{2.19}$$

The symbol '.' now becomes a *binary point*, with bits on the left being weighted by nonnegative powers of 2, and those on the right being weighted by negative powers of 2. For example, 101.11_2 represents the number $1 \times 2^2 + 0 \times 2^1 + 1 \times 2^0 + 1 \times 2^{-1} + 1 \times 2^{-2} = 4 + 0 + 1 + \frac{1}{2} + \frac{1}{4} = 5\frac{3}{4}$.

One can readily see from Equation 2.19 that shifting the binary point one position to the left has the effect of dividing the number by 2. For example, while 101.11_2 represents the number $5\frac{3}{4}$, 10.111_2 represents the number $2 + 0 + \frac{1}{2} +$

$\frac{1}{4} + \frac{1}{8} = 2\frac{7}{8}$. Similarly, shifting the binary point one position to the right has the effect of multiplying the number by 2. For example, 1011.1_2 represents the number $8 + 0 + 2 + 1 + \frac{1}{2} = 11\frac{1}{2}$.

Note that numbers of the form $0.11\cdots1_2$ represent numbers just below 1. For example, 0.111111_2 represents $\frac{63}{64}$. We will use the shorthand notation $1.0 - \epsilon$ to represent such values.

Assuming we consider only finite-length encodings, decimal notation cannot represent numbers such as $\frac{1}{3}$ and $\frac{5}{7}$ exactly. Similarly, fractional binary notation can only represent numbers that can be written $x \times 2^y$. Other values can only be approximated. For example, the number $\frac{1}{5}$ can be represented exactly as the fractional decimal number 0.20. As a fractional binary number, however, we cannot represent it exactly and instead must approximate it with increasing accuracy by lengthening the binary representation:

Representation	Value	Decimal
0.0_2	$\frac{0}{2}$	0.0_{10}
0.01_2	$\frac{1}{4}$	0.25_{10}
0.010_2	$\frac{2}{8}$	0.25_{10}
0.0011_2	$\frac{3}{16}$	0.1875_{10}
0.00110_2	$\frac{6}{32}$	0.1875_{10}
0.001101_2	$\frac{13}{64}$	0.203125_{10}
0.0011010_2	$\frac{26}{128}$	0.203125_{10}
0.00110011_2	$\frac{51}{256}$	0.19921875_{10}

Practice Problem 2.45 (solution page 157)

Fill in the missing information in the following table:

Fractional value	Binary representation	Decimal representation
$\frac{1}{8}$	0.001	0.125
$\frac{3}{4}$	_____	_____
$\frac{5}{16}$	_____	_____
_____	10.1011	_____
_____	1.001	_____
_____	_____	5.875
_____	_____	3.1875

Practice Problem 2.46 (solution page 158)

The imprecision of floating-point arithmetic can have disastrous effects. On February 25, 1991, during the first Gulf War, an American Patriot Missile battery in Dharan, Saudi Arabia, failed to intercept an incoming Iraqi Scud missile. The Scud struck an American Army barracks and killed 28 soldiers. The US General

Accounting Office (GAO) conducted a detailed analysis of the failure [76] and determined that the underlying cause was an imprecision in a numeric calculation. In this exercise, you will reproduce part of the GAO's analysis.

The Patriot system contains an internal clock, implemented as a counter that is incremented every 0.1 seconds. To determine the time in seconds, the program would multiply the value of this counter by a 24-bit quantity that was a fractional binary approximation to $\frac{1}{10}$. In particular, the binary representation of $\frac{1}{10}$ is the nonterminating sequence $0.000110011[0011] \cdots _2$, where the portion in brackets is repeated indefinitely. The program approximated 0.1, as a value x, by considering just the first 23 bits of the sequence to the right of the binary point: $x = 0.00011001100110011001100$. (See Problem 2.51 for a discussion of how they could have approximated 0.1 more precisely.)

A. What is the binary representation of $0.1 - x$?

B. What is the approximate decimal value of $0.1 - x$?

C. The clock starts at 0 when the system is first powered up and keeps counting up from there. In this case, the system had been running for around 100 hours. What was the difference between the actual time and the time computed by the software?

D. The system predicts where an incoming missile will appear based on its velocity and the time of the last radar detection. Given that a Scud travels at around 2,000 meters per second, how far off was its prediction?

Normally, a slight error in the absolute time reported by a clock reading would not affect a tracking computation. Instead, it should depend on the relative time between two successive readings. The problem was that the Patriot software had been upgraded to use a more accurate function for reading time, but not all of the function calls had been replaced by the new code. As a result, the tracking software used the accurate time for one reading and the inaccurate time for the other [103].

2.4.2   IEEE Floating-Point Representation

Positional notation such as considered in the previous section would not be efficient for representing very large numbers. For example, the representation of 5×2^{100} would consist of the bit pattern 101 followed by 100 zeros. Instead, we would like to represent numbers in a form $x \times 2^y$ by giving the values of x and y.

The IEEE floating-point standard represents a number in a form $V = (-1)^s \times M \times 2^E$:

- The *sign* s determines whether the number is negative ($s = 1$) or positive ($s = 0$), where the interpretation of the sign bit for numeric value 0 is handled as a special case.
- The *significand* M is a fractional binary number that ranges either between 1 and $2 - \epsilon$ or between 0 and $1 - \epsilon$.
- The *exponent* E weights the value by a (possibly negative) power of 2.

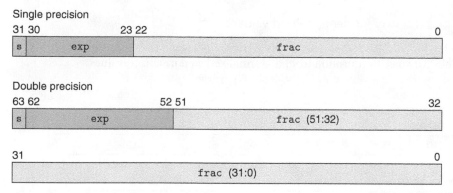

Figure 2.32 Standard floating-point formats. Floating-point numbers are represented by three fields. For the two most common formats, these are packed in 32-bit (single-precision) or 64-bit (double-precision) words.

The bit representation of a floating-point number is divided into three fields to encode these values:

- The single sign bit s directly encodes the sign s.
- The k-bit exponent field $\texttt{exp} = e_{k-1} \cdots e_1 e_0$ encodes the exponent E.
- The n-bit fraction field $\texttt{frac} = f_{n-1} \cdots f_1 f_0$ encodes the significand M, but the value encoded also depends on whether or not the exponent field equals 0.

Figure 2.32 shows the packing of these three fields into words for the two most common formats. In the single-precision floating-point format (a `float` in C), fields s, exp, and frac are 1, $k = 8$, and $n = 23$ bits each, yielding a 32-bit representation. In the double-precision floating-point format (a `double` in C), fields s, exp, and frac are 1, $k = 11$, and $n = 52$ bits each, yielding a 64-bit representation.

The value encoded by a given bit representation can be divided into three different cases (the latter having two variants), depending on the value of exp. These are illustrated in Figure 2.33 for the single-precision format.

Case 1: Normalized Values

This is the most common case. It occurs when the bit pattern of exp is neither all zeros (numeric value 0) nor all ones (numeric value 255 for single precision, 2047 for double). In this case, the exponent field is interpreted as representing a signed integer in *biased* form. That is, the exponent value is $E = e - Bias$, where e is the unsigned number having bit representation $e_{k-1} \cdots e_1 e_0$ and *Bias* is a bias value equal to $2^{k-1} - 1$ (127 for single precision and 1023 for double). This yields exponent ranges from -126 to $+127$ for single precision and -1022 to $+1023$ for double precision.

The fraction field frac is interpreted as representing the fractional value f, where $0 \le f < 1$, having binary representation $0.f_{n-1} \cdots f_1 f_0$, that is, with the

---

Aside   Why set the bias this way for denormalized values?

Having the exponent value be $1 - Bias$ rather than simply $-Bias$ might seem counterintuitive. We will see shortly that it provides for smooth transition from denormalized to normalized values.

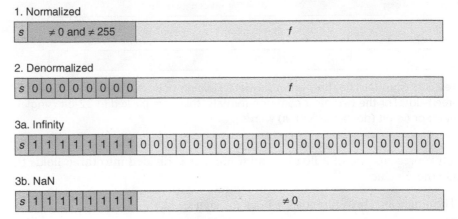

Figure 2.33   Categories of single-precision floating-point values. The value of the exponent determines whether the number is (1) normalized, (2) denormalized, or (3) a special value.

binary point to the left of the most significant bit. The significand is defined to be $M = 1 + f$. This is sometimes called an *implied leading 1* representation, because we can view M to be the number with binary representation $1. f_{n-1} f_{n-2} \cdots f_0$. This representation is a trick for getting an additional bit of precision for free, since we can always adjust the exponent E so that significand M is in the range $1 \leq M < 2$ (assuming there is no overflow). We therefore do not need to explicitly represent the leading bit, since it always equals 1.

Case 2: Denormalized Values

When the exponent field is all zeros, the represented number is in *denormalized* form. In this case, the exponent value is $E = 1 - Bias$, and the significand value is $M = f$, that is, the value of the fraction field without an implied leading 1.

Denormalized numbers serve two purposes. First, they provide a way to represent numeric value 0, since with a normalized number we must always have $M \geq 1$, and hence we cannot represent 0. In fact, the floating-point representation of $+0.0$ has a bit pattern of all zeros: the sign bit is 0, the exponent field is all zeros (indicating a denormalized value), and the fraction field is all zeros, giving $M = f = 0$. Curiously, when the sign bit is 1, but the other fields are all zeros, we get the value -0.0. With IEEE floating-point format, the values -0.0 and $+0.0$ are considered different in some ways and the same in others.

A second function of denormalized numbers is to represent numbers that are very close to 0.0. They provide a property known as *gradual underflow* in which possible numeric values are spaced evenly near 0.0.

Case 3: Special Values

A final category of values occurs when the exponent field is all ones. When the fraction field is all zeros, the resulting values represent infinity, either $+\infty$ when $s = 0$ or $-\infty$ when $s = 1$. Infinity can represent results that *overflow*, as when we multiply two very large numbers, or when we divide by zero. When the fraction field is nonzero, the resulting value is called a *NaN*, short for "not a number." Such values are returned as the result of an operation where the result cannot be given as a real number or as infinity, as when computing $\sqrt{-1}$ or $\infty - \infty$. They can also be useful in some applications for representing uninitialized data.

2.4.3   Example Numbers

Figure 2.34 shows the set of values that can be represented in a hypothetical 6-bit format having $k = 3$ exponent bits and $n = 2$ fraction bits. The bias is $2^{3-1} - 1 = 3$. Part (a) of the figure shows all representable values (other than *NaN*). The two infinities are at the extreme ends. The normalized numbers with maximum magnitude are ± 14. The denormalized numbers are clustered around 0. These can be seen more clearly in part (b) of the figure, where we show just the numbers between -1.0 and $+1.0$. The two zeros are special cases of denormalized numbers. Observe that the representable numbers are not uniformly distributed—they are denser nearer the origin.

Figure 2.35 shows some examples for a hypothetical 8-bit floating-point format having $k = 4$ exponent bits and $n = 3$ fraction bits. The bias is $2^{4-1} - 1 = 7$. The figure is divided into three regions representing the three classes of numbers. The different columns show how the exponent field encodes the exponent E, while the fraction field encodes the significand M, and together they form the

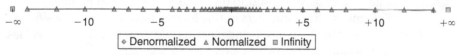

(a) Complete range

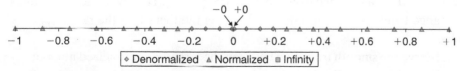

(b) Values between -1.0 and $+1.0$

Figure 2.34   Representable values for 6-bit floating-point format. There are $k = 3$ exponent bits and $n = 2$ fraction bits. The bias is 3.

Description	Bit representation	Exponent			Fraction		Value		
		e	E	2^E	f	M	$2^E \times M$	V	Decimal
Zero	0 0000 000	0	-6	$\frac{1}{64}$	$\frac{0}{8}$	$\frac{0}{8}$	$\frac{0}{512}$	0	0.0
Smallest positive	0 0000 001	0	-6	$\frac{1}{64}$	$\frac{1}{8}$	$\frac{1}{8}$	$\frac{1}{512}$	$\frac{1}{512}$	0.001953
	0 0000 010	0	-6	$\frac{1}{64}$	$\frac{2}{8}$	$\frac{2}{8}$	$\frac{2}{512}$	$\frac{1}{256}$	0.003906
	0 0000 011	0	-6	$\frac{1}{64}$	$\frac{3}{8}$	$\frac{3}{8}$	$\frac{3}{512}$	$\frac{3}{512}$	0.005859
	$\vdots$								
Largest denormalized	0 0000 111	0	-6	$\frac{1}{64}$	$\frac{7}{8}$	$\frac{7}{8}$	$\frac{7}{512}$	$\frac{7}{512}$	0.013672
Smallest normalized	0 0001 000	1	-6	$\frac{1}{64}$	$\frac{0}{8}$	$\frac{8}{8}$	$\frac{8}{512}$	$\frac{1}{64}$	0.015625
	0 0001 001	1	-6	$\frac{1}{64}$	$\frac{1}{8}$	$\frac{9}{8}$	$\frac{9}{512}$	$\frac{9}{512}$	0.017578
	$\vdots$								
	0 0110 110	6	-1	$\frac{1}{2}$	$\frac{6}{8}$	$\frac{14}{8}$	$\frac{14}{16}$	$\frac{7}{8}$	0.875
	0 0110 111	6	-1	$\frac{1}{2}$	$\frac{7}{8}$	$\frac{15}{8}$	$\frac{15}{16}$	$\frac{15}{16}$	0.9375
One	0 0111 000	7	0	1	$\frac{0}{8}$	$\frac{8}{8}$	$\frac{8}{8}$	1	1.0
	0 0111 001	7	0	1	$\frac{1}{8}$	$\frac{9}{8}$	$\frac{9}{8}$	$\frac{9}{8}$	1.125
	0 0111 010	7	0	1	$\frac{2}{8}$	$\frac{10}{8}$	$\frac{10}{8}$	$\frac{5}{4}$	1.25
	$\vdots$								
	0 1110 110	14	7	128	$\frac{6}{8}$	$\frac{14}{8}$	$\frac{1792}{8}$	224	224.0
Largest normalized	0 1110 111	14	7	128	$\frac{7}{8}$	$\frac{15}{8}$	$\frac{1920}{8}$	240	240.0
Infinity	0 1111 000	—	—	—	—	—	—	∞	—

Figure 2.35   Example nonnegative values for 8-bit floating-point format. There are $k = 4$ exponent bits and $n = 3$ fraction bits. The bias is 7.

represented value $V = 2^E \times M$. Closest to 0 are the denormalized numbers, starting with 0 itself. Denormalized numbers in this format have $E = 1 - 7 = -6$, giving a weight $2^E = \frac{1}{64}$. The fractions f and significands M range over the values $0, \frac{1}{8}, \ldots, \frac{7}{8}$, giving numbers V in the range 0 to $\frac{1}{64} \times \frac{7}{8} = \frac{7}{512}$.

The smallest normalized numbers in this format also have $E = 1 - 7 = -6$, and the fractions also range over the values $0, \frac{1}{8}, \ldots \frac{7}{8}$. However, the significands then range from $1 + 0 = 1$ to $1 + \frac{7}{8} = \frac{15}{8}$, giving numbers V in the range $\frac{8}{512} = \frac{1}{64}$ to $\frac{15}{512}$.

Observe the smooth transition between the largest denormalized number $\frac{7}{512}$ and the smallest normalized number $\frac{8}{512}$. This smoothness is due to our definition of E for denormalized values. By making it $1 - Bias$ rather than $-Bias$, we compensate for the fact that the significand of a denormalized number does not have an implied leading 1.

As we increase the exponent, we get successively larger normalized values, passing through 1.0 and then to the largest normalized number. This number has exponent $E = 7$, giving a weight $2^E = 128$. The fraction equals $\frac{7}{8}$, giving a significand $M = \frac{15}{8}$. Thus, the numeric value is $V = 240$. Going beyond this overflows to $+\infty$.

One interesting property of this representation is that if we interpret the bit representations of the values in Figure 2.35 as unsigned integers, they occur in ascending order, as do the values they represent as floating-point numbers. This is no accident—the IEEE format was designed so that floating-point numbers could be sorted using an integer sorting routine. A minor difficulty occurs when dealing with negative numbers, since they have a leading 1 and occur in descending order, but this can be overcome without requiring floating-point operations to perform comparisons (see Problem 2.84).

Practice Problem 2.47 (solution page 158)

Consider a 5-bit floating-point representation based on the IEEE floating-point format, with one sign bit, two exponent bits ($k = 2$), and two fraction bits ($n = 2$). The exponent bias is $2^{2-1} - 1 = 1$.

The table that follows enumerates the entire nonnegative range for this 5-bit floating-point representation. Fill in the blank table entries using the following directions:

e: The value represented by considering the exponent field to be an unsigned integer

E: The value of the exponent after biasing

2^E: The numeric weight of the exponent

f: The value of the fraction

M: The value of the significand

$2^E \times M$: The (unreduced) fractional value of the number

V: The reduced fractional value of the number

Decimal: The decimal representation of the number

Express the values of 2^E, f, M, $2^E \times M$, and V either as integers (when possible) or as fractions of the form $\frac{x}{y}$, where y is a power of 2. You need not fill in entries marked —.

Bits	e	E	2^E	f	M	$2^E \times M$	V	Decimal
0 00 00								
0 00 01								
0 00 10								
0 00 11								
0 01 00								

Bits	e	E	2^E	f	M	$2^E \times M$	V	Decimal
	0 01 01	1		0	1	$\frac{1}{4}$	$\frac{5}{4}$	$\frac{5}{4}$	$\frac{5}{4}$	1.
0 01 10	___	___	___	___	___	___	___	___
0 01 11	___	___	___	___	___	___	___	___
0 10 00	___	___	___	___	___	___	___	___
0 10 01	___	___	___	___	___	___	___	___
0 10 10	___	___	___	___	___	___	___	___
0 10 11	___	___	___	___	___	___	___	___
0 11 00	—	—	—	—	—	—	___	—
0 11 01	—	—	—	—	—	—	___	—
0 11 10	—	—	—	—	—	—	___	—
0 11 11	—	—	—	—	—	—	___	—

Figure 2.36 shows the representations and numeric values of some important single- and double-precision floating-point numbers. As with the 8-bit format shown in Figure 2.35, we can see some general properties for a floating-point representation with a k-bit exponent and an n-bit fraction:

- The value $+0.0$ always has a bit representation of all zeros.
- The smallest positive denormalized value has a bit representation consisting of a 1 in the least significant bit position and otherwise all zeros. It has a fraction (and significand) value $M = f = 2^{-n}$ and an exponent value $E = -2^{k-1} + 2$. The numeric value is therefore $V = 2^{-n-2^{k-1}+2}$.
- The largest denormalized value has a bit representation consisting of an exponent field of all zeros and a fraction field of all ones. It has a fraction (and significand) value $M = f = 1 - 2^{-n}$ (which we have written $1 - \epsilon$) and an exponent value $E = -2^{k-1} + 2$. The numeric value is therefore $V = (1 - 2^{-n}) \times 2^{-2^{k-1}+2}$, which is just slightly smaller than the smallest normalized value.

Description	exp	frac	Single precision		Double precision	
			Value	Decimal	Value	Decimal
Zero	$00\cdots00$	$0\cdots00$	0	0.0	0	0.0
Smallest denormalized	$00\cdots00$	$0\cdots01$	$2^{-23} \times 2^{-126}$	1.4×10^{-45}	$2^{-52} \times 2^{-1022}$	4.9×10^{-324}
Largest denormalized	$00\cdots00$	$1\cdots11$	$(1-\epsilon) \times 2^{-126}$	1.2×10^{-38}	$(1-\epsilon) \times 2^{-1022}$	2.2×10^{-308}
Smallest normalized	$00\cdots01$	$0\cdots00$	1×2^{-126}	1.2×10^{-38}	1×2^{-1022}	2.2×10^{-308}
One	$01\cdots11$	$0\cdots00$	1×2^0	1.0	1×2^0	1.0
Largest normalized	$11\cdots10$	$1\cdots11$	$(2-\epsilon) \times 2^{127}$	3.4×10^{38}	$(2-\epsilon) \times 2^{1023}$	1.8×10^{308}

Figure 2.36 Examples of nonnegative floating-point numbers.

- The smallest positive normalized value has a bit representation with a 1 in the least significant bit of the exponent field and otherwise all zeros. It has a significand value $M = 1$ and an exponent value $E = -2^{k-1} + 2$. The numeric value is therefore $V = 2^{-2^{k-1}+2}$.

- The value 1.0 has a bit representation with all but the most significant bit of the exponent field equal to 1 and all other bits equal to 0. Its significand value is $M = 1$ and its exponent value is $E = 0$.

- The largest normalized value has a bit representation with a sign bit of 0, the least significant bit of the exponent equal to 0, and all other bits equal to 1. It has a fraction value of $f = 1 - 2^{-n}$, giving a significand $M = 2 - 2^{-n}$ (which we have written $2 - \epsilon$.) It has an exponent value $E = 2^{k-1} - 1$, giving a numeric value $V = (2 - 2^{-n}) \times 2^{2^{k-1}-1} = (1 - 2^{-n-1}) \times 2^{2^{k-1}}$.

One useful exercise for understanding floating-point representations is to convert sample integer values into floating-point form. For example, we saw in Figure 2.15 that 12,345 has binary representation [11000000111001]. We create a normalized representation of this by shifting 13 positions to the right of a binary point, giving $12,345 = 1.1000000111001_2 \times 2^{13}$. To encode this in IEEE single-precision format, we construct the fraction field by dropping the leading 1 and adding 10 zeros to the end, giving binary representation [10000001110010000000000]. To construct the exponent field, we add bias 127 to 13, giving 140, which has binary representation [10001100]. We combine this with a sign bit of 0 to get the floating-point representation in binary of [01000110010000001110010000000000]. Recall from Section 2.1.3 that we observed the following correlation in the bit-level representations of the integer value 12345 (0x3039) and the single-precision floating-point value 12345.0 (0x4640E400):

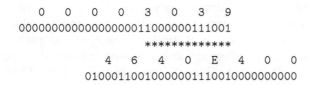

We can now see that the region of correlation corresponds to the low-order bits of the integer, stopping just before the most significant bit equal to 1 (this bit forms the implied leading 1), matching the high-order bits in the fraction part of the floating-point representation.

Practice Problem 2.48 (solution page 159)

As mentioned in Problem 2.6, the integer 3,510,593 has hexadecimal representation 0x00359141, while the single-precision floating-point number 3,510,593.0 has hexadecimal representation 0x4A564504. Derive this floating-point representation and explain the correlation between the bits of the integer and floating-point representations.

Practice Problem 2.49 (solution page 159)

A. For a floating-point format with an n-bit fraction, give a formula for the smallest positive integer that cannot be represented exactly (because it would require an $(n + 1)$-bit fraction to be exact). Assume the exponent field size k is large enough that the range of representable exponents does not provide a limitation for this problem.

B. What is the numeric value of this integer for single-precision format ($n = 23$)?

2.4.4 Rounding

Floating-point arithmetic can only approximate real arithmetic, since the representation has limited range and precision. Thus, for a value x, we generally want a systematic method of finding the "closest" matching value x' that can be represented in the desired floating-point format. This is the task of the *rounding* operation. One key problem is to define the direction to round a value that is halfway between two possibilities. For example, if I have $1.50 and want to round it to the nearest dollar, should the result be $1 or $2? An alternative approach is to maintain a lower and an upper bound on the actual number. For example, we could determine representable values x^- and x^+ such that the value x is guaranteed to lie between them: $x^- \le x \le x^+$. The IEEE floating-point format defines four different *rounding modes*. The default method finds a closest match, while the other three can be used for computing upper and lower bounds.

Figure 2.37 illustrates the four rounding modes applied to the problem of rounding a monetary amount to the nearest whole dollar. Round-to-even (also called round-to-nearest) is the default mode. It attempts to find a closest match. Thus, it rounds $1.40 to $1 and $1.60 to $2, since these are the closest whole dollar values. The only design decision is to determine the effect of rounding values that are halfway between two possible results. Round-to-even mode adopts the convention that it rounds the number either upward or downward such that the least significant digit of the result is even. Thus, it rounds both $1.50 and $2.50 to $2.

The other three modes produce guaranteed bounds on the actual value. These can be useful in some numerical applications. Round-toward-zero mode rounds positive numbers downward and negative numbers upward, giving a value $\hat{x}$ such

Mode	$1.40	$1.60	$1.50	$2.50	$–1.50
Round-to-even	$1	$2	$2	$2	$–2
Round-toward-zero	$1	$1	$1	$2	$–1
Round-down	$1	$1	$1	$2	$–2
Round-up	$2	$2	$2	$3	$–1

Figure 2.37 Illustration of rounding modes for dollar rounding. The first rounds to a nearest value, while the other three bound the result above or below.

that $|\hat{x}| \le |x|$. Round-down mode rounds both positive and negative numbers downward, giving a value x^- such that $x^- \le x$. Round-up mode rounds both positive and negative numbers upward, giving a value x^+ such that $x \le x^+$.

Round-to-even at first seems like it has a rather arbitrary goal—why is there any reason to prefer even numbers? Why not consistently round values halfway between two representable values upward? The problem with such a convention is that one can easily imagine scenarios in which rounding a set of data values would then introduce a statistical bias into the computation of an average of the values. The average of a set of numbers that we rounded by this means would be slightly higher than the average of the numbers themselves. Conversely, if we always rounded numbers halfway between downward, the average of a set of rounded numbers would be slightly lower than the average of the numbers themselves. Rounding toward even numbers avoids this statistical bias in most real-life situations. It will round upward about 50% of the time and round downward about 50% of the time.

Round-to-even rounding can be applied even when we are not rounding to a whole number. We simply consider whether the least significant digit is even or odd. For example, suppose we want to round decimal numbers to the nearest hundredth. We would round 1.2349999 to 1.23 and 1.2350001 to 1.24, regardless of rounding mode, since they are not halfway between 1.23 and 1.24. On the other hand, we would round both 1.2350000 and 1.2450000 to 1.24, since 4 is even.

Similarly, round-to-even rounding can be applied to binary fractional numbers. We consider least significant bit value 0 to be even and 1 to be odd. In general, the rounding mode is only significant when we have a bit pattern of the form $XX \cdots X.YY \cdots Y100 \cdots$, where X and Y denote arbitrary bit values with the rightmost Y being the position to which we wish to round. Only bit patterns of this form denote values that are halfway between two possible results. As examples, consider the problem of rounding values to the nearest quarter (i.e., 2 bits to the right of the binary point.) We would round 10.00011_2 ($2\frac{3}{32}$) down to 10.00_2 (2), and 10.00110_2 ($2\frac{3}{16}$) up to 10.01_2 ($2\frac{1}{4}$), because these values are not halfway between two possible values. We would round 10.11100_2 ($2\frac{7}{8}$) up to 11.00_2 (3) and 10.10100_2 ($2\frac{5}{8}$) down to 10.10_2 ($2\frac{1}{2}$), since these values are halfway between two possible results, and we prefer to have the least significant bit equal to zero.

Practice Problem 2.50 (solution page 159)

Show how the following binary fractional values would be rounded to the nearest half (1 bit to the right of the binary point), according to the round-to-even rule. In each case, show the numeric values, both before and after rounding.

A. 10.010_2

B. 10.011_2

C. 10.110_2

D. 11.001_2

Practice Problem 2.51 (solution page 159)

We saw in Problem 2.46 that the Patriot missile software approximated 0.1 as $x = 0.00011001100110011001100_2$. Suppose instead that they had used IEEE round-to-even mode to determine an approximation x' to 0.1 with 23 bits to the right of the binary point.

A. What is the binary representation of x'?

B. What is the approximate decimal value of $x' - 0.1$?

C. How far off would the computed clock have been after 100 hours of operation?

D. How far off would the program's prediction of the position of the Scud missile have been?

Practice Problem 2.52 (solution page 160)

Consider the following two 7-bit floating-point representations based on the IEEE floating-point format. Neither has a sign bit—they can only represent nonnegative numbers.

1. Format A
   - There are $k = 3$ exponent bits. The exponent bias is 3.
   - There are $n = 4$ fraction bits.
2. Format B
   - There are $k = 4$ exponent bits. The exponent bias is 7.
   - There are $n = 3$ fraction bits.

Below, you are given some bit patterns in format A, and your task is to convert them to the closest value in format B. If necessary, you should apply the round-to-even rounding rule. In addition, give the values of numbers given by the format A and format B bit patterns. Give these as whole numbers (e.g., 17) or as fractions (e.g., 17/64).

Format A		Format B	
Bits	Value	Bits	Value
011 0000	1	0111 000	1
101 1110	_____	_____	_____
010 1001	_____	_____	_____
110 1111	_____	_____	_____
000 0001	_____	_____	_____

2.4.5 Floating-Point Operations

The IEEE standard specifies a simple rule for determining the result of an arithmetic operation such as addition or multiplication. Viewing floating-point values x

and y as real numbers, and some operation $\odot$ defined over real numbers, the computation should yield $Round(x \odot y)$, the result of applying rounding to the exact result of the real operation. In practice, there are clever tricks floating-point unit designers use to avoid performing this exact computation, since the computation need only be sufficiently precise to guarantee a correctly rounded result. When one of the arguments is a special value, such as -0, ∞, or NaN, the standard specifies conventions that attempt to be reasonable. For example, $1/-0$ is defined to yield $-\infty$, while $1/+0$ is defined to yield $+\infty$.

One strength of the IEEE standard's method of specifying the behavior of floating-point operations is that it is independent of any particular hardware or software realization. Thus, we can examine its abstract mathematical properties without considering how it is actually implemented.

We saw earlier that integer addition, both unsigned and two's complement, forms an abelian group. Addition over real numbers also forms an abelian group, but we must consider what effect rounding has on these properties. Let us define $x +^f y$ to be $Round(x + y)$. This operation is defined for all values of x and y, although it may yield infinity even when both x and y are real numbers due to overflow. The operation is commutative, with $x +^f y = y +^f x$ for all values of x and y. On the other hand, the operation is not associative. For example, with single-precision floating point the expression (3.14+1e10)-1e10 evaluates to 0.0—the value 3.14 is lost due to rounding. On the other hand, the expression 3.14+(1e10-1e10) evaluates to 3.14. As with an abelian group, most values have inverses under floating-point addition, that is, $x +^f -x = 0$. The exceptions are infinities (since $+\infty - \infty = NaN$), and NaNs, since $NaN +^f x = NaN$ for any x.

The lack of associativity in floating-point addition is the most important group property that is lacking. It has important implications for scientific programmers and compiler writers. For example, suppose a compiler is given the following code fragment:

```
x = a + b + c;
y = b + c + d;
```

The compiler might be tempted to save one floating-point addition by generating the following code:

```
t = b + c;
x = a + t;
y = t + d;
```

However, this computation might yield a different value for x than would the original, since it uses a different association of the addition operations. In most applications, the difference would be so small as to be inconsequential. Unfortunately, compilers have no way of knowing what trade-offs the user is willing to make between efficiency and faithfulness to the exact behavior of the original program. As a result, they tend to be very conservative, avoiding any optimizations that could have even the slightest effect on functionality.

On the other hand, floating-point addition satisfies the following monotonicity property: if $a \geq b$, then $x +^f a \geq x +^f b$ for any values of a, b, and x other than *NaN*. This property of real (and integer) addition is not obeyed by unsigned or two's-complement addition.

Floating-point multiplication also obeys many of the properties one normally associates with multiplication. Let us define $x *^f y$ to be $Round(x \times y)$. This operation is closed under multiplication (although possibly yielding infinity or *NaN*), it is commutative, and it has 1.0 as a multiplicative identity. On the other hand, it is not associative, due to the possibility of overflow or the loss of precision due to rounding. For example, with single-precision floating point, the expression (1e20*1e20)*1e-20 evaluates to $+\infty$, while 1e20*(1e20*1e-20) evaluates to 1e20. In addition, floating-point multiplication does not distribute over addition. For example, with single-precision floating point, the expression 1e20*(1e20-1e20) evaluates to 0.0, while 1e20*1e20-1e20*1e20 evaluates to NaN.

On the other hand, floating-point multiplication satisfies the following monotonicity properties for any values of a, b, and c other than *NaN*:

$$a \geq b \quad \text{and} \quad c \geq 0 \Rightarrow a *^f c \geq b *^f c$$
$$a \geq b \quad \text{and} \quad c \leq 0 \Rightarrow a *^f c \leq b *^f c$$

In addition, we are also guaranteed that $a *^f a \geq 0$, as long as $a \neq NaN$. As we saw earlier, none of these monotonicity properties hold for unsigned or two's-complement multiplication.

This lack of associativity and distributivity is of serious concern to scientific programmers and to compiler writers. Even such a seemingly simple task as writing code to determine whether two lines intersect in three-dimensional space can be a major challenge.

2.4.6 Floating Point in C

All versions of C provide two different floating-point data types: float and double. On machines that support IEEE floating point, these data types correspond to single- and double-precision floating point. In addition, the machines use the round-to-even rounding mode. Unfortunately, since the C standards do not require the machine to use IEEE floating point, there are no standard methods to change the rounding mode or to get special values such as -0, $+\infty$, $-\infty$, or *NaN*. Most systems provide a combination of include (.h) files and procedure libraries to provide access to these features, but the details vary from one system to another. For example, the GNU compiler GCC defines program constants INFINITY (for $+\infty$) and NAN (for *NaN*) when the following sequence occurs in the program file:

```
#define _GNU_SOURCE 1
#include <math.h>
```

Practice Problem 2.53 (solution page 160)

Fill in the following macro definitions to generate the double-precision values $+\infty$, $-\infty$, and -0:

```
#define POS_INFINITY
#define NEG_INFINITY
#define NEG_ZERO
```

You cannot use any include files (such as math.h), but you can make use of the fact that the largest finite number that can be represented with double precision is around 1.8×10^{308}.

When casting values between int, float, and double formats, the program changes the numeric values and the bit representations as follows (assuming data type int is 32 bits):

- From int to float, the number cannot overflow, but it may be rounded.
- From int or float to double, the exact numeric value can be preserved because double has both greater range (i.e., the range of representable values), as well as greater precision (i.e., the number of significant bits).
- From double to float, the value can overflow to $+\infty$ or $-\infty$, since the range is smaller. Otherwise, it may be rounded, because the precision is smaller.
- From float or double to int, the value will be rounded toward zero. For example, 1.999 will be converted to 1, while -1.999 will be converted to -1. Furthermore, the value may overflow. The C standards do not specify a fixed result for this case. Intel-compatible microprocessors designate the bit pattern $[10 \cdots 00]$ ($TMin_w$ for word size w) as an *integer indefinite* value. Any conversion from floating point to integer that cannot assign a reasonable integer approximation yields this value. Thus, the expression (int) +1e10 yields -21483648, generating a negative value from a positive one.

Practice Problem 2.54 (solution page 160)

Assume variables x, f, and d are of type int, float, and double, respectively. Their values are arbitrary, except that neither f nor d equals $+\infty$, $-\infty$, or *NaN*. For each of the following C expressions, either argue that it will always be true (i.e., evaluate to 1) or give a value for the variables such that it is not true (i.e., evaluates to 0).

A. x == (int)(double) x

B. x == (int)(float) x

C. d == (double)(float) d

D. f == (float)(double) f

E. f == -(-f)

    F. `1.0/2 == 1/2.0`

    G. `d*d >= 0.0`

    H. `(f+d)-f == d`

2.5   Summary

Computers encode information as bits, generally organized as sequences of bytes. Different encodings are used for representing integers, real numbers, and character strings. Different models of computers use different conventions for encoding numbers and for ordering the bytes within multi-byte data.

The C language is designed to accommodate a wide range of different implementations in terms of word sizes and numeric encodings. Machines with 64-bit word sizes have become increasingly common, replacing the 32-bit machines that dominated the market for around 30 years. Because 64-bit machines can also run programs compiled for 32-bit machines, we have focused on the distinction between 32- and 64-bit programs, rather than machines. The advantage of 64-bit programs is that they can go beyond the 4 GB address limitation of 32-bit programs.

Most machines encode signed numbers using a two's-complement representation and encode floating-point numbers using IEEE Standard 754. Understanding these encodings at the bit level, as well as understanding the mathematical characteristics of the arithmetic operations, is important for writing programs that operate correctly over the full range of numeric values.

When casting between signed and unsigned integers of the same size, most C implementations follow the convention that the underlying bit pattern does not change. On a two's-complement machine, this behavior is characterized by functions $T2U_w$ and $U2T_w$, for a w-bit value. The implicit casting of C gives results that many programmers do not anticipate, often leading to program bugs.

Due to the finite lengths of the encodings, computer arithmetic has properties quite different from conventional integer and real arithmetic. The finite length can cause numbers to overflow, when they exceed the range of the representation. Floating-point values can also underflow, when they are so close to 0.0 that they are changed to zero.

The finite integer arithmetic implemented by C, as well as most other programming languages, has some peculiar properties compared to true integer arithmetic. For example, the expression x*x can evaluate to a negative number due to overflow. Nonetheless, both unsigned and two's-complement arithmetic satisfy many of the other properties of integer arithmetic, including associativity, commutativity, and distributivity. This allows compilers to do many optimizations. For example, in replacing the expression 7*x by (x<<3)-x, we make use of the associative, commutative, and distributive properties, along with the relationship between shifting and multiplying by powers of 2.

We have seen several clever ways to exploit combinations of bit-level operations and arithmetic operations. For example, we saw that with two's-complement arithmetic, ~x+1 is equivalent to -x. As another example, suppose we want a bit

> **Aside**   Ariane 5: The high cost of floating-point overflow
>
> Converting large floating-point numbers to integers is a common source of programming errors. Such an error had disastrous consequences for the maiden voyage of the Ariane 5 rocket, on June 4, 1996. Just 37 seconds after liftoff, the rocket veered off its flight path, broke up, and exploded. Communication satellites valued at $500 million were on board the rocket.
>
> A later investigation [73, 33] showed that the computer controlling the inertial navigation system had sent invalid data to the computer controlling the engine nozzles. Instead of sending flight control information, it had sent a diagnostic bit pattern indicating that an overflow had occurred during the conversion of a 64-bit floating-point number to a 16-bit signed integer.
>
> The value that overflowed measured the horizontal velocity of the rocket, which could be more than five times higher than that achieved by the earlier Ariane 4 rocket. In the design of the Ariane 4 software, they had carefully analyzed the numeric values and determined that the horizontal velocity would never overflow a 16-bit number. Unfortunately, they simply reused this part of the software in the Ariane 5 without checking the assumptions on which it had been based.

pattern of the form $[0, \ldots, 0, 1, \ldots, 1]$, consisting of $w - k$ zeros followed by k ones. Such bit patterns are useful for masking operations. This pattern can be generated by the C expression `(1<<k)-1`, exploiting the property that the desired bit pattern has numeric value $2^k - 1$. For example, the expression `(1<<8)-1` will generate the bit pattern `0xFF`.

Floating-point representations approximate real numbers by encoding numbers of the form $x \times 2^y$. IEEE Standard 754 provides for several different precisions, with the most common being single (32 bits) and double (64 bits). IEEE floating point also has representations for special values representing plus and minus infinity, as well as not-a-number.

Floating-point arithmetic must be used very carefully, because it has only limited range and precision, and because it does not obey common mathematical properties such as associativity.

Bibliographic Notes

Reference books on C [45, 61] discuss properties of the different data types and operations. Of these two, only Steele and Harbison [45] cover the newer features found in ISO C99. There do not yet seem to be any books that cover the features found in ISO C11. The C standards do not specify details such as precise word sizes or numeric encodings. Such details are intentionally omitted to make it possible to implement C on a wide range of different machines. Several books have been written giving advice to C programmers [59, 74] that warn about problems with overflow, implicit casting to unsigned, and some of the other pitfalls we have covered in this chapter. These books also provide helpful advice on variable naming, coding styles, and code testing. Seacord's book on security issues in C and C++ programs [97] combines information about C programs, how they are compiled and executed, and how vulnerabilities may arise. Books on Java (we recommend the one coauthored by James Gosling, the creator of the language [5]) describe the data formats and arithmetic operations supported by Java.

Most books on logic design [58, 116] have a section on encodings and arithmetic operations. Such books describe different ways of implementing arithmetic circuits. Overton's book on IEEE floating point [82] provides a detailed description of the format as well as the properties from the perspective of a numerical applications programmer.

Homework Problems

2.55 ◆
Compile and run the sample code that uses show_bytes (file show-bytes.c) on different machines to which you have access. Determine the byte orderings used by these machines.

2.56 ◆
Try running the code for show_bytes for different sample values.

2.57 ◆
Write procedures show_short, show_long, and show_double that print the byte representations of C objects of types short, long, and double, respectively. Try these out on several machines.

2.58 ◆◆
Write a procedure is_little_endian that will return 1 when compiled and run on a little-endian machine, and will return 0 when compiled and run on a big-endian machine. This program should run on any machine, regardless of its word size.

2.59 ◆◆
Write a C expression that will yield a word consisting of the least significant byte of x and the remaining bytes of y. For operands x = 0x89ABCDEF and y = 0x76543210, this would give 0x765432EF.

2.60 ◆◆
Suppose we number the bytes in a w-bit word from 0 (least significant) to $w/8 - 1$ (most significant). Write code for the following C function, which will return an unsigned value in which byte i of argument x has been replaced by byte b:

```
unsigned replace_byte (unsigned x, int i, unsigned char b);
```

Here are some examples showing how the function should work:

```
replace_byte(0x12345678, 2, 0xAB) --> 0x12AB5678
replace_byte(0x12345678, 0, 0xAB) --> 0x123456AB
```

Bit-Level Integer Coding Rules

In several of the following problems, we will artificially restrict what programming constructs you can use to help you gain a better understanding of the bit-level, logic, and arithmetic operations of C. In answering these problems, your code must follow these rules:

- Assumptions
  - Integers are represented in two's-complement form.
  - Right shifts of signed data are performed arithmetically.
  - Data type `int` is w bits long. For some of the problems, you will be given a specific value for w, but otherwise your code should work as long as w is a multiple of 8. You can use the expression `sizeof(int)<<3` to compute w.
- Forbidden
  - Conditionals (`if` or `?:`), loops, switch statements, function calls, and macro invocations.
  - Division, modulus, and multiplication.
  - Relative comparison operators (`<`, `>`, `<=`, and `>=`).
- Allowed operations
  - All bit-level and logic operations.
  - Left and right shifts, but only with shift amounts between 0 and $w - 1$.
  - Addition and subtraction.
  - Equality (`==`) and inequality (`!=`) tests. (Some of the problems do not allow these.)
  - Integer constants `INT_MIN` and `INT_MAX`.
  - Casting between data types `int` and `unsigned`, either explicitly or implicitly.

Even with these rules, you should try to make your code readable by choosing descriptive variable names and using comments to describe the logic behind your solutions. As an example, the following code extracts the most significant byte from integer argument x:

```
/* Get most significant byte from x */
int get_msb(int x) {
    /* Shift by w-8 */
    int shift_val = (sizeof(int)-1)<<3;
    /* Arithmetic shift */
    int xright = x >> shift_val;
    /* Zero all but LSB */
    return xright & 0xFF;
}
```

2.61 ◆◆
Write C expressions that evaluate to 1 when the following conditions are true and to 0 when they are false. Assume x is of type `int`.

A. Any bit of x equals 1.
B. Any bit of x equals 0.

C. Any bit in the least significant byte of x equals 1.

D. Any bit in the most significant byte of x equals 0.

Your code should follow the bit-level integer coding rules (page 128), with the additional restriction that you may not use equality (==) or inequality (!=) tests.

2.62 ◆◆◆

Write a function `int_shifts_are_arithmetic()` that yields 1 when run on a machine that uses arithmetic right shifts for data type `int` and yields 0 otherwise. Your code should work on a machine with any word size. Test your code on several machines.

2.63 ◆◆◆

Fill in code for the following C functions. Function `srl` performs a logical right shift using an arithmetic right shift (given by value `xsra`), followed by other operations not including right shifts or division. Function `sra` performs an arithmetic right shift using a logical right shift (given by value `xsrl`), followed by other operations not including right shifts or division. You may use the computation `8*sizeof(int)` to determine w, the number of bits in data type `int`. The shift amount k can range from 0 to $w - 1$.

```
unsigned srl(unsigned x, int k) {
    /* Perform shift arithmetically */
    unsigned xsra = (int) x >> k;
    .
    .
    .
    .
}
```

```
int sra(int x, int k) {
    /* Perform shift logically */
    int xsrl = (unsigned) x >> k;
    .
    .
    .
    .
}
```

2.64 ◆

Write code to implement the following function:

```
/* Return 1 when any odd bit of x equals 1; 0 otherwise.
   Assume w=32 */
int any_odd_one(unsigned x);
```

Your function should follow the bit-level integer coding rules (page 128), except that you may assume that data type `int` has $w = 32$ bits.

2.65 ◆◆◆◆
Write code to implement the following function:

```
/* Return 1 when x contains an odd number of 1s; 0 otherwise.
   Assume w=32 */
int odd_ones(unsigned x);
```

Your function should follow the bit-level integer coding rules (page 128), except that you may assume that data type int has $w = 32$ bits.

Your code should contain a total of at most 12 arithmetic, bitwise, and logical operations.

2.66 ◆◆◆
Write code to implement the following function:

```
/*
 * Generate mask indicating leftmost 1 in x.  Assume w=32.
 * For example, 0xFF00 -> 0x8000, and 0x6600 --> 0x4000.
 * If x = 0, then return 0.
 */
int leftmost_one(unsigned x);
```

Your function should follow the bit-level integer coding rules (page 128), except that you may assume that data type int has $w = 32$ bits.

Your code should contain a total of at most 15 arithmetic, bitwise, and logical operations.

Hint: First transform x into a bit vector of the form $[0 \cdots 011 \cdots 1]$.

2.67 ◆◆
You are given the task of writing a procedure int_size_is_32() that yields 1 when run on a machine for which an int is 32 bits, and yields 0 otherwise. You are not allowed to use the sizeof operator. Here is a first attempt:

```
1    /* The following code does not run properly on some machines */
2    int bad_int_size_is_32() {
3        /* Set most significant bit (msb) of 32-bit machine */
4        int set_msb = 1 << 31;
5        /* Shift past msb of 32-bit word */
6        int beyond_msb = 1 << 32;
7
8        /* set_msb is nonzero when word size >= 32
9           beyond_msb is zero when word size <= 32  */
10        return set_msb && !beyond_msb;
11    }
```

When compiled and run on a 32-bit SUN SPARC, however, this procedure returns 0. The following compiler message gives us an indication of the problem:

```
warning: left shift count >= width of type
```

A. In what way does our code fail to comply with the C standard?

B. Modify the code to run properly on any machine for which data type int is at least 32 bits.

C. Modify the code to run properly on any machine for which data type int is at least 16 bits.

2.68 ◆◆

Write code for a function with the following prototype:

```
/*
 * Mask with least signficant n bits set to 1
 * Examples: n = 6 --> 0x3F, n = 17 --> 0x1FFFF
 * Assume 1 <= n <= w
 */
int lower_one_mask(int n);
```

Your function should follow the bit-level integer coding rules (page 128). Be careful of the case $n = w$.

2.69 ◆◆◆

Write code for a function with the following prototype:

```
/*
 * Do rotating left shift.  Assume 0 <= n < w
 * Examples when x = 0x12345678 and w = 32:
 *    n=4 -> 0x23456781, n=20 -> 0x67812345
 */
unsigned rotate_left(unsigned x, int n);
```

Your function should follow the bit-level integer coding rules (page 128). Be careful of the case $n = 0$.

2.70 ◆◆

Write code for the function with the following prototype:

```
/*
 * Return 1 when x can be represented as an n-bit, 2's-complement
 * number; 0 otherwise
 * Assume 1 <= n <= w
 */
int fits_bits(int x, int n);
```

Your function should follow the bit-level integer coding rules (page 128).

2.71 ◆

You just started working for a company that is implementing a set of procedures to operate on a data structure where 4 signed bytes are packed into a 32-bit unsigned. Bytes within the word are numbered from 0 (least significant) to 3 (most significant). You have been assigned the task of implementing a function for a machine using two's-complement arithmetic and arithmetic right shifts with the following prototype:

```
/* Declaration of data type where 4 bytes are packed
   into an unsigned */
typedef unsigned packed_t;

/* Extract byte from word.  Return as signed integer */
int xbyte(packed_t word, int bytenum);
```

That is, the function will extract the designated byte and sign extend it to be a 32-bit `int`.

Your predecessor (who was fired for incompetence) wrote the following code:

```
/* Failed attempt at xbyte */
int xbyte(packed_t word, int bytenum)
{
    return (word >> (bytenum << 3)) & 0xFF;
}
```

 A. What is wrong with this code?

 B. Give a correct implementation of the function that uses only left and right shifts, along with one subtraction.

2.72 ◆◆
You are given the task of writing a function that will copy an integer `val` into a buffer `buf`, but it should do so only if enough space is available in the buffer.

Here is the code you write:

```
/* Copy integer into buffer if space is available */
/* WARNING: The following code is buggy */
void copy_int(int val, void *buf, int maxbytes) {
    if (maxbytes-sizeof(val) >= 0)
            memcpy(buf, (void *) &val, sizeof(val));
}
```

This code makes use of the library function `memcpy`. Although its use is a bit artificial here, where we simply want to copy an `int`, it illustrates an approach commonly used to copy larger data structures.

You carefully test the code and discover that it *always* copies the value to the buffer, even when `maxbytes` is too small.

 A. Explain why the conditional test in the code always succeeds. *Hint:* The `sizeof` operator returns a value of type `size_t`.

 B. Show how you can rewrite the conditional test to make it work properly.

2.73 ◆◆
Write code for a function with the following prototype:

```
/* Addition that saturates to TMin or TMax */
int saturating_add(int x, int y);
```

Instead of overflowing the way normal two's-complement addition does, saturating addition returns *TMax* when there would be positive overflow, and *TMin* when there would be negative overflow. Saturating arithmetic is commonly used in programs that perform digital signal processing.

Your function should follow the bit-level integer coding rules (page 128).

2.74 ◆◆
Write a function with the following prototype:

```
/* Determine whether arguments can be subtracted without overflow */
int tsub_ok(int x, int y);
```

This function should return 1 if the computation x-y does not overflow.

2.75 ◆◆◆
Suppose we want to compute the complete $2w$-bit representation of $x \cdot y$, where both x and y are unsigned, on a machine for which data type unsigned is w bits. The low-order w bits of the product can be computed with the expression x*y, so we only require a procedure with prototype

```
    unsigned unsigned_high_prod(unsigned x, unsigned y);
```

that computes the high-order w bits of $x \cdot y$ for unsigned variables.

We have access to a library function with prototype

```
    int signed_high_prod(int x, int y);
```

that computes the high-order w bits of $x \cdot y$ for the case where x and y are in two's-complement form. Write code calling this procedure to implement the function for unsigned arguments. Justify the correctness of your solution.

Hint: Look at the relationship between the signed product $x \cdot y$ and the unsigned product $x' \cdot y'$ in the derivation of Equation 2.18.

2.76 ◆
The library function calloc has the following declaration:

```
    void *calloc(size_t nmemb, size_t size);
```

According to the library documentation, "The calloc function allocates memory for an array of nmemb elements of size bytes each. The memory is set to zero. If nmemb or size is zero, then calloc returns NULL."

Write an implementation of calloc that performs the allocation by a call to malloc and sets the memory to zero via memset. Your code should not have any vulnerabilities due to arithmetic overflow, and it should work correctly regardless of the number of bits used to represent data of type size_t.

As a reference, functions malloc and memset have the following declarations:

```
void *malloc(size_t size);
void *memset(void *s, int c, size_t n);
```

2.77 ◆◆

Suppose we are given the task of generating code to multiply integer variable x by various different constant factors K. To be efficient, we want to use only the operations +, −, and <<. For the following values of K, write C expressions to perform the multiplication using at most three operations per expression.

- A. $K = 17$
- B. $K = -7$
- C. $K = 60$
- D. $K = -112$

2.78 ◆◆

Write code for a function with the following prototype:

```
/* Divide by power of 2. Assume 0 <= k < w-1 */
int divide_power2(int x, int k);
```

The function should compute $x/2^k$ with correct rounding, and it should follow the bit-level integer coding rules (page 128).

2.79 ◆◆

Write code for a function mul3div4 that, for integer argument x, computes 3 ∗ x/4 but follows the bit-level integer coding rules (page 128). Your code should replicate the fact that the computation 3∗x can cause overflow.

2.80 ◆◆◆

Write code for a function threefourths that, for integer argument x, computes the value of $\frac{3}{4}x$, rounded toward zero. It should not overflow. Your function should follow the bit-level integer coding rules (page 128).

2.81 ◆◆

Write C expressions to generate the bit patterns that follow, where a^k represents k repetitions of symbol a. Assume a w-bit data type. Your code may contain references to parameters j and k, representing the values of j and k, but not a parameter representing w.

- A. $1^{w-k}0^k$
- B. $0^{w-k-j}1^k0^j$

2.82 ◆

We are running programs where values of type int are 32 bits. They are represented in two's complement, and they are right shifted arithmetically. Values of type unsigned are also 32 bits.

We generate arbitrary values x and y, and convert them to unsigned values as follows:

```
/* Create some arbitrary values */
int x = random();
int y = random();
/* Convert to unsigned */
unsigned ux = (unsigned) x;
unsigned uy = (unsigned) y;
```

For each of the following C expressions, you are to indicate whether or not the expression *always* yields 1. If it always yields 1, describe the underlying mathematical principles. Otherwise, give an example of arguments that make it yield 0.

A. `(x<y) == (-x>-y)`

B. `((x+y)<<4) + y-x == 17*y+15*x`

C. `~x+~y+1 == ~(x+y)`

D. `(ux-uy) == -(unsigned)(y-x)`

E. `((x >> 2) << 2) <= x`

2.83 ◆◆

Consider numbers having a binary representation consisting of an infinite string of the form $0.y\,y\,y\,y\,y\,y\cdots$, where y is a k-bit sequence. For example, the binary representation of $\frac{1}{3}$ is $0.01010101\cdots$ $(y = 01)$, while the representation of $\frac{1}{5}$ is $0.001100110011\cdots$ $(y = 0011)$.

A. Let $Y = B2U_k(y)$, that is, the number having binary representation y. Give a formula in terms of Y and k for the value represented by the infinite string. *Hint:* Consider the effect of shifting the binary point k positions to the right.

B. What is the numeric value of the string for the following values of y?
   (a) 101
   (b) 0110
   (c) 010011

2.84 ◆

Fill in the return value for the following procedure, which tests whether its first argument is less than or equal to its second. Assume the function f2u returns an unsigned 32-bit number having the same bit representation as its floating-point argument. You can assume that neither argument is *NaN*. The two flavors of zero, $+0$ and -0, are considered equal.

```
int float_le(float x, float y) {
    unsigned ux = f2u(x);
    unsigned uy = f2u(y);
```

```
    /* Get the sign bits */
    unsigned sx = ux >> 31;
    unsigned sy = uy >> 31;

    /* Give an expression using only ux, uy, sx, and sy */
    return          ;
}
```

2.85 ◆

Given a floating-point format with a k-bit exponent and an n-bit fraction, write formulas for the exponent E, the significand M, the fraction f, and the value V for the quantities that follow. In addition, describe the bit representation.

A. The number 7.0

B. The largest odd integer that can be represented exactly

C. The reciprocal of the smallest positive normalized value

2.86 ◆

Intel-compatible processors also support an "extended-precision" floating-point format with an 80-bit word divided into a sign bit, $k = 15$ exponent bits, a single *integer* bit, and $n = 63$ fraction bits. The integer bit is an explicit copy of the implied bit in the IEEE floating-point representation. That is, it equals 1 for normalized values and 0 for denormalized values. Fill in the following table giving the approximate values of some "interesting" numbers in this format:

Description	Extended precision	
	Value	Decimal
Smallest positive denormalized	_____	_____
Smallest positive normalized	_____	_____
Largest normalized	_____	_____

This format can be used in C programs compiled for Intel-compatible machines by declaring the data to be of type `long double`. However, it forces the compiler to generate code based on the legacy 8087 floating-point instructions. The resulting program will most likely run much slower than would be the case for data type `float` or `double`.

2.87 ◆

The 2008 version of the IEEE floating-point standard, named IEEE 754-2008, includes a 16-bit "half-precision" floating-point format. It was originally devised by computer graphics companies for storing data in which a higher dynamic range is required than can be achieved with 16-bit integers. This format has 1 sign bit, 5 exponent bits ($k = 5$), and 10 fraction bits ($n = 10$). The exponent bias is $2^{5-1} - 1 = 15$.

Fill in the table that follows for each of the numbers given, with the following instructions for each column:

Hex: The four hexadecimal digits describing the encoded form.

M: The value of the significand. This should be a number of the form x or $\frac{x}{y}$, where x is an integer and y is an integral power of 2. Examples include 0, $\frac{67}{64}$, and $\frac{1}{256}$.

E: The integer value of the exponent.

V: The numeric value represented. Use the notation x or $x \times 2^z$, where x and z are integers.

D: The (possibly approximate) numerical value, as is printed using the %f formatting specification of printf.

As an example, to represent the number $\frac{7}{8}$, we would have $s = 0$, $M = \frac{7}{4}$, and $E = -1$. Our number would therefore have an exponent field of 01110_2 (decimal value $15 - 1 = 14$) and a significand field of 1100000000_2, giving a hex representation 3B00. The numerical value is 0.875.

You need not fill in entries marked —.

Description	Hex	M	E	V	D
-0	_____	_____	_____	-0	-0.0
Smallest value > 2	_____	_____	_____	_____	_____
512	_____	_____	_____	512	512.0
Largest denormalized	_____	_____	_____	_____	_____
$-\infty$	_____	—	—	$-\infty$	$-\infty$
Number with hex representation 3BB0	3BB0	_____	_____	_____	_____

2.88 ◆◆
Consider the following two 9-bit floating-point representations based on the IEEE floating-point format.

1. Format A
   - There is 1 sign bit.
   - There are $k = 5$ exponent bits. The exponent bias is 15.
   - There are $n = 3$ fraction bits.

2. Format B
   - There is 1 sign bit.
   - There are $k = 4$ exponent bits. The exponent bias is 7.
   - There are $n = 4$ fraction bits.

In the following table, you are given some bit patterns in format A, and your task is to convert them to the closest value in format B. If rounding is necessary you should *round toward* $+\infty$. In addition, give the values of numbers given by the format A and format B bit patterns. Give these as whole numbers (e.g., 17) or as fractions (e.g., 17/64 or $17/2^6$).

Format A		Format B	
Bits	Value	Bits	Value
1 01111 001	$\frac{-9}{8}$	1 0111 0010	$\frac{-9}{8}$
0 10110 011	_____	_____	_____
1 00111 010	_____	_____	_____
0 00000 111	_____	_____	_____
1 11100 000	_____	_____	_____
0 10111 100	_____	_____	_____

2.89 ◆

We are running programs on a machine where values of type int have a 32-bit two's-complement representation. Values of type float use the 32-bit IEEE format, and values of type double use the 64-bit IEEE format.

We generate arbitrary integer values x, y, and z, and convert them to values of type double as follows:

```
/* Create some arbitrary values */
int x = random();
int y = random();
int z = random();
/* Convert to double */
double   dx = (double) x;
double   dy = (double) y;
double   dz = (double) z;
```

For each of the following C expressions, you are to indicate whether or not the expression *always* yields 1. If it always yields 1, describe the underlying mathematical principles. Otherwise, give an example of arguments that make it yield 0. Note that you cannot use an IA32 machine running GCC to test your answers, since it would use the 80-bit extended-precision representation for both float and double.

   A. (float) x == (float) dx

   B. dx - dy == (double) (x-y)

   C. (dx + dy) + dz == dx + (dy + dz)

   D. (dx * dy) * dz == dx * (dy * dz)

   E. dx / dx == dz / dz

2.90 ◆

You have been assigned the task of writing a C function to compute a floating-point representation of 2^x. You decide that the best way to do this is to directly construct the IEEE single-precision representation of the result. When x is too small, your routine will return 0.0. When x is too large, it will return $+\infty$. Fill in the blank portions of the code that follows to compute the correct result. Assume the function u2f returns a floating-point value having an identical bit representation as its unsigned argument.

```c
float fpwr2(int x)
{
    /* Result exponent and fraction */
    unsigned exp, frac;
    unsigned u;

    if (x < _____) {
        /* Too small.  Return 0.0 */
        exp = _____;
        frac = _____;
    } else if (x < _____) {
        /* Denormalized result */
        exp = _____;
        frac = _____;
    } else if (x < _____) {
        /* Normalized result. */
        exp = _____;
        frac = _____;
    } else {
        /* Too big.  Return +oo */
        exp = _____;
        frac = _____;
    }

    /* Pack exp and frac into 32 bits */
    u = exp << 23 | frac;
    /* Return as float */
    return u2f(u);
}
```

2.91 ◆

Around 250 B.C., the Greek mathematician Archimedes proved that $\frac{223}{71} < \pi < \frac{22}{7}$. Had he had access to a computer and the standard library <math.h>, he would have been able to determine that the single-precision floating-point approximation of π has the hexadecimal representation 0x40490FDB. Of course, all of these are just approximations, since π is not rational.

A. What is the fractional binary number denoted by this floating-point value?

B. What is the fractional binary representation of $\frac{22}{7}$? *Hint:* See Problem 2.83.

C. At what bit position (relative to the binary point) do these two approximations to π diverge?

Bit-Level Floating-Point Coding Rules

In the following problems, you will write code to implement floating-point functions, operating directly on bit-level representations of floating-point numbers. Your code should exactly replicate the conventions for IEEE floating-point operations, including using round-to-even mode when rounding is required.

To this end, we define data type `float_bits` to be equivalent to `unsigned`:

```
/* Access bit-level representation floating-point number */
typedef unsigned float_bits;
```

Rather than using data type `float` in your code, you will use `float_bits`. You may use both `int` and `unsigned` data types, including unsigned and integer constants and operations. You may not use any unions, structs, or arrays. Most significantly, you may not use any floating-point data types, operations, or constants. Instead, your code should perform the bit manipulations that implement the specified floating-point operations.

The following function illustrates the use of these coding rules. For argument f, it returns ± 0 if f is denormalized (preserving the sign of f), and returns f otherwise.

```
/* If f is denorm, return 0.  Otherwise, return f */
float_bits float_denorm_zero(float_bits f) {
    /* Decompose bit representation into parts */
    unsigned sign = f>>31;
    unsigned exp =  f>>23 & 0xFF;
    unsigned frac = f     & 0x7FFFFF;
    if (exp == 0) {
        /* Denormalized.  Set fraction to 0 */
        frac = 0;
    }
    /* Reassemble bits */
    return (sign << 31) | (exp << 23) | frac;
}
```

2.92 ◆◆
Following the bit-level floating-point coding rules, implement the function with the following prototype:

```
/* Compute -f.  If f is NaN, then return f. */
float_bits float_negate(float_bits f);
```

For floating-point number f, this function computes $-f$. If f is *NaN*, your function should simply return f.

Test your function by evaluating it for all 2^{32} values of argument `f` and comparing the result to what would be obtained using your machine's floating-point operations.

2.93 ◆◆

Following the bit-level floating-point coding rules, implement the function with the following prototype:

```
/* Compute |f|.  If f is NaN, then return f. */
float_bits float_absval(float_bits f);
```

For floating-point number f, this function computes $|f|$. If f is *NaN*, your function should simply return f.

Test your function by evaluating it for all 2^{32} values of argument f and comparing the result to what would be obtained using your machine's floating-point operations.

2.94 ◆◆◆

Following the bit-level floating-point coding rules, implement the function with the following prototype:

```
/* Compute 2*f.  If f is NaN, then return f. */
float_bits float_twice(float_bits f);
```

For floating-point number f, this function computes $2.0 \cdot f$. If f is *NaN*, your function should simply return f.

Test your function by evaluating it for all 2^{32} values of argument f and comparing the result to what would be obtained using your machine's floating-point operations.

2.95 ◆◆◆

Following the bit-level floating-point coding rules, implement the function with the following prototype:

```
/* Compute 0.5*f.  If f is NaN, then return f. */
float_bits float_half(float_bits f);
```

For floating-point number f, this function computes $0.5 \cdot f$. If f is *NaN*, your function should simply return f.

Test your function by evaluating it for all 2^{32} values of argument f and comparing the result to what would be obtained using your machine's floating-point operations.

2.96 ◆◆◆◆

Following the bit-level floating-point coding rules, implement the function with the following prototype:

```
/*
 * Compute (int) f.
 * If conversion causes overflow or f is NaN, return 0x80000000
 */
int float_f2i(float_bits f);
```

For floating-point number f, this function computes (int) f. Your function should round toward zero. If f cannot be represented as an integer (e.g., it is out of range, or it is *NaN*), then the function should return 0x80000000.

Test your function by evaluating it for all 2^{32} values of argument f and comparing the result to what would be obtained using your machine's floating-point operations.

2.97 ◆◆◆◆
Following the bit-level floating-point coding rules, implement the function with the following prototype:

```
/* Compute (float) i */
float_bits float_i2f(int i);
```

For argument i, this function computes the bit-level representation of (float) i.

Test your function by evaluating it for all 2^{32} values of argument f and comparing the result to what would be obtained using your machine's floating-point operations.

Solutions to Practice Problems

Solution to Problem 2.1 (page 37)
Understanding the relation between hexadecimal and binary formats will be important once we start looking at machine-level programs. The method for doing these conversions is in the text, but it takes a little practice to become familiar.

A. 0x39A7F8 to binary:

Hexadecimal	3	9	A	7	F	8
Binary	0011	1001	1010	0111	1111	1000

B. Binary 1100100101111011 to hexadecimal:

Binary	1100	1001	0111	1011
Hexadecimal	C	9	7	B

C. 0xD5E4C to binary:

Hexadecimal	D	5	E	4	C
Binary	1101	0101	1110	0100	1100

D. Binary 1001101110011110110101 to hexadecimal:

Binary	10	0110	1110	0111	1011	0101
Hexadecimal	2	6	E	7	B	5

Solution to Problem 2.2 (page 37)
This problem gives you a chance to think about powers of 2 and their hexadecimal representations.

n	2^n (decimal)	2^n (hexadecimal)
9	512	0x200
19	524,288	0x80000
14	16,384	0x4000
16	65,536	0x10000
17	131,072	0x20000
5	32	0x20
7	128	0x80

Solution to Problem 2.3 (page 38)

This problem gives you a chance to try out conversions between hexadecimal and decimal representations for some smaller numbers. For larger ones, it becomes much more convenient and reliable to use a calculator or conversion program.

Decimal	Binary	Hexadecimal
0	0000 0000	0x00
$167 = 10 \cdot 16 + 7$	1010 0111	0xA7
$62 = 3 \cdot 16 + 14$	0011 1110	0x3E
$188 = 11 \cdot 16 + 12$	1011 1100	0xBC
$3 \cdot 16 + 7 = 55$	0011 0111	0x37
$8 \cdot 16 + 8 = 136$	1000 1000	0x88
$15 \cdot 16 + 3 = 243$	1111 0011	0xF3
$5 \cdot 16 + 2 = 82$	0101 0010	0x52
$10 \cdot 16 + 12 = 172$	1010 1100	0xAC
$14 \cdot 16 + 7 = 231$	1110 0111	0xE7

Solution to Problem 2.4 (page 39)

When you begin debugging machine-level programs, you will find many cases where some simple hexadecimal arithmetic would be useful. You can always convert numbers to decimal, perform the arithmetic, and convert them back, but being able to work directly in hexadecimal is more efficient and informative.

A. 0x503c + 0x8 = 0x5044. Adding 8 to hex c gives 4 with a carry of 1.

B. 0x503c − 0x40 = 0x4ffc. Subtracting 4 from 3 in the second digit position requires a borrow from the third. Since this digit is 0, we must also borrow from the fourth position.

C. 0x503c + 64 = 0x507c. Decimal 64 (2^6) equals hexadecimal 0x40.

D. 0x50ea − 0x503c = 0xae. To subtract hex c (decimal 12) from hex a (decimal 10), we borrow 16 from the second digit, giving hex e (decimal 14). In the second digit, we now subtract 3 from hex d (decimal 13), giving hex a (decimal 10).

Solution to Problem 2.5 (page 48)

This problem tests your understanding of the byte representation of data and the two different byte orderings.

A.   Little endian: 21   Big endian: 87
B.   Little endian: 21 43   Big endian: 87 65
C.   Little endian: 21 43 65   Big endian: 87 65 43

Recall that show_bytes enumerates a series of bytes starting from the one with lowest address and working toward the one with highest address. On a little-endian machine, it will list the bytes from least significant to most. On a big-endian machine, it will list bytes from the most significant byte to the least.

Solution to Problem 2.6 (page 49)

This problem is another chance to practice hexadecimal to binary conversion. It also gets you thinking about integer and floating-point representations. We will explore these representations in more detail later in this chapter.

A. Using the notation of the example in the text, we write the two strings as follows:

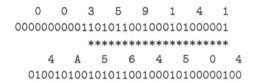

B. With the second word shifted two positions to the right relative to the first, we find a sequence with 21 matching bits.

C. We find all bits of the integer embedded in the floating-point number, except for the most significant bit having value 1. Such is the case for the example in the text as well. In addition, the floating-point number has some nonzero high-order bits that do not match those of the integer.

Solution to Problem 2.7 (page 49)

It prints 61 62 63 64 65 66. Recall also that the library routine strlen does not count the terminating null character, and so show_bytes printed only through the character 'f'.

Solution to Problem 2.8 (page 51)

This problem is a drill to help you become more familiar with Boolean operations.

Operation	Result
a	[01101001]
b	[01010101]
$\sim a$	[10010110]
$\sim b$	[10101010]
$a \,\&\, b$	[01000001]
$a \mid b$	[01111101]
$a \,\hat{}\, b$	[00111100]

Solution to Problem 2.9 (page 53)

This problem illustrates how Boolean algebra can be used to describe and reason about real-world systems. We can see that this color algebra is identical to the Boolean algebra over bit vectors of length 3.

A. Colors are complemented by complementing the values of R, G, and B. From this, we can see that white is the complement of black, yellow is the complement of blue, magenta is the complement of green, and cyan is the complement of red.

B. We perform Boolean operations based on a bit-vector representation of the colors. From this we get the following:

$$
\begin{array}{rclcl}
\text{Blue (001)} & | & \text{Green (010)} & = & \text{Cyan (011)} \\
\text{Yellow (110)} & \& & \text{Cyan (011)} & = & \text{Green (010)} \\
\text{Red (100)} & \hat{} & \text{Magenta (101)} & = & \text{Blue (001)}
\end{array}
$$

Solution to Problem 2.10 (page 54)

This procedure relies on the fact that EXCLUSIVE-OR is commutative and associative, and that $a \hat{} \, a = 0$ for any a.

Step	*x	*y
Initially	a	b
Step 1	a	$a \hat{} \, b$
Step 2	$a \hat{} \, (a \hat{} \, b) = (a \hat{} \, a) \hat{} \, b = b$	$a \hat{} \, b$
Step 3	b	$b \hat{} \, (a \hat{} \, b) = (b \hat{} \, b) \hat{} \, a = a$

See Problem 2.11 for a case where this function will fail.

Solution to Problem 2.11 (page 55)

This problem illustrates a subtle and interesting feature of our inplace swap routine.

A. Both `first` and `last` have value k, so we are attempting to swap the middle element with itself.

B. In this case, arguments x and y to `inplace_swap` both point to the same location. When we compute *x ^ *y, we get 0. We then store 0 as the middle element of the array, and the subsequent steps keep setting this element to 0. We can see that our reasoning in Problem 2.10 implicitly assumed that x and y denote different locations.

C. Simply replace the test in line 4 of `reverse_array` to be `first < last`, since there is no need to swap the middle element with itself.

Solution to Problem 2.12 (page 55)

Here are the expressions:

A. x & 0xFF

B. x ^ ~0xFF

C. x | 0xFF

These expressions are typical of the kind commonly found in performing low-level bit operations. The expression ~0xFF creates a mask where the 8 least-significant bits equal 0 and the rest equal 1. Observe that such a mask will be generated regardless of the word size. By contrast, the expression 0xFFFFFF00 would only work when data type int is 32 bits.

Solution to Problem 2.13 (page 56)

These problems help you think about the relation between Boolean operations and typical ways that programmers apply masking operations. Here is the code:

```
/* Declarations of functions implementing operations bis and bic */
int bis(int x, int m);
int bic(int x, int m);

/* Compute x|y using only calls to functions bis and bic */
int bool_or(int x, int y) {
  int result = bis(x,y);
  return result;
}

/* Compute x^y using only calls to functions bis and bic */
int bool_xor(int x, int y) {
  int result = bis(bic(x,y), bic(y,x));
  return result;
}
```

The bis operation is equivalent to Boolean OR—a bit is set in z if either this bit is set in x or it is set in m. On the other hand, bic(x, m) is equivalent to x & ~m; we want the result to equal 1 only when the corresponding bit of x is 1 and of m is 0.

Given that, we can implement | with a single call to bis. To implement ^, we take advantage of the property

$$x \wedge y = (x \ \& \ {\sim}y) \ | \ ({\sim}x \ \& \ y)$$

Solution to Problem 2.14 (page 57)

This problem highlights the relation between bit-level Boolean operations and logical operations in C. A common programming error is to use a bit-level operation when a logical one is intended, or vice versa.

Expression	Value	Expression	Value
x & y	0x20	x && y	0x01
x | y	0x7F	x || y	0x01
~x | ~y	0xDF	!x || !y	0x00
x & !y	0x00	x && ~y	0x01

Solution to Problem 2.15 (page 57)

The expression is ! (x ^ y).

That is, x^y will be zero if and only if every bit of x matches the corresponding bit of y. We then exploit the ability of ! to determine whether a word contains any nonzero bit.

There is no real reason to use this expression rather than simply writing x == y, but it demonstrates some of the nuances of bit-level and logical operations.

Solution to Problem 2.16 (page 58)

This problem is a drill to help you understand the different shift operations.

x		x << 3		Logical x >> 2		Arithmetic x >> 2	
Hex	Binary	Binary	Hex	Binary	Hex	Binary	Hex
0xC3	[11000011]	[00011000]	0x18	[00110000]	0x30	[11110000]	0xF0
0x75	[01110101]	[10101000]	0xA8	[00011101]	0x1D	[00011101]	0x1D
0x87	[10000111]	[00111000]	0x38	[00100001]	0x21	[11100001]	0xE1
0x66	[01100110]	[00110000]	0x30	[00011001]	0x19	[00011001]	0x19

Solution to Problem 2.17 (page 65)

In general, working through examples for very small word sizes is a very good way to understand computer arithmetic.

The unsigned values correspond to those in Figure 2.2. For the two's-complement values, hex digits 0 through 7 have a most significant bit of 0, yielding nonnegative values, while hex digits 8 through F have a most significant bit of 1, yielding a negative value.

Hexadecimal $\vec{x}$	Binary	$B2U_4(\vec{x})$	$B2T_4(\vec{x})$
0xE	[1110]	$2^3 + 2^2 + 2^1 = 14$	$-2^3 + 2^2 + 2^1 = -2$
0x0	[0000]	0	0
0x5	[0101]	$2^2 + 2^0 = 5$	$2^2 + 2^0 = 5$
0x8	[1000]	$2^3 = 8$	$-2^3 = -8$
0xD	[1101]	$2^3 + 2^2 + 2^0 = 13$	$-2^3 + 2^2 + 2^0 = -3$
0xF	[1111]	$2^3 + 2^2 + 2^1 + 2^0 = 15$	$-2^3 + 2^2 + 2^1 + 2^0 = -1$

Solution to Problem 2.18 (page 69)

For a 32-bit word, any value consisting of 8 hexadecimal digits beginning with one of the digits 8 through f represents a negative number. It is quite common to see numbers beginning with a string of f's, since the leading bits of a negative number are all ones. You must look carefully, though. For example, the number 0x8048337 has only 7 digits. Filling this out with a leading zero gives 0x08048337, a positive number.

4004d0:	48 81 ec e0 02 00 00	sub	$0x2e0,%rsp	A.	736
4004d7:	48 8b 44 24 a8	mov	-0x58(%rsp),%rax	B.	-88
4004dc:	48 03 47 28	add	0x28(%rdi),%rax	C.	40
4004e0:	48 89 44 24 d0	mov	%rax,-0x30(%rsp)	D.	-48
4004e5:	48 8b 44 24 78	mov	0x78(%rsp),%rax	E.	120
4004ea:	48 89 87 88 00 00 00	mov	%rax,0x88(%rdi)	F.	136
4004f1:	48 8b 84 24 f8 01 00	mov	0x1f8(%rsp),%rax	G.	504
4004f8:	00				
4004f9:	48 03 44 24 08	add	0x8(%rsp),%rax		
4004fe:	48 89 84 24 c0 00 00	mov	%rax,0xc0(%rsp)	H.	192
400505:	00				
400506:	48 8b 44 d4 b8	mov	-0x48(%rsp,%rdx,8),%rax	I.	-72

Solution to Problem 2.19 (page 71)

The functions *T2U* and *U2T* are very peculiar from a mathematical perspective. It is important to understand how they behave.

We solve this problem by reordering the rows in the solution of Problem 2.17 according to the two's-complement value and then listing the unsigned value as the result of the function application. We show the hexadecimal values to make this process more concrete.

$\vec{x}$ (hex)	x	$T2U_4(x)$
0x8	-8	8
0xD	-3	13
0xE	-2	14
0xF	-1	15
0x0	0	0
0x5	5	5

Solution to Problem 2.20 (page 73)

This exercise tests your understanding of Equation 2.5.

For the first four entries, the values of x are negative and $T2U_4(x) = x + 2^4$. For the remaining two entries, the values of x are nonnegative and $T2U_4(x) = x$.

Solution to Problem 2.21 (page 76)

This problem reinforces your understanding of the relation between two's-complement and unsigned representations, as well as the effects of the C promotion rules. Recall that $TMin_{32}$ is $-2{,}147{,}483{,}648$, and that when cast to unsigned it becomes 2,147,483,648. In addition, if either operand is unsigned, then the other operand will be cast to unsigned before comparing.

Expression	Type	Evaluation
-2147483647-1 == 2147483648U	Unsigned	1
-2147483647-1 < 2147483647	Signed	1
-2147483647-1U < 2147483647	Unsigned	0
-2147483647-1 < -2147483647	Signed	1
-2147483647-1U < -2147483647	Unsigned	1

Solution to Problem 2.22 (page 79)
This exercise provides a concrete demonstration of how sign extension preserves the numeric value of a two's-complement representation.

A.   [1011] $-2^3 + 2^1 + 2^0$ = $-8 + 2 + 1$ = -5
B.   [11011] $-2^4 + 2^3 + 2^1 + 2^0$ = $-16 + 8 + 2 + 1$ = -5
C.   [111011] $-2^5 + 2^4 + 2^3 + 2^1 + 2^0$ = $-32 + 16 + 8 + 2 + 1$ = -5

Solution to Problem 2.23 (page 80)
The expressions in these functions are common program "idioms" for extracting values from a word in which multiple bit fields have been packed. They exploit the zero-filling and sign-extending properties of the different shift operations. Note carefully the ordering of the cast and shift operations. In fun1, the shifts are performed on unsigned variable word and hence are logical. In fun2, shifts are performed after casting word to int and hence are arithmetic.

A.

w	fun1(w)	fun2(w)
0x00000076	0x00000076	0x00000076
0x87654321	0x00000021	0x00000021
0x000000C9	0x000000C9	0xFFFFFFC9
0xEDCBA987	0x00000087	0xFFFFFF87

B. Function fun1 extracts a value from the low-order 8 bits of the argument, giving an integer ranging between 0 and 255. Function fun2 extracts a value from the low-order 8 bits of the argument, but it also performs sign extension. The result will be a number between −128 and 127.

Solution to Problem 2.24 (page 82)
The effect of truncation is fairly intuitive for unsigned numbers, but not for two's-complement numbers. This exercise lets you explore its properties using very small word sizes.

Hex		Unsigned		Two's complement	
Original	Truncated	Original	Truncated	Original	Truncated
0	0	0	0	0	0
2	2	2	2	2	2
9	1	9	1	−7	1
B	3	11	3	−5	3
F	7	15	7	−1	−1

As Equation 2.9 states, the effect of this truncation on unsigned values is to simply find their residue, modulo 8. The effect of the truncation on signed values is a bit more complex. According to Equation 2.10, we first compute the modulo 8 residue of the argument. This will give values 0 through 7 for arguments 0 through 7, and also for arguments −8 through −1. Then we apply function $U2T_3$ to these residues, giving two repetitions of the sequences 0 through 3 and −4 through −1.

Solution to Problem 2.25 (page 83)

This problem is designed to demonstrate how easily bugs can arise due to the implicit casting from signed to unsigned. It seems quite natural to pass parameter length as an unsigned, since one would never want to use a negative length. The stopping criterion i <= length-1 also seems quite natural. But combining these two yields an unexpected outcome!

Since parameter length is unsigned, the computation 0 − 1 is performed using unsigned arithmetic, which is equivalent to modular addition. The result is then *UMax*. The ≤ comparison is also performed using an unsigned comparison, and since any number is less than or equal to *UMax*, the comparison always holds! Thus, the code attempts to access invalid elements of array a.

The code can be fixed either by declaring length to be an int or by changing the test of the for loop to be i < length.

Solution to Problem 2.26 (page 83)

This example demonstrates a subtle feature of unsigned arithmetic, and also the property that we sometimes perform unsigned arithmetic without realizing it. This can lead to very tricky bugs.

A. *For what cases will this function produce an incorrect result?* The function will incorrectly return 1 when s is shorter than t.

B. *Explain how this incorrect result comes about.* Since strlen is defined to yield an unsigned result, the difference and the comparison are both computed using unsigned arithmetic. When s is shorter than t, the difference strlen(s) - strlen(t) should be negative, but instead becomes a large, unsigned number, which is greater than 0.

C. *Show how to fix the code so that it will work reliably.* Replace the test with the following:

```
return strlen(s) > strlen(t);
```

Solution to Problem 2.27 (page 89)

This function is a direct implementation of the rules given to determine whether or not an unsigned addition overflows.

```
/* Determine whether arguments can be added without overflow */
int uadd_ok(unsigned x, unsigned y) {
    unsigned sum = x+y;
    return sum >= x;
}
```

Solution to Problem 2.28 (page 89)

This problem is a simple demonstration of arithmetic modulo 16. The easiest way to solve it is to convert the hex pattern into its unsigned decimal value. For nonzero values of x, we must have $(-_4^u x) + x = 16$. Then we convert the complemented value back to hex.

x		$-_4^u x$	
Hex	Decimal	Decimal	Hex
0	0	0	0
5	5	11	B
8	8	8	8
D	13	3	3
F	15	1	1

Solution to Problem 2.29 (page 93)

This problem is an exercise to make sure you understand two's-complement addition.

x	y	$x + y$	$x +_5^t y$	Case
−12	−15	−27	5	1
[10100]	[10001]	[100101]	[00101]	
−8	−8	−16	−16	2
[11000]	[11000]	[110000]	[10000]	
−9	8	−1	−1	2
[10111]	[01000]	[111111]	[11111]	
2	5	7	7	3
[00010]	[00101]	[000111]	[00111]	
12	4	16	−16	4
[01100]	[00100]	[010000]	[10000]	

Solution to Problem 2.30 (page 94)

This function is a direct implementation of the rules given to determine whether or not a two's-complement addition overflows.

```
/* Determine whether arguments can be added without overflow */
int tadd_ok(int x, int y) {
    int sum = x+y;
    int neg_over = x <  0 && y <  0 && sum >= 0;
    int pos_over = x >= 0 && y >= 0 && sum <  0;
    return !neg_over && !pos_over;
}
```

Solution to Problem 2.31 (page 94)

Your coworker could have learned, by studying Section 2.3.2, that two's-complement addition forms an abelian group, and so the expression (x+y)-x will evaluate to y regardless of whether or not the addition overflows, and that (x+y)-y will always evaluate to x.

Solution to Problem 2.32 (page 94)

This function will give correct values, except when y is *TMin*. In this case, we will have −y also equal to *TMin*, and so the call to function tadd_ok will indicate overflow when x is negative and no overflow when x is nonnegative. In fact, the opposite is true: tsub_ok(x, *TMin*) should yield 0 when x is negative and 1 when it is nonnegative.

One lesson to be learned from this exercise is that *TMin* should be included as one of the cases in any test procedure for a function.

Solution to Problem 2.33 (page 95)

This problem helps you understand two's-complement negation using a very small word size.

For $w = 4$, we have $TMin_4 = -8$. So -8 is its own additive inverse, while other values are negated by integer negation.

x		$-_4^t x$	
Hex	Decimal	Decimal	Hex
0	0	0	0
5	5	−5	B
8	−8	−8	8
D	−3	3	3
F	−1	1	1

The bit patterns are the same as for unsigned negation.

Solution to Problem 2.34 (page 98)

This problem is an exercise to make sure you understand two's-complement multiplication.

Mode	x		y		$x \cdot y$		Truncated $x \cdot y$	
Unsigned	4	[100]	5	[101]	20	[010100]	4	[100]
Two's complement	−4	[100]	−3	[101]	12	[001100]	−4	[100]
Unsigned	2	[010]	7	[111]	14	[001110]	6	[110]
Two's complement	2	[010]	−1	[111]	−2	[111110]	−2	[110]
Unsigned	6	[110]	6	[110]	36	[100100]	4	[100]
Two's complement	−2	[110]	−2	[110]	4	[000100]	−4	[100]

Solution to Problem 2.35 (page 99)

It is not realistic to test this function for all possible values of x and y. Even if you could run 10 billion tests per second, it would require over 58 years to test all combinations when data type int is 32 bits. On the other hand, it is feasible to test your code by writing the function with data type short or char and then testing it exhaustively.

Here's a more principled approach, following the proposed set of arguments:

1. We know that $x \cdot y$ can be written as a $2w$-bit two's-complement number. Let u denote the unsigned number represented by the lower w bits, and v denote the two's-complement number represented by the upper w bits. Then, based on Equation 2.3, we can see that $x \cdot y = v2^w + u$.

   We also know that $u = T2U_w(p)$, since they are unsigned and two's-complement numbers arising from the same bit pattern, and so by Equation 2.6, we can write $u = p + p_{w-1}2^w$, where p_{w-1} is the most significant bit of p. Letting $t = v + p_{w-1}$, we have $x \cdot y = p + t2^w$.

   When $t = 0$, we have $x \cdot y = p$; the multiplication does not overflow. When $t \neq 0$, we have $x \cdot y \neq p$; the multiplication does overflow.

2. By definition of integer division, dividing p by nonzero x gives a quotient q and a remainder r such that $p = x \cdot q + r$, and $|r| < |x|$. (We use absolute values here, because the signs of x and r may differ. For example, dividing -7 by 2 gives quotient -3 and remainder -1.)

3. Suppose $q = y$. Then we have $x \cdot y = x \cdot y + r + t2^w$. From this, we can see that $r + t2^w = 0$. But $|r| < |x| \leq 2^w$, and so this identity can hold only if $t = 0$, in which case $r = 0$.

   Suppose $r = t = 0$. Then we will have $x \cdot y = x \cdot q$, implying that $y = q$.

   When x equals 0, multiplication does not overflow, and so we see that our code provides a reliable way to test whether or not two's-complement multiplication causes overflow.

Solution to Problem 2.36 (page 99)

With 64 bits, we can perform the multiplication without overflowing. We then test whether casting the product to 32 bits changes the value:

```
1   /* Determine whether the arguments can be multiplied
2       without overflow */
3   int tmult_ok(int x, int y) {
4       /* Compute product without overflow */
5       int64_t pll = (int64_t) x*y;
6       /* See if casting to int preserves value */
7       return pll == (int) pll;
8   }
```

Note that the casting on the right-hand side of line 5 is critical. If we instead wrote the line as

```
int64_t pll = x*y;
```

the product would be computed as a 32-bit value (possibly overflowing) and then sign extended to 64 bits.

Solution to Problem 2.37 (page 99)

A. This change does not help at all. Even though the computation of asize will be accurate, the call to malloc will cause this value to be converted to a 32-bit unsigned number, and so the same overflow conditions will occur.

B. With malloc having a 32-bit unsigned number as its argument, it cannot possibly allocate a block of more than 2^{32} bytes, and so there is no point attempting to allocate or copy this much memory. Instead, the function should abort and return NULL, as illustrated by the following replacement to the original call to malloc (line 9):

```
uint64_t required_size = ele_cnt * (uint64_t) ele_size;
size_t request_size = (size_t) required_size;
if (required_size != request_size)
    /* Overflow must have occurred. Abort operation */
    return NULL;
void *result = malloc(request_size);
if (result == NULL)
    /* malloc failed */
    return NULL;
```

Solution to Problem 2.38 (page 102)

In Chapter 3, we will see many examples of the LEA instruction in action. The instruction is provided to support pointer arithmetic, but the C compiler often uses it as a way to perform multiplication by small constants.

For each value of k, we can compute two multiples: 2^k (when b is 0) and $2^k + 1$ (when b is a). Thus, we can compute multiples 1, 2, 3, 4, 5, 8, and 9.

Solution to Problem 2.39 (page 103)

The expression simply becomes $-(x<<m)$. To see this, let the word size be w so that $n = w - 1$. Form B states that we should compute $(x<<w) - (x<<m)$, but shifting x to the left by w will yield the value 0.

Solution to Problem 2.40 (page 103)

This problem requires you to try out the optimizations already described and also to supply a bit of your own ingenuity.

K	Shifts	Add/Subs	Expression
6	2	1	$(x<<2) + (x<<1)$
31	1	1	$(x<<5) - x$
-6	2	1	$(x<<1) - (x<<3)$
55	2	2	$(x<<6) - (x<<3) - x$

Observe that the fourth case uses a modified version of form B. We can view the bit pattern [110111] as having a run of 6 ones with a zero in the middle, and so we apply the rule for form B, but then we subtract the term corresponding to the middle zero bit.

Solution to Problem 2.41 (page 103)

Assuming that addition and subtraction have the same performance, the rule is to choose form A when $n = m$, either form when $n = m + 1$, and form B when $n > m + 1$.

The justification for this rule is as follows. Assume first that $m > 0$. When $n = m$, form A requires only a single shift, while form B requires two shifts and a subtraction. When $n = m + 1$, both forms require two shifts and either an addition or a subtraction. When $n > m + 1$, form B requires only two shifts and one subtraction, while form A requires $n - m + 1 > 2$ shifts and $n - m > 1$ additions. For the case of $m = 0$, we get one fewer shift for both forms A and B, and so the same rules apply for choosing between the two.

Solution to Problem 2.42 (page 107)

The only challenge here is to compute the bias without any testing or conditional operations. We use the trick that the expression x >> 31 generates a word with all ones if x is negative, and all zeros otherwise. By masking off the appropriate bits, we get the desired bias value.

```
int div16(int x) {
    /* Compute bias to be either 0 (x >= 0) or 15 (x < 0) */
    int bias = (x >> 31) & 0xF;
    return (x + bias) >> 4;
}
```

Solution to Problem 2.43 (page 107)

We have found that people have difficulty with this exercise when working directly with assembly code. It becomes more clear when put in the form shown in optarith.

We can see that M is 31; x*M is computed as (x<<5)-x.

We can see that N is 8; a bias value of 7 is added when y is negative, and the right shift is by 3.

Solution to Problem 2.44 (page 108)

These "C puzzle" problems provide a clear demonstration that programmers must understand the properties of computer arithmetic:

A. (x > 0) || (x-1 < 0)
   False. Let x be $-2,147,483,648$ ($TMin_{32}$). We will then have x-1 equal to $2,147,483,647$ ($TMax_{32}$).

B. (x & 7) != 7 || (x<<29 < 0)
   True. If (x & 7) != 7 evaluates to 0, then we must have bit x_2 equal to 1. When shifted left by 29, this will become the sign bit.

C. (x * x) >= 0
   False. When x is 65,535 (0xFFFF), x*x is $-131,071$ (0xFFFE0001).

D. x < 0 || -x <= 0
   True. If x is nonnegative, then -x is nonpositive.

E. x > 0 || -x >= 0
   False. Let x be $-2,147,483,648$ ($TMin_{32}$). Then both x and -x are negative.

F. x+y == uy+ux
   True. Two's-complement and unsigned addition have the same bit-level behavior, and they are commutative.

G. x*~y + uy*ux == -x
   True. ~y equals -y-1. uy*ux equals x*y. Thus, the left-hand side is equivalent to x*-y-x+x*y.

Solution to Problem 2.45 (page 111)

Understanding fractional binary representations is an important step to understanding floating-point encodings. This exercise lets you try out some simple examples.

$\frac{1}{8}$	0.001	0.125
$\frac{3}{4}$	0.11	0.75
$\frac{25}{16}$	1.1001	1.5625
$\frac{43}{16}$	10.1011	2.6875
$\frac{9}{8}$	1.001	1.125
$\frac{47}{8}$	101.111	5.875
$\frac{51}{16}$	11.0011	3.1875

One simple way to think about fractional binary representations is to represent a number as a fraction of the form $\frac{x}{2^k}$. We can write this in binary using the binary representation of x, with the binary point inserted k positions from the right. As an example, for $\frac{25}{16}$, we have $25_{10} = 11001_2$. We then put the binary point four positions from the right to get 1.1001_2.

Solution to Problem 2.46 (page 111)

In most cases, the limited precision of floating-point numbers is not a major problem, because the *relative* error of the computation is still fairly low. In this example, however, the system was sensitive to the *absolute* error.

A. We can see that $0.1 - x$ has the binary representation

$$0.00000000000000000000000001100[1100]\cdots_2$$

B. Comparing this to the binary representation of $\frac{1}{10}$, we can see that it is simply $2^{-20} \times \frac{1}{10}$, which is around 9.54×10^{-8}.

C. $9.54 \times 10^{-8} \times 100 \times 60 \times 60 \times 10 \approx 0.343$ seconds.

D. $0.343 \times 2{,}000 \approx 687$ meters.

Solution to Problem 2.47 (page 117)

Working through floating-point representations for very small word sizes helps clarify how IEEE floating point works. Note especially the transition between denormalized and normalized values.

Bits	e	E	2^E	f	M	$2^E \times M$	V	Decimal
0 00 00	0	0	1	$\frac{0}{4}$	$\frac{0}{4}$	$\frac{0}{4}$	0	0.0
0 00 01	0	0	1	$\frac{1}{4}$	$\frac{1}{4}$	$\frac{1}{4}$	$\frac{1}{4}$	0.25
0 00 10	0	0	1	$\frac{2}{4}$	$\frac{2}{4}$	$\frac{2}{4}$	$\frac{1}{2}$	0.5
0 00 11	0	0	1	$\frac{3}{4}$	$\frac{3}{4}$	$\frac{3}{4}$	$\frac{3}{4}$	0.75
0 01 00	1	0	1	$\frac{0}{4}$	$\frac{4}{4}$	$\frac{4}{4}$	1	1.0
0 01 01	1	0	1	$\frac{1}{4}$	$\frac{5}{4}$	$\frac{5}{4}$	$\frac{5}{4}$	1.25
0 01 10	1	0	1	$\frac{2}{4}$	$\frac{6}{4}$	$\frac{6}{4}$	$\frac{3}{2}$	1.5
0 01 11	1	0	1	$\frac{3}{4}$	$\frac{7}{4}$	$\frac{7}{4}$	$\frac{7}{4}$	1.75
0 10 00	2	1	2	$\frac{0}{4}$	$\frac{4}{4}$	$\frac{8}{4}$	2	2.0
0 10 01	2	1	2	$\frac{1}{4}$	$\frac{5}{4}$	$\frac{10}{4}$	$\frac{5}{2}$	2.5
0 10 10	2	1	2	$\frac{2}{4}$	$\frac{6}{4}$	$\frac{12}{4}$	3	3.0
0 10 11	2	1	2	$\frac{3}{4}$	$\frac{7}{4}$	$\frac{14}{4}$	$\frac{7}{2}$	3.5
0 11 00	—	—	—	—	—	—	∞	—
0 11 01	—	—	—	—	—	—	NaN	—
0 11 10	—	—	—	—	—	—	NaN	—
0 11 11	—	—	—	—	—	—	NaN	—

Solution to Problem 2.48 (page 119)

Hexadecimal 0x359141 is equivalent to binary [1101011001000101000001]. Shifting this right 21 places gives $1.1010110010001010000001_2 \times 2^{21}$. We form the fraction field by dropping the leading 1 and adding two zeros, giving

$$[10101100100010100000100]$$

The exponent is formed by adding bias 127 to 21, giving 148 (binary [10010100]). We combine this with a sign field of 0 to give a binary representation

$$[01001010010101100100010100000100]$$

We see that the matching bits in the two representations correspond to the low-order bits of the integer, up to the most significant bit equal to 1 matching the high-order 21 bits of the fraction:

```
   0    0    3    5    9    1    4    1
00000000000110101100100010100000 1
           ********************
   4    A    5    6    4    5    0    4
01001010010101100100010100000100
```

Solution to Problem 2.49 (page 120)

This exercise helps you think about what numbers cannot be represented exactly in floating point.

A. The number has binary representation 1, followed by n zeros, followed by 1, giving value $2^{n+1} + 1$.

B. When $n = 23$, the value is $2^{24} + 1 = 16,777,217$.

Solution to Problem 2.50 (page 121)

Performing rounding by hand helps reinforce the idea of round-to-even with binary numbers.

Original		Rounded	
10.010_2	$2\frac{1}{4}$	10.0	2
10.011_2	$2\frac{3}{8}$	10.1	$2\frac{1}{2}$
10.110_2	$2\frac{3}{4}$	11.0	3
11.001_2	$3\frac{1}{8}$	11.0	3

Solution to Problem 2.51 (page 122)

A. Looking at the nonterminating sequence for $\frac{1}{10}$, we see that the 2 bits to the right of the rounding position are 1, so a better approximation to $\frac{1}{10}$ would be obtained by incrementing x to get $x' = 0.000110011001100110011001101_2$, which is larger than 0.1.

B. We can see that $x' - 0.1$ has binary representation

$$0.0000000000000000000000000000[1100]$$

Comparing this to the binary representation of $\frac{1}{10}$, we can see that it is $2^{-22} \times \frac{1}{10}$, which is around 2.38×10^{-8}.

C. $2.38 \times 10^{-8} \times 100 \times 60 \times 60 \times 10 \approx 0.086$ seconds, a factor of 4 less than the error in the Patriot system.

D. $0.086 \times 2{,}000 \approx 171$ meters.

Solution to Problem 2.52 (page 122)

This problem tests a lot of concepts about floating-point representations, including the encoding of normalized and denormalized values, as well as rounding.

Format A		Format B		
Bits	Value	Bits	Value	Comments
011 0000	1	0111 000	1	
101 1110	$\frac{15}{2}$	1001 111	$\frac{15}{2}$	
010 1001	$\frac{25}{32}$	0110 100	$\frac{3}{4}$	Round down
110 1111	$\frac{31}{2}$	1011 000	16	Round up
000 0001	$\frac{1}{64}$	0001 000	$\frac{1}{64}$	Denorm → norm

Solution to Problem 2.53 (page 125)

In general, it is better to use a library macro rather than inventing your own code. This code seems to work on a variety of machines, however.

We assume that the value 1e400 overflows to infinity.

```
#define POS_INFINITY 1e400
#define NEG_INFINITY (-POS_INFINITY)
#define NEG_ZERO (-1.0/POS_INFINITY)
```

Solution to Problem 2.54 (page 125)

Exercises such as this one help you develop your ability to reason about floating-point operations from a programmer's perspective. Make sure you understand each of the answers.

A. `x == (int)(double) x`
   Yes, since `double` has greater precision and range than `int`.

B. `x == (int)(float) x`
   No. For example, when x is *TMax*.

C. `d == (double)(float) d`
   No. For example, when d is 1e40, we will get $+\infty$ on the right.

D. `f == (float)(double) f`
   Yes, since `double` has greater precision and range than `float`.

E. `f == -(-f)`
   Yes, since a floating-point number is negated by simply inverting its sign bit.

F. `1.0/2 == 1/2.0`

Yes, the numerators and denominators will both be converted to floating-point representations before the division is performed.

G. `d*d >= 0.0`

Yes, although it may overflow to $+\infty$.

H. `(f+d)-f == d`

No. For example, when `f` is `1.0e20` and `d` is 1.0, the expression `f+d` will be rounded to `1.0e20`, and so the expression on the left-hand side will evaluate to 0.0, while the right-hand side will be 1.0.

3

Machine-Level Representation of Programs

Computers execute *machine code*, sequences of bytes encoding the low-level operations that manipulate data, manage memory, read and write data on storage devices, and communicate over networks. A compiler generates machine code through a series of stages, based on the rules of the programming language, the instruction set of the target machine, and the conventions followed by the operating system. The GCC C compiler generates its output in the form of *assembly code*, a textual representation of the machine code giving the individual instructions in the program. Gcc then invokes both an *assembler* and a *linker* to generate the executable machine code from the assembly code. In this chapter, we will take a close look at machine code and its human-readable representation as assembly code.

When programming in a high-level language such as C, and even more so in Java, we are shielded from the detailed machine-level implementation of our program. In contrast, when writing programs in assembly code (as was done in the early days of computing) a programmer must specify the low-level instructions the program uses to carry out a computation. Most of the time, it is much more productive and reliable to work at the higher level of abstraction provided by a high-level language. The type checking provided by a compiler helps detect many program errors and makes sure we reference and manipulate data in consistent ways. With modern optimizing compilers, the generated code is usually at least as efficient as what a skilled assembly-language programmer would write by hand. Best of all, a program written in a high-level language can be compiled and executed on a number of different machines, whereas assembly code is highly machine specific.

So why should we spend our time learning machine code? Even though compilers do most of the work in generating assembly code, being able to read and understand it is an important skill for serious programmers. By invoking the compiler with appropriate command-line parameters, the compiler will generate a file showing its output in assembly-code form. By reading this code, we can understand the optimization capabilities of the compiler and analyze the underlying inefficiencies in the code. As we will experience in Chapter 5, programmers seeking to maximize the performance of a critical section of code often try different variations of the source code, each time compiling and examining the generated assembly code to get a sense of how efficiently the program will run. Furthermore, there are times when the layer of abstraction provided by a high-level language hides information about the run-time behavior of a program that we need to understand. For example, when writing concurrent programs using a thread package, as covered in Chapter 12, it is important to understand how program data are shared or kept private by the different threads and precisely how and where shared data are accessed. Such information is visible at the machine-code level. As another example, many of the ways programs can be attacked, allowing malware to infest a system, involve nuances of the way programs store their run-time control information. Many attacks involve exploiting weaknesses in system programs to overwrite information and thereby take control of the system. Understanding how these vulnerabilities arise and how to guard against them requires a knowledge of the machine-level representation of programs. The need for programmers to learn machine code has shifted over the years from one of being able to write programs directly in assembly code to one of being able to read and understand the code generated by compilers.

In this chapter, we will learn the details of one particular assembly language and see how C programs get compiled into this form of machine code. Reading the assembly code generated by a compiler involves a different set of skills than writing assembly code by hand. We must understand the transformations typical compilers make in converting the constructs of C into machine code. Relative to the computations expressed in the C code, optimizing compilers can rearrange execution order, eliminate unneeded computations, replace slow operations with faster ones, and even change recursive computations into iterative ones. Understanding the relation between source code and the generated assembly can often be a challenge—it's much like putting together a puzzle having a slightly different design than the picture on the box. It is a form of *reverse engineering*—trying to understand the process by which a system was created by studying the system and working backward. In this case, the system is a machine-generated assembly-language program, rather than something designed by a human. This simplifies the task of reverse engineering because the generated code follows fairly regular patterns and we can run experiments, having the compiler generate code for many different programs. In our presentation, we give many examples and provide a number of exercises illustrating different aspects of assembly language and compilers. This is a subject where mastering the details is a prerequisite to understanding the deeper and more fundamental concepts. Those who say "I understand the general principles, I don't want to bother learning the details" are deluding themselves. It is critical for you to spend time studying the examples, working through the exercises, and checking your solutions with those provided.

Our presentation is based on x86-64, the machine language for most of the processors found in today's laptop and desktop machines, as well as those that power very large data centers and supercomputers. This language has evolved over a long history, starting with Intel Corporation's first 16-bit processor in 1978, through to the expansion to 32 bits, and most recently to 64 bits. Along the way, features have been added to make better use of the available semiconductor technology, and to satisfy the demands of the marketplace. Much of the development has been driven by Intel, but its rival Advanced Micro Devices (AMD) has also made important contributions. The result is a rather peculiar design with features that make sense only when viewed from a historical perspective. It is also laden with features providing backward compatibility that are not used by modern compilers and operating systems. We will focus on the subset of the features used by GCC and Linux. This allows us to avoid much of the complexity and many of the arcane features of x86-64.

Our technical presentation starts with a quick tour to show the relation between C, assembly code, and machine code. We then proceed to the details of x86-64, starting with the representation and manipulation of data and the implementation of control. We see how control constructs in C, such as `if`, `while`, and `switch` statements, are implemented. We then cover the implementation of procedures, including how the program maintains a run-time stack to support the

Web Aside ASM:IA32   IA32 programming

IA32, the 32-bit predecessor to x86-64, was introduced by Intel in 1985. It served as the machine language of choice for several decades. Most x86 microprocessors sold today, and most operating systems installed on these machines, are designed to run x86-64. However, they can also execute IA32 programs in a backward compatibility mode. As a result, many application programs are still based on IA32. In addition, many existing systems cannot execute x86-64, due to limitations of their hardware or system software. IA32 continues to be an important machine language. You will find that having a background in x86-64 will enable you to learn the IA32 machine language quite readily.

passing of data and control between procedures, as well as storage for local variables. Next, we consider how data structures such as arrays, structures, and unions are implemented at the machine level. With this background in machine-level programming, we can examine the problems of out-of-bounds memory references and the vulnerability of systems to buffer overflow attacks. We finish this part of the presentation with some tips on using the GDB debugger for examining the run-time behavior of a machine-level program. The chapter concludes with a presentation on machine-program representations of code involving floating-point data and operations.

The computer industry has recently made the transition from 32-bit to 64-bit machines. A 32-bit machine can only make use of around 4 gigabytes (2^{32} bytes) of random access memory, With memory prices dropping at dramatic rates, and our computational demands and data sizes increasing, it has become both economically feasible and technically desirable to go beyond this limitation. Current 64-bit machines can use up to 256 terabytes (2^{48} bytes) of memory, and could readily be extended to use up to 16 exabytes (2^{64} bytes). Although it is hard to imagine having a machine with that much memory, keep in mind that 4 gigabytes seemed like an extreme amount of memory when 32-bit machines became commonplace in the 1970s and 1980s.

Our presentation focuses on the types of machine-level programs generated when compiling C and similar programming languages targeting modern operating systems. As a consequence, we make no attempt to describe many of the features of x86-64 that arise out of its legacy support for the styles of programs written in the early days of microprocessors, when much of the code was written manually and where programmers had to struggle with the limited range of addresses allowed by 16-bit machines.

3.1 A Historical Perspective

The Intel processor line, colloquially referred to as *x86*, has followed a long evolutionary development. It started with one of the first single-chip 16-bit microprocessors, where many compromises had to be made due to the limited capabilities of integrated circuit technology at the time. Since then, it has grown to take advantage of technology improvements as well as to satisfy the demands for higher performance and for supporting more advanced operating systems.

The list that follows shows some models of Intel processors and some of their key features, especially those affecting machine-level programming. We use the number of transistors required to implement the processors as an indication of how they have evolved in complexity. In this table, "K" denotes 1,000 (10^3), "M" denotes 1,000,000 (10^6), and "G" denotes 1,000,000,000 (10^9).

8086 (1978, 29 K transistors). One of the first single-chip, 16-bit microprocessors. The 8088, a variant of the 8086 with an 8-bit external bus, formed the heart of the original IBM personal computers. IBM contracted with then-tiny Microsoft to develop the MS-DOS operating system. The original models came with 32,768 bytes of memory and two floppy drives (no hard drive). Architecturally, the machines were limited to a 655,360-byte address space—addresses were only 20 bits long (1,048,576 bytes addressable), and the operating system reserved 393,216 bytes for its own use. In 1980, Intel introduced the 8087 floating-point coprocessor (45 K transistors) to operate alongside an 8086 or 8088 processor, executing the floating-point instructions. The 8087 established the floating-point model for the x86 line, often referred to as "x87."

80286 (1982, 134 K transistors). Added more (and now obsolete) addressing modes. Formed the basis of the IBM PC-AT personal computer, the original platform for MS Windows.

i386 (1985, 275 K transistors). Expanded the architecture to 32 bits. Added the flat addressing model used by Linux and recent versions of the Windows operating system. This was the first machine in the series that could fully support a Unix operating system.

i486 (1989, 1.2 M transistors). Improved performance and integrated the floating-point unit onto the processor chip but did not significantly change the instruction set.

Pentium (1993, 3.1 M transistors). Improved performance but only added minor extensions to the instruction set.

PentiumPro (1995, 5.5 M transistors). Introduced a radically new processor design, internally known as the *P6* microarchitecture. Added a class of "conditional move" instructions to the instruction set.

Pentium/MMX (1997, 4.5 M transistors). Added new class of instructions to the Pentium processor for manipulating vectors of integers. Each datum can be 1, 2, or 4 bytes long. Each vector totals 64 bits.

Pentium II (1997, 7 M transistors). Continuation of the P6 microarchitecture.

Pentium III (1999, 8.2 M transistors). Introduced SSE, a class of instructions for manipulating vectors of integer or floating-point data. Each datum can be 1, 2, or 4 bytes, packed into vectors of 128 bits. Later versions of this chip went up to 24 M transistors, due to the incorporation of the level-2 cache on chip.

Pentium 4 (2000, 42 M transistors). Extended SSE to SSE2, adding new data types (including double-precision floating point), along with 144 new instructions for these formats. With these extensions, compilers can use SSE instructions, rather than x87 instructions, to compile floating-point code.

Pentium 4E (2004, 125 M transistors). Added *hyperthreading*, a method to run two programs simultaneously on a single processor, as well as EM64T, Intel's implementation of a 64-bit extension to IA32 developed by Advanced Micro Devices (AMD), which we refer to as x86-64.

Core 2 (2006, 291 M transistors). Returned to a microarchitecture similar to P6. First *multi-core* Intel microprocessor, where multiple processors are implemented on a single chip. Did not support hyperthreading.

Core i7, Nehalem (2008, 781 M transistors). Incorporated both hyperthreading and multi-core, with the initial version supporting two executing programs on each core and up to four cores on each chip.

Core i7, Sandy Bridge (2011, 1.17 G transistors). Introduced AVX, an extension of the SSE to support data packed into 256-bit vectors.

Core i7, Haswell (2013, 1.4 G transistors). Extended AVX to AVX2, adding more instructions and instruction formats.

Each successive processor has been designed to be backward compatible—able to run code compiled for any earlier version. As we will see, there are many strange artifacts in the instruction set due to this evolutionary heritage. Intel has had several names for their processor line, including *IA32*, for "Intel Architecture 32-bit" and most recently *Intel64*, the 64-bit extension to IA32, which we will refer to as *x86-64*. We will refer to the overall line by the commonly used colloquial name "x86," reflecting the processor naming conventions up through the i486.

Over the years, several companies have produced processors that are compatible with Intel processors, capable of running the exact same machine-level programs. Chief among these is Advanced Micro Devices (AMD). For years, AMD lagged just behind Intel in technology, forcing a marketing strategy where they produced processors that were less expensive although somewhat lower in performance. They became more competitive around 2002, being the first to break the 1-gigahertz clock-speed barrier for a commercially available microprocessor, and introducing x86-64, the widely adopted 64-bit extension to Intel's IA32. Although we will talk about Intel processors, our presentation holds just as well for the compatible processors produced by Intel's rivals.

Much of the complexity of x86 is not of concern to those interested in programs for the Linux operating system as generated by the GCC compiler. The memory model provided in the original 8086 and its extensions in the 80286 became obsolete with the i386. The original x87 floating-point instructions became obsolete

Aside   Moore's Law

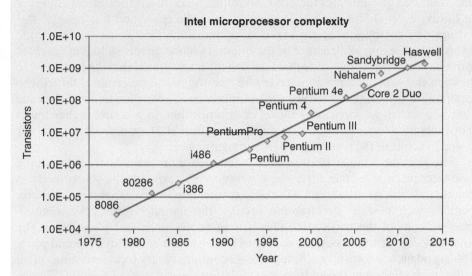

If we plot the number of transistors in the different Intel processors versus the year of introduction, and use a logarithmic scale for the y-axis, we can see that the growth has been phenomenal. Fitting a line through the data, we see that the number of transistors increases at an annual rate of approximately 37%, meaning that the number of transistors doubles about every 26 months. This growth has been sustained over the multiple-decade history of x86 microprocessors.

In 1965, Gordon Moore, a founder of Intel Corporation, extrapolated from the chip technology of the day (by which they could fabricate circuits with around 64 transistors on a single chip) to predict that the number of transistors per chip would double every year for the next 10 years. This prediction became known as *Moore's Law*. As it turns out, his prediction was just a little bit optimistic, but also too short-sighted. Over more than 50 years, the semiconductor industry has been able to double transistor counts on average every 18 months.

Similar exponential growth rates have occurred for other aspects of computer technology, including the storage capacities of magnetic disks and semiconductor memories. These remarkable growth rates have been the major driving forces of the computer revolution.

with the introduction of SSE2. Although we see vestiges of the historical evolution of x86 in x86-64 programs, many of the most arcane features of x86 do not appear.

3.2   Program Encodings

Suppose we write a C program as two files p1.c and p2.c. We can then compile this code using a Unix command line:

```
linux> gcc -Og -o p p1.c p2.c
```

The command gcc indicates the GCC C compiler. Since this is the default compiler on Linux, we could also invoke it as simply cc. The command-line option -Og[1] instructs the compiler to apply a level of optimization that yields machine code that follows the overall structure of the original C code. Invoking higher levels of optimization can generate code that is so heavily transformed that the relationship between the generated machine code and the original source code is difficult to understand. We will therefore use -Og optimization as a learning tool and then see what happens as we increase the level of optimization. In practice, higher levels of optimization (e.g., specified with the option -O1 or -O2) are considered a better choice in terms of the resulting program performance.

The gcc command invokes an entire sequence of programs to turn the source code into executable code. First, the C *preprocessor* expands the source code to include any files specified with #include commands and to expand any macros, specified with #define declarations. Second, the *compiler* generates assembly-code versions of the two source files having names p1.s and p2.s. Next, the *assembler* converts the assembly code into binary *object-code* files p1.o and p2.o. Object code is one form of machine code—it contains binary representations of all of the instructions, but the addresses of global values are not yet filled in. Finally, the *linker* merges these two object-code files along with code implementing library functions (e.g., printf) and generates the final executable code file p (as specified by the command-line directive -o p). Executable code is the second form of machine code we will consider—it is the exact form of code that is executed by the processor. The relation between these different forms of machine code and the linking process is described in more detail in Chapter 7.

3.2.1 Machine-Level Code

As described in Section 1.9.3, computer systems employ several different forms of abstraction, hiding details of an implementation through the use of a simpler abstract model. Two of these are especially important for machine-level programming. First, the format and behavior of a machine-level program is defined by the *instruction set architecture*, or ISA, defining the processor state, the format of the instructions, and the effect each of these instructions will have on the state. Most ISAs, including x86-64, describe the behavior of a program as if each instruction is executed in sequence, with one instruction completing before the next one begins. The processor hardware is far more elaborate, executing many instructions concurrently, but it employs safeguards to ensure that the overall behavior matches the sequential operation dictated by the ISA. Second, the memory addresses used by a machine-level program are *virtual addresses*, providing a memory model that

---

1. This optimization level was introduced in GCC version 4.8. Earlier versions of GCC, as well as non-GNU compilers, will not recognize this option. For these, using optimization level one (specified with the command-line flag -O1) is probably the best choice for generating code that follows the original program structure.

appears to be a very large byte array. The actual implementation of the memory system involves a combination of multiple hardware memories and operating system software, as described in Chapter 9.

The compiler does most of the work in the overall compilation sequence, transforming programs expressed in the relatively abstract execution model provided by C into the very elementary instructions that the processor executes. The assembly-code representation is very close to machine code. Its main feature is that it is in a more readable textual format, as compared to the binary format of machine code. Being able to understand assembly code and how it relates to the original C code is a key step in understanding how computers execute programs.

The machine code for x86-64 differs greatly from the original C code. Parts of the processor state are visible that normally are hidden from the C programmer:

- The *program counter* (commonly referred to as the PC, and called %rip in x86-64) indicates the address in memory of the next instruction to be executed.

- The integer *register file* contains 16 named locations storing 64-bit values. These registers can hold addresses (corresponding to C pointers) or integer data. Some registers are used to keep track of critical parts of the program state, while others are used to hold temporary data, such as the arguments and local variables of a procedure, as well as the value to be returned by a function.

- The condition code registers hold status information about the most recently executed arithmetic or logical instruction. These are used to implement conditional changes in the control or data flow, such as is required to implement if and while statements.

- A set of vector registers can each hold one or more integer or floating-point values.

Whereas C provides a model in which objects of different data types can be declared and allocated in memory, machine code views the memory as simply a large byte-addressable array. Aggregate data types in C such as arrays and structures are represented in machine code as contiguous collections of bytes. Even for scalar data types, assembly code makes no distinctions between signed or unsigned integers, between different types of pointers, or even between pointers and integers.

The program memory contains the executable machine code for the program, some information required by the operating system, a run-time stack for managing procedure calls and returns, and blocks of memory allocated by the user (e.g., by using the malloc library function). As mentioned earlier, the program memory is addressed using virtual addresses. At any given time, only limited subranges of virtual addresses are considered valid. For example, x86-64 virtual addresses are represented by 64-bit words. In current implementations of these machines, the upper 16 bits must be set to zero, and so an address can potentially specify a byte over a range of 2^{48}, or 64 terabytes. More typical programs will only have access to a few megabytes, or perhaps several gigabytes. The operating system manages

Aside The ever-changing forms of generated code

In our presentation, we will show the code generated by a particular version of GCC with particular settings of the command-line options. If you compile code on your own machine, chances are you will be using a different compiler or a different version of GCC and hence will generate different code. The open-source community supporting GCC keeps changing the code generator, attempting to generate more efficient code according to changing code guidelines provided by the microprocessor manufacturers.

Our goal in studying the examples shown in our presentation is to demonstrate how to examine assembly code and map it back to the constructs found in high-level programming languages. You will need to adapt these techniques to the style of code generated by your particular compiler.

this virtual address space, translating virtual addresses into the physical addresses of values in the actual processor memory.

A single machine instruction performs only a very elementary operation. For example, it might add two numbers stored in registers, transfer data between memory and a register, or conditionally branch to a new instruction address. The compiler must generate sequences of such instructions to implement program constructs such as arithmetic expression evaluation, loops, or procedure calls and returns.

3.2.2 Code Examples

Suppose we write a C code file `mstore.c` containing the following function definition:

```
long mult2(long, long);

void multstore(long x, long y, long *dest) {
    long t = mult2(x, y);
    *dest = t;
}
```

To see the assembly code generated by the C compiler, we can use the -S option on the command line:

```
linux> gcc -Og -S mstore.c
```

This will cause GCC to run the compiler, generating an assembly file `mstore.s`, and go no further. (Normally it would then invoke the assembler to generate an object-code file.)

The assembly-code file contains various declarations, including the following set of lines:

```
multstore:
  pushq   %rbx
```

```
movq    %rdx, %rbx
call    mult2
movq    %rax, (%rbx)
popq    %rbx
ret
```

Each indented line in the code corresponds to a single machine instruction. For example, the pushq instruction indicates that the contents of register %rbx should be pushed onto the program stack. All information about local variable names or data types has been stripped away.

If we use the –c command-line option, GCC will both compile and assemble the code

linux> *gcc -Og -c mstore.c*

This will generate an object-code file mstore.o that is in binary format and hence cannot be viewed directly. Embedded within the 1,368 bytes of the file mstore.o is a 14-byte sequence with the hexadecimal representation

53 48 89 d3 e8 00 00 00 00 48 89 03 5b c3

This is the object code corresponding to the assembly instructions listed previously. A key lesson to learn from this is that the program executed by the machine is simply a sequence of bytes encoding a series of instructions. The machine has very little information about the source code from which these instructions were generated.

To inspect the contents of machine-code files, a class of programs known as *disassemblers* can be invaluable. These programs generate a format similar to assembly code from the machine code. With Linux systems, the program OBJDUMP (for "object dump") can serve this role given the –d command-line flag:

linux> *objdump -d mstore.o*

The result (where we have added line numbers on the left and annotations in italicized text) is as follows:

```
          Disassembly of function sum in binary file mstore.o
1    0000000000000000 <multstore>:
     Offset  Bytes                    Equivalent assembly language
2      0:    53                       push    %rbx
3      1:    48 89 d3                 mov     %rdx,%rbx
4      4:    e8 00 00 00 00           callq   9 <multstore+0x9>
5      9:    48 89 03                 mov     %rax,(%rbx)
6      c:    5b                       pop     %rbx
7      d:    c3                       retq
```

On the left we see the 14 hexadecimal byte values, listed in the byte sequence shown earlier, partitioned into groups of 1 to 5 bytes each. Each of these groups is a single instruction, with the assembly-language equivalent shown on the right.

Several features about machine code and its disassembled representation are worth noting:

- x86-64 instructions can range in length from 1 to 15 bytes. The instruction encoding is designed so that commonly used instructions and those with fewer operands require a smaller number of bytes than do less common ones or ones with more operands.

- The instruction format is designed in such a way that from a given starting position, there is a unique decoding of the bytes into machine instructions. For example, only the instruction pushq %rbx can start with byte value 53.

- The disassembler determines the assembly code based purely on the byte sequences in the machine-code file. It does not require access to the source or assembly-code versions of the program.

- The disassembler uses a slightly different naming convention for the instructions than does the assembly code generated by GCC. In our example, it has omitted the suffix 'q' from many of the instructions. These suffixes are size designators and can be omitted in most cases. Conversely, the disassembler adds the suffix 'q' to the call and ret instructions. Again, these suffixes can safely be omitted.

Generating the actual executable code requires running a linker on the set of object-code files, one of which must contain a function main. Suppose in file main.c we had the following function:

```c
#include <stdio.h>

void multstore(long, long, long *);

int main() {
    long d;
    multstore(2, 3, &d);
    printf("2 * 3 --> %ld\n", d);
    return 0;
}
```

```
long mult2(long a, long b) {
    long s = a * b;
    return s;
}
```

Then we could generate an executable program `prog` as follows:

```
linux> gcc -Og -o prog main.c mstore.c
```

The file `prog` has grown to 8,655 bytes, since it contains not just the machine code for the procedures we provided but also code used to start and terminate the program as well as to interact with the operating system.

   We can disassemble the file `prog`:

```
linux> objdump -d prog
```

The disassembler will extract various code sequences, including the following:

```
    Disassembly of function sum in binary file prog
1   0000000000400540 <multstore>:
2     400540:  53                 push   %rbx
3     400541:  48 89 d3           mov    %rdx,%rbx
4     400544:  e8 42 00 00 00     callq  40058b <mult2>
5     400549:  48 89 03           mov    %rax,(%rbx)
6     40054c:  5b                 pop    %rbx
7     40054d:  c3                 retq
8     40054e:  90                 nop
9     40054f:  90                 nop
```

This code is almost identical to that generated by the disassembly of `mstore.c`. One important difference is that the addresses listed along the left are different—the linker has shifted the location of this code to a different range of addresses. A second difference is that the linker has filled in the address that the `callq` instruction should use in calling the function `mult2` (line 4 of the disassembly). One task for the linker is to match function calls with the locations of the executable code for those functions. A final difference is that we see two additional lines of code (lines 8–9). These instructions will have no effect on the program, since they occur after the return instruction (line 7). They have been inserted to grow the code for the function to 16 bytes, enabling a better placement of the next block of code in terms of memory system performance.

3.2.3 Notes on Formatting

The assembly code generated by GCC is difficult for a human to read. On one hand, it contains information with which we need not be concerned, while on the other hand, it does not provide any description of the program or how it works. For example, suppose we give the command

```
linux> gcc -Og -S mstore.c
```

to generate the file `mstore.s`. The full content of the file is as follows:

```
        .file    "010-mstore.c"
        .text
        .globl   multstore
        .type    multstore, @function
multstore:
        pushq    %rbx
        movq     %rdx, %rbx
        call     mult2
        movq     %rax, (%rbx)
        popq     %rbx
        ret
        .size    multstore, .-multstore
        .ident   "GCC: (Ubuntu 4.8.1-2ubuntu1~12.04) 4.8.1"
        .section        .note.GNU-stack,"",@progbits
```

All of the lines beginning with '.' are directives to guide the assembler and linker. We can generally ignore these. On the other hand, there are no explanatory remarks about what the instructions do or how they relate to the source code.

To provide a clearer presentation of assembly code, we will show it in a form that omits most of the directives, while including line numbers and explanatory annotations. For our example, an annotated version would appear as follows:

```
     void multstore(long x, long y, long *dest)
     x in %rdi, y in %rsi, dest in %rdx
1    multstore:
2        pushq    %rbx                   Save %rbx
3        movq     %rdx, %rbx             Copy dest to %rbx
4        call     mult2                  Call mult2(x, y)
5        movq     %rax, (%rbx)           Store result at *dest
6        popq     %rbx                   Restore %rbx
7        ret                             Return
```

We typically show only the lines of code relevant to the point being discussed. Each line is numbered on the left for reference and annotated on the right by a brief description of the effect of the instruction and how it relates to the computations of the original C code. This is a stylized version of the way assembly-language programmers format their code.

We also provide Web asides to cover material intended for dedicated machine-language enthusiasts. One Web aside describes IA32 machine code. Having a background in x86-64 makes learning IA32 fairly simple. Another Web aside gives a brief presentation of ways to incorporate assembly code into C programs. For some applications, the programmer must drop down to assembly code to access low-level features of the machine. One approach is to write entire functions in assembly code and combine them with C functions during the linking stage. A

Aside ATT versus Intel assembly-code formats

In our presentation, we show assembly code in ATT format (named after AT&T, the company that operated Bell Laboratories for many years), the default format for GCC, OBJDUMP, and the other tools we will consider. Other programming tools, including those from Microsoft as well as the documentation from Intel, show assembly code in *Intel* format. The two formats differ in a number of ways. As an example, GCC can generate code in Intel format for the sum function using the following command line:

```
linux> gcc -Og -S -masm=intel mstore.c
```

This gives the following assembly code:

```
multstore:
  push    rbx
  mov     rbx, rdx
  call    mult2
  mov     QWORD PTR [rbx], rax
  pop     rbx
  ret
```

We see that the Intel and ATT formats differ in the following ways:

- The Intel code omits the size designation suffixes. We see instruction push and mov instead of pushq and movq.
- The Intel code omits the '%' character in front of register names, using rbx instead of %rbx.
- The Intel code has a different way of describing locations in memory—for example, QWORD PTR [rbx] rather than (%rbx).
- Instructions with multiple operands list them in the reverse order. This can be very confusing when switching between the two formats.

Although we will not be using Intel format in our presentation, you will encounter it in documentation from Intel and Microsoft.

second is to use GCC's support for embedding assembly code directly within C programs.

3.3 Data Formats

Due to its origins as a 16-bit architecture that expanded into a 32-bit one, Intel uses the term "word" to refer to a 16-bit data type. Based on this, they refer to 32-bit quantities as "double words," and 64-bit quantities as "quad words." Figure 3.1 shows the x86-64 representations used for the primitive data types of C. Standard int values are stored as double words (32 bits). Pointers (shown here as char *) are stored as 8-byte quad words, as would be expected in a 64-bit machine. With x86-64, data type long is implemented with 64 bits, allowing a very wide range of values. Most of our code examples in this chapter use pointers and long data

Web Aside ASM:EASM Combining assembly code with C programs

Although a C compiler does a good job of converting the computations expressed in a program into machine code, there are some features of a machine that cannot be accessed by a C program. For example, every time an x86-64 processor executes an arithmetic or logical operation, it sets a 1-bit *condition code* flag, named PF (for "parity flag"), to 1 when the lower 8 bits in the resulting computation have an even number of ones and to 0 otherwise. Computing this information in C requires at least seven shifting, masking, and EXCLUSIVE-OR operations (see Problem 2.65). Even though the hardware performs this computation as part of every arithmetic or logical operation, there is no way for a C program to determine the value of the PF condition code flag. This task can readily be performed by incorporating a small number of assembly-code instructions into the program.

There are two ways to incorporate assembly code into C programs. First, we can write an entire function as a separate assembly-code file and let the assembler and linker combine this with code we have written in C. Second, we can use the *inline assembly* feature of GCC, where brief sections of assembly code can be incorporated into a C program using the asm directive. This approach has the advantage that it minimizes the amount of machine-specific code.

Of course, including assembly code in a C program makes the code specific to a particular class of machines (such as x86-64), and so it should only be used when the desired feature can only be accessed in this way.

C declaration	Intel data type	Assembly-code suffix	Size (bytes)
char	Byte	b	1
short	Word	w	2
int	Double word	l	4
long	Quad word	q	8
char *	Quad word	q	8
float	Single precision	s	4
double	Double precision	l	8

Figure 3.1 Sizes of C data types in x86-64. With a 64-bit machine, pointers are 8 bytes long.

types, and so they will operate on quad words. The x86-64 instruction set includes a full complement of instructions for bytes, words, and double words as well.

Floating-point numbers come in two principal formats: single-precision (4-byte) values, corresponding to C data type float, and double-precision (8-byte) values, corresponding to C data type double. Microprocessors in the x86 family historically implemented all floating-point operations with a special 80-bit (10-byte) floating-point format (see Problem 2.86). This format can be specified in C programs using the declaration long double. We recommend against using this format, however. It is not portable to other classes of machines, and it is typically not implemented with the same high-performance hardware as is the case for single- and double-precision arithmetic.

As the table of Figure 3.1 indicates, most assembly-code instructions generated by GCC have a single-character suffix denoting the size of the operand. For example, the data movement instruction has four variants: movb (move byte), movw (move word), movl (move double word), and movq (move quad word). The suffix '1' is used for double words, since 32-bit quantities are considered to be "long words." The assembly code uses the suffix '1' to denote a 4-byte integer as well as an 8-byte double-precision floating-point number. This causes no ambiguity, since floating-point code involves an entirely different set of instructions and registers.

3.4   Accessing Information

An x86-64 central processing unit (CPU) contains a set of 16 *general-purpose registers* storing 64-bit values. These registers are used to store integer data as well as pointers. Figure 3.2 diagrams the 16 registers. Their names all begin with %r, but otherwise follow multiple different naming conventions, owing to the historical evolution of the instruction set. The original 8086 had eight 16-bit registers, shown in Figure 3.2 as registers %ax through %bp. Each had a specific purpose, and hence they were given names that reflected how they were to be used. With the extension to IA32, these registers were expanded to 32-bit registers, labeled %eax through %ebp. In the extension to x86-64, the original eight registers were expanded to 64 bits, labeled %rax through %rbp. In addition, eight new registers were added, and these were given labels according to a new naming convention: %r8 through %r15.

As the nested boxes in Figure 3.2 indicate, instructions can operate on data of different sizes stored in the low-order bytes of the 16 registers. Byte-level operations can access the least significant byte, 16-bit operations can access the least significant 2 bytes, 32-bit operations can access the least significant 4 bytes, and 64-bit operations can access entire registers.

In later sections, we will present a number of instructions for copying and generating 1-, 2-, 4-, and 8-byte values. When these instructions have registers as destinations, two conventions arise for what happens to the remaining bytes in the register for instructions that generate less than 8 bytes: Those that generate 1- or 2-byte quantities leave the remaining bytes unchanged. Those that generate 4-byte quantities set the upper 4 bytes of the register to zero. The latter convention was adopted as part of the expansion from IA32 to x86-64.

As the annotations along the right-hand side of Figure 3.2 indicate, different registers serve different roles in typical programs. Most unique among them is the stack pointer, %rsp, used to indicate the end position in the run-time stack. Some instructions specifically read and write this register. The other 15 registers have more flexibility in their uses. A small number of instructions make specific use of certain registers. More importantly, a set of standard programming conventions governs how the registers are to be used for managing the stack, passing function

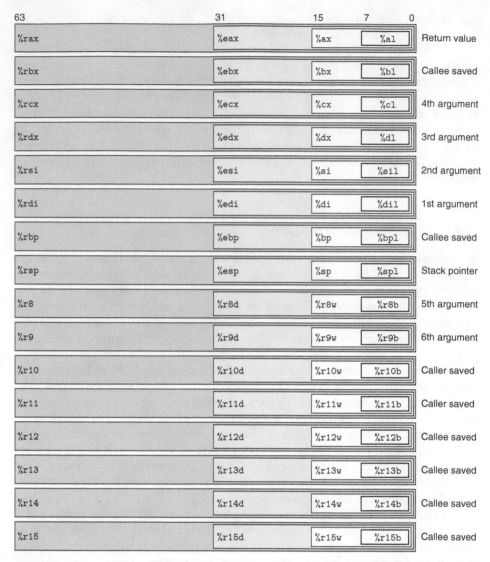

Figure 3.2 Integer registers. The low-order portions of all 16 registers can be accessed as byte, word (16-bit), double word (32-bit), and quad word (64-bit) quantities.

arguments, returning values from functions, and storing local and temporary data. We will cover these conventions in our presentation, especially in Section 3.7, where we describe the implementation of procedures.

3.4.1 Operand Specifiers

Most instructions have one or more *operands* specifying the source values to use in performing an operation and the destination location into which to place the

Type	Form	Operand value	Name
Immediate	$\$Imm$	Imm	Immediate
Register	r_a	$R[r_a]$	Register
Memory	Imm	$M[Imm]$	Absolute
Memory	(r_a)	$M[R[r_a]]$	Indirect
Memory	$Imm(r_b)$	$M[Imm + R[r_b]]$	Base + displacement
Memory	(r_b, r_i)	$M[R[r_b] + R[r_i]]$	Indexed
Memory	$Imm(r_b, r_i)$	$M[Imm + R[r_b] + R[r_i]]$	Indexed
Memory	$(, r_i, s)$	$M[R[r_i] \cdot s]$	Scaled indexed
Memory	$Imm(, r_i, s)$	$M[Imm + R[r_i] \cdot s]$	Scaled indexed
Memory	(r_b, r_i, s)	$M[R[r_b] + R[r_i] \cdot s]$	Scaled indexed
Memory	$Imm(r_b, r_i, s)$	$M[Imm + R[r_b] + R[r_i] \cdot s]$	Scaled indexed

Figure 3.3   Operand forms. Operands can denote immediate (constant) values, register values, or values from memory. The scaling factor s must be either 1, 2, 4, or 8.

result. x86-64 supports a number of operand forms (see Figure 3.3). Source values can be given as constants or read from registers or memory. Results can be stored in either registers or memory. Thus, the different operand possibilities can be classified into three types. The first type, *immediate*, is for constant values. In ATT-format assembly code, these are written with a '$' followed by an integer using standard C notation—for example, $-577 or $0x1F. Different instructions allow different ranges of immediate values; the assembler will automatically select the most compact way of encoding a value. The second type, *register*, denotes the contents of a register, one of the sixteen 8-, 4-, 2-, or 1-byte low-order portions of the registers for operands having 64, 32, 16, or 8 bits, respectively. In Figure 3.3, we use the notation r_a to denote an arbitrary register a and indicate its value with the reference $R[r_a]$, viewing the set of registers as an array R indexed by register identifiers.

The third type of operand is a *memory* reference, in which we access some memory location according to a computed address, often called the *effective address*. Since we view the memory as a large array of bytes, we use the notation $M_b[Addr]$ to denote a reference to the b-byte value stored in memory starting at address $Addr$. To simplify things, we will generally drop the subscript b.

As Figure 3.3 shows, there are many different *addressing modes* allowing different forms of memory references. The most general form is shown at the bottom of the table with syntax $Imm(r_b, r_i, s)$. Such a reference has four components: an immediate offset Imm, a base register r_b, an index register r_i, and a scale factor s, where s must be 1, 2, 4, or 8. Both the base and index must be 64-bit registers. The effective address is computed as $Imm + R[r_b] + R[r_i] \cdot s$. This general form is often seen when referencing elements of arrays. The other forms are simply special cases of this general form where some of the components are omitted. As we will see, the more complex addressing modes are useful when referencing array and structure elements.

Practice Problem 3.1 (solution page 325)

Assume the following values are stored at the indicated memory addresses and registers:

Address	Value	Register	Value
0x100	0xFF	%rax	0x100
0x104	0xAB	%rcx	0x1
0x108	0x13	%rdx	0x3
0x10C	0x11		

Fill in the following table showing the values for the indicated operands:

Operand	Value
%rax	_____
0x104	_____
$0x108	_____
(%rax)	_____
4(%rax)	_____
9(%rax,%rdx)	_____
260(%rcx,%rdx)	_____
0xFC(,%rcx,4)	_____
(%rax,%rdx,4)	_____

3.4.2 Data Movement Instructions

Among the most heavily used instructions are those that copy data from one location to another. The generality of the operand notation allows a simple data movement instruction to express a range of possibilities that in many machines would require a number of different instructions. We present a number of different data movement instructions, differing in their source and destination types, what conversions they perform, and other side effects they may have. In our presentation, we group the many different instructions into *instruction classes*, where the instructions in a class perform the same operation but with different operand sizes.

Figure 3.4 lists the simplest form of data movement instructions—MOV class. These instructions copy data from a source location to a destination location, without any transformation. The class consists of four instructions: movb, movw, movl, and movq. All four of these instructions have similar effects; they differ primarily in that they operate on data of different sizes: 1, 2, 4, and 8 bytes, respectively.

Instruction		Effect	Description
MOV	*S, D*	*D ← S*	Move
movb			Move byte
movw			Move word
movl			Move double word
movq			Move quad word
movabsq	*I, R*	*R ← I*	Move absolute quad word

Figure 3.4   Simple data movement instructions.

The source operand designates a value that is immediate, stored in a register, or stored in memory. The destination operand designates a location that is either a register or a memory address. x86-64 imposes the restriction that a move instruction cannot have both operands refer to memory locations. Copying a value from one memory location to another requires two instructions—the first to load the source value into a register, and the second to write this register value to the destination. Referring to Figure 3.2, register operands for these instructions can be the labeled portions of any of the 16 registers, where the size of the register must match the size designated by the last character of the instruction ('b', 'w', 'l', or 'q'). For most cases, the MOV instructions will only update the specific register bytes or memory locations indicated by the destination operand. The only exception is that when movl has a register as the destination, it will also set the high-order 4 bytes of the register to 0. This exception arises from the convention, adopted in x86-64, that any instruction that generates a 32-bit value for a register also sets the high-order portion of the register to 0.

The following MOV instruction examples show the five possible combinations of source and destination types. Recall that the source operand comes first and the destination second.

```
1    movl $0x4050,%eax        Immediate--Register, 4 bytes
2    movw %bp,%sp             Register--Register, 2 bytes
3    movb (%rdi,%rcx),%al     Memory--Register,   1 byte
4    movb $-17,(%esp)         Immediate--Memory,  1 byte
5    movq %rax,-12(%rbp)      Register--Memory,   8 bytes
```

A final instruction documented in Figure 3.4 is for dealing with 64-bit immediate data. The regular movq instruction can only have immediate source operands that can be represented as 32-bit two's-complement numbers. This value is then sign extended to produce the 64-bit value for the destination. The movabsq instruction can have an arbitrary 64-bit immediate value as its source operand and can only have a register as a destination.

Figures 3.5 and 3.6 document two classes of data movement instructions for use when copying a smaller source value to a larger destination. All of these instructions copy data from a source, which can be either a register or stored

Aside   Understanding how data movement changes a destination register

As described, there are two different conventions regarding whether and how data movement instructions modify the upper bytes of a destination register. This distinction is illustrated by the following code sequence:

```
1    movabsq   $0x0011223344556677, %rax      %rax = 0011223344556677
2    movb      $-1, %al                        %rax = 00112233445566FF
3    movw      $-1, %ax                        %rax = 001122334455FFFF
4    movl      $-1, %eax                       %rax = 00000000FFFFFFFF
5    movq      $-1, %rax                       %rax = FFFFFFFFFFFFFFFF
```

In the following discussion, we use hexadecimal notation. In the example, the instruction on line 1 initializes register %rax to the pattern 0011223344556677. The remaining instructions have immediate value -1 as their source values. Recall that the hexadecimal representation of -1 is of the form FF$\cdots$F, where the number of F's is twice the number of bytes in the representation. The movb instruction (line 2) therefore sets the low-order byte of %rax to FF, while the movw instruction (line 3) sets the low-order 2 bytes to FFFF, with the remaining bytes unchanged. The movl instruction (line 4) sets the low-order 4 bytes to FFFFFFFF, but it also sets the high-order 4 bytes to 00000000. Finally, the movq instruction (line 5) sets the complete register to FFFFFFFFFFFFFFFF.

Instruction	Effect		Description
MOVZ S, R	$R \leftarrow$	ZeroExtend(S)	Move with zero extension
movzbw			Move zero-extended byte to word
movzbl			Move zero-extended byte to double word
movzwl			Move zero-extended word to double word
movzbq			Move zero-extended byte to quad word
movzwq			Move zero-extended word to quad word

Figure 3.5   Zero-extending data movement instructions. These instructions have a register or memory location as the source and a register as the destination.

in memory, to a register destination. Instructions in the MOVZ class fill out the remaining bytes of the destination with zeros, while those in the MOVS class fill them out by sign extension, replicating copies of the most significant bit of the source operand. Observe that each instruction name has size designators as its final two characters—the first specifying the source size, and the second specifying the destination size. As can be seen, there are three instructions in each of these classes, covering all cases of 1- and 2-byte source sizes and 2- and 4-byte destination sizes, considering only cases where the destination is larger than the source, of course.

Instruction	Effect	Description
MOVS S, R	$R \leftarrow$ SignExtend(S)	Move with sign extension
movsbw		Move sign-extended byte to word
movsbl		Move sign-extended byte to double word
movswl		Move sign-extended word to double word
movsbq		Move sign-extended byte to quad word
movswq		Move sign-extended word to quad word
movslq		Move sign-extended double word to quad word
cltq	$\%rax \leftarrow$ SignExtend($\%eax$)	Sign-extend %eax to %rax

Figure 3.6 Sign-extending data movement instructions. The MOVS instructions have a register or memory location as the source and a register as the destination. The cltq instruction is specific to registers %eax and %rax.

Note the absence of an explicit instruction to zero-extend a 4-byte source value to an 8-byte destination in Figure 3.5. Such an instruction would logically be named movzlq, but this instruction does not exist. Instead, this type of data movement can be implemented using a movl instruction having a register as the destination. This technique takes advantage of the property that an instruction generating a 4-byte value with a register as the destination will fill the upper 4 bytes with zeros. Otherwise, for 64-bit destinations, moving with sign extension is supported for all three source types, and moving with zero extension is supported for the two smaller source types.

Figure 3.6 also documents the cltq instruction. This instruction has no operands—it always uses register %eax as its source and %rax as the destination for the sign-extended result. It therefore has the exact same effect as the instruction movslq %eax, %rax, but it has a more compact encoding.

Practice Problem 3.2 (solution page 325)

For each of the following lines of assembly language, determine the appropriate instruction suffix based on the operands. (For example, mov can be rewritten as movb, movw, movl, or movq.)

```
mov___    %eax, (%rsp)
mov___    (%rax), %dx
mov___    $0xFF, %bl
mov___    (%rsp,%rdx,4), %dl
mov___    (%rdx), %rax
mov___    %dx, (%rax)
```

Aside   Comparing byte movement instructions

The following example illustrates how different data movement instructions either do or do not change the high-order bytes of the destination. Observe that the three byte-movement instructions movb, movsbq, and movzbq differ from each other in subtle ways. Here is an example:

```
1    movabsq $0x0011223344556677, %rax    %rax = 0011223344556677
2    movb    $0xAA, %dl                    %dl  = AA
3    movb %dl,%al                          %rax = 00112233445566AA
4    movsbq %dl,%rax                       %rax = FFFFFFFFFFFFFFAA
5    movzbq %dl,%rax                       %rax = 00000000000000AA
```

In the following discussion, we use hexadecimal notation for all of the values. The first two lines of the code initialize registers %rax and %dl to 0011223344556677 and AA, respectively. The remaining instructions all copy the low-order byte of %rdx to the low-order byte of %rax. The movb instruction (line 3) does not change the other bytes. The movsbq instruction (line 4) sets the other 7 bytes to either all ones or all zeros depending on the high-order bit of the source byte. Since hexadecimal A represents binary value 1010, sign extension causes the higher-order bytes to each be set to FF. The movzbq instruction (line 5) always sets the other 7 bytes to zero.

Practice Problem 3.3 (solution page 326)

Each of the following lines of code generates an error message when we invoke the assembler. Explain what is wrong with each line.

```
movb $0xF, (%ebx)
movl %rax, (%rsp)
movw (%rax),4(%rsp)
movb %al,%sl
movq %rax,$0x123
movl %eax,%rdx
movb %si, 8(%rbp)
```

3.4.3   Data Movement Example

As an example of code that uses data movement instructions, consider the data exchange routine shown in Figure 3.7, both as C code and as assembly code generated by GCC.

As Figure 3.7(b) shows, function exchange is implemented with just three instructions: two data movements (movq) plus an instruction to return back to the point from which the function was called (ret). We will cover the details of function call and return in Section 3.7. Until then, it suffices to say that arguments are passed to functions in registers. Our annotated assembly code documents these. A function returns a value by storing it in register %rax, or in one of the low-order portions of this register.

(a) C code

```
long exchange(long *xp, long y)
{
    long x = *xp;
    *xp = y;
    return x;
}
```

(b) Assembly code

```
    long exchange(long *xp, long y)
    xp in %rdi, y in %rsi
1   exchange:
2     movq    (%rdi), %rax    Get x at xp. Set as return value.
3     movq    %rsi, (%rdi)    Store y at xp.
4     ret                     Return.
```

Figure 3.7 C and assembly code for exchange routine. Registers %rdi and %rsi hold parameters xp and y, respectively.

When the procedure begins execution, procedure parameters xp and y are stored in registers %rdi and %rsi, respectively. Instruction 2 then reads x from memory and stores the value in register %rax, a direct implementation of the operation x = *xp in the C program. Later, register %rax will be used to return a value from the function, and so the return value will be x. Instruction 3 writes y to the memory location designated by xp in register %rdi, a direct implementation of the operation *xp = y. This example illustrates how the MOV instructions can be used to read from memory to a register (line 2), and to write from a register to memory (line 3).

Two features about this assembly code are worth noting. First, we see that what we call "pointers" in C are simply addresses. Dereferencing a pointer involves copying that pointer into a register, and then using this register in a memory reference. Second, local variables such as x are often kept in registers rather than stored in memory locations. Register access is much faster than memory access.

Practice Problem 3.4 (solution page 326)

Assume variables sp and dp are declared with types

```
src_t  *sp;
dest_t *dp;
```

where src_t and dest_t are data types declared with typedef. We wish to use the appropriate pair of data movement instructions to implement the operation

```
*dp = (dest_t) *sp;
```

New to C?   Some examples of pointers

Function exchange (Figure 3.7(a)) provides a good illustration of the use of pointers in C. Argument xp is a pointer to a long integer, while y is a long integer itself. The statement

```
long x = *xp;
```

indicates that we should read the value stored in the location designated by xp and store it as a local variable named x. This read operation is known as pointer *dereferencing*. The C operator '*' performs pointer dereferencing.

The statement

```
*xp = y;
```

does the reverse—it writes the value of parameter y at the location designated by xp. This is also a form of pointer dereferencing (and hence the operator *), but it indicates a write operation since it is on the left-hand side of the assignment.

The following is an example of exchange in action:

```
long a = 4;
long b = exchange(&a, 3);
printf("a = %ld, b = %ld\verb@\@n", a, b);
```

This code will print

```
a = 3, b = 4
```

The C operator '&' (called the "address of" operator) *creates* a pointer, in this case to the location holding local variable a. Function exchange overwrites the value stored in a with 3 but returns the previous value, 4, as the function value. Observe how by passing a pointer to exchange, it could modify data held at some remote location.

Assume that the values of sp and dp are stored in registers %rdi and %rsi, respectively. For each entry in the table, show the two instructions that implement the specified data movement. The first instruction in the sequence should read from memory, do the appropriate conversion, and set the appropriate portion of register %rax. The second instruction should then write the appropriate portion of %rax to memory. In both cases, the portions may be %rax, %eax, %ax, or %al, and they may differ from one another.

Recall that when performing a cast that involves both a size change and a change of "signedness" in C, the operation should change the size first (Section 2.2.6).

src_t	dest_t	Instruction
long	long	movq (%rdi), %rax
		movq %rax, (%rsi)
char	int	_____
		_____

char	unsigned	_____
unsigned char	long	_____
int	char	_____
unsigned	unsigned char	_____
char	short	_____

Practice Problem 3.5 (solution page 327)

You are given the following information. A function with prototype

```
void decode1(long *xp, long *yp, long *zp);
```

is compiled into assembly code, yielding the following:

```
  void decode1(long *xp, long *yp, long *zp)
  xp in %rdi, yp in %rsi, zp in %rdx
decode1:
  movq    (%rdi), %r8
  movq    (%rsi), %rcx
  movq    (%rdx), %rax
  movq    %r8, (%rsi)
  movq    %rcx, (%rdx)
  movq    %rax, (%rdi)
  ret
```

Parameters xp, yp, and zp are stored in registers %rdi, %rsi, and %rdx, respectively.

Write C code for decode1 that will have an effect equivalent to the assembly code shown.

3.4.4 Pushing and Popping Stack Data

The final two data movement operations are used to push data onto and pop data from the program stack, as documented in Figure 3.8. As we will see, the stack plays a vital role in the handling of procedure calls. By way of background, a stack is a data structure where values can be added or deleted, but only according to a "last-in, first-out" discipline. We add data to a stack via a *push* operation and remove it via a *pop* operation, with the property that the value popped will always be the value that was most recently pushed and is still on the stack. A stack can be implemented as an array, where we always insert and remove elements from one

Instruction	Effect	Description
pushq *S*	R[%rsp] ← R[%rsp] − 8; M[R[%rsp]] ← *S*	Push quad word
popq *D*	*D* ← M[R[%rsp]]; R[%rsp] ← R[%rsp] + 8	Pop quad word

Figure 3.8 Push and pop instructions.

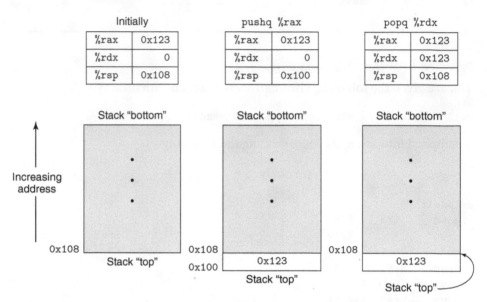

Figure 3.9 Illustration of stack operation. By convention, we draw stacks upside down, so that the "top" of the stack is shown at the bottom. With x86-64, stacks grow toward lower addresses, so pushing involves decrementing the stack pointer (register %rsp) and storing to memory, while popping involves reading from memory and incrementing the stack pointer.

end of the array. This end is called the *top* of the stack. With x86-64, the program stack is stored in some region of memory. As illustrated in Figure 3.9, the stack grows downward such that the top element of the stack has the lowest address of all stack elements. (By convention, we draw stacks upside down, with the stack "top" shown at the bottom of the figure.) The stack pointer %rsp holds the address of the top stack element.

The pushq instruction provides the ability to push data onto the stack, while the popq instruction pops it. Each of these instructions takes a single operand—the data source for pushing and the data destination for popping.

Pushing a quad word value onto the stack involves first decrementing the stack pointer by 8 and then writing the value at the new top-of-stack address.

Therefore, the behavior of the instruction pushq %rbp is equivalent to that of the pair of instructions

```
subq $8,%rsp          Decrement stack pointer
movq %rbp,(%rsp)      Store %rbp on stack
```

except that the pushq instruction is encoded in the machine code as a single byte, whereas the pair of instructions shown above requires a total of 8 bytes. The first two columns in Figure 3.9 illustrate the effect of executing the instruction pushq %rax when %rsp is 0x108 and %rax is 0x123. First %rsp is decremented by 8, giving 0x100, and then 0x123 is stored at memory address 0x100.

Popping a quad word involves reading from the top-of-stack location and then incrementing the stack pointer by 8. Therefore, the instruction popq %rax is equivalent to the following pair of instructions:

```
movq (%rsp),%rax      Read %rax from stack
addq $8,%rsp          Increment stack pointer
```

The third column of Figure 3.9 illustrates the effect of executing the instruction popq %edx immediately after executing the pushq. Value 0x123 is read from memory and written to register %rdx. Register %rsp is incremented back to 0x108. As shown in the figure, the value 0x123 remains at memory location 0x104 until it is overwritten (e.g., by another push operation). However, the stack top is always considered to be the address indicated by %rsp.

Since the stack is contained in the same memory as the program code and other forms of program data, programs can access arbitrary positions within the stack using the standard memory addressing methods. For example, assuming the topmost element of the stack is a quad word, the instruction movq 8(%rsp),%rdx will copy the second quad word from the stack to register %rdx.

3.5   Arithmetic and Logical Operations

Figure 3.10 lists some of the x86-64 integer and logic operations. Most of the operations are given as instruction classes, as they can have different variants with different operand sizes. (Only leaq has no other size variants.) For example, the instruction class ADD consists of four addition instructions: addb, addw, addl, and addq, adding bytes, words, double words, and quad words, respectively. Indeed, each of the instruction classes shown has instructions for operating on these four different sizes of data. The operations are divided into four groups: load effective address, unary, binary, and shifts. *Binary* operations have two operands, while *unary* operations have one operand. These operands are specified using the same notation as described in Section 3.4.

3.5.1   Load Effective Address

The *load effective address* instruction leaq is actually a variant of the movq instruction. It has the form of an instruction that reads from memory to a register,

Instruction		Effect	Description
leaq	S, D	$D \leftarrow \&S$	Load effective address
INC	D	$D \leftarrow D+1$	Increment
DEC	D	$D \leftarrow D-1$	Decrement
NEG	D	$D \leftarrow -D$	Negate
NOT	D	$D \leftarrow \sim D$	Complement
ADD	S, D	$D \leftarrow D + S$	Add
SUB	S, D	$D \leftarrow D - S$	Subtract
IMUL	S, D	$D \leftarrow D * S$	Multiply
XOR	S, D	$D \leftarrow D \,\hat{}\, S$	Exclusive-or
OR	S, D	$D \leftarrow D \mid S$	Or
AND	S, D	$D \leftarrow D \,\&\, S$	And
SAL	k, D	$D \leftarrow D << k$	Left shift
SHL	k, D	$D \leftarrow D << k$	Left shift (same as SAL)
SAR	k, D	$D \leftarrow D >>_A k$	Arithmetic right shift
SHR	k, D	$D \leftarrow D >>_L k$	Logical right shift

Figure 3.10 Integer arithmetic operations. The load effective address (leaq) instruction is commonly used to perform simple arithmetic. The remaining ones are more standard unary or binary operations. We use the notation $>>_A$ and $>>_L$ to denote arithmetic and logical right shift, respectively. Note the nonintuitive ordering of the operands with ATT-format assembly code.

but it does not reference memory at all. Its first operand appears to be a memory reference, but instead of reading from the designated location, the instruction copies the effective address to the destination. We indicate this computation in Figure 3.10 using the C address operator $\&S$. This instruction can be used to generate pointers for later memory references. In addition, it can be used to compactly describe common arithmetic operations. For example, if register %rdx contains value x, then the instruction leaq 7(%rdx,%rdx,4), %rax will set register %rax to $5x + 7$. Compilers often find clever uses of leaq that have nothing to do with effective address computations. The destination operand must be a register.

Practice Problem 3.6 (solution page 327)

Suppose register %rax holds value x and %rcx holds value y. Fill in the table below with formulas indicating the value that will be stored in register %rdx for each of the given assembly-code instructions:

Instruction	Result
leaq 6(%rax), %rdx	_____
leaq (%rax,%rcx), %rdx	_____
leaq (%rax,%rcx,4), %rdx	_____
leaq 7(%rax,%rax,8), %rdx	_____

```
leaq 0xA(,%rcx,4), %rdx        _____
leaq 9(%rax,%rcx,2), %rdx      _____
```

As an illustration of the use of `leaq` in compiled code, consider the following C program:

```
long scale(long x, long y, long z) {
    long t = x + 4 * y + 12 * z;
    return t;
}
```

When compiled, the arithmetic operations of the function are implemented by a sequence of three `leaq` functions, as is documented by the comments on the right-hand side:

```
long scale(long x, long y, long z)
 x in %rdi, y in %rsi, z in %rdx
scale:
  leaq    (%rdi,%rsi,4), %rax     x + 4*y
  leaq    (%rdx,%rdx,2), %rdx     z + 2*z = 3*z
  leaq    (%rax,%rdx,4), %rax     (x+4*y) + 4*(3*z) = x + 4*y + 12*z
  ret
```

The ability of the `leaq` instruction to perform addition and limited forms of multiplication proves useful when compiling simple arithmetic expressions such as this example.

Practice Problem 3.7 (solution page 328)

Consider the following code, in which we have omitted the expression being computed:

```
long scale2(long x, long y, long z) {
    long t = _____;
    return t;
}
```

Compiling the actual function with GCC yields the following assembly code:

```
long scale2(long x, long y, long z)
 x in %rdi, y in %rsi, z in %rdx
scale2:
  leaq    (%rdi,%rdi,4), %rax
  leaq    (%rax,%rsi,2), %rax
  leaq    (%rax,%rdx,8), %rax
  ret
```

Fill in the missing expression in the C code.

3.5.2   Unary and Binary Operations

Operations in the second group are unary operations, with the single operand serving as both source and destination. This operand can be either a register or a memory location. For example, the instruction incq (%rsp) causes the 8-byte element on the top of the stack to be incremented. This syntax is reminiscent of the C increment (++) and decrement (--) operators.

The third group consists of binary operations, where the second operand is used as both a source and a destination. This syntax is reminiscent of the C assignment operators, such as x -= y. Observe, however, that the source operand is given first and the destination second. This looks peculiar for noncommutative operations. For example, the instruction subq %rax,%rdx decrements register %rdx by the value in %rax. (It helps to read the instruction as "Subtract %rax from %rdx.") The first operand can be either an immediate value, a register, or a memory location. The second can be either a register or a memory location. As with the MOV instructions, the two operands cannot both be memory locations. Note that when the second operand is a memory location, the processor must read the value from memory, perform the operation, and then write the result back to memory.

Practice Problem 3.8 (solution page 328)

Assume the following values are stored at the indicated memory addresses and registers:

Address	Value		Register	Value
0x100	0xFF		%rax	0x100
0x108	0xAB		%rcx	0x1
0x110	0x13		%rdx	0x3
0x118	0x11			

Fill in the following table showing the effects of the following instructions, in terms of both the register or memory location that will be updated and the resulting value:

Instruction	Destination	Value
addq %rcx,(%rax)	_____	_____
subq %rdx,8(%rax)	_____	_____
imulq $16,(%rax,%rdx,8)	_____	_____
incq 16(%rax)	_____	_____
decq %rcx	_____	_____
subq %rdx,%rax	_____	_____

3.5.3   Shift Operations

The final group consists of shift operations, where the shift amount is given first and the value to shift is given second. Both arithmetic and logical right shifts are possible. The different shift instructions can specify the shift amount either as an immediate value or with the single-byte register %cl. (These instructions are unusual in only allowing this specific register as the operand.) In principle, having a 1-byte shift amount would make it possible to encode shift amounts ranging up to $2^8 - 1 = 255$. With x86-64, a shift instruction operating on data values that are w bits long determines the shift amount from the low-order m bits of register %cl, where $2^m = w$. The higher-order bits are ignored. So, for example, when register %cl has hexadecimal value 0xFF, then instruction salb would shift by 7, while salw would shift by 15, sall would shift by 31, and salq would shift by 63.

As Figure 3.10 indicates, there are two names for the left shift instruction: SAL and SHL. Both have the same effect, filling from the right with zeros. The right shift instructions differ in that SAR performs an arithmetic shift (fill with copies of the sign bit), whereas SHR performs a logical shift (fill with zeros). The destination operand of a shift operation can be either a register or a memory location. We denote the two different right shift operations in Figure 3.10 as $>>_A$ (arithmetic) and $>>_L$ (logical).

Practice Problem 3.9 (solution page 328)

Suppose we want to generate assembly code for the following C function:

```
long shift_left4_rightn(long x, long n)
{
    x <<= 4;
    x >>= n;
    return x;
}
```

The code that follows is a portion of the assembly code that performs the actual shifts and leaves the final value in register %rax. Two key instructions have been omitted. Parameters x and n are stored in registers %rdi and %rsi, respectively.

```
  long shift_left4_rightn(long x, long n)
  x in %rdi, n in %rsi
shift_left4_rightn:
  movq    %rdi, %rax      Get x
  _____          x <<= 4
  movl    %esi, %ecx      Get n (4 bytes)
  _____          x >>= n
```

Fill in the missing instructions, following the annotations on the right. The right shift should be performed arithmetically.

(a) C code

```
long arith(long x, long y, long z)
{
    long t1 = x ^ y;
    long t2 = z * 48;
    long t3 = t1 & 0x0F0F0F0F;
    long t4 = t2 - t3;
    return t4;
}
```

(b) Assembly code

```
     long arith(long x, long y, long z)
     x in %rdi, y in %rsi, z in %rdx
1    arith:
2      xorq    %rsi, %rdi              t1 = x ^ y
3      leaq    (%rdx,%rdx,2), %rax     3*z
4      salq    $4, %rax               t2 = 16 * (3*z) = 48*z
5      andl    $252645135, %edi       t3 = t1 & 0x0F0F0F0F
6      subq    %rdi, %rax             Return t2 - t3
7      ret
```

Figure 3.11   C and assembly code for arithmetic function.

3.5.4   Discussion

We see that most of the instructions shown in Figure 3.10 can be used for either unsigned or two's-complement arithmetic. Only right shifting requires instructions that differentiate between signed versus unsigned data. This is one of the features that makes two's-complement arithmetic the preferred way to implement signed integer arithmetic.

Figure 3.11 shows an example of a function that performs arithmetic operations and its translation into assembly code. Arguments x, y, and z are initially stored in registers %rdi, %rsi, and %rdx, respectively. The assembly-code instructions correspond closely with the lines of C source code. Line 2 computes the value of x^y. Lines 3 and 4 compute the expression z*48 by a combination of leaq and shift instructions. Line 5 computes the AND of t1 and 0x0F0F0F0F. The final subtraction is computed by line 6. Since the destination of the subtraction is register %rax, this will be the value returned by the function.

In the assembly code of Figure 3.11, the sequence of values in register %rax corresponds to program values 3*z, z*48, and t4 (as the return value). In general, compilers generate code that uses individual registers for multiple program values and moves program values among the registers.

Practice Problem 3.10 (solution page 329)

In the following variant of the function of Figure 3.11(a), the expressions have been replaced by blanks:

```
long arith2(long x, long y, long z)
{
    long t1 = _____;
    long t2 = _____;
    long t3 = _____;
    long t4 = _____;
    return t4;
}
```

The portion of the generated assembly code implementing these expressions is as follows:

```
long arith2(long x, long y, long z)
x in %rdi, y in %rsi, z in %rdx
arith2:
    orq     %rsi, %rdi
    sarq    $3, %rdi
    notq    %rdi
    movq    %rdx, %rax
    subq    %rdi, %rax
    ret
```

Based on this assembly code, fill in the missing portions of the C code.

Practice Problem 3.11 (solution page 329)

It is common to find assembly-code lines of the form

```
xorq %rdx,%rdx
```

in code that was generated from C where no EXCLUSIVE-OR operations were present.

A. Explain the effect of this particular EXCLUSIVE-OR instruction and what useful operation it implements.

B. What would be the more straightforward way to express this operation in assembly code?

C. Compare the number of bytes to encode these two different implementations of the same operation.

3.5.5 Special Arithmetic Operations

As we saw in Section 2.3, multiplying two 64-bit signed or unsigned integers can yield a product that requires 128 bits to represent. The x86-64 instruction set provides limited support for operations involving 128-bit (16-byte) numbers. Continuing with the naming convention of word (2 bytes), double word (4 bytes), and quad word (8 bytes), Intel refers to a 16-byte quantity as an *oct word*. Figure 3.12

Instruction		Effect	Description
imulq	S	R[%rdx]:R[%rax] ← S × R[%rax]	Signed full multiply
mulq	S	R[%rdx]:R[%rax] ← S × R[%rax]	Unsigned full multiply
cqto		R[%rdx]:R[%rax] ← SignExtend(R[%rax])	Convert to oct word
idivq	S	R[%rdx] ← R[%rdx]:R[%rax] mod S; R[%rax] ← R[%rdx]:R[%rax] ÷ S	Signed divide
divq	S	R[%rdx] ← R[%rdx]:R[%rax] mod S; R[%rax] ← R[%rdx]:R[%rax] ÷ S	Unsigned divide

Figure 3.12 Special arithmetic operations. These operations provide full 128-bit multiplication and division, for both signed and unsigned numbers. The pair of registers %rdx and %rax are viewed as forming a single 128-bit oct word.

describes instructions that support generating the full 128-bit product of two 64-bit numbers, as well as integer division.

The imulq instruction has two different forms One form, shown in Figure 3.10, is as a member of the IMUL instruction class. In this form, it serves as a "two-operand" multiply instruction, generating a 64-bit product from two 64-bit operands. It implements the operations $*_{64}^u$ and $*_{64}^t$ described in Sections 2.3.4 and 2.3.5. (Recall that when truncating the product to 64 bits, both unsigned multiply and two's-complement multiply have the same bit-level behavior.)

Additionally, the x86-64 instruction set includes two different "one-operand" multiply instructions to compute the full 128-bit product of two 64-bit values—one for unsigned (mulq) and one for two's-complement (imulq) multiplication. For both of these instructions, one argument must be in register %rax, and the other is given as the instruction source operand. The product is then stored in registers %rdx (high-order 64 bits) and %rax (low-order 64 bits). Although the name imulq is used for two distinct multiplication operations, the assembler can tell which one is intended by counting the number of operands.

As an example, the following C code demonstrates the generation of a 128-bit product of two unsigned 64-bit numbers x and y:

```
#include <inttypes.h>

typedef unsigned __int128 uint128_t;

void store_uprod(uint128_t *dest, uint64_t x, uint64_t y) {
    *dest = x * (uint128_t) y;
}
```

In this program, we explicitly declare x and y to be 64-bit numbers, using definitions declared in the file inttypes.h, as part of an extension of the C standard. Unfortunately, this standard does not make provisions for 128-bit values. Instead, we rely on support provided by GCC for 128-bit integers, declared using the name `__int128`. Our code uses a `typedef` declaration to define data type `uint128_t`, following the naming pattern for other data types found in `inttypes.h`. The code specifies that the resulting product should be stored at the 16 bytes designated by pointer `dest`.

The assembly code generated by GCC for this function is as follows:

```
      void store_uprod(uint128_t *dest, uint64_t x, uint64_t y)
      dest in %rdi, x in %rsi, y in %rdx
1   store_uprod:
2     movq    %rsi, %rax        Copy x to multiplicand
3     mulq    %rdx              Multiply by y
4     movq    %rax, (%rdi)      Store lower 8 bytes at dest
5     movq    %rdx, 8(%rdi)     Store upper 8 bytes at dest+8
6     ret
```

Observe that storing the product requires two `movq` instructions: one for the low-order 8 bytes (line 4), and one for the high-order 8 bytes (line 5). Since the code is generated for a little-endian machine, the high-order bytes are stored at higher addresses, as indicated by the address specification `8(%rdi)`.

Our earlier table of arithmetic operations (Figure 3.10) does not list any division or modulus operations. These operations are provided by the single-operand divide instructions similar to the single-operand multiply instructions. The signed division instruction `idivl` takes as its dividend the 128-bit quantity in registers `%rdx` (high-order 64 bits) and `%rax` (low-order 64 bits). The divisor is given as the instruction operand. The instruction stores the quotient in register `%rax` and the remainder in register `%rdx`.

For most applications of 64-bit addition, the dividend is given as a 64-bit value. This value should be stored in register `%rax`. The bits of `%rdx` should then be set to either all zeros (unsigned arithmetic) or the sign bit of `%rax` (signed arithmetic). The latter operation can be performed using the instruction `cqto`.[2] This instruction takes no operands—it implicitly reads the sign bit from `%rax` and copies it across all of `%rdx`.

As an illustration of the implementation of division with x86-64, the following C function computes the quotient and remainder of two 64-bit, signed numbers:

```
void remdiv(long x, long y,
            long *qp, long *rp) {
    long q = x/y;
    long r = x%y;
    *qp = q;
    *rp = r;
}
```

---

2. This instruction is called cqo in the Intel documentation, one of the few cases where the ATT-format name for an instruction does not match the Intel name.

This compiles to the following assembly code:

```
void remdiv(long x, long y, long *qp, long *rp)
x in %rdi, y in %rsi, qp in %rdx, rp in %rcx
1   remdiv:
2       movq    %rdx, %r8       Copy qp
3       movq    %rdi, %rax      Move x to lower 8 bytes of dividend
4       cqto                    Sign-extend to upper 8 bytes of dividend
5       idivq   %rsi            Divide by y
6       movq    %rax, (%r8)     Store quotient at qp
7       movq    %rdx, (%rcx)    Store remainder at rp
8       ret
```

In this code, argument rp must first be saved in a different register (line 2), since argument register %rdx is required for the division operation. Lines 3–4 then prepare the dividend by copying and sign-extending x. Following the division, the quotient in register %rax gets stored at qp (line 6), while the remainder in register %rdx gets stored at rp (line 7).

Unsigned division makes use of the divq instruction. Typically, register %rdx is set to zero beforehand.

Practice Problem 3.12 (solution page 329)

Consider the following function for computing the quotient and remainder of two unsigned 64-bit numbers:

```
void uremdiv(unsigned long x, unsigned long y,
             unsigned long *qp, unsigned long *rp) {
    unsigned long q = x/y;
    unsigned long r = x%y;
    *qp = q;
    *rp = r;
}
```

Modify the assembly code shown for signed division to implement this function.

3.6 Control

So far, we have only considered the behavior of *straight-line* code, where instructions follow one another in sequence. Some constructs in C, such as conditionals, loops, and switches, require conditional execution, where the sequence of operations that get performed depends on the outcomes of tests applied to the data. Machine code provides two basic low-level mechanisms for implementing conditional behavior: it tests data values and then alters either the control flow or the data flow based on the results of these tests.

Data-dependent control flow is the more general and more common approach for implementing conditional behavior, and so we will examine this first. Normally, both statements in C and instructions in machine code are executed *sequentially*, in the order they appear in the program. The execution order of a set of machine-code instructions can be altered with a *jump* instruction, indicating that control should pass to some other part of the program, possibly contingent on the result of some test. The compiler must generate instruction sequences that build upon this low-level mechanism to implement the control constructs of C.

In our presentation, we first cover the two ways of implementing conditional operations. We then describe methods for presenting loops and switch statements.

3.6.1 Condition Codes

In addition to the integer registers, the CPU maintains a set of single-bit *condition code* registers describing attributes of the most recent arithmetic or logical operation. These registers can then be tested to perform conditional branches. These condition codes are the most useful:

CF: Carry flag. The most recent operation generated a carry out of the most significant bit. Used to detect overflow for unsigned operations.

ZF: Zero flag. The most recent operation yielded zero.

SF: Sign flag. The most recent operation yielded a negative value.

OF: Overflow flag. The most recent operation caused a two's-complement overflow—either negative or positive.

For example, suppose we used one of the ADD instructions to perform the equivalent of the C assignment t = a+b, where variables a, b, and t are integers. Then the condition codes would be set according to the following C expressions:

CF	(unsigned) t < (unsigned) a	Unsigned overflow
ZF	(t == 0)	Zero
SF	(t < 0)	Negative
OF	(a < 0 == b < 0) && (t < 0 != a < 0)	Signed overflow

The leaq instruction does not alter any condition codes, since it is intended to be used in address computations. Otherwise, all of the instructions listed in Figure 3.10 cause the condition codes to be set. For the logical operations, such as XOR, the carry and overflow flags are set to zero. For the shift operations, the carry flag is set to the last bit shifted out, while the overflow flag is set to zero. For reasons that we will not delve into, the INC and DEC instructions set the overflow and zero flags, but they leave the carry flag unchanged.

In addition to the setting of condition codes by the instructions of Figure 3.10, there are two instruction classes (having 8-, 16-, 32-, and 64-bit forms) that set condition codes without altering any other registers; these are listed in Figure 3.13. The CMP instructions set the condition codes according to the differences of their two operands. They behave in the same way as the SUB instructions, except that they set the condition codes without updating their destinations. With ATT format,

Instruction		Based on	Description
CMP	S_1, S_2	$S_2 - S_1$	Compare
cmpb			Compare byte
cmpw			Compare word
cmpl			Compare double word
cmpq			Compare quad word
TEST	S_1, S_2	S_1 & S_2	Test
testb			Test byte
testw			Test word
testl			Test double word
testq			Test quad word

Figure 3.13 Comparison and test instructions. These instructions set the condition codes without updating any other registers.

the operands are listed in reverse order, making the code difficult to read. These instructions set the zero flag if the two operands are equal. The other flags can be used to determine ordering relations between the two operands. The TEST instructions behave in the same manner as the AND instructions, except that they set the condition codes without altering their destinations. Typically, the same operand is repeated (e.g., testq %rax,%rax to see whether %rax is negative, zero, or positive), or one of the operands is a mask indicating which bits should be tested.

3.6.2 Accessing the Condition Codes

Rather than reading the condition codes directly, there are three common ways of using the condition codes: (1) we can set a single byte to 0 or 1 depending on some combination of the condition codes, (2) we can conditionally jump to some other part of the program, or (3) we can conditionally transfer data. For the first case, the instructions described in Figure 3.14 set a single byte to 0 or to 1 depending on some combination of the condition codes. We refer to this entire class of instructions as the SET instructions; they differ from one another based on which combinations of condition codes they consider, as indicated by the different suffixes for the instruction names. It is important to recognize that the suffixes for these instructions denote different conditions and not different operand sizes. For example, instructions setl and setb denote "set less" and "set below," not "set long word" or "set byte."

A SET instruction has either one of the low-order single-byte register elements (Figure 3.2) or a single-byte memory location as its destination, setting this byte to either 0 or 1. To generate a 32-bit or 64-bit result, we must also clear the high-order bits. A typical instruction sequence to compute the C expression a < b, where a and b are both of type long, proceeds as follows:

Instruction		Synonym	Effect	Set condition
sete	D	setz	$D \leftarrow$ ZF	Equal / zero
setne	D	setnz	$D \leftarrow$ ~ ZF	Not equal / not zero
sets	D		$D \leftarrow$ SF	Negative
setns	D		$D \leftarrow$ ~ SF	Nonnegative
setg	D	setnle	$D \leftarrow$ ~ (SF ^ OF) & ~ZF	Greater (signed >)
setge	D	setnl	$D \leftarrow$ ~ (SF ^ OF)	Greater or equal (signed >=)
setl	D	setnge	$D \leftarrow$ SF ^ OF	Less (signed <)
setle	D	setng	$D \leftarrow$ (SF ^ OF) | ZF	Less or equal (signed <=)
seta	D	setnbe	$D \leftarrow$ ~ CF & ~ZF	Above (unsigned >)
setae	D	setnb	$D \leftarrow$ ~ CF	Above or equal (unsigned >=)
setb	D	setnae	$D \leftarrow$ CF	Below (unsigned <)
setbe	D	setna	$D \leftarrow$ CF | ZF	Below or equal (unsigned <=)

Figure 3.14   The SET instructions. Each instruction sets a single byte to 0 or 1 based on some combination of the condition codes. Some instructions have "synonyms," that is, alternate names for the same machine instruction.

```
   int comp(data_t a, data_t b)
   a in %rdi, b in %rsi
1  comp:
2    cmpq    %rsi, %rdi      Compare a:b
3    setl    %al             Set low-order byte of %eax to 0 or 1
4    movzbl  %al, %eax       Clear rest of %eax (and rest of %rax)
5    ret
```

Note the comparison order of the cmpq instruction (line 2). Although the arguments are listed in the order %rsi (b), then %rdi (a), the comparison is really between a and b. Recall also, as discussed in Section 3.4.2, that the movzbl instruction (line 4) clears not just the high-order 3 bytes of %eax, but the upper 4 bytes of the entire register, %rax, as well.

For some of the underlying machine instructions, there are multiple possible names, which we list as "synonyms." For example, both setg (for "set greater") and setnle (for "set not less or equal") refer to the same machine instruction. Compilers and disassemblers make arbitrary choices of which names to use.

Although all arithmetic and logical operations set the condition codes, the descriptions of the different SET instructions apply to the case where a comparison instruction has been executed, setting the condition codes according to the computation t = a−b. More specifically, let a, b, and t be the integers represented in two's-complement form by variables a, b, and t, respectively, and so $t = a -^t_w b$, where w depends on the sizes associated with a and b.

Consider the sete, or "set when equal," instruction. When $a = b$, we will have $t = 0$, and hence the zero flag indicates equality. Similarly, consider testing for signed comparison with the setl, or "set when less," instruction. When no overflow occurs (indicated by having OF set to 0), we will have $a < b$ when $a -_w^t b < 0$, indicated by having SF set to 1, and $a \geq b$ when $a -_w^t b \geq 0$, indicated by having SF set to 0. On the other hand, when overflow occurs, we will have $a < b$ when $a -_w^t b > 0$ (negative overflow) and $a > b$ when $a -_w^t b < 0$ (positive overflow). We cannot have overflow when $a = b$. Thus, when OF is set to 1, we will have $a < b$ if and only if SF is set to 0. Combining these cases, the EXCLUSIVE-OR of the overflow and sign bits provides a test for whether $a < b$. The other signed comparison tests are based on other combinations of SF ^ OF and ZF.

For the testing of unsigned comparisons, we now let a and b be the integers represented in unsigned form by variables a and b. In performing the computation t = a-b, the carry flag will be set by the CMP instruction when $a - b < 0$, and so the unsigned comparisons use combinations of the carry and zero flags.

It is important to note how machine code does or does not distinguish between signed and unsigned values. Unlike in C, it does not associate a data type with each program value. Instead, it mostly uses the same instructions for the two cases, because many arithmetic operations have the same bit-level behavior for unsigned and two's-complement arithmetic. Some circumstances require different instructions to handle signed and unsigned operations, such as using different versions of right shifts, division and multiplication instructions, and different combinations of condition codes.

Practice Problem 3.13 (solution page 330)

The C code

```
int comp(data_t a, data_t b) {
    return a COMP b;
}
```

shows a general comparison between arguments a and b, where data_t, the data type of the arguments, is defined (via typedef) to be one of the integer data types listed in Figure 3.1 and either signed or unsigned. The comparison COMP is defined via #define.

Suppose a is in some portion of %rdx while b is in some portion of %rsi. For each of the following instruction sequences, determine which data types data_t and which comparisons COMP could cause the compiler to generate this code. (There can be multiple correct answers; you should list them all.)

A. ```
    cmpl   %esi, %edi
    setl   %al
    ```

B.  ```
    cmpw    %si, %di
    setge   %al
    ```

C. cmpb   %sil, %dil
    setbe   %al

D. cmpq   %rsi, %rdi
    setne   %a

Practice Problem 3.14 (solution page 330)

The C code

```
int test(data_t a) {
    return a TEST 0;
}
```

shows a general comparison between argument a and 0, where we can set the data type of the argument by declaring data_t with a typedef, and the nature of the comparison by declaring TEST with a #define declaration. The following instruction sequences implement the comparison, where a is held in some portion of register %rdi. For each sequence, determine which data types data_t and which comparisons TEST could cause the compiler to generate this code. (There can be multiple correct answers; list all correct ones.)

A. testq   %rdi, %rdi
    setge   %al

B. testw   %di, %di
    sete   %al

C. testb   %dil, %dil
    seta   %al

D. testl   %edi, %edi
    setle   %al

3.6.3 Jump Instructions

Under normal execution, instructions follow each other in the order they are listed. A *jump* instruction can cause the execution to switch to a completely new position in the program. These jump destinations are generally indicated in assembly code by a *label*. Consider the following (very contrived) assembly-code sequence:

```
movq $0,%rax        Set %rax to 0
jmp .L1             Goto .L1
movq (%rax),%rdx    Null pointer dereference (skipped)
.L1:
popq %rdx           Jump target
```

Instruction		Synonym	Jump condition	Description
jmp	*Label*		1	Direct jump
jmp	**Operand*		1	Indirect jump
je	*Label*	jz	ZF	Equal / zero
jne	*Label*	jnz	~ZF	Not equal / not zero
js	*Label*		SF	Negative
jns	*Label*		~SF	Nonnegative
jg	*Label*	jnle	~(SF ^ OF) & ~ZF	Greater (signed >)
jge	*Label*	jnl	~(SF ^ OF)	Greater or equal (signed >=)
jl	*Label*	jnge	SF ^ OF	Less (signed <)
jle	*Label*	jng	(SF ^ OF) | ZF	Less or equal (signed <=)
ja	*Label*	jnbe	~CF & ~ZF	Above (unsigned >)
jae	*Label*	jnb	~CF	Above or equal (unsigned >=)
jb	*Label*	jnae	CF	Below (unsigned <)
jbe	*Label*	jna	CF | ZF	Below or equal (unsigned <=)

Figure 3.15 The jump instructions. These instructions jump to a labeled destination when the jump condition holds. Some instructions have "synonyms," alternate names for the same machine instruction.

The instruction jmp .L1 will cause the program to skip over the movq instruction and instead resume execution with the popq instruction. In generating the object-code file, the assembler determines the addresses of all labeled instructions and encodes the *jump targets* (the addresses of the destination instructions) as part of the jump instructions.

Figure 3.15 shows the different jump instructions. The jmp instruction jumps unconditionally. It can be either a *direct* jump, where the jump target is encoded as part of the instruction, or an *indirect* jump, where the jump target is read from a register or a memory location. Direct jumps are written in assembly code by giving a label as the jump target, for example, the label .L1 in the code shown. Indirect jumps are written using '*' followed by an operand specifier using one of the memory operand formats described in Figure 3.3. As examples, the instruction

```
jmp *%rax
```

uses the value in register %rax as the jump target, and the instruction

```
jmp *(%rax)
```

reads the jump target from memory, using the value in %rax as the read address.

The remaining jump instructions in the table are *conditional*—they either jump or continue executing at the next instruction in the code sequence, depending on some combination of the condition codes. The names of these instructions and the conditions under which they jump match those of the SET instructions (see Figure 3.14). As with the SET instructions, some of the underlying machine instructions have multiple names. Conditional jumps can only be direct.

3.6.4 Jump Instruction Encodings

For the most part, we will not concern ourselves with the detailed format of machine code. On the other hand, understanding how the targets of jump instructions are encoded will become important when we study linking in Chapter 7. In addition, it helps when interpreting the output of a disassembler. In assembly code, jump targets are written using symbolic labels. The assembler, and later the linker, generate the proper encodings of the jump targets. There are several different encodings for jumps, but some of the most commonly used ones are *PC relative*. That is, they encode the difference between the address of the target instruction and the address of the instruction immediately following the jump. These offsets can be encoded using 1, 2, or 4 bytes. A second encoding method is to give an "absolute" address, using 4 bytes to directly specify the target. The assembler and linker select the appropriate encodings of the jump destinations.

As an example of PC-relative addressing, the following assembly code for a function was generated by compiling a file branch.c. It contains two jumps: the jmp instruction on line 2 jumps forward to a higher address, while the jg instruction on line 7 jumps back to a lower one.

```
1       movq    %rdi, %rax
2       jmp     .L2
3     .L3:
4       sarq    %rax
5     .L2:
6       testq   %rax, %rax
7       jg      .L3
8       rep; ret
```

The disassembled version of the .o format generated by the assembler is as follows:

```
1     0:    48 89 f8         mov     %rdi,%rax
2     3:    eb 03            jmp     8 <loop+0x8>
3     5:    48 d1 f8         sar     %rax
4     8:    48 85 c0         test    %rax,%rax
5     b:    7f f8            jg      5 <loop+0x5>
6     d:    f3 c3            repz retq
```

In the annotations on the right generated by the disassembler, the jump targets are indicated as 0x8 for the jump instruction on line 2 and 0x5 for the jump instruction on line 5 (the disassembler lists all numbers in hexadecimal). Looking at the byte encodings of the instructions, however, we see that the target of the first jump instruction is encoded (in the second byte) as 0x03. Adding this to 0x5, the

---

Aside What do the instructions `rep` and `repz` do?

Line 8 of the assembly code shown on page 207 contains the instruction combination `rep; ret`. These are rendered in the disassembled code (line 6) as `repz retq`. One can infer that `repz` is a synonym for `rep`, just as `retq` is a synonym for `ret`. Looking at the Intel and AMD documentation for the `rep` instruction, we find that it is normally used to implement a repeating string operation [3, 51]. It seems completely inappropriate here. The answer to this puzzle can be seen in AMD's guidelines to compiler writers [1]. They recommend using the combination of `rep` followed by `ret` to avoid making the `ret` instruction the destination of a conditional jump instruction. Without the `rep` instruction, the `jg` instruction (line 7 of the assembly code) would proceed to the `ret` instruction when the branch is not taken. According to AMD, their processors cannot properly predict the destination of a `ret` instruction when it is reached from a jump instruction. The `rep` instruction serves as a form of no-operation here, and so inserting it as the jump destination does not change behavior of the code, except to make it faster on AMD processors. We can safely ignore any `rep` or `repz` instruction we see in the rest of the code presented in this book.

---

address of the following instruction, we get jump target address 0x8, the address of the instruction on line 4.

Similarly, the target of the second jump instruction is encoded as 0xf8 (decimal −8) using a single-byte two's-complement representation. Adding this to 0xd (decimal 13), the address of the instruction on line 6, we get 0x5, the address of the instruction on line 3.

As these examples illustrate, the value of the program counter when performing PC-relative addressing is the address of the instruction following the jump, not that of the jump itself. This convention dates back to early implementations, when the processor would update the program counter as its first step in executing an instruction.

The following shows the disassembled version of the program after linking:

```
1    4004d0:   48 89 f8              mov     %rdi,%rax
2    4004d3:   eb 03                 jmp     4004d8 <loop+0x8>
3    4004d5:   48 d1 f8              sar     %rax
4    4004d8:   48 85 c0              test    %rax,%rax
5    4004db:   7f f8                 jg      4004d5 <loop+0x5>
6    4004dd:   f3 c3                 repz retq
```

The instructions have been relocated to different addresses, but the encodings of the jump targets in lines 2 and 5 remain unchanged. By using a PC-relative encoding of the jump targets, the instructions can be compactly encoded (requiring just 2 bytes), and the object code can be shifted to different positions in memory without alteration.

Practice Problem 3.15 (solution page 330)

In the following excerpts from a disassembled binary, some of the information has been replaced by X's. Answer the following questions about these instructions.

A. What is the target of the `je` instruction below? (You do not need to know anything about the `callq` instruction here.)

```
4003fa: 74 02                je     XXXXXX
4003fc: ff d0                callq  *%rax
```

B. What is the target of the `je` instruction below?

```
40042f: 74 f4                je     XXXXXX
400431: 5d                   pop    %rbp
```

C. What is the address of the `ja` and `pop` instructions?

```
XXXXXX: 77 02                ja     400547
XXXXXX: 5d                   pop    %rbp
```

D. In the code that follows, the jump target is encoded in PC-relative form as a 4-byte two's-complement number. The bytes are listed from least significant to most, reflecting the little-endian byte ordering of x86-64. What is the address of the jump target?

```
4005e8: e9 73 ff ff ff       jmpq   XXXXXXX
4005ed: 90                   nop
```

The jump instructions provide a means to implement conditional execution (`if`), as well as several different loop constructs.

3.6.5   Implementing Conditional Branches with Conditional Control

The most general way to translate conditional expressions and statements from C into machine code is to use combinations of conditional and unconditional jumps. (As an alternative, we will see in Section 3.6.6 that some conditionals can be implemented by conditional transfers of data rather than control.) For example, Figure 3.16(a) shows the C code for a function that computes the absolute value of the difference of two numbers.[3] The function also has a side effect of incrementing one of two counters, encoded as global variables `lt_cnt` and `ge_cnt`. Gcc generates the assembly code shown as Figure 3.16(c). Our rendition of the machine code into C is shown as the function `gotodiff_se` (Figure 3.16(b)). It uses the `goto` statement in C, which is similar to the unconditional jump of

---

3. Actually, it can return a negative value if one of the subtractions overflows. Our interest here is to demonstrate machine code, not to implement robust code.

(a) Original C code

```
long lt_cnt = 0;
long ge_cnt = 0;

long absdiff_se(long x, long y)
{
    long result;
    if (x < y) {
        lt_cnt++;
        result = y - x;
    }
    else {
        ge_cnt++;
        result = x - y;
    }
    return result;
}
```

(b) Equivalent goto version

```
1   long gotodiff_se(long x, long y)
2   {
3       long result;
4       if (x >= y)
5           goto x_ge_y;
6       lt_cnt++;
7       result =  y - x;
8       return result;
9   x_ge_y:
10      ge_cnt++;
11      result = x - y;
12      return result;
13  }
```

(c) Generated assembly code

```
    long absdiff_se(long x, long y)
    x in %rdi, y in %rsi
1   absdiff_se:
2       cmpq    %rsi, %rdi          Compare x:y
3       jge     .L2                 If >= goto x_ge_y
4       addq    $1, lt_cnt(%rip)    lt_cnt++
5       movq    %rsi, %rax
6       subq    %rdi, %rax          result = y - x
7       ret                         Return
8   .L2:                            x_ge_y:
9       addq    $1, ge_cnt(%rip)    ge_cnt++
10      movq    %rdi, %rax
11      subq    %rsi, %rax          result = x - y
12      ret                         Return
```

Figure 3.16 Compilation of conditional statements. (a) C procedure absdiff_se contains an if-else statement. The generated assembly code is shown (c), along with (b) a C procedure gotodiff_se that mimics the control flow of the assembly code.

assembly code. Using goto statements is generally considered a bad programming style, since their use can make code very difficult to read and debug. We use them in our presentation as a way to construct C programs that describe the control flow of machine code. We call this style of programming "goto code."

In the goto code (Figure 3.16(b)), the statement goto x_ge_y on line 5 causes a jump to the label x_ge_y (since it occurs when $x \geq y$) on line 9. Continuing the execution from this point, it completes the computations specified by the `else` portion of function `absdiff_se` and returns. On the other hand, if the test `x >= y` fails, the program procedure will carry out the steps specified by the `if` portion of `absdiff_se` and return.

The assembly-code implementation (Figure 3.16(c)) first compares the two operands (line 2), setting the condition codes. If the comparison result indicates that x is greater than or equal to y, it then jumps to a block of code starting at line 8 that increments global variable `ge_cnt`, computes `x-y` as the return value, and returns. Otherwise, it continues with the execution of code beginning at line 4 that increments global variable `lt_cnt`, computes `y-x` as the return value, and returns. We can see, then, that the control flow of the assembly code generated for `absdiff_se` closely follows the goto code of `gotodiff_se`.

The general form of an if-else statement in C is given by the template

```
if (test-expr)
    then-statement
else
    else-statement
```

where *test-expr* is an integer expression that evaluates either to zero (interpreted as meaning "false") or to a nonzero value (interpreted as meaning "true"). Only one of the two branch statements (*then-statement* or *else-statement*) is executed.

For this general form, the assembly implementation typically adheres to the following form, where we use C syntax to describe the control flow:

```
    t = test-expr;
    if (!t)
        goto false;
    then-statement
    goto done;
false:
    else-statement
done:
```

That is, the compiler generates separate blocks of code for *then-statement* and *else-statement*. It inserts conditional and unconditional branches to make sure the correct block is executed.

Practice Problem 3.16 (solution page 331)

When given the C code

```
void cond(long a, long *p)
{
    if (p && a > *p)
        *p = a;
}
```

GCC generates the following assembly code:

```
    void cond(long a, long *p)
    a in %rdi, p in %rsi
cond:
    testq   %rsi, %rsi
    je      .L1
    cmpq    %rdi, (%rsi)
    jge     .L1
    movq    %rdi, (%rsi)
.L1:
    rep; ret
```

A. Write a goto version in C that performs the same computation and mimics the control flow of the assembly code, in the style shown in Figure 3.16(b). You might find it helpful to first annotate the assembly code as we have done in our examples.

B. Explain why the assembly code contains two conditional branches, even though the C code has only one if statement.

Practice Problem 3.17 (solution page 331)

An alternate rule for translating if statements into goto code is as follows:

```
    t = test-expr;
    if (t)
        goto true;
    else-statement
    goto done;
true:
    then-statement
done:
```

A. Rewrite the goto version of absdiff_se based on this alternate rule.

B. Can you think of any reasons for choosing one rule over the other?

Practice Problem 3.18 (solution page 332)

Starting with C code of the form

```
long test(long x, long y, long z) {
    long val = _____;
    if (_____) {
        if (_____)
            val = _____;
        else
            val = _____;
    } else if (_____)
        val = _____;
    return val;
}
```

GCC generates the following assembly code:

```
long test(long x, long y, long z)
x in %rdi, y in %rsi, z in %rdx
test:
  leaq     (%rdi,%rsi), %rax
  addq     %rdx, %rax
  cmpq     $-3, %rdi
  jge      .L2
  cmpq     %rdx, %rsi
  jge      .L3
  movq     %rdi, %rax
  imulq    %rsi, %rax
  ret
.L3:
  movq     %rsi, %rax
  imulq    %rdx, %rax
  ret
.L2:
  cmpq     $2, %rdi
  jle      .L4
  movq     %rdi, %rax
  imulq    %rdx, %rax
.L4:
  rep; ret
```

Fill in the missing expressions in the C code.

3.6.6 Implementing Conditional Branches with Conditional Moves

The conventional way to implement conditional operations is through a conditional transfer of *control*, where the program follows one execution path when a condition holds and another when it does not. This mechanism is simple and general, but it can be very inefficient on modern processors.

An alternate strategy is through a conditional transfer of *data*. This approach computes both outcomes of a conditional operation and then selects one based on whether or not the condition holds. This strategy makes sense only in restricted cases, but it can then be implemented by a simple *conditional move* instruction that is better matched to the performance characteristics of modern processors. Here, we examine this strategy and its implementation with x86-64.

Figure 3.17(a) shows an example of code that can be compiled using a conditional move. The function computes the absolute value of its arguments x and y, as did our earlier example (Figure 3.16). Whereas the earlier example had side effects in the branches, modifying the value of either lt_cnt or ge_cnt, this version simply computes the value to be returned by the function.

(a) Original C code

```
long absdiff(long x, long y)
{
    long result;
    if (x < y)
        result = y - x;
    else
        result = x - y;
    return result;
}
```

(b) Implementation using conditional assignment

```
1   long cmovdiff(long x, long y)
2   {
3       long rval = y-x;
4       long eval = x-y;
5       long ntest = x >= y;
6       /* Line below requires
7          single instruction: */
8       if (ntest) rval = eval;
9       return rval;
10  }
```

(c) Generated assembly code

```
    long absdiff(long x, long y)
    x in %rdi, y in %rsi
1   absdiff:
2     movq    %rsi, %rax
3     subq    %rdi, %rax      rval = y-x
4     movq    %rdi, %rdx
5     subq    %rsi, %rdx      eval = x-y
6     cmpq    %rsi, %rdi      Compare x:y
7     cmovge  %rdx, %rax      If >=, rval = eval
8     ret                     Return tval
```

Figure 3.17 Compilation of conditional statements using conditional assignment. (a) C function absdiff contains a conditional expression. The generated assembly code is shown (c), along with (b) a C function cmovdiff that mimics the operation of the assembly code.

For this function, GCC generates the assembly code shown in Figure 3.17(c), having an approximate form shown by the C function cmovdiff shown in Figure 3.17(b). Studying the C version, we can see that it computes both y-x and x-y, naming these rval and eval, respectively. It then tests whether x is greater than or equal to y, and if so, copies eval to rval before returning rval. The assembly code in Figure 3.17(c) follows the same logic. The key is that the single cmovge instruction (line 7) of the assembly code implements the conditional assignment (line 8) of cmovdiff. It will transfer the data from the source register to the destination, only if the cmpq instruction of line 6 indicates that one value is greater than or equal to the other (as indicated by the suffix ge).

To understand why code based on conditional data transfers can outperform code based on conditional control transfers (as in Figure 3.16), we must understand something about how modern processors operate. As we will see in Chapters 4 and 5, processors achieve high performance through *pipelining*, where an instruction is processed via a sequence of stages, each performing one small portion of the required operations (e.g., fetching the instruction from memory, determining the instruction type, reading from memory, performing an arithmetic operation, writing to memory, and updating the program counter). This approach achieves high performance by overlapping the steps of the successive instructions, such as fetching one instruction while performing the arithmetic operations for a previous instruction. To do this requires being able to determine the sequence of instructions to be executed well ahead of time in order to keep the pipeline full of instructions to be executed. When the machine encounters a conditional jump (referred to as a "branch"), it cannot determine which way the branch will go until it has evaluated the branch condition. Processors employ sophisticated *branch prediction logic* to try to guess whether or not each jump instruction will be followed. As long as it can guess reliably (modern microprocessor designs try to achieve success rates on the order of 90%), the instruction pipeline will be kept full of instructions. Mispredicting a jump, on the other hand, requires that the processor discard much of the work it has already done on future instructions and then begin filling the pipeline with instructions starting at the correct location. As we will see, such a misprediction can incur a serious penalty, say, 15–30 clock cycles of wasted effort, causing a serious degradation of program performance.

As an example, we ran timings of the absdiff function on an Intel Haswell processor using both methods of implementing the conditional operation. In a typical application, the outcome of the test x < y is highly unpredictable, and so even the most sophisticated branch prediction hardware will guess correctly only around 50% of the time. In addition, the computations performed in each of the two code sequences require only a single clock cycle. As a consequence, the branch misprediction penalty dominates the performance of this function. For x86-64 code with conditional jumps, we found that the function requires around 8 clock cycles per call when the branching pattern is easily predictable, and around 17.50 clock cycles per call when the branching pattern is random. From this, we can infer that the branch misprediction penalty is around 19 clock cycles. That means time required by the function ranges between around 8 and 27 cycles, depending on whether or not the branch is predicted correctly.

Aside   How did you determine this penalty?

Assume the probability of misprediction is p, the time to execute the code without misprediction is T_{OK}, and the misprediction penalty is T_{MP}. Then the average time to execute the code as a function of p is $T_{avg}(p) = (1 - p)T_{OK} + p(T_{OK} + T_{MP}) = T_{OK} + pT_{MP}$. We are given T_{OK} and T_{ran}, the average time when $p = 0.5$, and we want to determine T_{MP}. Substituting into the equation, we get $T_{ran} = T_{avg}(0.5) = T_{OK} + 0.5T_{MP}$, and therefore $T_{MP} = 2(T_{ran} - T_{OK})$. So, for $T_{OK} = 8$ and $T_{ran} = 17.5$, we get $T_{MP} = 19$.

On the other hand, the code compiled using conditional moves requires around 8 clock cycles regardless of the data being tested. The flow of control does not depend on data, and this makes it easier for the processor to keep its pipeline full.

Practice Problem 3.19 (solution page 332)

Running on an older processor model, our code required around 16 cycles when the branching pattern was highly predictable, and around 31 cycles when the pattern was random.

A. What is the approximate miss penalty?

B. How many cycles would the function require when the branch is mispre-dicted?

Figure 3.18 illustrates some of the conditional move instructions available with x86-64. Each of these instructions has two operands: a source register or memory location S, and a destination register R. As with the different SET (Section 3.6.2) and jump (Section 3.6.3) instructions, the outcome of these instructions depends on the values of the condition codes. The source value is read from either memory or the source register, but it is copied to the destination only if the specified condition holds.

The source and destination values can be 16, 32, or 64 bits long. Single-byte conditional moves are not supported. Unlike the unconditional instructions, where the operand length is explicitly encoded in the instruction name (e.g., movw and movl), the assembler can infer the operand length of a conditional move instruction from the name of the destination register, and so the same instruction name can be used for all operand lengths.

Unlike conditional jumps, the processor can execute conditional move instructions without having to predict the outcome of the test. The processor simply reads the source value (possibly from memory), checks the condition code, and then either updates the destination register or keeps it the same. We will explore the implementation of conditional moves in Chapter 4.

To understand how conditional operations can be implemented via conditional data transfers, consider the following general form of conditional expression and assignment:

Instruction		Synonym	Move condition	Description
cmove	*S, R*	cmovz	ZF	Equal / zero
cmovne	*S, R*	cmovnz	~ZF	Not equal / not zero
cmovs	*S, R*		SF	Negative
cmovns	*S, R*		~SF	Nonnegative
cmovg	*S, R*	cmovnle	~(SF ^ OF) & ~ZF	Greater (signed >)
cmovge	*S, R*	cmovnl	~(SF ^ OF)	Greater or equal (signed >=)
cmovl	*S, R*	cmovnge	SF ^ OF	Less (signed <)
cmovle	*S, R*	cmovng	(SF ^ OF) | ZF	Less or equal (signed <=)
cmova	*S, R*	cmovnbe	~CF & ~ZF	Above (unsigned >)
cmovae	*S, R*	cmovnb	~CF	Above or equal (Unsigned >=)
cmovb	*S, R*	cmovnae	CF	Below (unsigned <)
cmovbe	*S, R*	cmovna	CF | ZF	Below or equal (unsigned <=)

Figure 3.18   The conditional move instructions. These instructions copy the source value S to its destination R when the move condition holds. Some instructions have "synonyms," alternate names for the same machine instruction.

v = *test-expr* ? *then-expr* : *else-expr*;

The standard way to compile this expression using conditional control transfer would have the following form:

```
    if (!test-expr)
        goto false;
    v = then-expr;
    goto done;
false:
    v = else-expr;
done:
```

This code contains two code sequences—one evaluating *then-expr* and one evaluating *else-expr*. A combination of conditional and unconditional jumps is used to ensure that just one of the sequences is evaluated.

For the code based on a conditional move, both the *then-expr* and the *else-expr* are evaluated, with the final value chosen based on the evaluation *test-expr*. This can be described by the following abstract code:

```
    v  = then-expr;
    ve = else-expr;
    t  = test-expr;
    if (!t) v = ve;
```

The final statement in this sequence is implemented with a conditional move—value ve is copied to v only if test condition t does not hold.

Not all conditional expressions can be compiled using conditional moves. Most significantly, the abstract code we have shown evaluates both *then-expr* and *else-expr* regardless of the test outcome. If one of those two expressions could possibly generate an error condition or a side effect, this could lead to invalid behavior. Such is the case for our earlier example (Figure 3.16). Indeed, we put the side effects into this example specifically to force GCC to implement this function using conditional transfers.

As a second illustration, consider the following C function:

```
long cread(long *xp) {
    return (xp ? *xp : 0);
}
```

At first, this seems like a good candidate to compile using a conditional move to set the result to zero when the pointer is null, as shown in the following assembly code:

```
     long cread(long *xp)
     Invalid implementation of function cread
     xp in register %rdi
1    cread:
2      movq    (%rdi), %rax      v = *xp
3      testq   %rdi, %rdi        Test x
4      movl    $0, %edx          Set ve = 0
5      cmove   %rdx, %rax        If x==0, v = ve
6      ret                       Return v
```

This implementation is invalid, however, since the dereferencing of xp by the movq instruction (line 2) occurs even when the test fails, causing a null pointer dereferencing error. Instead, this code must be compiled using branching code.

Using conditional moves also does not always improve code efficiency. For example, if either the *then-expr* or the *else-expr* evaluation requires a significant computation, then this effort is wasted when the corresponding condition does not hold. Compilers must take into account the relative performance of wasted computation versus the potential for performance penalty due to branch misprediction. In truth, they do not really have enough information to make this decision reliably; for example, they do not know how well the branches will follow predictable patterns. Our experiments with GCC indicate that it only uses conditional moves when the two expressions can be computed very easily, for example, with single add instructions. In our experience, GCC uses conditional control transfers even in many cases where the cost of branch misprediction would exceed even more complex computations.

Overall, then, we see that conditional data transfers offer an alternative strategy to conditional control transfers for implementing conditional operations. They can only be used in restricted cases, but these cases are fairly common and provide a much better match to the operation of modern processors.

Practice Problem 3.20 (solution page 333)

In the following C function, we have left the definition of operation OP incomplete:

```
#define OP _____  /* Unknown operator */

long arith(long x) {
    return x OP 8;
}
```

When compiled, GCC generates the following assembly code:

```
long arith(long x)
x in %rdi
arith:
  leaq    7(%rdi), %rax
  testq   %rdi, %rdi
  cmovns  %rdi, %rax
  sarq    $3, %rax
  ret
```

A. What operation is OP?

B. Annotate the code to explain how it works.

Practice Problem 3.21 (solution page 333)

Starting with C code of the form

```
long test(long x, long y) {
    long val = _____;
    if (_____) {
        if (_____)
            val = _____;
        else
            val = _____;
    } else if (_____)
        val = _____;
    return val;
}
```

GCC generates the following assembly code:

```
long test(long x, long y)
x in %rdi, y in %rsi
test:
  leaq    0(,%rdi,8), %rax
  testq   %rsi, %rsi
  jle     .L2
```

```
        movq      %rsi, %rax
        subq      %rdi, %rax
        movq      %rdi, %rdx
        andq      %rsi, %rdx
        cmpq      %rsi, %rdi
        cmovge    %rdx, %rax
        ret
.L2:
        addq      %rsi, %rdi
        cmpq      $-2, %rsi
        cmovle    %rdi, %rax
        ret
```

Fill in the missing expressions in the C code.

3.6.7 Loops

C provides several looping constructs—namely, do-while, while, and for. No corresponding instructions exist in machine code. Instead, combinations of conditional tests and jumps are used to implement the effect of loops. Gcc and other compilers generate loop code based on the two basic loop patterns. We will study the translation of loops as a progression, starting with do-while and then working toward ones with more complex implementations, covering both patterns.

Do-While Loops

The general form of a do-while statement is as follows:

```
do
        body-statement
        while (test-expr);
```

The effect of the loop is to repeatedly execute *body-statement*, evaluate *test-expr*, and continue the loop if the evaluation result is nonzero. Observe that *body-statement* is executed at least once.

This general form can be translated into conditionals and goto statements as follows:

```
loop:
        body-statement
        t = test-expr;
        if (t)
            goto loop;
```

That is, on each iteration the program evaluates the body statement and then the test expression. If the test succeeds, the program goes back for another iteration.

(a) C code

```
long fact_do(long n)
{
    long result = 1;
    do {
        result *= n;
        n = n-1;
    } while (n > 1);
    return result;
}
```

(b) Equivalent goto version

```
long fact_do_goto(long n)
{
    long result = 1;
 loop:
    result *= n;
    n = n-1;
    if (n > 1)
        goto loop;
    return result;
}
```

(c) Corresponding assembly-language code

```
    long fact_do(long n)
    n in %rdi
1   fact_do:
2     movl    $1, %eax        Set result = 1
3   .L2:                      loop:
4     imulq   %rdi, %rax      Compute result *= n
5     subq    $1, %rdi        Decrement n
6     cmpq    $1, %rdi        Compare n:1
7     jg      .L2             If >, goto loop
8     rep; ret                Return
```

Figure 3.19 Code for do-while **version of factorial program.** A conditional jump causes the program to loop.

As an example, Figure 3.19(a) shows an implementation of a routine to compute the factorial of its argument, written $n!$, with a do-while loop. This function only computes the proper value for $n > 0$.

Practice Problem 3.22 (solution page 333)

A. What is the maximum value of n for which we can represent $n!$ with a 32-bit int?

B. What about for a 64-bit long?

The goto code shown in Figure 3.19(b) shows how the loop gets turned into a lower-level combination of tests and conditional jumps. Following the initialization of result, the program begins looping. First it executes the body of the loop, consisting here of updates to variables result and n. It then tests whether $n > 1$, and, if so, it jumps back to the beginning of the loop. Figure 3.19(c) shows

> **Aside** Reverse engineering loops
>
> A key to understanding how the generated assembly code relates to the original source code is to find a mapping between program values and registers. This task was simple enough for the loop of Figure 3.19, but it can be much more challenging for more complex programs. The C compiler will often rearrange the computations, so that some variables in the C code have no counterpart in the machine code, and new values are introduced into the machine code that do not exist in the source code. Moreover, it will often try to minimize register usage by mapping multiple program values onto a single register.
>
> The process we described for `fact_do` works as a general strategy for reverse engineering loops. Look at how registers are initialized before the loop, updated and tested within the loop, and used after the loop. Each of these provides a clue that can be combined to solve a puzzle. Be prepared for surprising transformations, some of which are clearly cases where the compiler was able to optimize the code, and others where it is hard to explain why the compiler chose that particular strategy.

the assembly code from which the goto code was generated. The conditional jump instruction `jg` (line 7) is the key instruction in implementing a loop. It determines whether to continue iterating or to exit the loop.

Reverse engineering assembly code, such as that of Figure 3.19(c), requires determining which registers are used for which program values. In this case, the mapping is fairly simple to determine: We know that n will be passed to the function in register `%rdi`. We can see register `%rax` getting initialized to 1 (line 2). (Recall that, although the instruction has `%eax` as its destination, it will also set the upper 4 bytes of `%rax` to 0.) We can see that this register is also updated by multiplication on line 4. Furthermore, since `%rax` is used to return the function value, it is often chosen to hold program values that are returned. We therefore conclude that `%rax` corresponds to program value `result`.

Practice Problem 3.23 (solution page 334)

For the C code

```
long dw_loop(long x) {
    long y = x*x;
    long *p = &x;
    long n = 2*x;
    do {
        x += y;
        (*p)++;
        n--;
    } while (n > 0);
    return x;
}
```

GCC generates the following assembly code:

```
    long dw_loop(long x)
    x initially in %rdi
1   dw_loop:
2     movq    %rdi, %rax
3     movq    %rdi, %rcx
4     imulq   %rdi, %rcx
5     leaq    (%rdi,%rdi), %rdx
6   .L2:
7     leaq    1(%rcx,%rax), %rax
8     subq    $1, %rdx
9     testq   %rdx, %rdx
10    jg      .L2
11    rep; ret
```

A. Which registers are used to hold program values x, y, and n?

B. How has the compiler eliminated the need for pointer variable p and the pointer dereferencing implied by the expression (*p)++?

C. Add annotations to the assembly code describing the operation of the program, similar to those shown in Figure 3.19(c).

While Loops

The general form of a while statement is as follows:

```
while (test-expr)
    body-statement
```

It differs from do-while in that *test-expr* is evaluated and the loop is potentially terminated before the first execution of *body-statement*. There are a number of ways to translate a while loop into machine code, two of which are used in code generated by GCC. Both use the same loop structure as we saw for do-while loops but differ in how to implement the initial test.

The first translation method, which we refer to as *jump to middle*, performs the initial test by performing an unconditional jump to the test at the end of the loop. It can be expressed by the following template for translating from the general while loop form to goto code:

```
    goto test;
loop:
    body-statement
test:
    t = test-expr;
    if (t)
        goto loop;
```

As an example, Figure 3.20(a) shows an implementation of the factorial function using a while loop. This function correctly computes $0! = 1$. The adjacent

(a) C code

```
long fact_while(long n)
{
    long result = 1;
    while (n > 1) {
        result *= n;
        n = n-1;
    }
    return result;
}
```

(b) Equivalent goto version

```
long fact_while_jm_goto(long n)
{
    long result = 1;
    goto test;
loop:
    result *= n;
    n = n-1;
test:
    if (n > 1)
        goto loop;
    return result;
}
```

(c) Corresponding assembly-language code

```
     long fact_while(long n)
      n in %rdi
fact_while:
   movl    $1, %eax       Set result = 1
   jmp     .L5            Goto test
.L6:                      loop:
   imulq   %rdi, %rax     Compute result *= n
   subq    $1, %rdi       Decrement n
.L5:                      test:
   cmpq    $1, %rdi       Compare n:1
   jg      .L6            If >, goto loop
   rep; ret               Return
```

Figure 3.20 **C and assembly code for while version of factorial using jump-to-middle translation.** The C function fact_while_jm_goto illustrates the operation of the assembly-code version.

function fact_while_jm_goto (Figure 3.20(b)) is a C rendition of the assembly code generated by GCC when optimization is specified with the command-line option –Og. Comparing the goto code generated for fact_while (Figure 3.20(b)) to that for fact_do (Figure 3.19(b)), we see that they are very similar, except that the statement goto test before the loop causes the program to first perform the test of n before modifying the values of result or n. The bottom portion of the figure (Figure 3.20(c)) shows the actual assembly code generated.

Practice Problem 3.24 (solution page 335)

For C code having the general form

```
long loop_while(long a, long b)
{
```

```
    long result = _____;
    while (_____) {
        result = _____;
        a = _____;
    }
    return result;
}
```

GCC, run with command-line option −Og, produces the following code:

```
       long loop_while(long a, long b)
       a in %rdi, b in %rsi
1    loop_while:
2        movl     $1, %eax
3        jmp      .L2
4    .L3:
5        leaq     (%rdi,%rsi), %rdx
6        imulq    %rdx, %rax
7        addq     $1, %rdi
8    .L2:
9        cmpq     %rsi, %rdi
10       jl       .L3
11       rep; ret
```

We can see that the compiler used a jump-to-middle translation, using the jmp instruction on line 3 to jump to the test starting with label .L2. Fill in the missing parts of the C code.

The second translation method, which we refer to as *guarded do*, first transforms the code into a do-while loop by using a conditional branch to skip over the loop if the initial test fails. Gcc follows this strategy when compiling with higher levels of optimization, for example, with command-line option −O1. This method can be expressed by the following template for translating from the general while loop form to a do-while loop:

```
t = test-expr;
if (!t)
    goto done;
do
    body-statement
    while (test-expr);
done:
```

This, in turn, can be transformed into goto code as

```
    t = test-expr;
    if (!t)
        goto done;
```

```
loop:
    body-statement
    t = test-expr;
    if (t)
        goto loop;
done:
```

Using this implementation strategy, the compiler can often optimize the initial test, for example, determining that the test condition will always hold.

As an example, Figure 3.21 shows the same C code for a factorial function as in Figure 3.20, but demonstrates the compilation that occurs when GCC is given command-line option -O1. Figure 3.21(c) shows the actual assembly code generated, while Figure 3.21(b) renders this assembly code in a more readable C representation. Referring to this goto code, we see that the loop will be skipped if $n \leq 1$, for the initial value of n. The loop itself has the same general structure as that generated for the do-while version of the function (Figure 3.19). One interesting feature, however, is that the loop test (line 9 of the assembly code) has been changed from $n > 1$ in the original C code to $n \neq 1$. The compiler has determined that the loop can only be entered when $n > 1$, and that decrementing n will result in either $n > 1$ or $n = 1$. Therefore, the test $n \neq 1$ will be equivalent to the test $n \leq 1$.

Practice Problem 3.25 (solution page 335)

For C code having the general form

```
long loop_while2(long a, long b)
{
    long result = _____;
    while (_____) {
        result = _____;
        b = _____;
    }
    return result;
}
```

GCC, run with command-line option -O1, produces the following code:

```
      a in %rdi, b in %rsi
1   loop_while2:
2       testq   %rsi, %rsi
3       jle     .L8
4       movq    %rsi, %rax
5   .L7:
6       imulq   %rdi, %rax
7       subq    %rdi, %rsi
8       testq   %rsi, %rsi
```

(a) C code

```
long fact_while(long n)
{
    long result = 1;
    while (n > 1) {
        result *= n;
        n = n-1;
    }
    return result;
}
```

(b) Equivalent goto version

```
long fact_while_gd_goto(long n)
{
    long result = 1;
    if (n <= 1)
        goto done;
loop:
    result *= n;
    n = n-1;
    if (n != 1)
        goto loop;
done:
    return result;
}
```

(c) Corresponding assembly-language code

```
    long fact_while(long n)
    n in %rdi
1   fact_while:
2       cmpq    $1, %rdi        Compare n:1
3       jle     .L7             If <=, goto done
4       movl    $1, %eax        Set result = 1
5   .L6:                        loop:
6       imulq   %rdi, %rax      Compute result *= n
7       subq    $1, %rdi        Decrement n
8       cmpq    $1, %rdi        Compare n:1
9       jne     .L6             If !=, goto loop
10      rep; ret                Return
11  .L7:                        done:
12      movl    $1, %eax        Compute result = 1
13      ret                     Return
```

Figure 3.21 C and assembly code for while version of factorial using guarded-do translation. The fact_while_gd_goto function illustrates the operation of the assembly-code version.

```
9       jg      .L7
10      rep; ret
11  .L8:
12      movq    %rsi, %rax
13      ret
```

We can see that the compiler used a guarded-do translation, using the jle instruction on line 3 to skip over the loop code when the initial test fails. Fill in the missing parts of the C code. Note that the control structure in the assembly code does not exactly match what would be obtained by a direct translation of the C code according to our translation rules. In particular, it has two different `ret` instructions (lines 10 and 13). However, you can fill out the missing portions of the C code in a way that it will have equivalent behavior to the assembly code.

Practice Problem 3.26 (solution page 336)

A function `fun_a` has the following overall structure:

```
long fun_a(unsigned long x) {
    long val = 0;
    while ( ... ) {
        .
        .
        .
    }
    return ...;
}
```

The GCC C compiler generates the following assembly code:

```
    long fun_a(unsigned long x)
    x in %rdi
1   fun_a:
2     movl    $0, %eax
3     jmp     .L5
4   .L6:
5     xorq    %rdi, %rax
6     shrq    %rdi           Shift right by 1
7   .L5:
8     testq   %rdi, %rdi
9     jne     .L6
10    andl    $1, %eax
11    ret
```

Reverse engineer the operation of this code and then do the following:

A. Determine what loop translation method was used.

B. Use the assembly-code version to fill in the missing parts of the C code.

C. Describe in English what this function computes.

For Loops

The general form of a `for` loop is as follows:

```
for (init-expr; test-expr; update-expr)
    body-statement
```

The C language standard states (with one exception, highlighted in Problem 3.29) that the behavior of such a loop is identical to the following code using a `while` loop:

```
init-expr;
while (test-expr) {
    body-statement
    update-expr;
}
```

The program first evaluates the initialization expression *init-expr*. It enters a loop where it first evaluates the test condition *test-expr*, exiting if the test fails, then executes the body of the loop *body-statement*, and finally evaluates the update expression *update-expr*.

The code generated by GCC for a `for` loop then follows one of our two translation strategies for `while` loops, depending on the optimization level. That is, the jump-to-middle strategy yields the goto code

```
    init-expr;
    goto test;
loop:
    body-statement
    update-expr;
test:
    t = test-expr;
    if (t)
        goto loop;
```

while the guarded-do strategy yields

```
    init-expr;
    t = test-expr;
    if (!t)
        goto done;
loop:
    body-statement
    update-expr;
    t = test-expr;
    if (t)
        goto loop;
done:
```

As examples, consider a factorial function written with a `for` loop:

```
long fact_for(long n)
{
    long i;
    long result = 1;
```

```
    for (i = 2; i <= n; i++)
        result *= i;
    return result;
}
```

As shown, the natural way of writing a factorial function with a `for` loop is to multiply factors from 2 up to n, and so this function is quite different from the code we showed using either a `while` or a do-while loop.

We can identify the different components of the `for` loop in this code as follows:

init-expr	i = 2
test-expr	i <= n
update-expr	i++
body-statement	result *= i;

Substituting these components into the template we have shown to transform a `for` loop into a `while` loop yields the following:

```
long fact_for_while(long n)
{
    long i = 2;
    long result = 1;
    while (i <= n) {
        result *= i;
        i++;
    }
    return result;
}
```

Applying the jump-to-middle transformation to the `while` loop then yields the following version in goto code:

```
long fact_for_jm_goto(long n)
{
    long i = 2;
    long result = 1;
    goto test;
 loop:
    result *= i;
    i++;
 test:
    if (i <= n)
        goto loop;
    return result;
}
```

Indeed, a close examination of the assembly code produced by GCC with command-line option -Og closely follows this template:

```
long fact_for(long n)
 n in %rdi
fact_for:
  movl    $1, %eax        Set result = 1
  movl    $2, %edx        Set i = 2
  jmp     .L8             Goto test
.L9:                          loop:
  imulq   %rdx, %rax      Compute result *= i
  addq    $1, %rdx        Increment i
.L8:                         test:
  cmpq    %rdi, %rdx      Compare i:n
  jle     .L9             If <=, goto loop
  rep; ret                Return
```

Practice Problem 3.27 (solution page 336)

Write goto code for fact_for based on first transforming it to a while loop and then applying the guarded-do transformation.

We see from this presentation that all three forms of loops in C—do-while, while, and for—can be translated by a simple strategy, generating code that contains one or more conditional branches. Conditional transfer of control provides the basic mechanism for translating loops into machine code.

Practice Problem 3.28 (solution page 336)

A function fun_b has the following overall structure:

```
long fun_b(unsigned long x) {
    long val = 0;
    long i;
    for ( ... ; ... ; ... ) {
        .
        .
        .
    }
    return val;
}
```

The GCC C compiler generates the following assembly code:

```
  long fun_b(unsigned long x)
  x in %rdi
1  fun_b:
2    movl    $64, %edx
```

```
 3        movl    $0, %eax
 4     .L10:
 5        movq    %rdi, %rcx
 6        andl    $1, %ecx
 7        addq    %rax, %rax
 8        orq     %rcx, %rax
 9        shrq    %rdi            Shift right by 1
10        subq    $1, %rdx
11        jne     .L10
12        rep; ret
```

Reverse engineer the operation of this code and then do the following:

A. Use the assembly-code version to fill in the missing parts of the C code.

B. Explain why there is neither an initial test before the loop nor an initial jump to the test portion of the loop.

C. Describe in English what this function computes.

Practice Problem 3.29 (solution page 337)

Executing a `continue` statement in C causes the program to jump to the end of the current loop iteration. The stated rule for translating a `for` loop into a `while` loop needs some refinement when dealing with `continue` statements. For example, consider the following code:

```c
/* Example of for loop containing a continue statement */
/* Sum even numbers between 0 and 9 */
long sum = 0;
long i;
for (i = 0; i < 10; i++) {
    if (i & 1)
        continue;
    sum += i;
}
```

A. What would we get if we naively applied our rule for translating the `for` loop into a `while` loop? What would be wrong with this code?

B. How could you replace the `continue` statement with a `goto` statement to ensure that the `while` loop correctly duplicates the behavior of the `for` loop?

3.6.8 Switch Statements

A `switch` statement provides a multiway branching capability based on the value of an integer index. They are particularly useful when dealing with tests where there can be a large number of possible outcomes. Not only do they make the C code more readable, but they also allow an efficient implementation using a data structure called a *jump table*. A jump table is an array where entry i is the address of a code segment implementing the action the program should take when the switch index equals i. The code performs an array reference into the jump table using the switch index to determine the target for a jump instruction. The advantage of using a jump table over a long sequence of if-else statements is that the time taken to perform the switch is independent of the number of switch cases. Gcc selects the method of translating a switch statement based on the number of cases and the sparsity of the case values. Jump tables are used when there are a number of cases (e.g., four or more) and they span a small range of values.

Figure 3.22(a) shows an example of a C switch statement. This example has a number of interesting features, including case labels that do not span a contiguous range (there are no labels for cases 101 and 105), cases with multiple labels (cases 104 and 106), and cases that *fall through* to other cases (case 102) because the code for the case does not end with a break statement.

Figure 3.23 shows the assembly code generated when compiling switch_eg. The behavior of this code is shown in C as the procedure switch_eg_impl in Figure 3.22(b). This code makes use of support provided by GCC for jump tables, as an extension to the C language. The array jt contains seven entries, each of which is the address of a block of code. These locations are defined by labels in the code and indicated in the entries in jt by code pointers, consisting of the labels prefixed by &&. (Recall that the operator '&' creates a pointer for a data value. In making this extension, the authors of GCC created a new operator && to create a pointer for a code location.) We recommend that you study the C procedure switch_eg_impl and how it relates to the assembly-code version.

Our original C code has cases for values 100, 102–104, and 106, but the switch variable n can be an arbitrary integer. The compiler first shifts the range to between 0 and 6 by subtracting 100 from n, creating a new program variable that we call index in our C version. It further simplifies the branching possibilities by treating index as an *unsigned* value, making use of the fact that negative numbers in a two's-complement representation map to large positive numbers in an unsigned representation. It can therefore test whether index is outside of the range 0–6 by testing whether it is greater than 6. In the C and assembly code, there are five distinct locations to jump to, based on the value of index. These are loc_A (identified in the assembly code as .L3), loc_B (.L5), loc_C (.L6), loc_D (.L7), and loc_def (.L8), where the latter is the destination for the default case. Each of these labels identifies a block of code implementing one of the case branches. In both the C and the assembly code, the program compares index to 6 and jumps to the code for the default case if it is greater.

The key step in executing a switch statement is to access a code location through the jump table. This occurs in line 16 in the C code, with a goto statement that references the jump table jt. This *computed goto* is supported by GCC as an extension to the C language. In our assembly-code version, a similar operation occurs on line 5, where the jmp instruction's operand is prefixed with '*', indicating

(a) Switch statement

```
void switch_eg(long x, long n,
               long *dest)
{
    long val = x;

    switch (n) {

    case 100:
        val *= 13;
        break;

    case 102:
        val += 10;
        /* Fall through */

    case 103:
        val += 11;
        break;

    case 104:
    case 106:
        val *= val;
        break;

    default:
        val = 0;
    }
    *dest = val;
}
```

(b) Translation into extended C

```
1    void switch_eg_impl(long x, long n,
2                        long *dest)
3    {
4        /* Table of code pointers */
5        static void *jt[7] = {
6            &&loc_A, &&loc_def, &&loc_B,
7            &&loc_C, &&loc_D, &&loc_def,
8            &&loc_D
9        };
10       unsigned long index = n - 100;
11       long val;
12
13       if (index > 6)
14           goto loc_def;
15       /* Multiway branch */
16       goto *jt[index];
17
18   loc_A:    /* Case 100 */
19       val = x * 13;
20       goto done;
21   loc_B:    /* Case 102 */
22       x = x + 10;
23       /* Fall through */
24   loc_C:    /* Case 103 */
25       val = x + 11;
26       goto done;
27   loc_D:    /* Cases 104, 106 */
28       val = x * x;
29       goto done;
30   loc_def:  /* Default case */
31       val = 0;
32   done:
33       *dest = val;
34   }
```

Figure 3.22   Example `switch` statement and its translation into extended C. The translation shows the structure of jump table `jt` and how it is accessed. Such tables are supported by GCC as an extension to the C language.

an indirect jump, and the operand specifies a memory location indexed by register %eax, which holds the value of index. (We will see in Section 3.8 how array references are translated into machine code.)

Our C code declares the jump table as an array of seven elements, each of which is a pointer to a code location. These elements span values 0–6 of

```
       void switch_eg(long x, long n, long *dest)
       x in %rdi, n in %rsi, dest in %rdx
1   switch_eg:
2      subq      $100, %rsi           Compute index = n-100
3      cmpq      $6, %rsi             Compare index:6
4      ja        .L8                  If >, goto loc_def
5      jmp       *.L4(,%rsi,8)        Goto *jg[index]
6   .L3:                              loc_A:
7      leaq      (%rdi,%rdi,2), %rax  3*x
8      leaq      (%rdi,%rax,4), %rdi  val = 13*x
9      jmp       .L2                  Goto done
10  .L5:                              loc_B:
11     addq      $10, %rdi            x = x + 10
12  .L6:                              loc_C:
13     addq      $11, %rdi            val = x + 11
14     jmp       .L2                  Goto done
15  .L7:                              loc_D:
16     imulq     %rdi, %rdi           val = x * x
17     jmp       .L2                  Goto done
18  .L8:                              loc_def:
19     movl      $0, %edi             val = 0
20  .L2:                              done:
21     movq      %rdi, (%rdx)         *dest = val
22     ret                           Return
```

Figure 3.23   Assembly code for `switch` statement example in Figure 3.22.

index, corresponding to values 100–106 of n. Observe that the jump table handles duplicate cases by simply having the same code label (`loc_D`) for entries 4 and 6, and it handles missing cases by using the label for the default case (`loc_def`) as entries 1 and 5.

In the assembly code, the jump table is indicated by the following declarations, to which we have added comments:

```
1      .section      .rodata
2      .align 8                    Align address to multiple of 8
3   .L4:
4      .quad    .L3                Case 100: loc_A
5      .quad    .L8                Case 101: loc_def
6      .quad    .L5                Case 102: loc_B
7      .quad    .L6                Case 103: loc_C
8      .quad    .L7                Case 104: loc_D
9      .quad    .L8                Case 105: loc_def
10     .quad    .L7                Case 106: loc_D
```

These declarations state that within the segment of the object-code file called .rodata (for "read-only data"), there should be a sequence of seven "quad" (8-byte) words, where the value of each word is given by the instruction address associated with the indicated assembly-code labels (e.g., .L3). Label .L4 marks the start of this allocation. The address associated with this label serves as the base for the indirect jump (line 5).

The different code blocks (C labels loc_A through loc_D and loc_def) implement the different branches of the switch statement. Most of them simply compute a value for val and then go to the end of the function. Similarly, the assembly-code blocks compute a value for register %rdi and jump to the position indicated by label .L2 at the end of the function. Only the code for case label 102 does not follow this pattern, to account for the way the code for this case falls through to the block with label 103 in the original C code. This is handled in the assembly-code block starting with label .L5, by omitting the jmp instruction at the end of the block, so that the code continues execution of the next block. Similarly, the C version switch_eg_impl has no goto statement at the end of the block starting with label loc_B.

Examining all of this code requires careful study, but the key point is to see that the use of a jump table allows a very efficient way to implement a multiway branch. In our case, the program could branch to five distinct locations with a single jump table reference. Even if we had a switch statement with hundreds of cases, they could be handled by a single jump table access.

Practice Problem 3.30 (solution page 338)

In the C function that follows, we have omitted the body of the switch statement. In the C code, the case labels did not span a contiguous range, and some cases had multiple labels.

```c
void switch2(long x, long *dest) {
    long val = 0;
    switch (x) {
        ⋮
            Body of switch statement omitted
        ⋮
    }
    *dest = val;
}
```

In compiling the function, GCC generates the assembly code that follows for the initial part of the procedure, with variable x in %rdi:

```
    void switch2(long x, long *dest)
    x in %rdi
1   switch2:
2     addq    $1, %rdi
3     cmpq    $8, %rdi
4     ja      .L2
5     jmp     *.L4(,%rdi,8)
```

It generates the following code for the jump table:

```
1    .L4:
2       .quad    .L9
3       .quad    .L5
4       .quad    .L6
5       .quad    .L7
6       .quad    .L2
7       .quad    .L7
8       .quad    .L8
9       .quad    .L2
10      .quad    .L5
```

Based on this information, answer the following questions:

A. What were the values of the case labels in the switch statement?

B. What cases had multiple labels in the C code?

Practice Problem 3.31 (solution page 338)

For a C function switcher with the general structure

```
void switcher(long a, long b, long c, long *dest)
{
    long val;
    switch(a) {
    case _____:          /* Case A */
        c = _____;
        /* Fall through */
    case _____:          /* Case B */
        val = _____;
        break;
    case _____:          /* Case C */
    case _____:          /* Case D */
        val = _____;
        break;
    case _____:          /* Case E */
        val = _____;
        break;
    default:
        val = _____;
    }
    *dest = val;
}
```

GCC generates the assembly code and jump table shown in Figure 3.24.

Fill in the missing parts of the C code. Except for the ordering of case labels C and D, there is only one way to fit the different cases into the template.

(a) Code

```
      void switcher(long a, long b, long c, long *dest)
      a in %rsi, b in %rdi, c in %rdx, d in %rcx
1     switcher:
2       cmpq     $7, %rdi
3       ja       .L2
4       jmp      *.L4(,%rdi,8)
5       .section         .rodata
6     .L7:
7       xorq     $15, %rsi
8       movq     %rsi, %rdx
9     .L3:
10      leaq     112(%rdx), %rdi
11      jmp      .L6
12    .L5:
13      leaq     (%rdx,%rsi), %rdi
14      salq     $2, %rdi
15      jmp      .L6
16    .L2:
17      movq     %rsi, %rdi
18    .L6:
19      movq     %rdi, (%rcx)
20      ret
```

(b) Jump table

```
1     .L4:
2       .quad    .L3
3       .quad    .L2
4       .quad    .L5
5       .quad    .L2
6       .quad    .L6
7       .quad    .L7
8       .quad    .L2
9       .quad    .L5
```

Figure 3.24 **Assembly code and jump table for Problem 3.31.**

3.7 Procedures

Procedures are a key abstraction in software. They provide a way to package code that implements some functionality with a designated set of arguments and an optional return value. This function can then be invoked from different points in a program. Well-designed software uses procedures as an abstraction mechanism, hiding the detailed implementation of some action while providing a clear and concise interface definition of what values will be computed and what effects the procedure will have on the program state. Procedures come in many guises in different programming languages—functions, methods, subroutines, handlers, and so on—but they all share a general set of features.

There are many different attributes that must be handled when providing machine-level support for procedures. For discussion purposes, suppose procedure P calls procedure Q, and Q then executes and returns back to P. These actions involve one or more of the following mechanisms:

Passing control. The program counter must be set to the starting address of the code for Q upon entry and then set to the instruction in P following the call to Q upon return.

Passing data. P must be able to provide one or more parameters to Q, and Q must be able to return a value back to P.

Allocating and deallocating memory. Q may need to allocate space for local variables when it begins and then free that storage before it returns.

The x86-64 implementation of procedures involves a combination of special instructions and a set of conventions on how to use the machine resources, such as the registers and the program memory. Great effort has been made to minimize the overhead involved in invoking a procedure. As a consequence, it follows what can be seen as a minimalist strategy, implementing only as much of the above set of mechanisms as is required for each particular procedure. In our presentation, we build up the different mechanisms step by step, first describing control, then data passing, and, finally, memory management.

3.7.1 The Run-Time Stack

A key feature of the procedure-calling mechanism of C, and of most other languages, is that it can make use of the last-in, first-out memory management discipline provided by a stack data structure. Using our example of procedure P calling procedure Q, we can see that while Q is executing, P, along with any of the procedures in the chain of calls up to P, is temporarily suspended. While Q is running, only it will need the ability to allocate new storage for its local variables or to set up a call to another procedure. On the other hand, when Q returns, any local storage it has allocated can be freed. Therefore, a program can manage the storage required by its procedures using a stack, where the stack and the program registers store the information required for passing control and data, and for allocating memory. As P calls Q, control and data information are added to the end of the stack. This information gets deallocated when P returns.

As described in Section 3.4.4, the x86-64 stack grows toward lower addresses and the stack pointer %rsp points to the top element of the stack. Data can be stored on and retrieved from the stack using the pushq and popq instructions. Space for data with no specified initial value can be allocated on the stack by simply decrementing the stack pointer by an appropriate amount. Similarly, space can be deallocated by incrementing the stack pointer.

When an x86-64 procedure requires storage beyond what it can hold in registers, it allocates space on the stack. This region is referred to as the procedure's

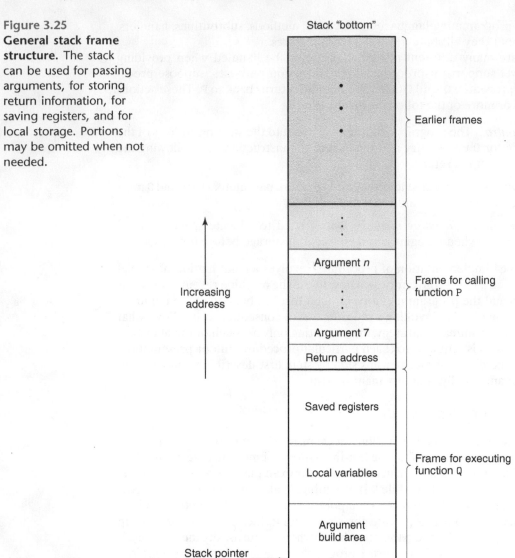

Figure 3.25

General stack frame structure. The stack can be used for passing arguments, for storing return information, for saving registers, and for local storage. Portions may be omitted when not needed.

stack frame. Figure 3.25 shows the overall structure of the run-time stack, including its partitioning into stack frames, in its most general form. The frame for the currently executing procedure is always at the top of the stack. When procedure P calls procedure Q, it will push the *return address* onto the stack, indicating where within P the program should resume execution once Q returns. We consider the return address to be part of P's stack frame, since it holds state relevant to P. The code for Q allocates the space required for its stack frame by extending the current stack boundary. Within that space, it can save the values of registers, allocate space for local variables, and set up arguments for the procedures it calls. The stack frames for most procedures are of fixed size, allocated at the beginning of the procedure. Some procedures, however, require variable-size frames. This issue is discussed in Section 3.10.5. Procedure P can pass up to six integral values (i.e., pointers and integers) on the stack, but if Q requires more arguments, these can be stored by P within its stack frame prior to the call.

In the interest of space and time efficiency, x86-64 procedures allocate only the portions of stack frames they require. For example, many procedures have six or fewer arguments, and so all of their parameters can be passed in registers. Thus, parts of the stack frame diagrammed in Figure 3.25 may be omitted. Indeed, many functions do not even require a stack frame. This occurs when all of the local variables can be held in registers and the function does not call any other functions (sometimes referred to as a *leaf procedure*, in reference to the tree structure of procedure calls). For example, none of the functions we have examined thus far required stack frames.

3.7.2 Control Transfer

Passing control from function P to function Q involves simply setting the program counter (PC) to the starting address of the code for Q. However, when it later comes time for Q to return, the processor must have some record of the code location where it should resume the execution of P. This information is recorded in x86-64 machines by invoking procedure Q with the instruction call Q. This instruction pushes an address A onto the stack and sets the PC to the beginning of Q. The pushed address A is referred to as the *return address* and is computed as the address of the instruction immediately following the call instruction. The counterpart instruction ret pops an address A off the stack and sets the PC to A.

The general forms of the call and ret instructions are described as follows:

Instruction	Description
call *Label*	Procedure call
call **Operand*	Procedure call
ret	Return from call

(These instructions are referred to as callq and retq in the disassembly outputs generated by the program OBJDUMP. The added suffix 'q' simply emphasizes that these are x86-64 versions of call and return instructions, not IA32. In x86-64 assembly code, both versions can be used interchangeably.)

The call instruction has a target indicating the address of the instruction where the called procedure starts. Like jumps, a call can be either direct or indirect. In assembly code, the target of a direct call is given as a label, while the target of an indirect call is given by '*' followed by an operand specifier using one of the formats described in Figure 3.3.

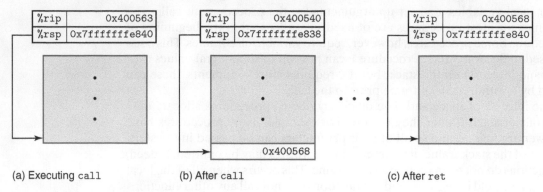

(a) Executing `call`　　　　(b) After `call`　　　　(c) After `ret`

Figure 3.26 Illustration of `call` and `ret` functions. The `call` instruction transfers control to the start of a function, while the `ret` instruction returns back to the instruction following the call.

Figure 3.26 illustrates the execution of the `call` and `ret` instructions for the `multstore` and `main` functions introduced in Section 3.2.2. The following are excerpts of the disassembled code for the two functions:

```
        Beginning of function multstore
1   0000000000400540 <multstore>:
2     400540:  53                      push    %rbx
3     400541:  48 89 d3                mov     %rdx,%rbx
      . . .
        Return from function multstore
4     40054d:  c3                      retq
      . . .
        Call to multstore from main
5     400563:  e8 d8 ff ff ff          callq   400540 <multstore>
6     400568:  48 8b 54 24 08          mov     0x8(%rsp),%rdx
```

In this code, we can see that the `call` instruction with address 0x400563 in `main` calls function `multstore`. This status is shown in Figure 3.26(a), with the indicated values for the stack pointer `%rsp` and the program counter `%rip`. The effect of the `call` is to push the return address 0x400568 onto the stack and to jump to the first instruction in function `multstore`, at address 0x0400540 (3.26(b)). The execution of function `multstore` continues until it hits the `ret` instruction at address 0x40054d. This instruction pops the value 0x400568 from the stack and jumps to this address, resuming the execution of `main` just after the `call` instruction (3.26(c)).

As a more detailed example of passing control to and from procedures, Figure 3.27(a) shows the disassembled code for two functions, `top` and `leaf`, as well as the portion of code in function `main` where `top` gets called. Each instruction is identified by labels L1–L2 (in `leaf`), T1–T4 (in `top`), and M1–M2 in `main`. Part (b) of the figure shows a detailed trace of the code execution, in which `main` calls `top(100)`, causing `top` to call `leaf(95)`. Function `leaf` returns 97 to `top`, which

(a) Disassembled code for demonstrating procedure calls and returns

```
        Disassembly of leaf(long y)
        y in %rdi
1   0000000000400540 <leaf>:
2       400540:   48 8d 47 02              lea     0x2(%rdi),%rax    L1: z+2
3       400544:   c3                       retq                      L2: Return

4   0000000000400545 <top>:
        Disassembly of top(long x)
        x in %rdi
5       400545:   48 83 ef 05              sub     $0x5,%rdi         T1: x-5
6       400549:   e8 f2 ff ff ff           callq   400540 <leaf>    T2: Call leaf(x-5)
7       40054e:   48 01 c0                 add     %rax,%rax        T3: Double result
8       400551:   c3                       retq                      T4: Return


        . . .

        Call to top from function main
9       40055b:   e8 e5 ff ff ff           callq   400545 <top>     M1: Call top(100)
10      400560:   48 89 c2                 mov     %rax,%rdx        M2: Resume
```

(b) Execution trace of example code

| Instruction | | | State values (at beginning) | | | | |
Label	PC	Instruction	%rdi	%rax	%rsp	*%rsp	Description
M1	0x40055b	callq	100	—	0x7fffffffe820	—	Call top(100)
T1	0x400545	sub	100	—	0x7fffffffe818	0x400560	Entry of top
T2	0x400549	callq	95	—	0x7fffffffe818	0x400560	Call leaf(95)
L1	0x400540	lea	95	—	0x7fffffffe810	0x40054e	Entry of leaf
L2	0x400544	retq	—	97	0x7fffffffe810	0x40054e	Return 97 from leaf
T3	0x40054e	add	—	97	0x7fffffffe818	0x400560	Resume top
T4	0x400551	retq	—	194	0x7fffffffe818	0x400560	Return 194 from top
M2	0x400560	mov	—	194	0x7fffffffe820	—	Resume main

Figure 3.27 Detailed execution of program involving procedure calls and returns. Using the stack to store return addresses makes it possible to return to the right point in the procedures.

then returns 194 to main. The first three columns describe the instruction being executed, including the instruction label, the address, and the instruction type. The next four columns show the state of the program *before* the instruction is executed, including the contents of registers %rdi, %rax, and %rsp, as well as the value at the top of the stack. The contents of this table should be studied carefully, as they demonstrate the important role of the run-time stack in managing the storage needed to support procedure calls and returns.

Instruction L1 of leaf sets %rax to 97, the value to be returned. Instruction L2 then returns. It pops 0x400054e from the stack. In setting the PC to this popped value, control transfers back to instruction T3 of top. The program has successfully completed the call to leaf and returned to top.

Instruction T3 sets %rax to 194, the value to be returned from top. Instruction T4 then returns. It pops 0x4000560 from the stack, thereby setting the PC to instruction M2 of main. The program has successfully completed the call to top and returned to main. We see that the stack pointer has also been restored to 0x7fffffffe820, the value it had before the call to top.

We can see that this simple mechanism of pushing the return address onto the stack makes it possible for the function to later return to the proper point in the program. The standard call/return mechanism of C (and of most programming languages) conveniently matches the last-in, first-out memory management discipline provided by a stack.

Practice Problem 3.32 (solution page 339)

The disassembled code for two functions first and last is shown below, along with the code for a call of first by function main:

```
    Disassembly of last(long u, long v)
    u in %rdi, v in %rsi
1   0000000000400540 <last>:
2     400540:   48 89 f8            mov    %rdi,%rax        L1: u
3     400543:   48 0f af c6         imul   %rsi,%rax        L2: u*v
4     400547:   c3                  retq                    L3: Return


    Disassembly of last(long x)
    x in %rdi
5   0000000000400548 <first>:
6     400548:   48 8d 77 01         lea    0x1(%rdi),%rsi   F1: x+1
7     40054c:   48 83 ef 01         sub    $0x1,%rdi        F2: x-1
8     400550:   e8 eb ff ff ff      callq  400540 <last>    F3: Call last(x-1,x+1)
9     400555:   f3 c3               repz retq               F4: Return
        .
        .
        .
10    400560:   e8 e3 ff ff ff      callq  400548 <first>   M1: Call first(10)
11    400565:   48 89 c2            mov    %rax,%rdx        M2: Resume
```

Each of these instructions is given a label, similar to those in Figure 3.27(a). Starting with the calling of first(10) by main, fill in the following table to trace instruction execution through to the point where the program returns back to main.

	Instruction		State values (at beginning)					
Label	PC	Instruction	%rdi	%rsi	%rax	%rsp	*%rsp	Description
M1	0x400560	callq	10	—	—	0x7fffffffe820	—	Call first(10)
F1								
F2								
F3								
L1								
L2								
L3								
F4								
M2								

3.7.3 Data Transfer

In addition to passing control to a procedure when called, and then back again when the procedure returns, procedure calls may involve passing data as arguments, and returning from a procedure may also involve returning a value. With x86-64, most of these data passing to and from procedures take place via registers. For example, we have already seen numerous examples of functions where arguments are passed in registers %rdi, %rsi, and others, and where values are returned in register %rax. When procedure P calls procedure Q, the code for P must first copy the arguments into the proper registers. Similarly, when Q returns back to P, the code for P can access the returned value in register %rax. In this section, we explore these conventions in greater detail.

With x86-64, up to six integral (i.e., integer and pointer) arguments can be passed via registers. The registers are used in a specified order, with the name used for a register depending on the size of the data type being passed. These are shown in Figure 3.28. Arguments are allocated to these registers according to their

Operand size (bits)	Argument number					
	1	2	3	4	5	6
64	%rdi	%rsi	%rdx	%rcx	%r8	%r9
32	%edi	%esi	%edx	%ecx	%r8d	%r9d
16	%di	%si	%dx	%cx	%r8w	%r9w
8	%dil	%sil	%dl	%cl	%r8b	%r9b

Figure 3.28 Registers for passing function arguments. The registers are used in a specified order and named according to the argument sizes.

ordering in the argument list. Arguments smaller than 64 bits can be accessed using the appropriate subsection of the 64-bit register. For example, if the first argument is 32 bits, it can be accessed as %edi.

When a function has more than six integral arguments, the other ones are passed on the stack. Assume that procedure P calls procedure Q with n integral arguments, such that $n > 6$. Then the code for P must allocate a stack frame with enough storage for arguments 7 through n, as illustrated in Figure 3.25. It copies arguments 1–6 into the appropriate registers, and it puts arguments 7 through n onto the stack, with argument 7 at the top of the stack. When passing parameters on the stack, all data sizes are rounded up to be multiples of eight. With the arguments in place, the program can then execute a call instruction to transfer control to procedure Q. Procedure Q can access its arguments via registers and possibly from the stack. If Q, in turn, calls some function that has more than six arguments, it can allocate space within its stack frame for these, as is illustrated by the area labeled "Argument build area" in Figure 3.25.

As an example of argument passing, consider the C function proc shown in Figure 3.29(a). This function has eight arguments, including integers with different numbers of bytes (8, 4, 2, and 1), as well as different types of pointers, each of which is 8 bytes.

The assembly code generated for proc is shown in Figure 3.29(b). The first six arguments are passed in registers. The last two are passed on the stack, as documented by the diagram of Figure 3.30. This diagram shows the state of the stack during the execution of proc. We can see that the return address was pushed onto the stack as part of the procedure call. The two arguments, therefore, are at positions 8 and 16 relative to the stack pointer. Within the code, we can see that different versions of the ADD instruction are used according to the sizes of the operands: addq for a1 (long), addl for a2 (int), addw for a3 (short), and addb for a4 (char). Observe that the movl instruction of line 6 reads 4 bytes from memory; the following addb instruction only makes use of the low-order byte.

Practice Problem 3.33 (solution page 339)

A C function procprob has four arguments u, a, v, and b. Each is either a signed number or a pointer to a signed number, where the numbers have different sizes. The function has the following body:

```
*u += a;
*v += b;
return sizeof(a) + sizeof(b);
```

It compiles to the following x86-64 code:

```
1   procprob:
2      movslq  %edi, %rdi
3      addq    %rdi, (%rdx)
4      addb    %sil, (%rcx)
```

(a) C code

```
void proc(long   a1, long   *a1p,
          int    a2, int    *a2p,
          short  a3, short  *a3p,
          char   a4, char   *a4p)
{
    *a1p += a1;
    *a2p += a2;
    *a3p += a3;
    *a4p += a4;
}
```

(b) Generated assembly code

```
    void proc(a1, a1p, a2, a2p, a3, a3p, a4, a4p)
    Arguments passed as follows:
      a1  in %rdi           (64 bits)
      a1p in %rsi           (64 bits)
      a2  in %edx           (32 bits)
      a2p in %rcx           (64 bits)
      a3  in %r8w           (16 bits)
      a3p in %r9            (64 bits)
      a4  at %rsp+8         ( 8 bits)
      a4p at %rsp+16        (64 bits)
1   proc:
2     movq    16(%rsp), %rax    Fetch a4p  (64 bits)
3     addq    %rdi, (%rsi)      *a1p += a1 (64 bits)
4     addl    %edx, (%rcx)      *a2p += a2 (32 bits)
5     addw    %r8w, (%r9)       *a3p += a3 (16 bits)
6     movl    8(%rsp), %edx     Fetch a4   ( 8 bits)
7     addb    %dl, (%rax)       *a4p += a4 ( 8 bits)
8     ret                       Return
```

Figure 3.29 Example of function with multiple arguments of different types.
Arguments 1–6 are passed in registers, while arguments 7–8 are passed on the stack.

**Figure 3.30
Stack frame structure for
function** proc. **Arguments**
a4 **and** a4p **are passed on
the stack.**

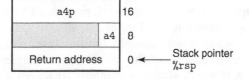

```
5       movl    $6, %eax
6       ret
```

Determine a valid ordering and types of the four parameters. There are two correct answers.

3.7.4   Local Storage on the Stack

Most of the procedure examples we have seen so far did not require any local storage beyond what could be held in registers. At times, however, local data must be stored in memory. Common cases of this include these:

- There are not enough registers to hold all of the local data.
- The address operator '&' is applied to a local variable, and hence we must be able to generate an address for it.
- Some of the local variables are arrays or structures and hence must be accessed by array or structure references. We will discuss this possibility when we describe how arrays and structures are allocated.

Typically, a procedure allocates space on the stack frame by decrementing the stack pointer. This results in the portion of the stack frame labeled "Local variables" in Figure 3.25.

As an example of the handling of the address operator, consider the two functions shown in Figure 3.31(a). The function swap_add swaps the two values designated by pointers xp and yp and also returns the sum of the two values. The function caller creates pointers to local variables arg1 and arg2 and passes these to swap_add. Figure 3.31(b) shows how caller uses a stack frame to implement these local variables. The code for caller starts by decrementing the stack pointer by 16; this effectively allocates 16 bytes on the stack. Letting S denote the value of the stack pointer, we can see that the code computes &arg2 as $S + 8$ (line 5), &arg1 as S (line 6). We can therefore infer that local variables arg1 and arg2 are stored within the stack frame at offsets 0 and 8 relative to the stack pointer. When the call to swap_add completes, the code for caller then retrieves the two values from the stack (lines 8–9), computes their difference, and multiplies this by the value returned by swap_add in register %rax (line 10). Finally, the function deallocates its stack frame by incrementing the stack pointer by 16 (line 11.) We can see with this example that the run-time stack provides a simple mechanism for allocating local storage when it is required and deallocating it when the function completes.

As a more complex example, the function call_proc, shown in Figure 3.32, illustrates many aspects of the x86-64 stack discipline. Despite the length of this example, it is worth studying carefully. It shows a function that must allocate storage on the stack for local variables, as well as to pass values to the 8-argument function proc (Figure 3.29). The function creates a stack frame, diagrammed in Figure 3.33.

Looking at the assembly code for call_proc (Figure 3.32(b)), we can see that a large portion of the code (lines 2–15) involves preparing to call function

(a) Code for swap_add and calling function

```
long swap_add(long *xp, long *yp)
{
    long x = *xp;
    long y = *yp;
    *xp = y;
    *yp = x;
    return x + y;
}


long caller()
{
    long arg1 = 534;
    long arg2 = 1057;
    long sum = swap_add(&arg1, &arg2);
    long diff = arg1 - arg2;
    return sum * diff;
}
```

(b) Generated assembly code for calling function

```
        long caller()
1   caller:
2       subq    $16, %rsp           Allocate 16 bytes for stack frame
3       movq    $534, (%rsp)        Store 534 in arg1
4       movq    $1057, 8(%rsp)      Store 1057 in arg2
5       leaq    8(%rsp), %rsi       Compute &arg2 as second argument
6       movq    %rsp, %rdi          Compute &arg1 as first argument
7       call    swap_add            Call swap_add(&arg1, &arg2)
8       movq    (%rsp), %rdx        Get arg1
9       subq    8(%rsp), %rdx       Compute diff = arg1 - arg2
10      imulq   %rdx, %rax          Compute sum * diff
11      addq    $16, %rsp           Deallocate stack frame
12      ret                         Return
```

Figure 3.31   Example of procedure definition and call. The calling code must allocate a stack frame due to the presence of address operators.

proc. This includes setting up the stack frame for the local variables and function parameters, and for loading function arguments into registers. As Figure 3.33 shows, local variables x1–x4 are allocated on the stack and have different sizes. Expressing their locations as offsets relative to the stack pointer, they occupy bytes 24–31 (x1), 20–23 (x2), 18–19 (x3), and 17 (s3). Pointers to these locations are generated by leaq instructions (lines 7, 10, 12, and 14). Arguments 7 (with value 4) and 8 (a pointer to the location of x4) are stored on the stack at offsets 0 and 8 relative to the stack pointer.

(a) C code for calling function

```
long call_proc()
{
    long  x1 = 1; int  x2 = 2;
    short x3 = 3; char x4 = 4;
    proc(x1, &x1, x2, &x2, x3, &x3, x4, &x4);
    return (x1+x2)*(x3-x4);
}
```

(b) Generated assembly code

```
         long call_proc()
1    call_proc:
       Set up arguments to proc
2        subq    $32, %rsp            Allocate 32-byte stack frame
3        movq    $1, 24(%rsp)         Store 1 in &x1
4        movl    $2, 20(%rsp)         Store 2 in &x2
5        movw    $3, 18(%rsp)         Store 3 in &x3
6        movb    $4, 17(%rsp)         Store 4 in &x4
7        leaq    17(%rsp), %rax       Create &x4
8        movq    %rax, 8(%rsp)        Store &x4 as argument 8
9        movl    $4, (%rsp)           Store 4 as argument 7
10       leaq    18(%rsp), %r9        Pass &x3 as argument 6
11       movl    $3, %r8d             Pass 3 as argument 5
12       leaq    20(%rsp), %rcx       Pass &x2 as argument 4
13       movl    $2, %edx             Pass 2 as argument 3
14       leaq    24(%rsp), %rsi       Pass &x1 as argument 2
15       movl    $1, %edi             Pass 1 as argument 1
       Call proc
16       call    proc
       Retrieve changes to memory
17       movslq  20(%rsp), %rdx       Get x2 and convert to long
18       addq    24(%rsp), %rdx       Compute x1+x2
19       movswl  18(%rsp), %eax       Get x3 and convert to int
20       movsbl  17(%rsp), %ecx       Get x4 and convert to int
21       subl    %ecx, %eax           Compute x3-x4
22       cltq                         Convert to long
23       imulq   %rdx, %rax           Compute (x1+x2) * (x3-x4)
24       addq    $32, %rsp            Deallocate stack frame
25       ret                          Return
```

Figure 3.32 Example of code to call function proc**, defined in Figure 3.29.** This code creates a stack frame.

Figure 3.33
Stack frame for function
`call_proc`. The stack
frame contains local
variables, as well as two of
the arguments to pass to
function `proc`.

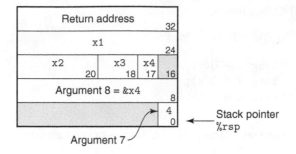

When procedure `proc` is called, the program will begin executing the code shown in Figure 3.29(b). As shown in Figure 3.30, arguments 7 and 8 are now at offsets 8 and 16 relative to the stack pointer, because the return address was pushed onto the stack.

When the program returns to `call_proc`, the code retrieves the values of the four local variables (lines 17–20) and performs the final computations. It finishes by incrementing the stack pointer by 32 to deallocate the stack frame.

3.7.5 Local Storage in Registers

The set of program registers acts as a single resource shared by all of the procedures. Although only one procedure can be active at a given time, we must make sure that when one procedure (the *caller*) calls another (the *callee*), the callee does not overwrite some register value that the caller planned to use later. For this reason, x86-64 adopts a uniform set of conventions for register usage that must be respected by all procedures, including those in program libraries.

By convention, registers `%rbx`, `%rbp`, and `%r12`–`%r15` are classified as *callee-saved* registers. When procedure P calls procedure Q, Q must *preserve* the values of these registers, ensuring that they have the same values when Q returns to P as they did when Q was called. Procedure Q can preserve a register value by either not changing it at all or by pushing the original value on the stack, altering it, and then popping the old value from the stack before returning. The pushing of register values has the effect of creating the portion of the stack frame labeled "Saved registers" in Figure 3.25. With this convention, the code for P can safely store a value in a callee-saved register (after saving the previous value on the stack, of course), call Q, and then use the value in the register without risk of it having been corrupted.

All other registers, except for the stack pointer `%rsp`, are classified as *caller-saved* registers. This means that they can be modified by any function. The name "caller saved" can be understood in the context of a procedure P having some local data in such a register and calling procedure Q. Since Q is free to alter this register, it is incumbent upon P (the caller) to first save the data before it makes the call.

As an example, consider the function P shown in Figure 3.34(a). It calls Q twice. During the first call, it must retain the value of x for use later. Similarly, during the second call, it must retain the value computed for Q(y). In Figure 3.34(b),

(a) Calling function

```
long P(long x, long y)
{
    long u = Q(y);
    long v = Q(x);
    return u + v;
}
```

(b) Generated assembly code for the calling function

```
        long P(long x, long y)
        x in %rdi, y in %rsi
1    P:
2        pushq    %rbp            Save %rbp
3        pushq    %rbx            Save %rbx
4        subq     $8, %rsp        Align stack frame
5        movq     %rdi, %rbp      Save x
6        movq     %rsi, %rdi      Move y to first argument
7        call     Q               Call Q(y)
8        movq     %rax, %rbx      Save result
9        movq     %rbp, %rdi      Move x to first argument
10       call     Q               Call Q(x)
11       addq     %rbx, %rax      Add saved Q(y) to Q(x)
12       addq     $8, %rsp        Deallocate last part of stack
13       popq     %rbx            Restore %rbx
14       popq     %rbp            Restore %rbp
15       ret
```

Figure 3.34 Code demonstrating use of callee-saved registers. Value x must be preserved during the first call, and value Q(y) must be preserved during the second.

we can see that the code generated by GCC uses two callee-saved registers: %rbp to hold x, and %rbx to hold the computed value of Q(y). At the beginning of the function, it saves the values of these two registers on the stack (lines 2–3). It copies argument x to %rbp before the first call to Q (line 5). It copies the result of this call to %rbx before the second call to Q (line 8). At the end of the function (lines 13–14), it restores the values of the two callee-saved registers by popping them off the stack. Note how they are popped in the reverse order from how they were pushed, to account for the last-in, first-out discipline of a stack.

Practice Problem 3.34 (solution page 340)

Consider a function P, which generates local values, named a0–a8. It then calls function Q using these generated values as arguments. Gcc produces the following code for the first part of P:

```
     long P(long x)
     x in %rdi
1    P:
2        pushq    %r15
3        pushq    %r14
4        pushq    %r13
5        pushq    %r12
6        pushq    %rbp
7        pushq    %rbx
8        subq     $24, %rsp
9        movq     %rdi, %rbx
10       leaq     1(%rdi), %r15
11       leaq     2(%rdi), %r14
12       leaq     3(%rdi), %r13
13       leaq     4(%rdi), %r12
14       leaq     5(%rdi), %rbp
15       leaq     6(%rdi), %rax
16       movq     %rax, (%rsp)
17       leaq     7(%rdi), %rdx
18       movq     %rdx, 8(%rsp)
19       movl     $0, %eax
20       call     Q
           . . .
```

A. Identify which local values get stored in callee-saved registers.

B. Identify which local values get stored on the stack.

C. Explain why the program could not store all of the local values in callee-saved registers.

3.7.6 Recursive Procedures

The conventions we have described for using the registers and the stack allow x86-64 procedures to call themselves recursively. Each procedure call has its own private space on the stack, and so the local variables of the multiple outstanding calls do not interfere with one another. Furthermore, the stack discipline naturally provides the proper policy for allocating local storage when the procedure is called and deallocating it before returning.

Figure 3.35 shows both the C code and the generated assembly code for a recursive factorial function. We can see that the assembly code uses register %rbx to hold the parameter n, after first saving the existing value on the stack (line 2) and later restoring the value before returning (line 11). Due to the stack discipline, and the register-saving conventions, we can be assured that when the recursive call to rfact(n-1) returns (line 9) that (1) the result of the call will be held in register

(a) C code

```c
long rfact(long n)
{
    long result;
    if (n <= 1)
        result = 1;
    else
        result = n * rfact(n-1);
    return result;
}
```

(b) Generated assembly code

```
    long rfact(long n)
    n in %rdi
1   rfact:
2     pushq   %rbx                Save %rbx
3     movq    %rdi, %rbx          Store n in callee-saved register
4     movl    $1, %eax            Set return value = 1
5     cmpq    $1, %rdi            Compare n:1
6     jle     .L35                If <=, goto done
7     leaq    -1(%rdi), %rdi      Compute n-1
8     call    rfact               Call rfact(n-1)
9     imulq   %rbx, %rax          Multiply result by n
10  .L35:                       done:
11    popq    %rbx                Restore %rbx
12    ret                         Return
```

Figure 3.35 Code for recursive factorial program. The standard procedure handling mechanisms suffice for implementing recursive functions.

%rax, and (2) the value of argument n will held in register %rbx. Multiplying these two values then computes the desired result.

We can see from this example that calling a function recursively proceeds just like any other function call. Our stack discipline provides a mechanism where each invocation of a function has its own private storage for state information (saved values of the return location and callee-saved registers). If need be, it can also provide storage for local variables. The stack discipline of allocation and deallocation naturally matches the call-return ordering of functions. This method of implementing function calls and returns even works for more complex patterns, including mutual recursion (e.g., when procedure P calls Q, which in turn calls P).

Practice Problem 3.35 (solution page 340)

For a C function having the general structure

```
long rfun(unsigned long x) {
    if ( _____ )
        return _____;
    unsigned long nx = _____;
    long rv = rfun(nx);
    return _____;
}
```

GCC generates the following assembly code:

```
     long rfun(unsigned long x)
     x in %rdi
1    rfun:
2      pushq   %rbx
3      movq    %rdi, %rbx
4      movl    $0, %eax
5      testq   %rdi, %rdi
6      je      .L2
7      shrq    $2, %rdi
8      call    rfun
9      addq    %rbx, %rax
10   .L2:
11     popq    %rbx
12     ret
```

A. What value does `rfun` store in the callee-saved register `%rbx`?

B. Fill in the missing expressions in the C code shown above.

3.8   Array Allocation and Access

Arrays in C are one means of aggregating scalar data into larger data types. C uses a particularly simple implementation of arrays, and hence the translation into machine code is fairly straightforward. One unusual feature of C is that we can generate pointers to elements within arrays and perform arithmetic with these pointers. These are translated into address computations in machine code.

Optimizing compilers are particularly good at simplifying the address computations used by array indexing. This can make the correspondence between the C code and its translation into machine code somewhat difficult to decipher.

3.8.1   Basic Principles

For data type T and integer constant N, consider a declaration of the form

T A[N];

Let us denote the starting location as x_A. The declaration has two effects. First, it allocates a contiguous region of $L \cdot N$ bytes in memory, where L is the size (in bytes) of data type T. Second, it introduces an identifier A that can be used as a pointer to the beginning of the array. The value of this pointer will be x_A. The array elements can be accessed using an integer index ranging between 0 and $N-1$. Array element i will be stored at address $x_A + L \cdot i$.

As examples, consider the following declarations:

```
char    A[12];
char    *B[8];
int     C[6];
double *D[5];
```

These declarations will generate arrays with the following parameters:

Array	Element size	Total size	Start address	Element i
A	1	12	x_A	$x_A + i$
B	8	64	x_B	$x_B + 8i$
C	4	24	x_C	$x_C + 4i$
D	8	40	x_D	$x_D + 8i$

Array A consists of 12 single-byte (char) elements. Array C consists of 6 integers, each requiring 4 bytes. B and D are both arrays of pointers, and hence the array elements are 8 bytes each.

The memory referencing instructions of x86-64 are designed to simplify array access. For example, suppose E is an array of values of type int and we wish to evaluate E[i], where the address of E is stored in register %rdx and i is stored in register %rcx. Then the instruction

```
movl (%rdx,%rcx,4),%eax
```

will perform the address computation $x_E + 4i$, read that memory location, and copy the result to register %eax. The allowed scaling factors of 1, 2, 4, and 8 cover the sizes of the common primitive data types.

Practice Problem 3.36 (solution page 341)

Consider the following declarations:

```
short    S[7];
short   *T[3];
short  **U[6];
int      V[8];
double  *W[4];
```

Fill in the following table describing the element size, the total size, and the address of element i for each of these arrays.

Array	Element size	Total size	Start address	Element i
S	_____	_____	x_S	_____
T	_____	_____	x_T	_____
U	_____	_____	x_U	_____
V	_____	_____	x_V	_____
W	_____	_____	x_W	_____

3.8.2 Pointer Arithmetic

C allows arithmetic on pointers, where the computed value is scaled according to the size of the data type referenced by the pointer. That is, if p is a pointer to data of type T, and the value of p is x_p, then the expression p+i has value $x_p + L \cdot i$, where L is the size of data type T.

The unary operators '&' and '*' allow the generation and dereferencing of pointers. That is, for an expression *Expr* denoting some object, &*Expr* is a pointer giving the address of the object. For an expression *AExpr* denoting an address, *AExpr* gives the value at that address. The expressions *Expr* and *&Expr* are therefore equivalent. The array subscripting operation can be applied to both arrays and pointers. The array reference A[i] is identical to the expression *(A+i). It computes the address of the ith array element and then accesses this memory location.

Expanding on our earlier example, suppose the starting address of integer array E and integer index i are stored in registers %rdx and %rcx, respectively. The following are some expressions involving E. We also show an assembly-code implementation of each expression, with the result being stored in either register %eax (for data) or register %rax (for pointers).

Expression	Type	Value	Assembly code
E	int *	x_E	movl %rdx,%rax
E[0]	int	$M[x_E]$	movl (%rdx),%eax
E[i]	int	$M[x_E + 4i]$	movl (%rdx,%rcx,4),%eax
&E[2]	int *	$x_E + 8$	leaq 8(%rdx),%rax
E+i-1	int *	$x_E + 4i - 4$	leaq -4(%rdx,%rcx,4),%rax
*(E+i-3)	int	$M[x_E + 4i - 12]$	movl -12(%rdx,%rcx,4),%eax
&E[i]-E	long	i	movq %rcx,%rax

In these examples, we see that operations that return array values have type int, and hence involve 4-byte operations (e.g., movl) and registers (e.g., %eax). Those that return pointers have type int *, and hence involve 8-byte operations (e.g., leaq) and registers (e.g., %rax). The final example shows that one can compute the difference of two pointers within the same data structure, with the result being data having type long and value equal to the difference of the two addresses divided by the size of the data type.

Practice Problem 3.37 (solution page 341)

Suppose x_S, the address of short integer array S, and long integer index i are stored in registers %rdx and %rcx, respectively. For each of the following expressions, give its type, a formula for its value, and an assembly-code implementation. The result should be stored in register %rax if it is a pointer and register element %ax if it has data type short.

Expression	Type	Value	Assembly code
S+1	_____	_____	_____
S[3]	_____	_____	_____
&S[i]	_____	_____	_____
S[4*i+1]	_____	_____	_____
S+i-5	_____	_____	_____

3.8.3 Nested Arrays

The general principles of array allocation and referencing hold even when we create arrays of arrays. For example, the declaration

```
int A[5][3];
```

is equivalent to the declaration

```
typedef int row3_t[3];
row3_t A[5];
```

Data type row3_t is defined to be an array of three integers. Array A contains five such elements, each requiring 12 bytes to store the three integers. The total array size is then $4 \cdot 5 \cdot 3 = 60$ bytes.

Array A can also be viewed as a two-dimensional array with five rows and three columns, referenced as A[0][0] through A[4][2]. The array elements are ordered in memory in *row-major* order, meaning all elements of row 0, which can be written A[0], followed by all elements of row 1 (A[1]), and so on. This is illustrated in Figure 3.36.

This ordering is a consequence of our nested declaration. Viewing A as an array of five elements, each of which is an array of three int's, we first have A[0], followed by A[1], and so on.

To access elements of multidimensional arrays, the compiler generates code to compute the offset of the desired element and then uses one of the MOV instructions with the start of the array as the base address and the (possibly scaled) offset as an index. In general, for an array declared as

T D[R][C];

array element D[i][j] is at memory address

$$\&D[i][j] = x_D + L(C \cdot i + j) \tag{3.1}$$

Figure 3.36

Elements of array in row-major order.

Row	Element	Address
A[0]	A[0][0]	x_A
	A[0][1]	$x_A + 4$
	A[0][2]	$x_A + 8$
A[1]	A[1][0]	$x_A + 12$
	A[1][1]	$x_A + 16$
	A[1][2]	$x_A + 20$
A[2]	A[2][0]	$x_A + 24$
	A[2][1]	$x_A + 28$
	A[2][2]	$x_A + 32$
A[3]	A[3][0]	$x_A + 36$
	A[3][1]	$x_A + 40$
	A[4][2]	$x_A + 44$
A[4]	A[4][0]	$x_A + 48$
	A[4][1]	$x_A + 52$
	A[4][2]	$x_A + 56$

where L is the size of data type T in bytes. As an example, consider the 5×3 integer array A defined earlier. Suppose x_A, i, and j are in registers %rdi, %rsi, and %rdx, respectively. Then array element A[i][j] can be copied to register %eax by the following code:

```
     A in %rdi, i in %rsi, and j in %rdx
1    leaq    (%rsi,%rsi,2), %rax      Compute 3i
2    leaq    (%rdi,%rax,4), %rax      Compute x_A + 12i
3    movl    (%rax,%rdx,4), %eax      Read from M[x_A + 12i + 4]
```

As can be seen, this code computes the element's address as $x_A + 12i + 4j = x_A + 4(3i + j)$ using the scaling and addition capabilities of x86-64 address arithmetic.

Practice Problem 3.38 (solution page 341)

Consider the following source code, where M and N are constants declared with #define:

```
long P[M][N];
long Q[N][M];

long sum_element(long i, long j) {
    return P[i][j] + Q[j][i];
}
```

In compiling this program, GCC generates the following assembly code:

```
     long sum_element(long i, long j)
     i in %rdi, j in %rsi
1    sum_element:
2        leaq    0(,%rdi,8), %rdx
3        subq    %rdi, %rdx
4        addq    %rsi, %rdx
5        leaq    (%rsi,%rsi,4), %rax
6        addq    %rax, %rdi
7        movq    Q(,%rdi,8), %rax
8        addq    P(,%rdx,8), %rax
9        ret
```

Use your reverse engineering skills to determine the values of M and N based on this assembly code.

3.8.4 Fixed-Size Arrays

The C compiler is able to make many optimizations for code operating on multi-dimensional arrays of fixed size. Here we demonstrate some of the optimizations made by GCC when the optimization level is set with the flag –O1. Suppose we declare data type fix_matrix to be 16×16 arrays of integers as follows:

```
#define N 16
typedef int fix_matrix[N][N];
```

(This example illustrates a good coding practice. Whenever a program uses some constant as an array dimension or buffer size, it is best to associate a name with it via a #define declaration, and then use this name consistently, rather than the numeric value. That way, if an occasion ever arises to change the value, it can be done by simply modifying the #define declaration.) The code in Figure 3.37(a) computes element i, k of the product of arrays A and B—that is, the inner product of row i from A and column k from B. This product is given by the formula $\sum_{0 \le j < N} a_{i,j} \cdot b_{j,k}$. Gcc generates code that we then recoded into C, shown as function fix_prod_ele_opt in Figure 3.37(b). This code contains a number of clever optimizations. It removes the integer index j and converts all array references to pointer dereferences. This involves (1) generating a pointer, which we have named Aptr, that points to successive elements in row i of A, (2) generating a pointer, which we have named Bptr, that points to successive elements in column k of B, and (3) generating a pointer, which we have named Bend, that equals the value Bptr will have when it is time to terminate the loop. The initial value for Aptr is the address of the first element of row i of A, given by the C expression &A[i][0]. The initial value for Bptr is the address of the first element of column k of B, given by the C expression &B[0][k]. The value for Bend is the index of what would be the $(n + 1)$st element in column j of B, given by the C expression &B[N][k].

(a) Original C code

```
/* Compute i,k of fixed matrix product */
int fix_prod_ele (fix_matrix A, fix_matrix B, long i, long k) {
    long j;
    int result = 0;

    for (j = 0; j < N; j++)
        result += A[i][j] * B[j][k];

    return result;
}
```

(b) Optimized C code

```
1    /* Compute i,k of fixed matrix product */
2    int fix_prod_ele_opt(fix_matrix A, fix_matrix B, long i, long k) {
3        int *Aptr = &A[i][0];    /* Points to elements in row i of A     */
4        int *Bptr = &B[0][k];    /* Points to elements in column k of B */
5        int *Bend = &B[N][k];    /* Marks stopping point for Bptr       */
6        int result = 0;
7        do {                     /* No need for initial test */
8            result += *Aptr * *Bptr;  /* Add next product to sum */
9            Aptr ++;             /* Move Aptr to next column */
10           Bptr += N;           /* Move Bptr to next row    */
11       } while (Bptr != Bend);  /* Test for stopping point  */
12       return result;
13   }
```

Figure 3.37   Original and optimized code to compute element i, k **of matrix product for fixed-length arrays.** The compiler performs these optimizations automatically.

The following is the actual assembly code generated by GCC for function fix_prod_ele. We see that four registers are used as follows: %eax holds result, %rdi holds Aptr, %rcx holds Bptr, and %rsi holds Bend.

```
     int fix_prod_ele_opt(fix_matrix A, fix_matrix B, long i, long k)
     A in %rdi, B in %rsi, i in %rdx, k in %rcx
1    fix_prod_ele:
2        salq    $6, %rdx              Compute 64 * i
3        addq    %rdx, %rdi            Compute Aptr = x_A + 64i = &A[i][0]
4        leaq    (%rsi,%rcx,4), %rcx   Compute Bptr = x_B + 4k = &B[0][k]
5        leaq    1024(%rcx), %rsi      Compute Bend = x_B + 4k + 1024 = &B[N][k]
6        movl    $0, %eax              Set result = 0
7    .L7:                              loop:
8        movl    (%rdi), %edx          Read *Aptr
9        imull   (%rcx), %edx          Multiply by *Bptr
10       addl    %edx, %eax            Add to result
```

```
11      addq    $4, %rdi          Increment Aptr ++
12      addq    $64, %rcx         Increment Bptr += N
13      cmpq    %rsi, %rcx        Compare Bptr:Bend
14      jne     .L7               If !=, goto loop
15      rep; ret                  Return
```

Practice Problem 3.39 (solution page 342)

Use Equation 3.1 to explain how the computations of the initial values for Aptr, Bptr, and Bend in the C code of Figure 3.37(b) (lines 3–5) correctly describe their computations in the assembly code generated for fix_prod_ele (lines 3–5).

Practice Problem 3.40 (solution page 342)

The following C code sets the diagonal elements of one of our fixed-size arrays to val:

```
/* Set all diagonal elements to val */
void fix_set_diag(fix_matrix A, int val) {
    long i;
    for (i = 0; i < N; i++)
        A[i][i] = val;
}
```

When compiled with optimization level –01, GCC generates the following assembly code:

```
1    fix_set_diag:
     void fix_set_diag(fix_matrix A, int val)
     A in %rdi, val in %rsi
2      movl    $0, %eax
3    .L13:
4      movl    %esi, (%rdi,%rax)
5      addq    $68, %rax
6      cmpq    $1088, %rax
7      jne     .L13
8      rep; ret
```

Create a C code program fix_set_diag_opt that uses optimizations similar to those in the assembly code, in the same style as the code in Figure 3.37(b). Use expressions involving the parameter N rather than integer constants, so that your code will work correctly if N is redefined.

3.8.5 Variable-Size Arrays

Historically, C only supported multidimensional arrays where the sizes (with the possible exception of the first dimension) could be determined at compile time.

Programmers requiring variable-size arrays had to allocate storage for these arrays using functions such as malloc or calloc, and they had to explicitly encode the mapping of multidimensional arrays into single-dimension ones via row-major indexing, as expressed in Equation 3.1. ISO C99 introduced the capability of having array dimension expressions that are computed as the array is being allocated.

In the C version of variable-size arrays, we can declare an array

```
int A[expr1][expr2]
```

either as a local variable or as an argument to a function, and then the dimensions of the array are determined by evaluating the expressions *expr1* and *expr2* at the time the declaration is encountered. So, for example, we can write a function to access element i, j of an $n \times n$ array as follows:

```
int var_ele(long n, int A[n][n], long i, long j) {
    return A[i][j];
}
```

The parameter n must precede the parameter A[n][n], so that the function can compute the array dimensions as the parameter is encountered.

Gcc generates code for this referencing function as

```
    int var_ele(long n, int A[n][n], long i, long j)
    n in %rdi, A in %rsi, i in %rdx, j in %rcx
1   var_ele:
2     imulq    %rdx, %rdi              Compute n · i
3     leaq     (%rsi,%rdi,4), %rax     Compute x_A + 4(n · i)
4     movl     (%rax,%rcx,4), %eax     Read from M[x_A + 4(n · i) + 4j]
5     ret
```

As the annotations show, this code computes the address of element i, j as $x_A + 4(n \cdot i) + 4j = x_A + 4(n \cdot i + j)$. The address computation is similar to that of the fixed-size array (Section 3.8.3), except that (1) the register usage changes due to added parameter n, and (2) a multiply instruction is used (line 2) to compute $n \cdot i$, rather than an leaq instruction to compute $3i$. We see therefore that referencing variable-size arrays requires only a slight generalization over fixed-size ones. The dynamic version must use a multiplication instruction to scale i by n, rather than a series of shifts and adds. In some processors, this multiplication can incur a significant performance penalty, but it is unavoidable in this case.

When variable-size arrays are referenced within a loop, the compiler can often optimize the index computations by exploiting the regularity of the access patterns. For example, Figure 3.38(a) shows C code to compute element i, k of the product of two $n \times n$ arrays A and B. Gcc generates assembly code, which we have recast into C (Figure 3.38(b)). This code follows a different style from the optimized code for the fixed-size array (Figure 3.37), but that is more an artifact of the choices made by the compiler, rather than a fundamental requirement for the two different functions. The code of Figure 3.38(b) retains loop variable j, both to detect when

(a) Original C code

```
1   /* Compute i,k of variable matrix product */
2   int var_prod_ele(long n, int A[n][n], int B[n][n], long i, long k) {
3       long j;
4       int result = 0;
5
6       for (j = 0; j < n; j++)
7           result += A[i][j] * B[j][k];
8
9       return result;
10  }
```

(b) Optimized C code

```
/* Compute i,k of variable matrix product */
int var_prod_ele_opt(long n, int A[n][n], int B[n][n], long i, long k) {
    int *Arow = A[i];
    int *Bptr = &B[0][k];
    int result = 0;
    long j;
    for (j = 0; j < n; j++) {
        result += Arow[j] * *Bptr;
        Bptr += n;
    }
    return result;
}
```

Figure 3.38 Original and optimized code to compute element i, k **of matrix product for variable-size arrays.** The compiler performs these optimizations automatically.

the loop has terminated and to index into an array consisting of the elements of row i of A.

The following is the assembly code for the loop of var_prod_ele:

```
        Registers: n in %rdi, Arow in %rsi, Bptr in %rcx
                   4n in %r9, result in %eax, j in %edx
1   .L24:                               loop:
2       movl    (%rsi,%rdx,4), %r8d     Read Arow[j]
3       imull   (%rcx), %r8d            Multiply by *Bptr
4       addl    %r8d, %eax              Add to result
5       addq    $1, %rdx                j++
6       addq    %r9, %rcx               Bptr += n
7       cmpq    %rdi, %rdx              Compare j:n
8       jne     .L24                    If !=, goto loop
```

We see that the program makes use of both a scaled value $4n$ (register %r9) for incrementing Bptr as well as the value of n (register %rdi) to check the loop bounds. The need for two values does not show up in the C code, due to the scaling of pointer arithmetic.

We have seen that, with optimizations enabled, GCC is able to recognize patterns that arise when a program steps through the elements of a multidimensional array. It can then generate code that avoids the multiplication that would result from a direct application of Equation 3.1. Whether it generates the pointer-based code of Figure 3.37(b) or the array-based code of Figure 3.38(b), these optimizations will significantly improve program performance.

3.9   Heterogeneous Data Structures

C provides two mechanisms for creating data types by combining objects of different types: *structures*, declared using the keyword struct, aggregate multiple objects into a single unit; *unions*, declared using the keyword union, allow an object to be referenced using several different types.

3.9.1   Structures

The C struct declaration creates a data type that groups objects of possibly different types into a single object. The different components of a structure are referenced by names. The implementation of structures is similar to that of arrays in that all of the components of a structure are stored in a contiguous region of memory and a pointer to a structure is the address of its first byte. The compiler maintains information about each structure type indicating the byte offset of each field. It generates references to structure elements using these offsets as displacements in memory referencing instructions.

As an example, consider the following structure declaration:

```
struct rec {
    int i;
    int j;
    int a[2];
    int *p;
};
```

This structure contains four fields: two 4-byte values of type int, a two-element array of type int, and an 8-byte integer pointer, giving a total of 24 bytes:

Offset	0	4	8	16	24
Contents	i	j	a[0]	a[1]	p

Observe that array a is embedded within the structure. The numbers along the top of the diagram give the byte offsets of the fields from the beginning of the structure.

To access the fields of a structure, the compiler generates code that adds the appropriate offset to the address of the structure. For example, suppose variable r

New to C?   Representing an object as a `struct`

The `struct` data type constructor is the closest thing C provides to the objects of C++ and Java. It allows the programmer to keep information about some entity in a single data structure and to reference that information with names.

For example, a graphics program might represent a rectangle as a structure:

```
struct rect {
    long llx;           /* X coordinate of lower-left corner */
    long lly;           /* Y coordinate of lower-left corner */
    unsigned long width;  /* Width (in pixels)                */
    unsigned long height; /* Height (in pixels)               */
    unsigned color;       /* Coding of color                  */
};
```

We can declare a variable r of type `struct rect` and set its field values as follows:

```
struct rect r;
r.llx = r.lly = 0;
r.color = 0xFF00FF;
r.width = 10;
r.height = 20;
```

where the expression `r.llx` selects field `llx` of structure `r`.

Alternatively, we can both declare the variable and initialize its fields with a single statement:

```
struct rect r = { 0, 0, 0xFF00FF, 10, 20 };
```

It is common to pass pointers to structures from one place to another rather than copying them. For example, the following function computes the area of a rectangle, where a pointer to the rectangle struct is passed to the function:

```
long area(struct rect *rp) {
    return (*rp).width * (*rp).height;
}
```

The expression `(*rp).width` dereferences the pointer and selects the `width` field of the resulting structure. Parentheses are required, because the compiler would interpret the expression `*rp.width` as `*(rp.width)`, which is not valid. This combination of dereferencing and field selection is so common that C provides an alternative notation using `->`. That is, `rp->width` is equivalent to the expression `(*rp).width`. For example, we can write a function that rotates a rectangle counterclockwise by 90 degrees as

```
void rotate_left(struct rect *rp) {
    /* Exchange width and height */
    long t = rp->height;
    rp->height = rp->width;
    rp->width  = t;
    /* Shift to new lower-left corner */
    rp->llx   -= t;
}
```

of type struct rec * is in register %rdi. Then the following code copies element r->i to element r->j:

```
        Registers: r in %rdi
1       movl    (%rdi), %eax            Get r->i
2       movl    %eax, 4(%rdi)           Store in r->j
```

Since the offset of field i is 0, the address of this field is simply the value of r. To store into field j, the code adds offset 4 to the address of r.

To generate a pointer to an object within a structure, we can simply add the field's offset to the structure address. For example, we can generate the pointer &(r->a[1]) by adding offset $8 + 4 \cdot 1 = 12$. For pointer r in register %rdi and long integer variable i in register %rsi, we can generate the pointer value &(r->a[i]) with the single instruction

```
        Registers: r in %rdi, i %rsi
1       leaq    8(%rdi,%rsi,4), %rax    Set %rax to &r->a[i]
```

As a final example, the following code implements the statement

```
    r->p = &r->a[r->i + r->j];
```

starting with r in register %rdi:

```
        Registers: r in %rdi
1       movl    4(%rdi), %eax          Get r->j
2       addl    (%rdi), %eax           Add r->i
3       cltq                           Extend to 8 bytes
4       leaq    8(%rdi,%rax,4), %rax   Compute &r->a[r->i + r->j]
5       movq    %rax, 16(%rdi)         Store in r->p
```

As these examples show, the selection of the different fields of a structure is handled completely at compile time. The machine code contains no information about the field declarations or the names of the fields.

Practice Problem 3.41 (solution page 343)

Consider the following structure declaration:

```
struct prob {
    int *p;
    struct {
        int x;
        int y;
    } s;
    struct prob *next;
};
```

This declaration illustrates that one structure can be embedded within another, just as arrays can be embedded within structures and arrays can be embedded within arrays.

The following procedure (with some expressions omitted) operates on this structure:

```
void sp_init(struct prob *sp) {
    sp->s.x  = _____;
    sp->p    = _____;
    sp->next = _____;
}
```

A. What are the offsets (in bytes) of the following fields?

        p: _____
      s.x: _____
      s.y: _____
     next: _____

B. How many total bytes does the structure require?

C. The compiler generates the following assembly code for sp_init:

```
        void sp_init(struct prob *sp)
        sp in %rdi
  1     sp_init:
  2       movl    12(%rdi), %eax
  3       movl    %eax, 8(%rdi)
  4       leaq    8(%rdi), %rax
  5       movq    %rax, (%rdi)
  6       movq    %rdi, 16(%rdi)
  7       ret
```

On the basis of this information, fill in the missing expressions in the code for sp_init.

Practice Problem 3.42 (solution page 343)

The following code shows the declaration of a structure of type ELE and the prototype for a function fun:

```
struct ELE {
    long    v;
    struct ELE *p;
};


long fun(struct ELE *ptr);
```

When the code for fun is compiled, GCC generates the following assembly code:

```
      long fun(struct ELE *ptr)
      ptr in %rdi
1   fun:
2       movl    $0, %eax
3       jmp     .L2
4   .L3:
5       addq    (%rdi), %rax
6       movq    8(%rdi), %rdi
7   .L2:
8       testq   %rdi, %rdi
9       jne     .L3
10      rep; ret
```

A. Use your reverse engineering skills to write C code for fun.

B. Describe the data structure that this structure implements and the operation performed by fun.

3.9.2   Unions

Unions provide a way to circumvent the type system of C, allowing a single object to be referenced according to multiple types. The syntax of a union declaration is identical to that for structures, but its semantics are very different. Rather than having the different fields reference different blocks of memory, they all reference the same block.

Consider the following declarations:

```
struct S3 {
    char c;
    int i[2];
    double v;
};
```

```
union U3 {
    char c;
    int i[2];
    double v;
};
```

When compiled on an x86-64 Linux machine, the offsets of the fields, as well as the total size of data types S3 and U3, are as shown in the following table:

Type	c	i	v	Size
S3	0	4	16	24
U3	0	0	0	8

(We will see shortly why i has offset 4 in S3 rather than 1, and why v has offset 16, rather than 9 or 12.) For pointer p of type union U3 *, references p->c, p->i[0], and p->v would all reference the beginning of the data structure. Observe also that the overall size of a union equals the maximum size of any of its fields.

Unions can be useful in several contexts. However, they can also lead to nasty bugs, since they bypass the safety provided by the C type system. One application is when we know in advance that the use of two different fields in a data structure will be mutually exclusive. Then, declaring these two fields as part of a union rather than a structure will reduce the total space allocated.

For example, suppose we want to implement a binary tree data structure where each leaf node has two double data values and each internal node has pointers to two children but no data. If we declare this as

```
struct node_s {
    struct node_s *left;
    struct node_s *right;
    double data[2];
};
```

then every node requires 32 bytes, with half the bytes wasted for each type of node. On the other hand, if we declare a node as

```
union node_u {
    struct {
        union node_u *left;
        union node_u *right;
    } internal;
    double data[2];
};
```

then every node will require just 16 bytes. If n is a pointer to a node of type union node_u *, we would reference the data of a leaf node as n->data[0] and n->data[1], and the children of an internal node as n->internal.left and n->internal.right.

With this encoding, however, there is no way to determine whether a given node is a leaf or an internal node. A common method is to introduce an enumerated type defining the different possible choices for the union, and then create a structure containing a tag field and the union:

```
typedef enum { N_LEAF, N_INTERNAL } nodetype_t;

struct node_t {
    nodetype_t type;
    union {
        struct {
            struct node_t *left;
            struct node_t *right;
        } internal;
        double data[2];
    } info;
};
```

This structure requires a total of 24 bytes: 4 for `type`, and either 8 each for `info.internal.left` and `info.internal.right` or 16 for `info.data`. As we will discuss shortly, an additional 4 bytes of padding is required between the field for `type` and the union elements, bringing the total structure size to $4 + 4 + 16 = 24$. In this case, the savings gain of using a union is small relative to the awkwardness of the resulting code. For data structures with more fields, the savings can be more compelling.

Unions can also be used to access the bit patterns of different data types. For example, suppose we use a simple cast to convert a value d of type `double` to a value u of type `unsigned long`:

```
unsigned long u = (unsigned long) d;
```

Value u will be an integer representation of d. Except for the case where d is 0.0, the bit representation of u will be very different from that of d. Now consider the following code to generate a value of type `unsigned long` from a `double`:

```
unsigned long double2bits(double d) {
    union {
        double d;
        unsigned long u;
    } temp;
    temp.d = d;
    return temp.u;
};
```

In this code, we store the argument in the union using one data type and access it using another. The result will be that u will have the same bit representation as d, including fields for the sign bit, the exponent, and the significand, as described in

Section 3.11. The numeric value of u will bear no relation to that of d, except for the case when d is 0.0.

When using unions to combine data types of different sizes, byte-ordering issues can become important. For example, suppose we write a procedure that will create an 8-byte double using the bit patterns given by two 4-byte unsigned values:

```
double uu2double(unsigned word0, unsigned word1)
{
    union {
        double d;
        unsigned u[2];
    } temp;

    temp.u[0] = word0;
    temp.u[1] = word1;
    return temp.d;
}
```

On a little-endian machine, such as an x86-64 processor, argument word0 will become the low-order 4 bytes of d, while word1 will become the high-order 4 bytes. On a big-endian machine, the role of the two arguments will be reversed.

Practice Problem 3.43 (solution page 344)

Suppose you are given the job of checking that a C compiler generates the proper code for structure and union access. You write the following structure declaration:

```
typedef union {
    struct {
        long    u;
        short   v;
        char    w;
    } t1;
    struct {
        int a[2];
        char *p;
    } t2;
} u_type;
```

You write a series of functions of the form

```
void get(u_type *up, type *dest) {
    *dest = expr;
}
```

with different access expressions *expr* and with destination data type *type* set according to type associated with *expr*. You then examine the code generated when compiling the functions to see if they match your expectations.

Suppose in these functions that up and dest are loaded into registers %rdi and %rsi, respectively. Fill in the following table with data type *type* and sequences of one to three instructions to compute the expression and store the result at dest.

expr	*type*	Code
up->t1.u	long	movq (%rdi), %rax movq %rax, (%rsi)
up->t1.v	_____	_____ _____ _____
&up->t1.w	_____	_____ _____ _____
up->t2.a	_____	_____ _____ _____
up->t2.a[up->t1.u]	_____	_____ _____ _____
*up->t2.p	_____	_____ _____ _____

3.9.3 Data Alignment

Many computer systems place restrictions on the allowable addresses for the primitive data types, requiring that the address for some objects must be a multiple of some value K (typically 2, 4, or 8). Such *alignment restrictions* simplify the design of the hardware forming the interface between the processor and the memory system. For example, suppose a processor always fetches 8 bytes from memory with an address that must be a multiple of 8. If we can guarantee that any double will be aligned to have its address be a multiple of 8, then the value can be read or written with a single memory operation. Otherwise, we may need to perform two memory accesses, since the object might be split across two 8-byte memory blocks.

The x86-64 hardware will work correctly regardless of the alignment of data. However, Intel recommends that data be aligned to improve memory system performance. Their alignment rule is based on the principle that any primitive object of K bytes must have an address that is a multiple of K. We can see that this rule leads to the following alignments:

K	Types
1	char
2	short
4	int, float
8	long, double, char *

Alignment is enforced by making sure that every data type is organized and allocated in such a way that every object within the type satisfies its alignment restrictions. The compiler places directives in the assembly code indicating the desired alignment for global data. For example, the assembly-code declaration of the jump table on page 235 contains the following directive on line 2:

```
.align 8
```

This ensures that the data following it (in this case the start of the jump table) will start with an address that is a multiple of 8. Since each table entry is 8 bytes long, the successive elements will obey the 8-byte alignment restriction.

For code involving structures, the compiler may need to insert gaps in the field allocation to ensure that each structure element satisfies its alignment requirement. The structure will then have some required alignment for its starting address.

For example, consider the structure declaration

```
struct S1 {
    int  i;
    char c;
    int  j;
};
```

Suppose the compiler used the minimal 9-byte allocation, diagrammed as follows:

Offset	0		4	5		9

Contents: i | c | j

Then it would be impossible to satisfy the 4-byte alignment requirement for both fields i (offset 0) and j (offset 5). Instead, the compiler inserts a 3-byte gap (shown here as shaded in blue) between fields c and j:

Offset	0		4	5		8		12

Contents: i | c | (gap) | j

As a result, j has offset 8, and the overall structure size is 12 bytes. Furthermore, the compiler must ensure that any pointer p of type struct S1* satisfies a 4-byte alignment. Using our earlier notation, let pointer p have value x_p. Then x_p must be a multiple of 4. This guarantees that both p->i (address x_p) and p->j (address $x_p + 8$) will satisfy their 4-byte alignment requirements.

In addition, the compiler may need to add padding to the end of the structure so that each element in an array of structures will satisfy its alignment requirement. For example, consider the following structure declaration:

```
struct S2 {
    int  i;
    int  j;
    char c;
};
```

If we pack this structure into 9 bytes, we can still satisfy the alignment requirements for fields i and j by making sure that the starting address of the structure satisfies a 4-byte alignment requirement. Consider, however, the following declaration:

```
struct S2 d[4];
```

With the 9-byte allocation, it is not possible to satisfy the alignment requirement for each element of d, because these elements will have addresses x_d, $x_d + 9$, $x_d + 18$, and $x_d + 27$. Instead, the compiler allocates 12 bytes for structure S2, with the final 3 bytes being wasted space:

Offset   0   4   8 9   12
Contents [i | j | c |]

That way, the elements of d will have addresses x_d, $x_d + 12$, $x_d + 24$, and $x_d + 36$. As long as x_d is a multiple of 4, all of the alignment restrictions will be satisfied.

Practice Problem 3.44 (solution page 345)

For each of the following structure declarations, determine the offset of each field, the total size of the structure, and its alignment requirement for x86-64:

A. `struct P1 { int i; char c; int j; char d; };`

B. `struct P2 { int i; char c; char d; long j; };`

C. `struct P3 { short w[3]; char c[3] };`

D. `struct P4 { short w[5]; char *c[3] };`

E. `struct P5 { struct P3 a[2]; struct P2 t };`

Practice Problem 3.45 (solution page 345)

Answer the following for the structure declaration

```
struct {
    char   *a;
    short   b;
    double  c;
    char    d;
    float   e;
    char    f;
```

Aside   A case of mandatory alignment

For most x86-64 instructions, keeping data aligned improves efficiency, but it does not affect program behavior. On the other hand, some models of Intel and AMD processors will not work correctly with unaligned data for some of the SSE instructions implementing multimedia operations. These instructions operate on 16-byte blocks of data, and the instructions that transfer data between the SSE unit and memory require the memory addresses to be multiples of 16. Any attempt to access memory with an address that does not satisfy this alignment will lead to an *exception* (see Section 8.1), with the default behavior for the program to terminate.

As a result, any compiler and run-time system for an x86-64 processor must ensure that any memory allocated to hold a data structure that may be read from or stored into an SSE register must satisfy a 16-byte alignment. This requirement has the following two consequences:

- The starting address for any block generated by a memory allocation function (`alloca`, `malloc`, `calloc`, or `realloc`) must be a multiple of 16.
- The stack frame for most functions must be aligned on a 16-byte boundary. (This requirement has a number of exceptions.)

More recent versions of x86-64 processors implement the AVX multimedia instructions. In addition to providing a superset of the SSE instructions, processors supporting AVX also do not have a mandatory alignment requirement.

```
    long    g;
    int     h;
} rec;
```

A. What are the byte offsets of all the fields in the structure?

B. What is the total size of the structure?

C. Rearrange the fields of the structure to minimize wasted space, and then show the byte offsets and total size for the rearranged structure.

3.10   Combining Control and Data in Machine-Level Programs

So far, we have looked separately at how machine-level code implements the control aspects of a program and how it implements different data structures. In this section, we look at ways in which data and control interact with each other. We start by taking a deep look into pointers, one of the most important concepts in the C programming language, but one for which many programmers only have a shallow understanding. We review the use of the symbolic debugger GDB for examining the detailed operation of machine-level programs. Next, we see how understanding machine-level programs enables us to study buffer overflow, an important security vulnerability in many real-world systems. Finally, we examine how machine-level programs implement cases where the amount of stack storage required by a function can vary from one execution to another.

3.10.1   Understanding Pointers

Pointers are a central feature of the C programming language. They serve as a uniform way to generate references to elements within different data structures. Pointers are a source of confusion for novice programmers, but the underlying concepts are fairly simple. Here we highlight some key principles of pointers and their mapping into machine code.

- *Every pointer has an associated type.* This type indicates what kind of object the pointer points to. Using the following pointer declarations as illustrations

  ```
  int *ip;
  char **cpp;
  ```

  variable ip is a pointer to an object of type int, while cpp is a pointer to an object that itself is a pointer to an object of type char. In general, if the object has type T, then the pointer has type $*T$. The special void $*$ type represents a generic pointer. For example, the malloc function returns a generic pointer, which is converted to a typed pointer via either an explicit cast or by the implicit casting of the assignment operation. Pointer types are not part of machine code; they are an abstraction provided by C to help programmers avoid addressing errors.

- *Every pointer has a value.* This value is an address of some object of the designated type. The special NULL (0) value indicates that the pointer does not point anywhere.

- *Pointers are created with the '&' operator.* This operator can be applied to any C expression that is categorized as an *lvalue*, meaning an expression that can appear on the left side of an assignment. Examples include variables and the elements of structures, unions, and arrays. We have seen that the machine-code realization of the '&' operator often uses the leaq instruction to compute the expression value, since this instruction is designed to compute the address of a memory reference.

- *Pointers are dereferenced with the '*' operator.* The result is a value having the type associated with the pointer. Dereferencing is implemented by a memory reference, either storing to or retrieving from the specified address.

- *Arrays and pointers are closely related.* The name of an array can be referenced (but not updated) as if it were a pointer variable. Array referencing (e.g., a[3]) has the exact same effect as pointer arithmetic and dereferencing (e.g., *(a+3)). Both array referencing and pointer arithmetic require scaling the offsets by the object size. When we write an expression p+i for pointer p with value p, the resulting address is computed as $p + L \cdot i$, where L is the size of the data type associated with p.

- *Casting from one type of pointer to another changes its type but not its value.* One effect of casting is to change any scaling of pointer arithmetic. So, for example, if p is a pointer of type char * having value p, then the expression (int *) p+7 computes $p + 28$, while (int *) (p+7) computes $p + 7$. (Recall that casting has higher precedence than addition.)

- *Pointers can also point to functions.* This provides a powerful capability for storing and passing references to code, which can be invoked in some other part of the program. For example, if we have a function defined by the prototype

```
int fun(int x, int *p);
```

then we can declare and assign a pointer fp to this function by the following code sequence:

```
int (*fp)(int, int *);
fp = fun;
```

We can then invoke the function using this pointer:

```
int y = 1;
int result = fp(3, &y);
```

The value of a function pointer is the address of the first instruction in the machine-code representation of the function.

New to C?   Function pointers

The syntax for declaring function pointers is especially difficult for novice programmers to understand. For a declaration such as

```
int (*f)(int*);
```

it helps to read it starting from the inside (starting with 'f') and working outward. Thus, we see that f is a pointer, as indicated by (*f). It is a pointer to a function that has a single int * as an argument, as indicated by (*f)(int*). Finally, we see that it is a pointer to a function that takes an int * as an argument and returns int.

The parentheses around *f are required, because otherwise the declaration

```
int *f(int*);
```

would be read as

```
(int *) f(int*);
```

That is, it would be interpreted as a function prototype, declaring a function f that has an int * as its argument and returns an int *.

Kernighan and Ritchie [61, Sect. 5.12] present a helpful tutorial on reading C declarations.

3.10.2   Life in the Real World: Using the GDB Debugger

The GNU debugger GDB provides a number of useful features to support the run-time evaluation and analysis of machine-level programs. With the examples and exercises in this book, we attempt to infer the behavior of a program by just looking at the code. Using GDB, it becomes possible to study the behavior by watching the program in action while having considerable control over its execution.

Figure 3.39 shows examples of some GDB commands that help when working with machine-level x86-64 programs. It is very helpful to first run OBJDUMP to get a disassembled version of the program. Our examples are based on running GDB on the file prog, described and disassembled on page 175. We start GDB with the following command line:

```
linux> gdb prog
```

The general scheme is to set breakpoints near points of interest in the program. These can be set to just after the entry of a function or at a program address. When one of the breakpoints is hit during program execution, the program will halt and return control to the user. From a breakpoint, we can examine different registers and memory locations in various formats. We can also single-step the program, running just a few instructions at a time, or we can proceed to the next breakpoint.

As our examples suggest, GDB has an obscure command syntax, but the online help information (invoked within GDB with the `help` command) overcomes this shortcoming. Rather than using the command-line interface to GDB, many programmers prefer using DDD, an extension to GDB that provides a graphical user interface.

3.10.3   Out-of-Bounds Memory References and Buffer Overflow

We have seen that C does not perform any bounds checking for array references, and that local variables are stored on the stack along with state information such as saved register values and return addresses. This combination can lead to serious program errors, where the state stored on the stack gets corrupted by a write to an out-of-bounds array element. When the program then tries to reload the register or execute a `ret` instruction with this corrupted state, things can go seriously wrong.

A particularly common source of state corruption is known as *buffer overflow*. Typically, some character array is allocated on the stack to hold a string, but the size of the string exceeds the space allocated for the array. This is demonstrated by the following program example:

```
/* Implementation of library function gets() */
char *gets(char *s)
{
    int c;
    char *dest = s;
```

Command	Effect
Starting and stopping	
quit	Exit GDB
run	Run your program (give command-line arguments here)
kill	Stop your program
Breakpoints	
break multstore	Set breakpoint at entry to function multstore
break *0x400540	Set breakpoint at address 0x400540
delete 1	Delete breakpoint 1
delete	Delete all breakpoints
Execution	
stepi	Execute one instruction
stepi 4	Execute four instructions
nexti	Like stepi, but proceed through function calls
continue	Resume execution
finish	Run until current function returns
Examining code	
disas	Disassemble current function
disas multstore	Disassemble function multstore
disas 0x400544	Disassemble function around address 0x400544
disas 0x400540, 0x40054d	Disassemble code within specified address range
print /x $rip	Print program counter in hex
Examining data	
print $rax	Print contents of %rax in decimal
print /x $rax	Print contents of %rax in hex
print /t $rax	Print contents of %rax in binary
print 0x100	Print decimal representation of 0x100
print /x 555	Print hex representation of 555
print /x ($rsp+8)	Print contents of %rsp plus 8 in hex
print *(long *) 0x7fffffffe818	Print long integer at address 0x7fffffffe818
print *(long *) ($rsp+8)	Print long integer at address %rsp + 8
x/2g 0x7fffffffe818	Examine two (8-byte) words starting at address 0x7fffffffe818
x/20b multstore	Examine first 20 bytes of function multstore
Useful information	
info frame	Information about current stack frame
info registers	Values of all the registers
help	Get information about GDB

Figure 3.39 Example GDB commands. These examples illustrate some of the ways GDB supports debugging of machine-level programs.

Figure 3.40
Stack organization for echo **function.** Character array buf is just part of the saved state. An out-of-bounds write to buf can corrupt the program state.

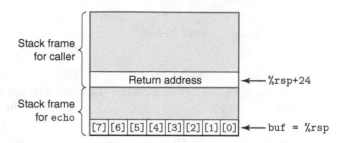

```
    while ((c = getchar()) != '\n' && c != EOF)
        *dest++ = c;
    if (c == EOF && dest == s)
        /* No characters read */
        return NULL;
    *dest++ = '\0'; /* Terminate string */
    return s;
}

/* Read input line and write it back */
void echo()
{
    char buf[8];   /* Way too small! */
    gets(buf);
    puts(buf);
}
```

The preceding code shows an implementation of the library function gets to demonstrate a serious problem with this function. It reads a line from the standard input, stopping when either a terminating newline character or some error condition is encountered. It copies this string to the location designated by argument s and terminates the string with a null character. We show the use of gets in the function echo, which simply reads a line from standard input and echos it back to standard output.

The problem with gets is that it has no way to determine whether sufficient space has been allocated to hold the entire string. In our echo example, we have purposely made the buffer very small—just eight characters long. Any string longer than seven characters will cause an out-of-bounds write.

By examining the assembly code generated by GCC for echo, we can infer how the stack is organized:

```
      void echo()
1     echo:
2       subq    $24, %rsp      Allocate 24 bytes on stack
3       movq    %rsp, %rdi     Compute buf as %rsp
4       call    gets           Call gets
5       movq    %rsp, %rdi     Compute buf as %rsp
```

```
6       call    puts                Call puts
7       addq    $24, %rsp           Deallocate stack space
8       ret                         Return
```

Figure 3.40 illustrates the stack organization during the execution of echo. The program allocates 24 bytes on the stack by subtracting 24 from the stack pointer (line 2). Character buf is positioned at the top of the stack, as can be seen by the fact that %rsp is copied to %rdi to be used as the argument to the calls to both gets and puts. The 16 bytes between buf and the stored return pointer are not used. As long as the user types at most seven characters, the string returned by gets (including the terminating null) will fit within the space allocated for buf. A longer string, however, will cause gets to overwrite some of the information stored on the stack. As the string gets longer, the following information will get corrupted:

Characters typed	Additional corrupted state
0–7	None
9–23	Unused stack space
24–31	Return address
32+	Saved state in caller

No serious consequence occurs for strings of up to 23 characters, but beyond that, the value of the return pointer, and possibly additional saved state, will be corrupted. If the stored value of the return address is corrupted, then the ret instruction (line 8) will cause the program to jump to a totally unexpected location. None of these behaviors would seem possible based on the C code. The impact of out-of-bounds writing to memory by functions such as gets can only be understood by studying the program at the machine-code level.

Our code for echo is simple but sloppy. A better version involves using the function fgets, which includes as an argument a count on the maximum number of bytes to read. Problem 3.71 asks you to write an echo function that can handle an input string of arbitrary length. In general, using gets or any function that can overflow storage is considered a bad programming practice. Unfortunately, a number of commonly used library functions, including strcpy, strcat, and sprintf, have the property that they can generate a byte sequence without being given any indication of the size of the destination buffer [97]. Such conditions can lead to vulnerabilities to buffer overflow.

Practice Problem 3.46 (solution page 346)

Figure 3.41 shows a (low-quality) implementation of a function that reads a line from standard input, copies the string to newly allocated storage, and returns a pointer to the result.

Consider the following scenario. Procedure get_line is called with the return address equal to 0x400776 and register %rbx equal to 0x0123456789ABCDEF. You type in the string

```
01234567890123456789901234
```

(a) C code

```
/* This is very low-quality code.
   It is intended to illustrate bad programming practices.
   See Practice Problem 3.46. */
char *get_line()
{
    char buf[4];
    char *result;
    gets(buf);
    result = malloc(strlen(buf));
    strcpy(result, buf);
    return result;
}
```

(b) Disassembly up through call to gets

```
      char *get_line()
1   0000000000400720 <get_line>:
2     400720:  53                        push   %rbx
3     400721:  48 83 ec 10               sub    $0x10,%rsp
      Diagram stack at this point
4     400725:  48 89 e7                  mov    %rsp,%rdi
5     400728:  e8 73 ff ff ff            callq  4006a0 <gets>
      Modify diagram to show stack contents at this point
```

Figure 3.41 C and disassembled code for Practice Problem 3.46.

The program terminates with a segmentation fault. You run GDB and determine that the error occurs during the execution of the ret instruction of get_line.

A. Fill in the diagram that follows, indicating as much as you can about the stack just after executing the instruction at line 3 in the disassembly. Label the quantities stored on the stack (e.g., "Return address") on the right, and their hexadecimal values (if known) within the box. Each box represents 8 bytes. Indicate the position of %rsp. Recall that the ASCII codes for characters 0–9 are 0x30–0x39.

```
┌─────────────────────────┐
│ 00 00 00 00 00 40 00 76 │ Return address
├─────────────────────────┤
│                         │
├─────────────────────────┤
│                         │
├─────────────────────────┤
│                         │
├─────────────────────────┤
│                         │
└─────────────────────────┘
```

B. Modify your diagram to show the effect of the call to gets (line 5).

C. To what address does the program attempt to return?

D. What register(s) have corrupted value(s) when `get_line` returns?

E. Besides the potential for buffer overflow, what two other things are wrong with the code for `get_line`?

A more pernicious use of buffer overflow is to get a program to perform a function that it would otherwise be unwilling to do. This is one of the most common methods to attack the security of a system over a computer network. Typically, the program is fed with a string that contains the byte encoding of some executable code, called the *exploit code*, plus some extra bytes that overwrite the return address with a pointer to the exploit code. The effect of executing the `ret` instruction is then to jump to the exploit code.

In one form of attack, the exploit code then uses a system call to start up a shell program, providing the attacker with a range of operating system functions. In another form, the exploit code performs some otherwise unauthorized task, repairs the damage to the stack, and then executes `ret` a second time, causing an (apparently) normal return to the caller.

As an example, the famous Internet worm of November 1988 used four different ways to gain access to many of the computers across the Internet. One was a buffer overflow attack on the finger daemon `fingerd`, which serves requests by the FINGER command. By invoking FINGER with an appropriate string, the worm could make the daemon at a remote site have a buffer overflow and execute code that gave the worm access to the remote system. Once the worm gained access to a system, it would replicate itself and consume virtually all of the machine's computing resources. As a consequence, hundreds of machines were effectively paralyzed until security experts could determine how to eliminate the worm. The author of the worm was caught and prosecuted. He was sentenced to 3 years probation, 400 hours of community service, and a $10,500 fine. Even to this day, however, people continue to find security leaks in systems that leave them vulnerable to buffer overflow attacks. This highlights the need for careful programming. Any interface to the external environment should be made "bulletproof" so that no behavior by an external agent can cause the system to misbehave.

3.10.4 Thwarting Buffer Overflow Attacks

Buffer overflow attacks have become so pervasive and have caused so many problems with computer systems that modern compilers and operating systems have implemented mechanisms to make it more difficult to mount these attacks and to limit the ways by which an intruder can seize control of a system via a buffer overflow attack. In this section, we will present mechanisms that are provided by recent versions of GCC for Linux.

Stack Randomization

In order to insert exploit code into a system, the attacker needs to inject both the code as well as a pointer to this code as part of the attack string. Generating

Aside   Worms and viruses

Both worms and viruses are pieces of code that attempt to spread themselves among computers. As described by Spafford [105], a *worm* is a program that can run by itself and can propagate a fully working version of itself to other machines. A *virus* is a piece of code that adds itself to other programs, including operating systems. It cannot run independently. In the popular press, the term "virus" is used to refer to a variety of different strategies for spreading attacking code among systems, and so you will hear people saying "virus" for what more properly should be called a "worm."

this pointer requires knowing the stack address where the string will be located. Historically, the stack addresses for a program were highly predictable. For all systems running the same combination of program and operating system version, the stack locations were fairly stable across many machines. So, for example, if an attacker could determine the stack addresses used by a common Web server, it could devise an attack that would work on many machines. Using infectious disease as an analogy, many systems were vulnerable to the exact same strain of a virus, a phenomenon often referred to as a *security monoculture* [96].

The idea of *stack randomization* is to make the position of the stack vary from one run of a program to another. Thus, even if many machines are running identical code, they would all be using different stack addresses. This is implemented by allocating a random amount of space between 0 and n bytes on the stack at the start of a program, for example, by using the allocation function `alloca`, which allocates space for a specified number of bytes on the stack. This allocated space is not used by the program, but it causes all subsequent stack locations to vary from one execution of a program to another. The allocation range n needs to be large enough to get sufficient variations in the stack addresses, yet small enough that it does not waste too much space in the program.

The following code shows a simple way to determine a "typical" stack address:

```
int main() {
    long local;
    printf("local at %p\n", &local);
    return 0;
}
```

This code simply prints the address of a local variable in the `main` function. Running the code 10,000 times on a Linux machine in 32-bit mode, the addresses ranged from 0xff7fc59c to 0xffffd09c, a range of around 2^{23}. Running in 64-bit mode on the newer machine, the addresses ranged from 0x7fff0001b698 to 0x7ffffffaa4a8, a range of nearly 2^{32}.

Stack randomization has become standard practice in Linux systems. It is one of a larger class of techniques known as *address-space layout randomization*, or ASLR [99]. With ASLR, different parts of the program, including program code, library code, stack, global variables, and heap data, are loaded into different regions of memory each time a program is run. That means that a program running on one machine will have very different address mappings than the same program running on other machines. This can thwart some forms of attack.

Overall, however, a persistent attacker can overcome randomization by brute force, repeatedly attempting attacks with different addresses. A common trick is to include a long sequence of nop (pronounced "no op," short for "no operation") instructions before the actual exploit code. Executing this instruction has no effect, other than incrementing the program counter to the next instruction. As long as the attacker can guess an address somewhere within this sequence, the program will run through the sequence and then hit the exploit code. The common term for this sequence is a "nop sled" [97], expressing the idea that the program "slides" through the sequence. If we set up a 256-byte nop sled, then the randomization over $n = 2^{23}$ can be cracked by enumerating $2^{15} = 32,768$ starting addresses, which is entirely feasible for a determined attacker. For the 64-bit case, trying to enumerate $2^{24} = 16,777,216$ is a bit more daunting. We can see that stack randomization and other aspects of ASLR can increase the effort required to successfully attack a system, and therefore greatly reduce the rate at which a virus or worm can spread, but it cannot provide a complete safeguard.

Practice Problem 3.47 (solution page 347)

Running our stack-checking code 10,000 times on a system running Linux version 2.6.16, we obtained addresses ranging from a minimum of 0xffffb754 to a maximum of 0xffffd754.

A. What is the approximate range of addresses?

B. If we attempted a buffer overrun with a 128-byte nop sled, about how many attempts would it take to test all starting addresses?

Stack Corruption Detection

A second line of defense is to be able to detect when a stack has been corrupted. We saw in the example of the echo function (Figure 3.40) that the corruption typically occurs when the program overruns the bounds of a local buffer. In C, there is no reliable way to prevent writing beyond the bounds of an array. Instead, the program can attempt to detect when such a write has occurred before it can have any harmful effects.

Recent versions of GCC incorporate a mechanism known as a *stack protector* into the generated code to detect buffer overruns. The idea is to store a special *canary* value[4] in the stack frame between any local buffer and the rest of the stack state, as illustrated in Figure 3.42 [26, 97]. This canary value, also referred to as a *guard value*, is generated randomly each time the program runs, and so there is no

---

4. The term "canary" refers to the historic use of these birds to detect the presence of dangerous gases in coal mines.

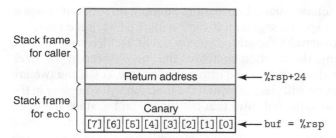

Figure 3.42   Stack organization for echo function with stack protector enabled. A special "canary" value is positioned between array buf and the saved state. The code checks the canary value to determine whether or not the stack state has been corrupted.

easy way for an attacker to determine what it is. Before restoring the register state and returning from the function, the program checks if the canary has been altered by some operation of this function or one that it has called. If so, the program aborts with an error.

Recent versions of GCC try to determine whether a function is vulnerable to a stack overflow and insert this type of overflow detection automatically. In fact, for our earlier demonstration of stack overflow, we had to give the command-line option −fno−stack−protector to prevent GCC from inserting this code. Compiling the function echo without this option, and hence with the stack protector enabled, gives the following assembly code:

```
     void echo()
1    echo:
2        subq    $24, %rsp              Allocate 24 bytes on stack
3        movq    %fs:40, %rax           Retrieve canary
4        movq    %rax, 8(%rsp)          Store on stack
5        xorl    %eax, %eax             Zero out register
6        movq    %rsp, %rdi             Compute buf as %rsp
7        call    gets                   Call gets
8        movq    %rsp, %rdi             Compute buf as %rsp
9        call    puts                   Call puts
10       movq    8(%rsp), %rax          Retrieve canary
11       xorq    %fs:40, %rax           Compare to stored value
12       je      .L9                    If =, goto ok
13       call    __stack_chk_fail       Stack corrupted!
14   .L9:                          ok:
15       addq    $24, %rsp              Deallocate stack space
16       ret
```

We see that this version of the function retrieves a value from memory (line 3) and stores it on the stack at offset 8 from %rsp, just beyond the region allocated for buf. The instruction argument %fs:40 is an indication that the canary value is read from memory using *segmented addressing*, an addressing mechanism that dates back to the 80286 and is seldom found in programs running on modern systems. By storing the canary in a special segment, it can be marked as "read only," so that an attacker cannot overwrite the stored canary value. Before restoring the register state and returning, the function compares the value stored at the stack location with the canary value (via the xorq instruction on line 11). If the two are identical, the xorq instruction will yield zero, and the function will complete in the normal fashion. A nonzero value indicates that the canary on the stack has been modified, and so the code will call an error routine.

Stack protection does a good job of preventing a buffer overflow attack from corrupting state stored on the program stack. It incurs only a small performance penalty, especially because GCC only inserts it when there is a local buffer of type char in the function. Of course, there are other ways to corrupt the state of an executing program, but reducing the vulnerability of the stack thwarts many common attack strategies.

Practice Problem 3.48 (solution page 347)

The functions intlen, len, and iptoa provide a very convoluted way to compute the number of decimal digits required to represent an integer. We will use this as a way to study some aspects of the GCC stack protector facility.

```c
int len(char *s) {
    return strlen(s);
}

void iptoa(char *s, long *p) {
    long val = *p;
    sprintf(s, "%ld", val);
}

int intlen(long x) {
    long v;
    char buf[12];
    v = x;
    iptoa(buf, &v);
    return len(buf);
}
```

The following show portions of the code for intlen, compiled both with and without stack protector:

(a) Without protector

```
      int intlen(long x)
      x in %rdi
  1   intlen:
  2     subq    $40, %rsp
  3     movq    %rdi, 24(%rsp)
```

```
4       leaq        24(%rsp), %rsi
5       movq        %rsp, %rdi
6       call        iptoa
```

(b) With protector

```
int intlen(long x)
x in %rdi
1       intlen:
2           subq        $56, %rsp
3           movq        %fs:40, %rax
4           movq        %rax, 40(%rsp)
5           xorl        %eax, %eax
6           movq        %rdi, 8(%rsp)
7           leaq        8(%rsp), %rsi
8           leaq        16(%rsp), %rdi
9           call        iptoa
```

A. For both versions: What are the positions in the stack frame for buf, v, and (when present) the canary value?

B. How does the rearranged ordering of the local variables in the protected code provide greater security against a buffer overrun attack?

Limiting Executable Code Regions

A final step is to eliminate the ability of an attacker to insert executable code into a system. One method is to limit which memory regions hold executable code. In typical programs, only the portion of memory holding the code generated by the compiler need be executable. The other portions can be restricted to allow just reading and writing. As we will see in Chapter 9, the virtual memory space is logically divided into *pages*, typically with 2,048 or 4,096 bytes per page. The hardware supports different forms of *memory protection*, indicating the forms of access allowed by both user programs and the operating system kernel. Many systems allow control over three forms of access: read (reading data from memory), write (storing data into memory), and execute (treating the memory contents as machine-level code). Historically, the x86 architecture merged the read and execute access controls into a single 1-bit flag, so that any page marked as readable was also executable. The stack had to be kept both readable and writable, and therefore the bytes on the stack were also executable. Various schemes were implemented to be able to limit some pages to being readable but not executable, but these generally introduced significant inefficiencies.

More recently, AMD introduced an NX (for "no-execute") bit into the memory protection for its 64-bit processors, separating the read and execute access modes, and Intel followed suit. With this feature, the stack can be marked as being readable and writable, but not executable, and the checking of whether a page is executable is performed in hardware, with no penalty in efficiency.

Some types of programs require the ability to dynamically generate and execute code. For example, "just-in-time" compilation techniques dynamically generate code for programs written in interpreted languages, such as Java, to improve execution performance. Whether or not the run-time system can restrict the executable code to just that part generated by the compiler in creating the original program depends on the language and the operating system.

The techniques we have outlined—randomization, stack protection, and limiting which portions of memory can hold executable code—are three of the most common mechanisms used to minimize the vulnerability of programs to buffer overflow attacks. They all have the properties that they require no special effort on the part of the programmer and incur very little or no performance penalty. Each separately reduces the level of vulnerability, and in combination they become even more effective. Unfortunately, there are still ways to attack computers [85, 97], and so worms and viruses continue to compromise the integrity of many machines.

3.10.5 Supporting Variable-Size Stack Frames

We have examined the machine-level code for a variety of functions so far, but they all have the property that the compiler can determine in advance the amount of space that must be allocated for their stack frames. Some functions, however, require a variable amount of local storage. This can occur, for example, when the function calls `alloca`, a standard library function that can allocate an arbitrary number of bytes of storage on the stack. It can also occur when the code declares a local array of variable size.

Although the information presented in this section should rightfully be considered an aspect of how procedures are implemented, we have deferred the presentation to this point, since it requires an understanding of arrays and alignment.

The code of Figure 3.43(a) gives an example of a function containing a variable-size array. The function declares local array p of n pointers, where n is given by the first argument. This requires allocating $8n$ bytes on the stack, where the value of n may vary from one call of the function to another. The compiler therefore cannot determine how much space it must allocate for the function's stack frame. In addition, the program generates a reference to the address of local variable i, and so this variable must also be stored on the stack. During execution, the program must be able to access both local variable i and the elements of array p. On returning, the function must deallocate the stack frame and set the stack pointer to the position of the stored return address.

To manage a variable-size stack frame, x86-64 code uses register %rbp to serve as a *frame pointer* (sometimes referred to as a *base pointer*, and hence the letters bp in %rbp). When using a frame pointer, the stack frame is organized as shown for the case of function vframe in Figure 3.44. We see that the code must save the previous version of %rbp on the stack, since it is a callee-saved register. It then keeps %rbp pointing to this position throughout the execution of the function, and it references fixed-length local variables, such as i, at offsets relative to %rbp.

(a) C code

```
long vframe(long n, long idx, long *q) {
    long i;
    long *p[n];
    p[0] = &i;
    for (i = 1; i < n; i++)
        p[i] = q;
    return *p[idx];
}
```

(b) Portions of generated assembly code

```
     long vframe(long n, long idx, long *q)
     n in %rdi, idx in %rsi, q in %rdx
     Only portions of code shown
1    vframe:
2      pushq    %rbp                         Save old %rbp
3      movq     %rsp, %rbp                   Set frame pointer
4      subq     $16, %rsp                    Allocate space for i (%rsp = s₁)
5      leaq     22(,%rdi,8), %rax
6      andq     $-16, %rax
7      subq     %rax, %rsp                   Allocate space for array p (%rsp = s₂)
8      leaq     7(%rsp), %rax
9      shrq     $3, %rax
10     leaq     0(,%rax,8), %r8              Set %r8 to &p[0]
11     movq     %r8, %rcx                    Set %rcx to &p[0] (%rcx = p)

     . . .
     Code for initialization loop
     i in %rax and on stack, n in %rdi, p in %rcx, q in %rdx
12   .L3:                                    loop:
13     movq     %rdx, (%rcx,%rax,8)          Set p[i] to q
14     addq     $1, %rax                     Increment i
15     movq     %rax, -8(%rbp)               Store on stack
16   .L2:
17     movq     -8(%rbp), %rax               Retrieve i from stack
18     cmpq     %rdi, %rax                   Compare i:n
19     jl       .L3                          If <, goto loop

     . . .
     Code for function exit
20     leave                                 Restore %rbp and %rsp
21     ret                                   Return
```

Figure 3.43   Function requiring the use of a frame pointer. The variable-size array implies that the size of the stack frame cannot be determined at compile time.

Figure 3.44

Stack frame structure for function vframe. The function uses register %rbp as a frame pointer. The annotations along the right-hand side are in reference to Practice Problem 3.49.

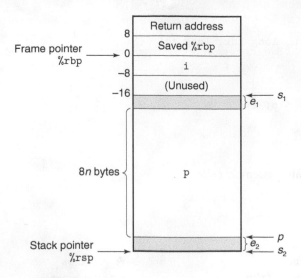

Figure 3.43(b) shows portions of the code GCC generates for function vframe. At the beginning of the function, we see code that sets up the stack frame and allocates space for array p. The code starts by pushing the current value of %rbp onto the stack and setting %rbp to point to this stack position (lines 2–3). Next, it allocates 16 bytes on the stack, the first 8 of which are used to store local variable i, and the second 8 of which are unused. Then it allocates space for array p (lines 5–11). The details of how much space it allocates and where it positions p within this space are explored in Practice Problem 3.49. Suffice it to say that by the time the program reaches line 11, it has (1) allocated at least $8n$ bytes on the stack and (2) positioned array p within the allocated region such that at least $8n$ bytes are available for its use.

The code for the initialization loop shows examples of how local variables i and p are referenced. Line 13 shows array element p[i] being set to q. This instruction uses the value in register %rcx as the address for the start of p. We can see instances where local variable i is updated (line 15) and read (line 17). The address of i is given by reference -8(%rbp)—that is, at offset -8 relative to the frame pointer.

At the end of the function, the frame pointer is restored to its previous value using the leave instruction (line 20). This instruction takes no arguments. It is equivalent to executing the following two instructions:

```
movq %rbp, %rsp      Set stack pointer to beginning of frame
popq %rbp            Restore saved %rbp and set stack ptr
                     to end of caller's frame
```

That is, the stack pointer is first set to the position of the saved value of %rbp, and then this value is popped from the stack into %rbp. This instruction combination has the effect of deallocating the entire stack frame.

In earlier versions of x86 code, the frame pointer was used with every function call. With x86-64 code, it is used only in cases where the stack frame may be of variable size, as is the case for function vframe. Historically, most compilers used frame pointers when generating IA32 code. Recent versions of GCC have dropped this convention. Observe that it is acceptable to mix code that uses frame pointers with code that does not, as long as all functions treat %rbp as a callee-saved register.

Practice Problem 3.49 (solution page 347)

In this problem, we will explore the logic behind the code in lines 5–11 of Figure 3.43(b), where space is allocated for variable-size array p. As the annotations of the code indicate, let us let s_1 denote the address of the stack pointer after executing the subq instruction of line 4. This instruction allocates the space for local variable i. Let s_2 denote the value of the stack pointer after executing the subq instruction of line 7. This instruction allocates the storage for local array p. Finally, let p denote the value assigned to registers %r8 and %rcx in the instructions of lines 10–11. Both of these registers are used to reference array p.

The right-hand side of Figure 3.44 diagrams the positions of the locations indicated by s_1, s_2, and p. It also shows that there may be an offset of e_2 bytes between the values of s_1 and p. This space will not be used. There may also be an offset of e_1 bytes between the end of array p and the position indicated by s_1.

A. Explain, in mathematical terms, the logic in the computation of s_2 on lines 5–7. *Hint:* Think about the bit-level representation of -16 and its effect in the andq instruction of line 6.

B. Explain, in mathematical terms, the logic in the computation of p on lines 8–10. *Hint:* You may want to refer to the discussion on division by powers of 2 in Section 2.3.7.

C. For the following values of n and s_1, trace the execution of the code to determine what the resulting values would be for s_2, p, e_1, and e_2.

n	s_1	s_2	p	e_1	e_2
5	2,065				
6	2,064				

D. What alignment properties does this code guarantee for the values of s_2 and p?

3.11 Floating-Point Code

The *floating-point architecture* for a processor consists of the different aspects that affect how programs operating on floating-point data are mapped onto the machine, including

- How floating-point values are stored and accessed. This is typically via some form of registers.

- The instructions that operate on floating-point data.
- The conventions used for passing floating-point values as arguments to functions and for returning them as results.
- The conventions for how registers are preserved during function calls—for example, with some registers designated as caller saved, and others as callee saved.

To understand the x86-64 floating-point architecture, it is helpful to have a brief historical perspective. Since the introduction of the Pentium/MMX in 1997, both Intel and AMD have incorporated successive generations of *media* instructions to support graphics and image processing. These instructions originally focused on allowing multiple operations to be performed in a parallel mode known as *single instruction, multiple data,* or *SIMD* (pronounced sim-dee). In this mode the same operation is performed on a number of different data values in parallel. Over the years, there has been a progression of these extensions. The names have changed through a series of major revisions from MMX to SSE (for "streaming SIMD extensions") and most recently AVX (for "advanced vector extensions"). Within each generation, there have also been different versions. Each of these extensions manages data in sets of registers, referred to as "MM" registers for MMX, "XMM" for SSE, and "YMM" for AVX, ranging from 64 bits for MM registers, to 128 for XMM, to 256 for YMM. So, for example, each YMM register can hold eight 32-bit values, or four 64-bit values, where these values can be either integer or floating point.

Starting with SSE2, introduced with the Pentium 4 in 2000, the media instructions have included ones to operate on *scalar* floating-point data, using single values in the low-order 32 or 64 bits of XMM or YMM registers. This scalar mode provides a set of registers and instructions that are more typical of the way other processors support floating point. All processors capable of executing x86-64 code support SSE2 or higher, and hence x86-64 floating point is based on SSE or AVX, including conventions for passing procedure arguments and return values [77].

Our presentation is based on AVX2, the second version of AVX, introduced with the Core i7 Haswell processor in 2013. Gcc will generate AVX2 code when given the command-line parameter –mavx2. Code based on the different versions of SSE, as well as the first version of AVX, is conceptually similar, although they differ in the instruction names and formats. We present only instructions that arise in compiling floating-point programs with GCC. These are, for the most part, the scalar AVX instructions, although we document occasions where instructions intended for operating on entire data vectors arise. A more complete coverage of how to exploit the SIMD capabilities of SSE and AVX is presented in Web Aside OPT:SIMD on page 546. Readers may wish to refer to the AMD and Intel documentation for the individual instructions [4, 51]. As with integer operations, note that the ATT format we use in our presentation differs from the Intel format used in these documents. In particular, the instruction operands are listed in a different order in these two versions.

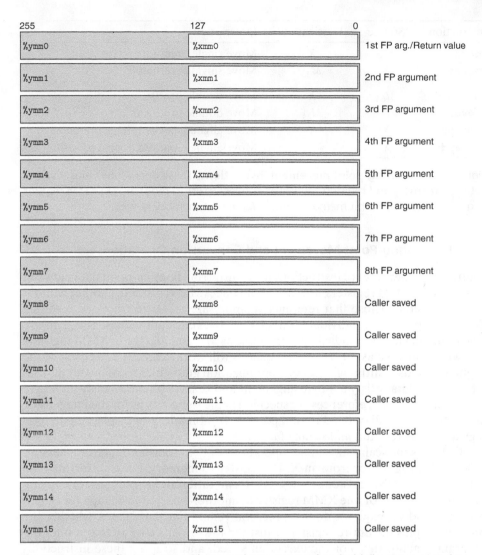

255	127	0	
%ymm0	%xmm0		1st FP arg./Return value
%ymm1	%xmm1		2nd FP argument
%ymm2	%xmm2		3rd FP argument
%ymm3	%xmm3		4th FP argument
%ymm4	%xmm4		5th FP argument
%ymm5	%xmm5		6th FP argument
%ymm6	%xmm6		7th FP argument
%ymm7	%xmm7		8th FP argument
%ymm8	%xmm8		Caller saved
%ymm9	%xmm9		Caller saved
%ymm10	%xmm10		Caller saved
%ymm11	%xmm11		Caller saved
%ymm12	%xmm12		Caller saved
%ymm13	%ymm13		Caller saved
%ymm14	%xmm14		Caller saved
%ymm15	%xmm15		Caller saved

Figure 3.45   Media registers. These registers are used to hold floating-point data. Each YMM register holds 32 bytes. The low-order 16 bytes can be accessed as an XMM register.

As is illustrated in Figure 3.45, the AVX floating-point architecture allows data to be stored in 16 YMM registers, named %ymm0–%ymm15. Each YMM register is 256 bits (32 bytes) long. When operating on scalar data, these registers only hold floating-point data, and only the low-order 32 bits (for `float`) or 64 bits (for `double`) are used. The assembly code refers to the registers by their SSE XMM register names %xmm0–%xmm15, where each XMM register is the low-order 128 bits (16 bytes) of the corresponding YMM register.

Instruction	Source	Destination	Description
vmovss	M_{32}	X	Move single precision
vmovss	X	M_{32}	Move single precision
vmovsd	M_{64}	X	Move double precision
vmovsd	X	M_{64}	Move double precision
vmovaps	X	X	Move aligned, packed single precision
vmovapd	X	X	Move aligned, packed double precision

Figure 3.46 Floating-point movement instructions. These operations transfer values between memory and registers, as well as between pairs of registers. (X: XMM register (e.g., %xmm3); M_{32}: 32-bit memory range; M_{64}: 64-bit memory range)

3.11.1 Floating-Point Movement and Conversion Operations

Figure 3.46 shows a set of instructions for transferring floating-point data between memory and XMM registers, as well as from one XMM register to another without any conversions. Those that reference memory are *scalar* instructions, meaning that they operate on individual, rather than packed, data values. The data are held either in memory (indicated in the table as M_{32} and M_{64}) or in XMM registers (shown in the table as X). These instructions will work correctly regardless of the alignment of data, although the code optimization guidelines recommend that 32-bit memory data satisfy a 4-byte alignment and that 64-bit data satisfy an 8-byte alignment. Memory references are specified in the same way as for the integer MOV instructions, with all of the different possible combinations of displacement, base register, index register, and scaling factor.

Gcc uses the scalar movement operations only to transfer data from memory to an XMM register or from an XMM register to memory. For transferring data between two XMM registers, it uses one of two different instructions for copying the entire contents of one XMM register to another—namely, vmovaps for single-precision and vmovapd for double-precision values. For these cases, whether the program copies the entire register or just the low-order value affects neither the program functionality nor the execution speed, and so using these instructions rather than ones specific to scalar data makes no real difference. The letter 'a' in these instruction names stands for "aligned." When used to read and write memory, they will cause an exception if the address does not satisfy a 16-byte alignment. For transferring between two registers, there is no possibility of an incorrect alignment.

As an example of the different floating-point move operations, consider the C function

```
float float_mov(float v1, float *src, float *dst) {
    float v2 = *src;
    *dst = v1;
    return v2;
}
```

Instruction	Source	Destination	Description
vcvttss2si	X/M_{32}	R_{32}	Convert with truncation single precision to integer
vcvttsd2si	X/M_{64}	R_{32}	Convert with truncation double precision to integer
vcvttss2siq	X/M_{32}	R_{64}	Convert with truncation single precision to quad word integer
vcvttsd2siq	X/M_{64}	R_{64}	Convert with truncation double precision to quad word integer

Figure 3.47 Two-operand floating-point conversion operations. These convert floating-point data to integers. (X: XMM register (e.g., %xmm3); R_{32}: 32-bit general-purpose register (e.g., %eax); R_{64}: 64-bit general-purpose register (e.g., %rax); M_{32}: 32-bit memory range; M_{64}: 64-bit memory range)

Instruction	Source 1	Source 2	Destination	Description
vcvtsi2ss	M_{32}/R_{32}	X	X	Convert integer to single precision
vcvtsi2sd	M_{32}/R_{32}	X	X	Convert integer to double precision
vcvtsi2ssq	M_{64}/R_{64}	X	X	Convert quad word integer to single precision
vcvtsi2sdq	M_{64}/R_{64}	X	X	Convert quad word integer to double precision

Figure 3.48 Three-operand floating-point conversion operations. These instructions convert from the data type of the first source to the data type of the destination. The second source value has no effect on the low-order bytes of the result. (X: XMM register (e.g., %xmm3); M_{32}: 32-bit memory range; M_{64}: 64-bit memory range)

and its associated x86-64 assembly code

```
    float float_mov(float v1, float *src, float *dst)
    v1 in %xmm0, src in %rdi, dst in %rsi
1   float_mov:
2       vmovaps %xmm0, %xmm1      Copy v1
3       vmovss  (%rdi), %xmm0     Read v2 from src
4       vmovss  %xmm1, (%rsi)     Write v1 to dst
5       ret                      Return v2 in %xmm0
```

We can see in this example the use of the vmovaps instruction to copy data from one register to another and the use of the vmovss instruction to copy data from memory to an XMM register and from an XMM register to memory.

Figures 3.47 and 3.48 show sets of instructions for converting between floating-point and integer data types, as well as between different floating-point formats. These are all scalar instructions operating on individual data values. Those in Figure 3.47 convert from a floating-point value read from either an XMM register or memory and write the result to a general-purpose register (e.g., %rax, %ebx, etc.). When converting floating-point values to integers, they perform *truncation*, rounding values toward zero, as is required by C and most other programming languages.

The instructions in Figure 3.48 convert from integer to floating point. They use an unusual three-operand format, with two sources and a destination. The first operand is read from memory or from a general-purpose register. For our purposes, we can ignore the second operand, since its value only affects the upper bytes of the result. The destination must be an XMM register. In common usage, both the second source and the destination operands are identical, as in the instruction

```
vcvtsi2sdq    %rax, %xmm1, %xmm1
```

This instruction reads a long integer from register %rax, converts it to data type double, and stores the result in the lower bytes of XMM register %xmm1.

Finally, for converting between two different floating-point formats, current versions of GCC generate code that requires separate documentation. Suppose the low-order 4 bytes of %xmm0 hold a single-precision value; then it would seem straightforward to use the instruction

```
vcvtss2sd    %xmm0, %xmm0, %xmm0
```

to convert this to a double-precision value and store the result in the lower 8 bytes of register %xmm0. Instead, we find the following code generated by GCC:

```
     Conversion from single to double precision
1    vunpcklps    %xmm0, %xmm0, %xmm0    Replicate first vector element
2    vcvtps2pd    %xmm0, %xmm0          Convert two vector elements to double
```

The vunpcklps instruction is normally used to interleave the values in two XMM registers and store them in a third. That is, if one source register contains words $[s_3, s_2, s_1, s_0]$ and the other contains words $[d_3, d_2, d_1, d_0]$, then the value of the destination register will be $[s_1, d_1, s_0, d_0]$. In the code above, we see the same register being used for all three operands, and so if the original register held values $[x_3, x_2, x_1, x_0]$, then the instruction will update the register to hold values $[x_1, x_1, x_0, x_0]$. The vcvtps2pd instruction expands the two low-order single-precision values in the source XMM register to be the two double-precision values in the destination XMM register. Applying this to the result of the preceding vunpcklps instruction would give values $[dx_0, dx_0]$, where dx_0 is the result of converting x to double precision. That is, the net effect of the two instructions is to convert the original single-precision value in the low-order 4 bytes of %xmm0 to double precision and store two copies of it in %xmm0. It is unclear why GCC generates this code. There is neither benefit nor need to have the value duplicated within the XMM register.

Gcc generates similar code for converting from double precision to single precision:

```
     Conversion from double to single precision
1    vmovddup     %xmm0, %xmm0    Replicate first vector element
2    vcvtpd2psx   %xmm0, %xmm0    Convert two vector elements to single
```

Suppose these instructions start with register %xmm0 holding two double-precision values $[x_1, x_0]$. Then the vmovddup instruction will set it to $[x_0, x_0]$. The vcvtpd2psx instruction will convert these values to single precision, pack them into the low-order half of the register, and set the upper half to 0, yielding a result $[0.0, 0.0, x_0, x_0]$ (recall that floating-point value 0.0 is represented by a bit pattern of all zeros). Again, there is no clear value in computing the conversion from one precision to another this way, rather than by using the single instruction

```
vcvtsd2ss %xmm0, %xmm0, %xmm0
```

As an example of the different floating-point conversion operations, consider the C function

```
double fcvt(int i, float *fp, double *dp, long *lp)
{
    float f = *fp; double d = *dp; long l = *lp;
    *lp = (long)    d;
    *fp = (float)   i;
    *dp = (double)  l;
    return (double) f;
}
```

and its associated x86-64 assembly code

```
    double fcvt(int i, float *fp, double *dp, long *lp)
    i in %edi, fp in %rsi, dp in %rdx, lp in %rcx
1   fcvt:
2     vmovss   (%rsi), %xmm0              Get f = *fp
3     movq     (%rcx), %rax               Get l = *lp
4     vcvttsd2siq    (%rdx), %r8          Get d = *dp and convert to long
5     movq     %r8, (%rcx)                Store at lp
6     vcvtsi2ss      %edi, %xmm1, %xmm1   Convert i to float
7     vmovss   %xmm1, (%rsi)              Store at fp
8     vcvtsi2sdq     %rax, %xmm1, %xmm1   Convert l to double
9     vmovsd   %xmm1, (%rdx)              Store at dp
    The following two instructions convert f to double
10    vunpcklps      %xmm0, %xmm0, %xmm0
11    vcvtps2pd      %xmm0, %xmm0
12    ret                                 Return f
```

All of the arguments to fcvt are passed through the general-purpose registers, since they are either integers or pointers. The result is returned in register %xmm0. As is documented in Figure 3.45, this is the designated return register for float or double values. In this code, we see a number of the movement and conversion instructions of Figures 3.46–3.48, as well as GCC's preferred method of converting from single to double precision.

Practice Problem 3.50 (solution page 347)

For the following C code, the expressions val1–val4 all map to the program values i, f, d, and l:

```
double fcvt2(int *ip, float *fp, double *dp, long l)
{
    int i = *ip; float f = *fp; double d = *dp;
    *ip = (int)      val1;
    *fp = (float)    val2;
    *dp = (double)   val3;
    return (double)  val4;
}
```

Determine the mapping, based on the following x86-64 code for the function:

```
    double fcvt2(int *ip, float *fp, double *dp, long l)
    ip in %rdi, fp in %rsi, dp in %rdx, l in %rcx
    Result returned in %xmm0
1   fcvt2:
2     movl      (%rdi), %eax
3     vmovss    (%rsi), %xmm0
4     vcvttsd2si        (%rdx), %r8d
5     movl      %r8d, (%rdi)
6     vcvtsi2ss         %eax, %xmm1, %xmm1
7     vmovss    %xmm1, (%rsi)
8     vcvtsi2sdq        %rcx, %xmm1, %xmm1
9     vmovsd    %xmm1, (%rdx)
10    vunpcklps         %xmm0, %xmm0, %xmm0
11    vcvtps2pd         %xmm0, %xmm0
12    ret
```

Practice Problem 3.51 (solution page 348)

The following C function converts an argument of type src_t to a return value of type dst_t, where these two types are defined using typedef:

```
dest_t cvt(src_t x)
{
    dest_t y = (dest_t) x;
    return y;
}
```

For execution on x86-64, assume that argument x is either in %xmm0 or in the appropriately named portion of register %rdi (i.e., %rdi or %edi). One or two instructions are to be used to perform the type conversion and to copy the value to the appropriately named portion of register %rax (integer result) or

%xmm0 (floating-point result). Show the instruction(s), including the source and destination registers.

T_x	T_y	Instruction(s)
long	double	vcvtsi2sdq %rdi, %xmm0
double	int	_____
double	float	_____
long	float	_____
float	long	_____

3.11.2   Floating-Point Code in Procedures

With x86-64, the XMM registers are used for passing floating-point arguments to functions and for returning floating-point values from them. As is illustrated in Figure 3.45, the following conventions are observed:

- Up to eight floating-point arguments can be passed in XMM registers %xmm0–%xmm7. These registers are used in the order the arguments are listed. Additional floating-point arguments can be passed on the stack.
- A function that returns a floating-point value does so in register %xmm0.
- All XMM registers are caller saved. The callee may overwrite any of these registers without first saving it.

When a function contains a combination of pointer, integer, and floating-point arguments, the pointers and integers are passed in general-purpose registers, while the floating-point values are passed in XMM registers. This means that the mapping of arguments to registers depends on both their types and their ordering. Here are several examples:

```
double f1(int x, double y, long z);
```

This function would have x in %edi, y in %xmm0, and z in %rsi.

```
double f2(double y, int x, long z);
```

This function would have the same register assignment as function f1.

```
double f1(float x, double *y, long *z);
```

This function would have x in %xmm0, y in %rdi, and z in %rsi.

Practice Problem 3.52 (solution page 348)

For each of the following function declarations, determine the register assignments for the arguments:

A. `double g1(double a, long b, float c, int d);`

B. `double g2(int a, double *b, float *c, long d);`

C. `double g3(double *a, double b, int c, float d);`

D. `double g4(float a, int *b, float c, double d);`

3.11.3 Floating-Point Arithmetic Operations

Figure 3.49 documents a set of scalar AVX2 floating-point instructions that perform arithmetic operations. Each has either one (S_1) or two (S_1, S_2) source operands and a destination operand D. The first source operand S_1 can be either an XMM register or a memory location. The second source operand and the destination operands must be XMM registers. Each operation has an instruction for single precision and an instruction for double precision. The result is stored in the destination register.

As an example, consider the following floating-point function:

```
double funct(double a, float x, double b, int i)
{
    return a*x - b/i;
}
```

The x86-64 code is as follows:

```
    double funct(double a, float x, double b, int i)
    a in %xmm0, x in %xmm1, b in %xmm2, i in %edi
1   funct:
    The following two instructions convert x to double
2     vunpcklps      %xmm1, %xmm1, %xmm1
3     vcvtps2pd      %xmm1, %xmm1
4     vmulsd  %xmm0, %xmm1, %xmm0          Multiply a by x
5     vcvtsi2sd      %edi, %xmm1, %xmm1    Convert i to double
6     vdivsd  %xmm1, %xmm2, %xmm2          Compute b/i
```

Single	Double	Effect	Description
vaddss	vaddsd	$D \leftarrow S_2 + S_1$	Floating-point add
vsubss	vsubsd	$D \leftarrow S_2 - S_1$	Floating-point subtract
vmulss	vmulsd	$D \leftarrow S_2 \times S_1$	Floating-point multiply
vdivss	vdivsd	$D \leftarrow S_2/S_1$	Floating-point divide
vmaxss	vmaxsd	$D \leftarrow \max(S_2, S_1)$	Floating-point maximum
vminss	vminsd	$D \leftarrow \min(S_2, S_1)$	Floating-point minimum
sqrtss	sqrtsd	$D \leftarrow \sqrt{S_1}$	Floating-point square root

Figure 3.49 Scalar floating-point arithmetic operations. These have either one or two source operands and a destination operand.

```
7    vsubsd  %xmm2, %xmm0, %xmm0        Subtract from a*x
8    ret                                Return
```

The three floating-point arguments a, x, and b are passed in XMM registers %xmm0–%xmm2, while integer argument i is passed in register %edi. The standard two-instruction sequence is used to convert argument x to double (lines 2–3). Another conversion instruction is required to convert argument i to double (line 5). The function value is returned in register %xmm0.

Practice Problem 3.53 (solution page 348)

For the following C function, the types of the four arguments are defined by typedef:

```
double funct1(arg1_t p, arg2_t q, arg3_t r, arg4_t s)
{
    return p/(q+r) - s;
}
```

When compiled, GCC generates the following code:

```
      double funct1(arg1_t p, arg2_t q, arg3_t r, arg4_t s)
1    funct1:
2      vcvtsi2ssq      %rsi, %xmm2, %xmm2
3      vaddss  %xmm0, %xmm2, %xmm0
4      vcvtsi2ss       %edi, %xmm2, %xmm2
5      vdivss  %xmm0, %xmm2, %xmm0
6      vunpcklps       %xmm0, %xmm0, %xmm0
7      vcvtps2pd       %xmm0, %xmm0
8      vsubsd  %xmm1, %xmm0, %xmm0
9      ret
```

Determine the possible combinations of types of the four arguments (there may be more than one).

Practice Problem 3.54 (solution page 349)

Function funct2 has the following prototype:

```
double funct2(double w, int x, float y, long z);
```

Gcc generates the following code for the function:

```
      double funct2(double w, int x, float y, long z)
      w in %xmm0, x in %edi, y in %xmm1, z in %rsi
1    funct2:
2      vcvtsi2ss       %edi, %xmm2, %xmm2
3      vmulss  %xmm1, %xmm2, %xmm1
```

```
4      vunpcklps          %xmm1, %xmm1, %xmm1
5      vcvtps2pd          %xmm1, %xmm2
6      vcvtsi2sdq         %rsi, %xmm1, %xmm1
7      vdivsd   %xmm1, %xmm0, %xmm0
8      vsubsd   %xmm0, %xmm2, %xmm0
9      ret
```

Write a C version of funct2.

3.11.4 Defining and Using Floating-Point Constants

Unlike integer arithmetic operations, AVX floating-point operations cannot have immediate values as operands. Instead, the compiler must allocate and initialize storage for any constant values. The code then reads the values from memory. This is illustrated by the following Celsius to Fahrenheit conversion function:

```
double cel2fahr(double temp)
{
    return 1.8 * temp + 32.0;
}
```

The relevant parts of the x86-64 assembly code are as follows:

```
       double cel2fahr(double temp)
       temp in %xmm0
1    cel2fahr:
2      vmulsd    .LC2(%rip), %xmm0, %xmm0     Multiply by 1.8
3      vaddsd    .LC3(%rip), %xmm0, %xmm0     Add 32.0
4      ret
5    .LC2:
6      .long     3435973837                   Low-order 4 bytes of 1.8
7      .long     1073532108                   High-order 4 bytes of 1.8
8    .LC3:
9      .long     0                            Low-order 4 bytes of 32.0
10     .long     1077936128                   High-order 4 bytes of 32.0
```

We see that the function reads the value 1.8 from the memory location labeled .LC2 and the value 32.0 from the memory location labeled .LC3. Looking at the values associated with these labels, we see that each is specified by a pair of .long declarations with the values given in decimal. How should these be interpreted as floating-point values? Looking at the declaration labeled .LC2, we see that the two values are 3435973837 (0xcccccccd) and 1073532108 (0x3ffcccccc.) Since the machine uses little-endian byte ordering, the first value gives the low-order 4 bytes, while the second gives the high-order 4 bytes. From the high-order bytes, we can extract an exponent field of 0x3ff (1023), from which we subtract a bias of 1023 to get an exponent of 0. Concatenating the fraction bits of the two values, we get a fraction field of 0xcccccccccccccd, which can be shown to be the fractional binary representation of 0.8, to which we add the implied leading one to get 1.8.

Single	Double	Effect	Description
vxorps	xorpd	$D \leftarrow S_2 \char`^ S_1$	Bitwise EXCLUSIVE-OR
vandps	andpd	$D \leftarrow S_2 \,\&\, S_1$	Bitwise AND

Figure 3.50   Bitwise operations on packed data. These instructions perform Boolean operations on all 128 bits in an XMM register.

Practice Problem 3.55 (solution page 349)

Show how the numbers declared at label .LC3 encode the number 32.0.

3.11.5   Using Bitwise Operations in Floating-Point Code

At times, we find GCC generating code that performs bitwise operations on XMM registers to implement useful floating-point results. Figure 3.50 shows some relevant instructions, similar to their counterparts for operating on general-purpose registers. These operations all act on packed data, meaning that they update the entire destination XMM register, applying the bitwise operation to all the data in the two source registers. Once again, our only interest for scalar data is the effect these instructions have on the low-order 4 or 8 bytes of the destination. These operations are often simple and convenient ways to manipulate floating-point values, as is explored in the following problem.

Practice Problem 3.56 (solution page 350)

Consider the following C function, where EXPR is a macro defined with #define:

```
double simplefun(double x) {
    return EXPR(x);
}
```

Below, we show the AVX2 code generated for different definitions of EXPR, where value x is held in %xmm0. All of them correspond to some useful operation on floating-point values. Identify what the operations are. Your answers will require you to understand the bit patterns of the constant words being retrieved from memory.

```
A.  1       vmovsd  .LC1(%rip), %xmm1
    2       vandpd  %xmm1, %xmm0, %xmm0
    3   .LC1:
    4       .long   4294967295
    5       .long   2147483647
    6       .long   0
    7       .long   0

B.  1       vxorpd  %xmm0, %xmm0, %xmm0
```

```
C.  1        vmovsd  .LC2(%rip), %xmm1
    2        vxorpd  %xmm1, %xmm0, %xmm0
    3    .LC2:
    4        .long   0
    5        .long   -2147483648
    6        .long   0
    7        .long   0
```

3.11.6 Floating-Point Comparison Operations

AVX2 provides two instructions for comparing floating-point values:

Instruction		Based on	Description
ucomiss	S_1, S_2	$S_2 - S_1$	Compare single precision
ucomisd	S_1, S_2	$S_2 - S_1$	Compare double precision

These instructions are similar to the CMP instructions (see Section 3.6), in that they compare operands S_1 and S_2 (but in the opposite order one might expect) and set the condition codes to indicate their relative values. As with cmpq, they follow the ATT-format convention of listing the operands in reverse order. Argument S_2 must be in an XMM register, while S_1 can be either in an XMM register or in memory.

The floating-point comparison instructions set three condition codes: the zero flag ZF, the carry flag CF, and the parity flag PF. We did not document the parity flag in Section 3.6.1, because it is not commonly found in GCC-generated x86 code. For integer operations, this flag is set when the most recent arithmetic or logical operation yielded a value where the least significant byte has even parity (i.e., an even number of ones in the byte). For floating-point comparisons, however, the flag is set when either operand is *NaN*. By convention, any comparison in C is considered to fail when one of the arguments is *NaN*, and this flag is used to detect such a condition. For example, even the comparison x == x yields 0 when x is *NaN*.

The condition codes are set as follows:

Ordering S_2:S_1	CF	ZF	PF
Unordered	1	1	1
$S_2 < S_1$	1	0	0
$S_2 = S_1$	0	1	0
$S_2 > S_1$	0	0	0

The *unordered* case occurs when either operand is *NaN*. This can be detected with the parity flag. Commonly, the jp (for "jump on parity") instruction is used to conditionally jump when a floating-point comparison yields an unordered result. Except for this case, the values of the carry and zero flags are the same as those for an unsigned comparison: ZF is set when the two operands are equal, and CF is

(a) C code

```
typedef enum {NEG, ZERO, POS, OTHER} range_t;

range_t find_range(float x)
{
    int result;
    if (x < 0)
        result = NEG;
    else if (x == 0)
        result = ZERO;
    else if (x > 0)
        result = POS;
    else
        result = OTHER;
    return result;
}
```

(b) Generated assembly code

```
      range_t find_range(float x)
      x in %xmm0
1     find_range:
2       vxorps   %xmm1, %xmm1, %xmm1         Set %xmm1 = 0
3       vucomiss         %xmm0, %xmm1        Compare 0:x
4       ja       .L5                         If >, goto neg
5       vucomiss         %xmm1, %xmm0        Compare x:0
6       jp       .L8                         If NaN, goto posornan
7       movl     $1, %eax                    result = ZERO
8       je       .L3                         If =, goto done
9     .L8:                                 posornan:
10      vucomiss         .LC0(%rip), %xmm0   Compare x:0
11      setbe    %al                         Set result = NaN ? 1 : 0
12      movzbl   %al, %eax                   Zero-extend
13      addl     $2, %eax                    result += 2 (POS for > 0, OTHER for NaN)
14      ret                                  Return
15    .L5:                                 neg:
16      movl     $0, %eax                    result = NEG
17    .L3:                                 done:
18      rep; ret                             Return
```

Figure 3.51 Illustration of conditional branching in floating-point code.

set when $S_2 < S_1$. Instructions such as ja and jb are used to conditionally jump on various combinations of these flags.

As an example of floating-point comparisons, the C function of Figure 3.51(a) classifies argument x according to its relation to 0.0, returning an enumerated type as the result. Enumerated types in C are encoded as integers, and so the possible function values are: 0 (NEG), 1 (ZERO), 2 (POS), and 3 (OTHER). This final outcome occurs when the value of x is *NaN*.

Gcc generates the code shown in Figure 3.51(b) for find_range. The code is not very efficient—it compares x to 0.0 three times, even though the required information could be obtained with a single comparison. It also generates floating-point constant 0.0 twice—once using vxorps, and once by reading the value from memory. Let us trace the flow of the function for the four possible comparison results:

x < 0.0   The ja branch on line 4 will be taken, jumping to the end with a return value of 0.

x = 0.0   The ja (line 4) and jp (line 6) branches will not be taken, but the je branch (line 8) will, returning with %eax equal to 1.

x > 0.0   None of the three branches will be taken. The setbe (line 11) will yield 0, and this will be incremented by the addl instruction (line 13) to give a return value of 2.

x = *NaN*   The jp branch (line 6) will be taken. The third vucomiss instruction (line 10) will set both the carry and the zero flag, and so the setbe instruction (line 11) and the following instruction will set %eax to 1. This gets incremented by the addl instruction (line 13) to give a return value of 3.

In Homework Problems 3.73 and 3.74, you are challenged to hand-generate more efficient implementations of find_range.

Practice Problem 3.57 (solution page 350)

Function funct3 has the following prototype:

```
double funct3(int *ap, double b, long c, float *dp);
```

For this function, GCC generates the following code:

```
   double funct3(int *ap, double b, long c, float *dp)
   ap in %rdi, b in %xmm0, c in %rsi, dp in %rdx
 1 funct3:
 2   vmovss    (%rdx), %xmm1
 3   vcvtsi2sd          (%rdi), %xmm2, %xmm2
 4   vucomisd          %xmm2, %xmm0
 5   jbe     .L8
 6   vcvtsi2ssq        %rsi, %xmm0, %xmm0
 7   vmulss  %xmm1, %xmm0, %xmm1
```

```
8      vunpcklps          %xmm1, %xmm1, %xmm1
9      vcvtps2pd          %xmm1, %xmm0
10     ret
11   .L8:
12     vaddss  %xmm1, %xmm1, %xmm1
13     vcvtsi2ssq         %rsi, %xmm0, %xmm0
14     vaddss  %xmm1, %xmm0, %xmm0
15     vunpcklps          %xmm0, %xmm0, %xmm0
16     vcvtps2pd          %xmm0, %xmm0
17     ret
```

Write a C version of `funct3`.

3.11.7 Observations about Floating-Point Code

We see that the general style of machine code generated for operating on floating-point data with AVX2 is similar to what we have seen for operating on integer data. Both use a collection of registers to hold and operate on values, and they use these registers for passing function arguments.

Of course, there are many complexities in dealing with the different data types and the rules for evaluating expressions containing a mixture of data types, and AVX2 code involves many more different instructions and formats than is usually seen with functions that perform only integer arithmetic.

AVX2 also has the potential to make computations run faster by performing parallel operations on packed data. Compiler developers are working on automating the conversion of scalar code to parallel code, but currently the most reliable way to achieve higher performance through parallelism is to use the extensions to the C language supported by GCC for manipulating vectors of data. See Web Aside OPT:SIMD on page 546 to see how this can be done.

3.12 Summary

In this chapter, we have peered beneath the layer of abstraction provided by the C language to get a view of machine-level programming. By having the compiler generate an assembly-code representation of the machine-level program, we gain insights into both the compiler and its optimization capabilities, along with the machine, its data types, and its instruction set. In Chapter 5, we will see that knowing the characteristics of a compiler can help when trying to write programs that have efficient mappings onto the machine. We have also gotten a more complete picture of how the program stores data in different memory regions. In Chapter 12, we will see many examples where application programmers need to know whether a program variable is on the run-time stack, in some dynamically allocated data structure, or part of the global program data. Understanding how programs map onto machines makes it easier to understand the differences between these kinds of storage.

Machine-level programs, and their representation by assembly code, differ in many ways from C programs. There is minimal distinction between different data types. The program is expressed as a sequence of instructions, each of which performs a single operation. Parts of the program state, such as registers and the run-time stack, are directly visible to the programmer. Only low-level operations are provided to support data manipulation and program control. The compiler must use multiple instructions to generate and operate on different data structures and to implement control constructs such as conditionals, loops, and procedures. We have covered many different aspects of C and how it gets compiled. We have seen that the lack of bounds checking in C makes many programs prone to buffer overflows. This has made many systems vulnerable to attacks by malicious intruders, although recent safeguards provided by the run-time system and the compiler help make programs more secure.

We have only examined the mapping of C onto x86-64, but much of what we have covered is handled in a similar way for other combinations of language and machine. For example, compiling C++ is very similar to compiling C. In fact, early implementations of C++ first performed a source-to-source conversion from C++ to C and generated object code by running a C compiler on the result. C++ objects are represented by structures, similar to a C struct. Methods are represented by pointers to the code implementing the methods. By contrast, Java is implemented in an entirely different fashion. The object code of Java is a special binary representation known as *Java byte code*. This code can be viewed as a machine-level program for a *virtual machine*. As its name suggests, this machine is not implemented directly in hardware. Instead, software interpreters process the byte code, simulating the behavior of the virtual machine. Alternatively, an approach known as *just-in-time compilation* dynamically translates byte code sequences into machine instructions. This approach provides faster execution when code is executed multiple times, such as in loops. The advantage of using byte code as the low-level representation of a program is that the same code can be "executed" on many different machines, whereas the machine code we have considered runs only on x86-64 machines.

Bibliographic Notes

Both Intel and AMD provide extensive documentation on their processors. This includes general descriptions of an assembly-language programmer's view of the hardware [2, 50], as well as detailed references about the individual instructions [3, 51]. Reading the instruction descriptions is complicated by the facts that (1) all documentation is based on the Intel assembly-code format, (2) there are many variations for each instruction due to the different addressing and execution modes, and (3) there are no illustrative examples. Still, these remain the authoritative references about the behavior of each instruction.

The organization x86-64.org has been responsible for defining the *application binary interface* (ABI) for x86-64 code running on Linux systems [77]. This interface describes details for procedure linkages, binary code files, and a number of other features that are required for machine-code programs to execute properly.

As we have discussed, the ATT format used by GCC is very different from the Intel format used in Intel documentation and by other compilers (including the Microsoft compilers).

Muchnick's book on compiler design [80] is considered the most comprehensive reference on code-optimization techniques. It covers many of the techniques we discuss here, such as register usage conventions.

Much has been written about the use of buffer overflow to attack systems over the Internet. Detailed analyses of the 1988 Internet worm have been published by Spafford [105] as well as by members of the team at MIT who helped stop its spread [35]. Since then a number of papers and projects have generated ways both to create and to prevent buffer overflow attacks. Seacord's book [97] provides a wealth of information about buffer overflow and other attacks on code generated by C compilers.

Homework Problems

3.58 ◆
For a function with prototype

```
long decode2(long x, long y, long z);
```

GCC generates the following assembly code:

```
1    decode2:
2        subq    %rdx, %rsi
3        imulq   %rsi, %rdi
4        movq    %rsi, %rax
5        salq    $63, %rax
6        sarq    $63, %rax
7        xorq    %rdi, %rax
8        ret
```

Parameters x, y, and z are passed in registers %rdi, %rsi, and %rdx. The code stores the return value in register %rax.

Write C code for decode2 that will have an effect equivalent to the assembly code shown.

3.59 ◆◆
The following code computes the 128-bit product of two 64-bit signed values x and y and stores the result in memory:

```
1    typedef __int128 int128_t;
2
3    void store_prod(int128_t *dest, int64_t x, int64_t y) {
4        *dest = x * (int128_t) y;
5    }
```

Gcc generates the following assembly code implementing the computation:

```
1   store_prod:
2     movq    %rdx, %rax
3     cqto
4     movq    %rsi, %rcx
5     sarq    $63, %rcx
6     imulq   %rax, %rcx
7     imulq   %rsi, %rdx
8     addq    %rdx, %rcx
9     mulq    %rsi
10    addq    %rcx, %rdx
11    movq    %rax, (%rdi)
12    movq    %rdx, 8(%rdi)
13    ret
```

This code uses three multiplications for the multiprecision arithmetic required to implement 128-bit arithmetic on a 64-bit machine. Describe the algorithm used to compute the product, and annotate the assembly code to show how it realizes your algorithm. *Hint:* When extending arguments of x and y to 128 bits, they can be rewritten as $x = 2^{64} \cdot x_h + x_l$ and $y = 2^{64} \cdot y_h + y_l$, where x_h, x_l, y_h, and y_l are 64-bit values. Similarly, the 128-bit product can be written as $p = 2^{64} \cdot p_h + p_l$, where p_h and p_l are 64-bit values. Show how the code computes the values of p_h and p_l in terms of x_h, x_l, y_h, and y_l.

3.60 ◆◆

Consider the following assembly code:

```
    long loop(long x, int n)
    x in %rdi, n in %esi
1   loop:
2     movl    %esi, %ecx
3     movl    $1, %edx
4     movl    $0, %eax
5     jmp     .L2
6   .L3:
7     movq    %rdi, %r8
8     andq    %rdx, %r8
9     orq     %r8, %rax
10    salq    %cl, %rdx
11  .L2:
12    testq   %rdx, %rdx
13    jne     .L3
14    rep; ret
```

The preceding code was generated by compiling C code that had the following overall form:

```
1   long loop(long x, long n)
2   {
3       long result = _____;
4       long mask;
5       for (mask = _____; mask _____ ; mask = _____ ) {
6           result |= _____ ;
7       }
8       return result;
9   }
```

Your task is to fill in the missing parts of the C code to get a program equivalent to the generated assembly code. Recall that the result of the function is returned in register %rax. You will find it helpful to examine the assembly code before, during, and after the loop to form a consistent mapping between the registers and the program variables.

A. Which registers hold program values x, n, result, and mask?

B. What are the initial values of result and mask?

C. What is the test condition for mask?

D. How does mask get updated?

E. How does result get updated?

F. Fill in all the missing parts of the C code.

3.61 ◆◆

In Section 3.6.6, we examined the following code as a candidate for the use of conditional data transfer:

```
long cread(long *xp) {
    return (xp ? *xp : 0);
}
```

We showed a trial implementation using a conditional move instruction but argued that it was not valid, since it could attempt to read from a null address.

Write a C function cread_alt that has the same behavior as cread, except that it can be compiled to use conditional data transfer. When compiled, the generated code should use a conditional move instruction rather than one of the jump instructions.

3.62 ◆◆

The code that follows shows an example of branching on an enumerated type value in a switch statement. Recall that enumerated types in C are simply a way to introduce a set of names having associated integer values. By default, the values assigned to the names count from zero upward. In our code, the actions associated with the different case labels have been omitted.

```
1    /* Enumerated type creates set of constants numbered 0 and upward */
2    typedef enum {MODE_A, MODE_B, MODE_C, MODE_D, MODE_E} mode_t;
3
4    long switch3(long *p1, long *p2, mode_t action)
5    {
6        long result = 0;
7        switch(action) {
8        case MODE_A:
9
10       case MODE_B:
11
12       case MODE_C:
13
14       case MODE_D:
15
16       case MODE_E:
17
18       default:
19
20       }
21       return result;
22   }
```

The part of the generated assembly code implementing the different actions is shown in Figure 3.52. The annotations indicate the argument locations, the register values, and the case labels for the different jump destinations.

Fill in the missing parts of the C code. It contained one case that fell through to another—try to reconstruct this.

3.63 ◆◆

This problem will give you a chance to reverse engineer a switch statement from disassembled machine code. In the following procedure, the body of the switch statement has been omitted:

```
1    long switch_prob(long x, long n) {
2        long result = x;
3        switch(n) {
4            /* Fill in code here */
5
6        }
7        return result;
8    }
```

```
        p1 in %rdi, p2 in %rsi, action in %edx
1    .L8:                        MODE_E
2      movl     $27, %eax
3      ret
4    .L3:                        MODE_A
5      movq     (%rsi), %rax
6      movq     (%rdi), %rdx
7      movq     %rdx, (%rsi)
8      ret
9    .L5:                        MODE_B
10     movq     (%rdi), %rax
11     addq     (%rsi), %rax
12     movq     %rax, (%rdi)
13     ret
14   .L6:                        MODE_C
15     movq     $59, (%rdi)
16     movq     (%rsi), %rax
17     ret
18   .L7:                        MODE_D
19     movq     (%rsi), %rax
20     movq     %rax, (%rdi)
21     movl     $27, %eax
22     ret
23   .L9:                        default
24     movl     $12, %eax
25     ret
```

Figure 3.52 Assembly code for Problem 3.62. This code implements the different branches of a switch statement.

Figure 3.53 shows the disassembled machine code for the procedure.

The jump table resides in a different area of memory. We can see from the indirect jump on line 5 that the jump table begins at address 0x4006f8. Using the GDB debugger, we can examine the six 8-byte words of memory comprising the jump table with the command x/6gx 0x4006f8. GDB prints the following:

```
(gdb) x/6gx 0x4006f8
0x4006f8:    0x00000000004005a1    0x00000000004005c3
0x400708:    0x00000000004005a1    0x00000000004005aa
0x400718:    0x00000000004005b2    0x00000000004005bf
```

Fill in the body of the switch statement with C code that will have the same behavior as the machine code.

```
        long switch_prob(long x, long n)
        x in %rdi, n in %rsi
1   0000000000400590 <switch_prob>:
2     400590:   48 83 ee 3c            sub     $0x3c,%rsi
3     400594:   48 83 fe 05            cmp     $0x5,%rsi
4     400598:   77 29                  ja      4005c3 <switch_prob+0x33>
5     40059a:   ff 24 f5 f8 06 40 00   jmpq    *0x4006f8(,%rsi,8)
6     4005a1:   48 8d 04 fd 00 00 00   lea     0x0(,%rdi,8),%rax
7     4005a8:   00
8     4005a9:   c3                     retq
9     4005aa:   48 89 f8               mov     %rdi,%rax
10    4005ad:   48 c1 f8 03            sar     $0x3,%rax
11    4005b1:   c3                     retq
12    4005b2:   48 89 f8               mov     %rdi,%rax
13    4005b5:   48 c1 e0 04            shl     $0x4,%rax
14    4005b9:   48 29 f8               sub     %rdi,%rax
15    4005bc:   48 89 c7               mov     %rax,%rdi
16    4005bf:   48 0f af ff            imul    %rdi,%rdi
17    4005c3:   48 8d 47 4b            lea     0x4b(%rdi),%rax
18    4005c7:   c3                     retq
```

Figure 3.53 Disassembled code for Problem 3.63.

3.64 ◆◆◆

Consider the following source code, where *R*, *S*, and *T* are constants declared with #define:

```
1   long A[R][S][T];
2
3   long store_ele(long i, long j, long k, long *dest)
4   {
5       *dest = A[i][j][k];
6       return sizeof(A);
7   }
```

In compiling this program, GCC generates the following assembly code:

```
        long store_ele(long i, long j, long k, long *dest)
        i in %rdi, j in %rsi, k in %rdx, dest in %rcx
1   store_ele:
2     leaq    (%rsi,%rsi,2), %rax
3     leaq    (%rsi,%rax,4), %rax
4     movq    %rdi, %rsi
5     salq    $6, %rsi
6     addq    %rsi, %rdi
7     addq    %rax, %rdi
```

```
8       addq    %rdi, %rdx
9       movq    A(,%rdx,8), %rax
10      movq    %rax, (%rcx)
11      movl    $3640, %eax
12      ret
```

A. Extend Equation 3.1 from two dimensions to three to provide a formula for the location of array element A[i][j][k].

B. Use your reverse engineering skills to determine the values of R, S, and T based on the assembly code.

3.65 ◆

The following code transposes the elements of an $M \times M$ array, where M is a constant defined by #define:

```
1   void transpose(long A[M][M]) {
2       long i, j;
3       for (i = 0; i < M; i++)
4           for (j = 0; j < i; j++) {
5               long t = A[i][j];
6               A[i][j] = A[j][i];
7               A[j][i] = t;
8           }
9   }
```

When compiled with optimization level –01, GCC generates the following code for the inner loop of the function:

```
1   .L6:
2       movq    (%rdx), %rcx
3       movq    (%rax), %rsi
4       movq    %rsi, (%rdx)
5       movq    %rcx, (%rax)
6       addq    $8, %rdx
7       addq    $120, %rax
8       cmpq    %rdi, %rax
9       jne     .L6
```

We can see that GCC has converted the array indexing to pointer code.

A. Which register holds a pointer to array element A[i][j]?

B. Which register holds a pointer to array element A[j][i]?

C. What is the value of M?

3.66 ◆

Consider the following source code, where NR and NC are macro expressions declared with #define that compute the dimensions of array A in terms of parameter n. This code computes the sum of the elements of column j of the array.

```
1   long sum_col(long n, long A[NR(n)][NC(n)], long j) {
2       long i;
3       long result = 0;
4       for (i = 0; i < NR(n); i++)
5           result += A[i][j];
6       return result;
7   }
```

In compiling this program, GCC generates the following assembly code:

```
long sum_col(long n, long A[NR(n)][NC(n)], long j)
n in %rdi, A in %rsi, j in %rdx
1   sum_col:
2       leaq    1(,%rdi,4), %r8
3       leaq    (%rdi,%rdi,2), %rax
4       movq    %rax, %rdi
5       testq   %rax, %rax
6       jle     .L4
7       salq    $3, %r8
8       leaq    (%rsi,%rdx,8), %rcx
9       movl    $0, %eax
10      movl    $0, %edx
11  .L3:
12      addq    (%rcx), %rax
13      addq    $1, %rdx
14      addq    %r8, %rcx
15      cmpq    %rdi, %rdx
16      jne     .L3
17      rep; ret
18  .L4:
19      movl    $0, %eax
20      ret
```

Use your reverse engineering skills to determine the definitions of NR and NC.

3.67 ◆◆

For this exercise, we will examine the code generated by GCC for functions that have structures as arguments and return values, and from this see how these language features are typically implemented.

The following C code has a function process having structures as argument and return values, and a function eval that calls process:

```
1   typedef struct {
2       long a[2];
3       long *p;
4   } strA;
5
```

```
6    typedef struct {
7        long u[2];
8        long q;
9    } strB;
10
11   strB process(strA s) {
12       strB r;
13       r.u[0] = s.a[1];
14       r.u[1] = s.a[0];
15       r.q =     *s.p;
16       return r;
17   }
18
19   long eval(long x, long y, long z) {
20       strA s;
21       s.a[0] = x;
22       s.a[1] = y;
23       s.p = &z;
24       strB r = process(s);
25       return r.u[0] + r.u[1] + r.q;
26   }
```

Gcc generates the following code for these two functions:

```
     strB process(strA s)
1    process:
2      movq      %rdi, %rax
3      movq      24(%rsp), %rdx
4      movq      (%rdx), %rdx
5      movq      16(%rsp), %rcx
6      movq      %rcx, (%rdi)
7      movq      8(%rsp), %rcx
8      movq      %rcx, 8(%rdi)
9      movq      %rdx, 16(%rdi)
10     ret
```

```
     long eval(long x, long y, long z)
     x in %rdi, y in %rsi, z in %rdx
1    eval:
2      subq      $104, %rsp
3      movq      %rdx, 24(%rsp)
4      leaq      24(%rsp), %rax
5      movq      %rdi, (%rsp)
6      movq      %rsi, 8(%rsp)
7      movq      %rax, 16(%rsp)
8      leaq      64(%rsp), %rdi
9      call      process
```

```
10      movq    72(%rsp), %rax
11      addq    64(%rsp), %rax
12      addq    80(%rsp), %rax
13      addq    $104, %rsp
14      ret
```

A. We can see on line 2 of function eval that it allocates 104 bytes on the stack. Diagram the stack frame for eval, showing the values that it stores on the stack prior to calling process.

B. What value does eval pass in its call to process?

C. How does the code for process access the elements of structure argument s?

D. How does the code for process set the fields of result structure r?

E. Complete your diagram of the stack frame for eval, showing how eval accesses the elements of structure r following the return from process.

F. What general principles can you discern about how structure values are passed as function arguments and how they are returned as function results?

3.68 ◆◆◆

In the following code, A and B are constants defined with #define:

```
1   typedef struct {
2       int x[A][B]; /* Unknown constants A and B */
3       long y;
4   } str1;
5
6   typedef struct {
7       char array[B];
8       int t;
9       short s[A];
10      long u;
11  } str2;
12
13  void setVal(str1 *p, str2 *q) {
14      long v1 = q->t;
15      long v2 = q->u;
16      p->y = v1+v2;
17  }
```

Gcc generates the following code for setVal:

```
    void setVal(str1 *p, str2 *q)
    p in %rdi, q in %rsi
1   setVal:
2     movslq  8(%rsi), %rax
3     addq    32(%rsi), %rax
```

```
4      movq    %rax, 184(%rdi)
5      ret
```

What are the values of *A* and *B*? (The solution is unique.)

3.69 ◆◆◆

You are charged with maintaining a large C program, and you come across the following code:

```
1    typedef struct {
2        int first;
3        a_struct a[CNT];
4        int last;
5    } b_struct;
6
7    void test(long i, b_struct *bp)
8    {
9        int n = bp->first + bp->last;
10       a_struct *ap = &bp->a[i];
11       ap->x[ap->idx] = n;
12   }
```

The declarations of the compile-time constant CNT and the structure a_struct are in a file for which you do not have the necessary access privilege. Fortunately, you have a copy of the .o version of code, which you are able to disassemble with the OBJDUMP program, yielding the following disassembly:

```
     void test(long i, b_struct *bp)
     i in %rdi, bp in %rsi
1    0000000000000000 <test>:
2       0:   8b 8e 20 01 00 00       mov     0x120(%rsi),%ecx
3       6:   03 0e                   add     (%rsi),%ecx
4       8:   48 8d 04 bf             lea     (%rdi,%rdi,4),%rax
5       c:   48 8d 04 c6             lea     (%rsi,%rax,8),%rax
6      10:   48 8b 50 08             mov     0x8(%rax),%rdx
7      14:   48 63 c9                movslq %ecx,%rcx
8      17:   48 89 4c d0 10          mov     %rcx,0x10(%rax,%rdx,8)
9      1c:   c3                      retq
```

Using your reverse engineering skills, deduce the following:

A. The value of CNT.

B. A complete declaration of structure a_struct. Assume that the only fields in this structure are idx and x, and that both of these contain signed values.

3.70 ◆◆◆

Consider the following union declaration:

```
1   union ele {
2       struct {
3           long *p;
4           long y;
5       } e1;
6       struct {
7           long x;
8           union ele *next;
9       } e2;
10  };
```

This declaration illustrates that structures can be embedded within unions.

The following function (with some expressions omitted) operates on a linked list having these unions as list elements:

```
1   void proc (union ele *up) {
2       up->_____ = *(_____) - _____;
3   }
```

A. What are the offsets (in bytes) of the following fields:

   e1.p   _____
   e1.y   _____
   e2.x   _____
   e2.next   _____

B. How many total bytes does the structure require?

C. The compiler generates the following assembly code for proc:

```
    void proc (union ele *up)
    up in %rdi
1   proc:
2       movq    8(%rdi), %rax
3       movq    (%rax), %rdx
4       movq    (%rdx), %rdx
5       subq    8(%rax), %rdx
6       movq    %rdx, (%rdi)
7       ret
```

On the basis of this information, fill in the missing expressions in the code for proc. *Hint:* Some union references can have ambiguous interpretations. These ambiguities get resolved as you see where the references lead. There is only one answer that does not perform any casting and does not violate any type constraints.

3.71 ◆

Write a function good_echo that reads a line from standard input and writes it to standard output. Your implementation should work for an input line of arbitrary length. You may use the library function fgets, but you must make sure your function works correctly even when the input line requires more space than you have allocated for your buffer. Your code should also check for error conditions and return when one is encountered. Refer to the definitions of the standard I/O functions for documentation [45, 61].

3.72 ◆◆

Figure 3.54(a) shows the code for a function that is similar to function vfunct (Figure 3.43(a)). We used vfunct to illustrate the use of a frame pointer in managing variable-size stack frames. The new function aframe allocates space for local

(a) C code

```
1    #include <alloca.h>
2
3    long aframe(long n, long idx, long *q)  {
4        long i;
5        long **p = alloca(n * sizeof(long *));
6        p[0] = &i;
7        for (i = 1; i < n; i++)
8            p[i] = q;
9        return *p[idx];
10   }
```

(b) Portions of generated assembly code

```
     long aframe(long n, long idx, long *q)
     n in %rdi, idx in %rsi, q in %rdx
1    aframe:
2        pushq   %rbp
3        movq    %rsp, %rbp
4        subq    $16, %rsp              Allocate space for i (%rsp = s₁)
5        leaq    30(,%rdi,8), %rax
6        andq    $-16, %rax
7        subq    %rax, %rsp             Allocate space for array p (%rsp = s₂)
8        leaq    15(%rsp), %r8
9        andq    $-16, %r8             Set %r8 to &p[0]
         .
         .
         .
```

Figure 3.54 Code for Problem 3.72. This function is similar to that of Figure 3.43.

array p by calling library function `alloca`. This function is similar to the more commonly used function `malloc`, except that it allocates space on the run-time stack. The space is automatically deallocated when the executing procedure returns.

Figure 3.54(b) shows the part of the assembly code that sets up the frame pointer and allocates space for local variables `i` and `p`. It is very similar to the corresponding code for `vframe`. Let us use the same notation as in Problem 3.49: The stack pointer is set to values s_1 at line 4 and s_2 at line 7. The start address of array p is set to value p at line 9. Extra space e_2 may arise between s_2 and p, and extra space e_1 may arise between the end of array p and s_1.

A. Explain, in mathematical terms, the logic in the computation of s_2.

B. Explain, in mathematical terms, the logic in the computation of p.

C. Find values of n and s_1 that lead to minimum and maximum values of e_1.

D. What alignment properties does this code guarantee for the values of s_2 and p?

3.73 ◆

Write a function in assembly code that matches the behavior of the function `find_range` in Figure 3.51. Your code should contain only one floating-point comparison instruction, and then it should use conditional branches to generate the correct result. Test your code on all 2^{32} possible argument values. Web Aside ASM:EASM on page 178 describes how to incorporate functions written in assembly code into C programs.

3.74 ◆◆

Write a function in assembly code that matches the behavior of the function `find_range` in Figure 3.51. Your code should contain only one floating-point comparison instruction, and then it should use conditional moves to generate the correct result. You might want to make use of the instruction `cmovp` (move if even parity). Test your code on all 2^{32} possible argument values. Web Aside ASM:EASM on page 178 describes how to incorporate functions written in assembly code into C programs.

3.75 ◆

ISO C99 includes extensions to support complex numbers. Any floating-point type can be modified with the keyword `complex`. Here are some sample functions that work with complex data and that call some of the associated library functions:

```
1   #include <complex.h>
2
3   double c_imag(double complex x) {
4       return cimag(x);
5   }
6
7   double c_real(double complex x) {
8       return creal(x);
9   }
10
```

```
11    double complex c_sub(double complex x, double complex y) {
12        return x - y;
13    }
```

When compiled, GCC generates the following assembly code for these functions:

```
    double c_imag(double complex x)
1   c_imag:
2       movapd  %xmm1, %xmm0
3       ret


    double c_real(double complex x)
4   c_real:
5       rep; ret


    double complex c_sub(double complex x, double complex y)
6   c_sub:
7       subsd   %xmm2, %xmm0
8       subsd   %xmm3, %xmm1
9       ret
```

Based on these examples, determine the following:

A. How are complex arguments passed to a function?

B. How are complex values returned from a function?

Solutions to Practice Problems

Solution to Problem 3.1 (page 182)
This exercise gives you practice with the different operand forms.

Operand	Value	Comment
%rax	0x100	Register
0x104	0xAB	Absolute address
$0x108	0x108	Immediate
(%rax)	0xFF	Address 0x100
4(%rax)	0xAB	Address 0x104
9(%rax,%rdx)	0x11	Address 0x10C
260(%rcx,%rdx)	0x13	Address 0x108
0xFC(,%rcx,4)	0xFF	Address 0x100
(%rax,%rdx,4)	0x11	Address 0x10C

Solution to Problem 3.2 (page 185)
As we have seen, the assembly code generated by GCC includes suffixes on the instructions, while the disassembler does not. Being able to switch between these

two forms is an important skill to learn. One important feature is that memory references in x86-64 are always given with quad word registers, such as %rax, even if the operand is a byte, single word, or double word.

Here is the code written with suffixes:

```
movl    %eax, (%rsp)
movw    (%rax), %dx
movb    $0xFF, %bl
movb    (%rsp,%rdx,4), %dl
movq    (%rdx), %rax
movw    %dx, (%rax)
```

Solution to Problem 3.3 (page 186)

Since we will rely on GCC to generate most of our assembly code, being able to write correct assembly code is not a critical skill. Nonetheless, this exercise will help you become more familiar with the different instruction and operand types.

Here is the code with explanations of the errors:

```
movb $0xF, (%ebx)        Cannot use %ebx as address register
movl %rax, (%rsp)        Mismatch between instruction suffix and register ID
movw (%rax),4(%rsp)      Cannot have both source and destination be memory references
movb %al,%sl             No register named %sl
movl %eax,$0x123         Cannot have immediate as destination
movl %eax,%dx            Destination operand incorrect size
movb %si, 8(%rbp)        Mismatch between instruction suffix and register ID
```

Solution to Problem 3.4 (page 187)

This exercise gives you more experience with the different data movement instructions and how they relate to the data types and conversion rules of C. The nuances of conversions of both signedness and size, as well as integral promotion, add challenge to this problem.

src_t	dest_t	Instruction	Comments
long	long	movq (%rdi), %rax	Read 8 bytes
		movq %rax, (%rsi)	Store 8 bytes
char	int	movsbl (%rdi), %eax	Convert char to int
		movl %eax, (%rsi)	Store 4 bytes
char	unsigned	movsbl (%rdi), %eax	Convert char to int
		movl %eax, (%rsi)	Store 4 bytes
unsigned char	long	movzbl (%rdi), %eax	Read byte and zero-extend
		movq %rax, (%rsi)	Store 8 bytes

int	char	`movl (%rdi), %eax` `movb %al, (%rsi)`	Read 4 bytes Store low-order byte
unsigned	unsigned char	`movl (%rdi), %eax` `movb %al, (%rsi)`	Read 4 bytes Store low-order byte
char	short	`movsbw (%rdi), %ax` `movw %ax, (%rsi)`	Read byte and sign-extend Store 2 bytes

Solution to Problem 3.5 (page 189)

Reverse engineering is a good way to understand systems. In this case, we want to reverse the effect of the C compiler to determine what C code gave rise to this assembly code. The best way is to run a "simulation," starting with values x, y, and z at the locations designated by pointers xp, yp, and zp, respectively. We would then get the following behavior:

```
void decode1(long *xp, long *yp, long *zp)
 xp in %rdi, yp in %rsi, zp in %rdx
decode1:
  movq    (%rdi), %r8      Get x = *xp
  movq    (%rsi), %rcx     Get y = *yp
  movq    (%rdx), %rax     Get z = *zp
  movq    %r8, (%rsi)      Store x at yp
  movq    %rcx, (%rdx)     Store y at zp
  movq    %rax, (%rdi)     Store z at xp
  ret
```

From this, we can generate the following C code:

```
void decode1(long *xp, long *yp, long *zp)
{
    long x = *xp;
    long y = *yp;
    long z = *zp;

    *yp = x;
    *zp = y;
    *xp = z;
}
```

Solution to Problem 3.6 (page 192)

This exercise demonstrates the versatility of the `leaq` instruction and gives you more practice in deciphering the different operand forms. Although the operand forms are classified as type "Memory" in Figure 3.3, no memory access occurs.

Instruction	Result
leaq 6(%rax), %rdx	$6 + x$
leaq (%rax,%rcx), %rdx	$x + y$
leaq (%rax,%rcx,4), %rdx	$x + 4y$
leaq 7(%rax,%rax,8), %rdx	$7 + 9x$
leaq 0xA(,%rcx,4), %rdx	$10 + 4y$
leaq 9(%rax,%rcx,2), %rdx	$9 + x + 2y$

Solution to Problem 3.7 (page 193)

Again, reverse engineering proves to be a useful way to learn the relationship between C code and the generated assembly code.

The best way to solve problems of this type is to annotate the lines of assembly code with information about the operations being performed. Here is a sample:

```
long scale2(long x, long y, long z)
x in %rdi, y in %rsi, z in %rdx
scale2:
  leaq    (%rdi,%rdi,4), %rax     5 * x
  leaq    (%rax,%rsi,2), %rax     5 * x + 2 * y
  leaq    (%rax,%rdx,8), %rax     5 * x + 2 * y + 8 * z
  ret
```

From this, it is easy to generate the missing expression:

```
long t = 5 * x + 2 * y + 8 * z;
```

Solution to Problem 3.8 (page 194)

This problem gives you a chance to test your understanding of operands and the arithmetic instructions. The instruction sequence is designed so that the result of each instruction does not affect the behavior of subsequent ones.

Instruction	Destination	Value
addq %rcx, (%rax)	0x100	0x100
subq %rdx,8(%rax)	0x108	0xA8
imulq $16,(%rax,%rdx,8)	0x118	0x110
incq 16(%rax)	0x110	0x14
decq %rcx	%rcx	0x0
subq %rdx,%rax	%rax	0xFD

Solution to Problem 3.9 (page 195)

This exercise gives you a chance to generate a little bit of assembly code. The solution code was generated by GCC. By loading parameter n in register %ecx, it can then use byte register %cl to specify the shift amount for the sarq instruction. It might seem odd to use a movl instruction, given that n is eight bytes long, but keep in mind that only the least significant byte is required to specify the shift amount.

```
long shift_left4_rightn(long x, long n)
x in %rdi, n in %rsi
shift_left4_rightn:
  movq    %rdi, %rax    Get x
  salq    $4, %rax      x <<= 4
  movl    %esi, %ecx    Get n (4 bytes)
  sarq    %cl, %rax     x >>= n
```

Solution to Problem 3.10 (page 196)

This problem is fairly straightforward, since the assembly code follows the structure of the C code closely.

```
long t1 = x | y;
long t2 = t1 >> 3;
long t3 = ~t2;
long t4 = z-t3;
```

Solution to Problem 3.11 (page 197)

A. This instruction is used to set register %rdx to zero, exploiting the property that $x \text{ ^ } x = 0$ for any x. It corresponds to the C statement x = 0.

B. A more direct way of setting register %rdx to zero is with the instruction movq $0,%rdx.

C. Assembling and disassembling this code, however, we find that the version with xorq requires only 3 bytes, while the version with movq requires 7. Other ways to set %rdx to zero rely on the property that any instruction that updates the lower 4 bytes will cause the high-order bytes to be set to zero. Thus, we could use either xorl %edx,%edx (2 bytes) or movl $0,%edx (5 bytes).

Solution to Problem 3.12 (page 200)

We can simply replace the cqto instruction with one that sets register %rdx to zero, and use divq rather than idivq as our division instruction, yielding the following code:

```
    void uremdiv(unsigned long x, unsigned long y,
                 unsigned long *qp, unsigned long *rp)
    x in %rdi, y in %rsi, qp in %rdx, rp in %rcx
1   uremdiv:
2     movq    %rdx, %r8       Copy qp
3     movq    %rdi, %rax      Move x to lower 8 bytes of dividend
4     movl    $0, %edx        Set upper 8 bytes of dividend to 0
5     divq    %rsi            Divide by y
6     movq    %rax, (%r8)     Store quotient at qp
7     movq    %rdx, (%rcx)    Store remainder at rp
8     ret
```

Solution to Problem 3.13 (page 204)

It is important to understand that assembly code does not keep track of the type of a program value. Instead, the different instructions determine the operand sizes and whether they are signed or unsigned. When mapping from instruction sequences back to C code, we must do a bit of detective work to infer the data types of the program values.

A. The suffix 'l' and the register identifiers indicate 32-bit operands, while the comparison is for a two's-complement <. We can infer that data_t must be int.

B. The suffix 'w' and the register identifiers indicate 16-bit operands, while the comparison is for a two's-complement >=. We can infer that data_t must be short.

C. The suffix 'b' and the register identifiers indicate 8-bit operands, while the comparison is for an unsigned <=. We can infer that data_t must be unsigned char.

D. The suffix 'q' and the register identifiers indicate 64-bit operands, while the comparison is for !=, which is the same whether the arguments are signed, unsigned, or pointers. We can infer that data_t could be either long, unsigned long, or some form of pointer.

Solution to Problem 3.14 (page 205)

This problem is similar to Problem 3.13, except that it involves TEST instructions rather than CMP instructions.

A. The suffix 'q' and the register identifiers indicate a 64-bit operand, while the comparison is for >=, which must be signed. We can infer that data_t must be long.

B. The suffix 'w' and the register identifier indicate a 16-bit operand, while the comparison is for ==, which is the same for signed or unsigned. We can infer that data_t must be either short or unsigned short.

C. The suffix 'b' and the register identifier indicate an 8-bit operand, while the comparison is for unsigned >. We can infer that data_t must be unsigned char.

D. The suffix 'l' and the register identifier indicate 32-bit operands, while the comparison is for <. We can infer that data_t must be int.

Solution to Problem 3.15 (page 209)

This exercise requires you to examine disassembled code in detail and reason about the encodings for jump targets. It also gives you practice in hexadecimal arithmetic.

A. The je instruction has as its target 0x4003fc + 0x02. As the original disassembled code shows, this is 0x4003fe:

```
4003fa: 74 02              je      4003fe
4003fc: ff d0              callq   *%rax
```

B. The `je` instruction has as its target 0x0x400431 − 12 (since 0xf4 is the 1-byte two's-complement representation of −12). As the original disassembled code shows, this is 0x400425:

```
40042f: 74 f4                je      400425
400431: 5d                   pop     %rbp
```

C. According to the annotation produced by the disassembler, the jump target is at absolute address 0x400547. According to the byte encoding, this must be at an address 0x2 bytes beyond that of the pop instruction. Subtracting these gives address 0x400545. Noting that the encoding of the `ja` instruction requires 2 bytes, it must be located at address 0x400543. These are confirmed by examining the original disassembly:

```
400543: 77 02                ja      400547
400545: 5d                   pop     %rbp
```

D. Reading the bytes in reverse order, we can see that the target offset is 0xffffff73, or decimal −141. Adding this to 0x0x4005ed (the address of the nop instruction) gives address 0x400560:

```
4005e8: e9 73 ff ff ff       jmpq    400560
4005ed: 90                   nop
```

Solution to Problem 3.16 (page 212)

Annotating assembly code and writing C code that mimics its control flow are good first steps in understanding assembly-language programs. This problem gives you practice for an example with simple control flow. It also gives you a chance to examine the implementation of logical operations.

A. Here is the C code:

```
void goto_cond(long a, long *p) {
    if (p == 0)
        goto done;
    if (*p >= a)
        goto done;
    *p = a;
 done:
    return;
}
```

B. The first conditional branch is part of the implementation of the && expression. If the test for p being non-null fails, the code will skip the test of a > *p.

Solution to Problem 3.17 (page 212)

This is an exercise to help you think about the idea of a general translation rule and how to apply it.

A. Converting to this alternate form involves only switching around a few lines of the code:

```
long gotodiff_se_alt(long x, long y) {
    long result;
    if (x < y)
        goto x_lt_y;
    ge_cnt++;
    result = x - y;
    return result;
  x_lt_y:
    lt_cnt++;
    result = y - x;
    return result;
}
```

B. In most respects, the choice is arbitrary. But the original rule works better for the common case where there is no else statement. For this case, we can simply modify the translation rule to be as follows:

```
    t = test-expr;
    if (!t)
        goto done;
    then-statement
done:
```

A translation based on the alternate rule is more cumbersome.

Solution to Problem 3.18 (page 213)

This problem requires that you work through a nested branch structure, where you will see how our rule for translating if statements has been applied. On the whole, the machine code is a straightforward translation of the C code.

```
long test(long x, long y, long z) {
    long val = x+y+z;
    if (x < -3) {
        if (y < z)
            val = x*y;
        else
            val = y*z;
    } else if (x > 2)
        val = x*z;
    return val;
}
```

Solution to Problem 3.19 (page 216)

This problem reinforces our method of computing the misprediction penalty.

A. We can apply our formula directly to get $T_{MP} = 2(31 - 16) = 30$.

B. When misprediction occurs, the function will require around $16 + 30 = 46$ cycles.

Solution to Problem 3.20 (page 219)

This problem provides a chance to study the use of conditional moves.

A. The operator is '/'. We see this is an example of dividing by a power of 3 by right shifting (see Section 2.3.7). Before shifting by $k = 3$, we must add a bias of $2^k - 1 = 7$ when the dividend is negative.

B. Here is an annotated version of the assembly code:

```
long arith(long x)
x in %rdi
arith:
  leaq    7(%rdi), %rax      temp = x+7
  testq   %rdi, %rdi         Text x
  cmovns  %rdi, %rax         If x>= 0, temp = x
  sarq    $3, %rax           result = temp >> 3 (= x/8)
  ret
```

The program creates a temporary value equal to $x + 7$, in anticipation of x being negative and therefore requiring biasing. The cmovns instruction conditionally changes this number to x when $x \geq 0$, and then it is shifted by 3 to generate $x/8$.

Solution to Problem 3.21 (page 219)

This problem is similar to Problem 3.18, except that some of the conditionals have been implemented by conditional data transfers. Although it might seem daunting to fit this code into the framework of the original C code, you will find that it follows the translation rules fairly closely.

```
long test(long x, long y) {
    long val = 8*x;
    if (y > 0) {
        if (x < y)
            val = y-x;
        else
            val = x&y;
    } else if (y <= -2)
        val = x+y;
    return val;
}
```

Solution to Problem 3.22 (page 221)

A. If we build up a table of factorials computed with data type int, we get the following:

n	$n!$	OK?
1	1	Y
2	2	Y
3	6	Y
4	24	Y
5	120	Y
6	720	Y
7	5,040	Y
8	40,320	Y
9	362,880	Y
10	3,628,800	Y
11	39,916,800	Y
12	479,001,600	Y
13	1,932,053,504	N

We can see that the computation of 13! has overflowed. As we learned in Problem 2.35, when we get value x while attempting to compute $n!$, we can test for overflow by computing x/n and seeing whether it equals $(n − 1)!$ (assuming that we have already ensured that the computation of $(n − 1)!$ did not overflow). In this case we get $1,932,053,504/13 = 161,004,458.667$. As a second test, we can see that any factorial beyond 10! must be a multiple of 100 and therefore have zeros for the last two digits. The correct value of 13! is 6,227,020,800.

B. Doing the computation with data type long lets us go up to 20!, yielding 2,432,902,008,176,640,000.

Solution to Problem 3.23 (page 222)

The code generated when compiling loops can be tricky to analyze, because the compiler can perform many different optimizations on loop code, and because it can be difficult to match program variables with registers. This particular example demonstrates several places where the assembly code is not just a direct translation of the C code.

A. Although parameter x is passed to the function in register %rdi, we can see that the register is never referenced once the loop is entered. Instead, we can see that registers %rax, %rcx, and %rdx are initialized in lines 2–5 to x, x*x, and x+x. We can conclude, therefore, that these registers contain the program variables.

B. The compiler determines that pointer p always points to x, and hence the expression (*p)++ simply increments x. It combines this incrementing by 1 with the increment by y, via the leaq instruction of line 7.

C. The annotated code is as follows:

```
       long dw_loop(long x)
       x initially in %rdi
 1    dw_loop:
 2       movq    %rdi, %rax              Copy x to %rax
 3       movq    %rdi, %rcx
 4       imulq   %rdi, %rcx              Compute y = x*x
 5       leaq    (%rdi,%rdi), %rdx       Compute n = 2*x
 6    .L2:                           loop:
 7       leaq    1(%rcx,%rax), %rax      Compute x += y + 1
 8       subq    $1, %rdx                Decrement n
 9       testq   %rdx, %rdx              Test n
10       jg      .L2                     If > 0, goto loop
11       rep; ret                        Return
```

Solution to Problem 3.24 (page 224)

This assembly code is a fairly straightforward translation of the loop using the jump-to-middle method. The full C code is as follows:

```
long loop_while(long a, long b)
{
    long result = 1;
    while (a < b) {
        result = result * (a+b);
        a = a+1;
    }
    return result;
}
```

Solution to Problem 3.25 (page 226)

While the generated code does not follow the exact pattern of the guarded-do translation, we can see that it is equivalent to the following C code:

```
long loop_while2(long a, long b)
{
    long result = b;
    while (b > 0) {
        result = result * a;
        b = b-a;
    }
    return result;
}
```

We will often see cases, especially when compiling with higher levels of optimization, where GCC takes some liberties in the exact form of the code it generates, while preserving the required functionality.

Solution to Problem 3.26 (page 228)

Being able to work backward from assembly code to C code is a prime example of reverse engineering.

A. We can see that the code uses the jump-to-middle translation, using the `jmp` instruction on line 3.

B. Here is the original C code:

```c
long fun_a(unsigned long x) {
    long val = 0;
    while (x) {
        val ^= x;
        x >>= 1;
    }
    return val & 0x1;
}
```

C. This code computes the *parity* of argument x. That is, it returns 1 if there is an odd number of ones in x and 0 if there is an even number.

Solution to Problem 3.27 (page 231)

This exercise is intended to reinforce your understanding of how loops are implemented.

```c
long fact_for_gd_goto(long n)
{
    long i = 2;
    long result = 1;
    if (n <= 1)
        goto done;
 loop:
    result *= i;
    i++;
    if (i <= n)
        goto loop;
 done:
    return result;
}
```

Solution to Problem 3.28 (page 231)

This problem is trickier than Problem 3.26, since the code within the loop is more complex and the overall operation is less familiar.

A. Here is the original C code:

```c
long fun_b(unsigned long x) {
    long val = 0;
    long i;
```

```
        for (i = 64; i != 0; i--) {
            val = (val << 1) | (x & 0x1);
            x >>= 1;
        }
        return val;
    }
```

B. The code was generated using the guarded-do transformation, but the compiler detected that, since i is initialized to 64, it will satisfy the test $i \neq 0$, and therefore the initial test is not required.

C. This code reverses the bits in x, creating a mirror image. It does this by shifting the bits of x from left to right, and then filling these bits in as it shifts val from right to left.

Solution to Problem 3.29 (page 232)

Our stated rule for translating a for loop into a while loop is just a bit too simplistic—this is the only aspect that requires special consideration.

A. Applying our translation rule would yield the following code:

```
        /* Naive translation of for loop into while loop */
        /* WARNING: This is buggy code */
        long sum = 0;
        long i = 0;
        while (i < 10) {
            if (i & 1)
                /* This will cause an infinite loop */
                continue;
            sum += i;
            i++;
        }
```

This code has an infinite loop, since the continue statement would prevent index variable i from being updated.

B. The general solution is to replace the continue statement with a goto statement that skips the rest of the loop body and goes directly to the update portion:

```
        /* Correct translation of for loop into while loop */
        long sum = 0;
        long i = 0;
        while (i < 10) {
            if (i & 1)
                goto update;
            sum += i;
        update:
            i++;
        }
```

Solution to Problem 3.30 (page 236)

This problem gives you a chance to reason about the control flow of a `switch` statement. Answering the questions requires you to combine information from several places in the assembly code.

- Line 2 of the assembly code adds 1 to x to set the lower range of the cases to zero. That means that the minimum case label is -1.
- Lines 3 and 4 cause the program to jump to the default case when the adjusted case value is greater than 8. This implies that the maximum case label is $-1 + 8 = 7$.
- In the jump table, we see that the entry on lines 6 (case value 3) and 9 (case value 6) have the same destination (.L2) as the jump instruction on line 4, indicating the default case behavior. Thus, case labels 3 and 5 are missing in the `switch` statement body.
- In the jump table, we see that the entries on lines 3 and 10 have the same destination. These correspond to cases 0 and 7.
- In the jump table, we see that the entries on lines 5 and 7 have the same destination. These correspond to cases 2 and 4.

From this reasoning, we draw the following conclusions:

A. The case labels in the `switch` statement body have values $-1, 0, 1, 2, 4, 5$, and 7.

B. The case with destination .L5 has labels 0 and 7.

C. The case with destination .L7 has labels 2 and 4.

Solution to Problem 3.31 (page 237)

The key to reverse engineering compiled `switch` statements is to combine the information from the assembly code and the jump table to sort out the different cases. We can see from the `ja` instruction (line 3) that the code for the default case has label .L2. We can see that the only other repeated label in the jump table is .L5, and so this must be the code for the cases C and D. We can see that the code falls through at line 8, and so label .L7 must match case A and label .L3 must match case B. That leaves only label .L6 to match case E.

The original C code is as follows:

```
void switcher(long a, long b, long c, long *dest)
{
    long val;
    switch(a) {
    case 5:
        c = b ^ 15;
        /* Fall through */
    case 0:
        val = c + 112;
        break;
```

```
    case 2:
    case 7:
        val = (c + b) << 2;
        break;
    case 4:
        val = a;
        break;
    default:
        val = b;
    }
    *dest = val;
}
```

Solution to Problem 3.32 (page 244)

Tracing through the program execution at this level of detail reinforces many aspects of procedure call and return. We can see clearly how control is passed to the function when it is called, and how the calling function resumes upon return. We can also see how arguments get passed through registers %rdi and %rsi, and how results are returned via register %rax.

	Instruction				State values (at beginning)			
Label	PC	Instruction	%rdi	%rsi	%rax	%rsp	*%rsp	Description
M1	0x400560	callq	10	—	—	0x7fffffffe820	—	Call first(10)
F1	0x400548	lea	10	—	—	0x7fffffffe818	0x400565	Entry of first
F2	0x40054c	sub	10	11	—	0x7fffffffe818	0x400565	
F3	0x400550	callq	9	11	—	0x7fffffffe818	0x400565	Call last(9, 11)
L1	0x400540	mov	9	11	—	0x7fffffffe810	0x400555	Entry of last
L2	0x400543	imul	9	11	9	0x7fffffffe810	0x400555	
L3	0x400547	retq	9	11	99	0x7fffffffe810	0x400555	Return 99 from last
F4	0x400555	repz repq	9	11	99	0x7fffffffe818	0x400565	Return 99 from first
M2	0x400565	mov	9	11	99	0x7fffffffe820	—	Resume main

Solution to Problem 3.33 (page 246)

This problem is a bit tricky due to the mixing of different data sizes.

Let us first describe one answer and then explain the second possibility. If we assume the first addition (line 3) implements *u += a, while the second (line 4) implements v += b, then we can see that a was passed as the first argument in %edi and converted from 4 bytes to 8 before adding it to the 8 bytes pointed to by %rdx. This implies that a must be of type int and u must be of type long *. We can also see that the low-order byte of argument b is added to the byte pointed to by %rcx. This implies that v must be of type char *, but the type of b is ambiguous—it could be 1, 2, 4, or 8 bytes long. This ambiguity is resolved by noting the return value of

6, computed as the sum of the sizes of a and b. Since we know a is 4 bytes long, we can deduce that b must be 2.

An annotated version of this function explains these details:

```
int procprob1(int a, short b, long *u, char *v)
a in %edi, b in %si, u in %rdx, v in %rcx
1   procprob:
2     movslq  %edi, %rdi        Convert a to long
3     addq    %rdi, (%rdx)      Add to *u (long)
4     addb    %sil, (%rcx)      Add low-order byte of b to *v
5     movl    $6, %eax          Return 4+2
6     ret
```

Alternatively, we can see that the same assembly code would be valid if the two sums were computed in the assembly code in the opposite ordering as they are in the C code. This would result in interchanging arguments a and b and arguments u and v, yielding the following prototype:

```
int procprob(int b, short a, long *v, char *u);
```

Solution to Problem 3.34 (page 252)

This example demonstrates the use of callee-saved registers as well as the stack for holding local data.

A. We can see that lines 9–14 save local values a0–a5 into callee-saved registers %rbx, %r15, %r14, %r13, %r12, and %rbp, respectively.

B. Local values a6 and a7 are stored on the stack at offsets 0 and 8 relative to the stack pointer (lines 16 and 18).

C. After storing six local variables, the program has used up the supply of callee-saved registers. It stores the remaining two local values on the stack.

Solution to Problem 3.35 (page 254)

This problem provides a chance to examine the code for a recursive function. An important lesson to learn is that recursive code has the exact same structure as the other functions we have seen. The stack and register-saving disciplines suffice to make recursive functions operate correctly.

A. Register %rbx holds the value of parameter x, so that it can be used to compute the result expression.

B. The assembly code was generated from the following C code:

```
long rfun(unsigned long x) {
    if (x == 0)
        return 0;
    unsigned long nx = x>>2;
    long rv = rfun(nx);
    return x + rv;
}
```

Solution to Problem 3.36 (page 256)

This exercise tests your understanding of data sizes and array indexing. Observe that a pointer of any kind is 8 bytes long. Data type short requires 2 bytes, while int requires 4.

Array	Element size	Total size	Start address	Element i
S	2	14	x_S	$x_S + 2i$
T	8	24	x_T	$x_T + 8i$
U	8	48	x_U	$x_U + 8i$
V	4	32	x_V	$x_V + 4i$
W	8	32	x_W	$x_W + 8i$

Solution to Problem 3.37 (page 258)

This problem is a variant of the one shown for integer array E. It is important to understand the difference between a pointer and the object being pointed to. Since data type short requires 2 bytes, all of the array indices are scaled by a factor of 2. Rather than using movl, as before, we now use movw.

Expression	Type	Value	Assembly
S+1	short *	$x_S + 2$	leaq 2(%rdx),%rax
S[3]	short	$M[x_S + 6]$	movw 6(%rdx),%ax
&S[i]	short *	$x_S + 2i$	leaq (%rdx,%rcx,2),%rax
S[4*i+1]	short	$M[x_S + 8i + 2]$	movw 2(%rdx,%rcx,8),%ax
S+i-5	short *	$x_S + 2i - 10$	leaq -10(%rdx,%rcx,2),%rax

Solution to Problem 3.38 (page 259)

This problem requires you to work through the scaling operations to determine the address computations, and to apply Equation 3.1 for row-major indexing. The first step is to annotate the assembly code to determine how the address references are computed:

```
       long sum_element(long i, long j)
       i in %rdi, j in %rsi
1    sum_element:
2      leaq    0(,%rdi,8), %rdx        Compute 8i
3      subq    %rdi, %rdx              Compute 7i
4      addq    %rsi, %rdx              Compute 7i + j
5      leaq    (%rsi,%rsi,4), %rax     Compute 5j
6      addq    %rax, %rdi             Compute i  + 5j
7      movq    Q(,%rdi,8), %rax       Retrieve M[xQ + 8 (5j + i)]
8      addq    P(,%rdx,8), %rax       Add M[xP + 8 (7i + j)]
9      ret
```

We can see that the reference to matrix P is at byte offset $8 \cdot (7i + j)$, while the reference to matrix Q is at byte offset $8 \cdot (5j + i)$. From this, we can determine that P has 7 columns, while Q has 5, giving $M = 5$ and $N = 7$.

Solution to Problem 3.39 (page 262)

These computations are direct applications of Equation 3.1:

- For $L = 4$, $C = 16$, and $j = 0$, pointer Aptr is computed as $x_A + 4 \cdot (16i + 0) = x_A + 64i$.
- For $L = 4$, $C = 16$, $i = 0$, and $j = k$, Bptr is computed as $x_B + 4 \cdot (16 \cdot 0 + k) = x_B + 4k$.
- For $L = 4$, $C = 16$, $i = 16$, and $j = k$, Bend is computed as $x_B + 4 \cdot (16 \cdot 16 + k) = x_B + 1{,}024 + 4k$.

Solution to Problem 3.40 (page 262)

This exercise requires that you be able to study compiler-generated assembly code to understand what optimizations have been performed. In this case, the compiler was clever in its optimizations.

Let us first study the following C code, and then see how it is derived from the assembly code generated for the original function.

```
/* Set all diagonal elements to val */
void fix_set_diag_opt(fix_matrix A, int val) {
    int *Abase = &A[0][0];
    long i = 0;
    long iend = N*(N+1);
    do {
        Abase[i] = val;
        i += (N+1);
    } while (i != iend);
}
```

This function introduces a variable Abase, of type int *, pointing to the start of array A. This pointer designates a sequence of 4-byte integers consisting of elements of A in row-major order. We introduce an integer variable index that steps through the diagonal elements of A, with the property that diagonal elements i and $i + 1$ are spaced $N + 1$ elements apart in the sequence, and that once we reach diagonal element N (index value $N(N + 1)$), we have gone beyond the end.

The actual assembly code follows this general form, but now the pointer increments must be scaled by a factor of 4. We label register %rax as holding a value index4 equal to index in our C version but scaled by a factor of 4. For $N = 16$, we can see that our stopping point for index4 will be $4 \cdot 16(16 + 1) = 1{,}088$.

```
1   fix_set_diag:
        void fix_set_diag(fix_matrix A, int val)
        A in %rdi, val in %rsi
2       movl    $0, %eax                    Set index4 = 0
3   .L13:                                   loop:
4       movl    %esi, (%rdi,%rax)           Set Abase[index4/4] to val
5       addq    $68, %rax                   Increment index4 += 4(N+1)
```

```
6       cmpq    $1088, %rax              Compare index4: 4N(N+1)
7       jne     .L13                     If !=, goto loop
8       rep; ret                         Return
```

Solution to Problem 3.41 (page 268)

This problem gets you to think about structure layout and the code used to access structure fields. The structure declaration is a variant of the example shown in the text. It shows that nested structures are allocated by embedding the inner structures within the outer ones.

A. The layout of the structure is as follows:

Offset	0		8	12	16		24
Contents		p	s.x	s.y	next		

B. It uses 24 bytes.

C. As always, we start by annotating the assembly code:

```
        void sp_init(struct prob *sp)
        sp in %rdi
1       sp_init:
2         movl    12(%rdi), %eax         Get sp->s.y
3         movl    %eax, 8(%rdi)          Save in sp->s.x
4         leaq    8(%rdi), %rax          Compute &(sp->s.x)
5         movq    %rax, (%rdi)           Store in sp->p
6         movq    %rdi, 16(%rdi)         Store sp in sp->next
7         ret
```

From this, we can generate C code as follows:

```
void sp_init(struct prob *sp)
{
    sp->s.x   = sp->s.y;
    sp->p     = &(sp->s.x);
    sp->next  = sp;
}
```

Solution to Problem 3.42 (page 269)

This problem demonstrates how a very common data structure and operation on it is implemented in machine code. We solve the problem by first annotating the assembly code, recognizing that the two fields of the structure are at offsets 0 (for v) and 8 (for p).

```
        long fun(struct ELE *ptr)
        ptr in %rdi
1       fun:
2         movl    $0, %eax                result = 0
3         jmp     .L2                      Goto middle
```

```
4     .L3:                            loop:
5       addq    (%rdi), %rax          result += ptr->v
6       movq    8(%rdi), %rdi         ptr = ptr->p
7     .L2:                            middle:
8       testq   %rdi, %rdi            Test ptr
9       jne     .L3                   If != NULL, goto loop
10      rep; ret
```

A. Based on the annotated code, we can generate a C version:

```
long fun(struct ELE *ptr) {
    long val = 0;
    while (ptr) {
        val += ptr->v;
        ptr  = ptr->p;
    }
    return val;
}
```

B. We can see that each structure is an element in a singly linked list, with field v being the value of the element and p being a pointer to the next element. Function fun computes the sum of the element values in the list.

Solution to Problem 3.43 (page 272)

Structures and unions involve a simple set of concepts, but it takes practice to be comfortable with the different referencing patterns and their implementations.

EXPR	TYPE	Code
up->t1.u	long	movq (%rdi), %rax movq %rax, (%rsi)
up->t1.v	short	movw 8(%rdi), %ax movw %ax, (%rsi)
&up->t1.w	char *	addq $10, %rdi movq %rdi, (%rsi)
up->t2.a	int *	movq %rdi, (%rsi)

up->t2.a[up->t1.u]	int	movq (%rdi), %rax
		movl (%rdi,%rax,4), %eax
		movl %eax, (%rsi)

*up->t2.p	char	movq 8(%rdi), %rax
		movb (%rax), %al
		movb %al, (%rsi)

Solution to Problem 3.44 (page 275)

Understanding structure layout and alignment is very important for understanding how much storage different data structures require and for understanding the code generated by the compiler for accessing structures. This problem lets you work out the details of some example structures.

A. struct P1 { int i; char c; int j; char d; };

i	c	j	d	Total	Alignment
0	4	8	12	16	4

B. struct P2 { int i; char c; char d; long j; };

i	c	d	j	Total	Alignment
0	4	5	8	16	8

C. struct P3 { short w[3]; char c[3] };

w	c	Total	Alignment
0	6	10	2

D. struct P4 { short w[5]; char *c[3] };

w	c	Total	Alignment
0	16	40	8

E. struct P5 { struct P3 a[2]; struct P2 t };

a	t	Total	Alignment
0	24	40	8

Solution to Problem 3.45 (page 275)

This is an exercise in understanding structure layout and alignment.

A. Here are the object sizes and byte offsets:

Field	a	b	c	d	e	f	g	h
Size	8	2	8	1	4	1	8	4
Offset	0	8	16	24	28	32	40	48

B. The structure is a total of 56 bytes long. The end of the structure must be padded by 4 bytes to satisfy the 8-byte alignment requirement.

C. One strategy that works, when all data elements have a length equal to a power of 2, is to order the structure elements in descending order of size. This leads to a declaration

```
struct {
    char      *a;
    double    c;
    long      g;
    float     e;
    int       h;
    short     b;
    char      d;
    char      f;
} rec;
```

with the following offsets:

					Field			
	a	c	g	e	h	b	d	f
Size	8	8	8	4	4	2	1	1
Offset	0	8	16	24	28	32	34	35

The structure must be padded by 4 bytes to satisfy the 8-byte alignment requirement, giving a total of 40 bytes.

Solution to Problem 3.46 (page 282)

This problem covers a wide range of topics, such as stack frames, string representations, ASCII code, and byte ordering. It demonstrates the dangers of out-of-bounds memory references and the basic ideas behind buffer overflow.

A. Stack after line 3:

00 00 00 00 00 40 00 76	Return address
01 23 45 67 89 AB CD EF	Saved %rbx
	← buf = %rsp

B. Stack after line 5:

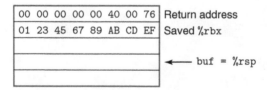

00 00 00 00 00 40 00 34	Return address
33 32 31 30 39 38 37 36	Saved %rbx
35 34 33 32 31 30 39 38	
37 36 35 34 33 32 31 30	← buf = %rsp

C. The program is attempting to return to address 0x040034. The low-order 2 bytes were overwritten by the code for character '4' and the terminating null character.

D. The saved value of register %rbx was set to 0x3332313039383736. This value will be loaded into the register before get_line returns.

E. The call to `malloc` should have had `strlen(buf)+1` as its argument, and the code should also check that the returned value is not equal to NULL.

Solution to Problem 3.47 (page 286)

A. This corresponds to a range of around 2^{13} addresses.

B. A 128-byte nop sled would cover 2^7 addresses with each test, and so we would only require around $2^6 = 64$ attempts.

This example clearly shows that the degree of randomization in this version of Linux would provide only minimal deterrence against an overflow attack.

Solution to Problem 3.48 (page 288)

This problem gives you another chance to see how x86-64 code manages the stack, and to also better understand how to defend against buffer overflow attacks.

A. For the unprotected code, we can see that lines 4 and 5 compute the positions of v and buf to be at offsets 24 and 0 relative to `%rsp`. In the protected code, the canary is stored at offset 40 (line 4), while v and buf are at offsets 8 and 16 (lines 7 and 8).

B. In the protected code, local variable v is positioned closer to the top of the stack than buf, and so an overrun of buf will not corrupt the value of v.

Solution to Problem 3.49 (page 293)

This code combines many of the tricks we have seen for performing bit-level arithmetic. It requires careful study to make any sense of it.

A. The `leaq` instruction of line 5 computes the value $8n + 22$, which is then rounded down to the nearest multiple of 16 by the `andq` instruction of line 6. The resulting value will be $8n + 8$ when n is odd and $8n + 16$ when n is even, and this value is subtracted from s_1 to give s_2.

B. The three instructions in this sequence round s_2 up to the nearest multiple of 8. They make use of the combination of biasing and shifting that we saw for dividing by a power of 2 in Section 2.3.7.

C. These two examples can be seen as the cases that minimize and maximize the values of e_1 and e_2.

n	s_1	s_2	p	e_1	e_2
5	2,065	2,017	2,024	1	7
6	2,064	2,000	2,000	16	0

D. We can see that s_2 is computed in a way that preserves whatever offset s_1 has with the nearest multiple of 16. We can also see that p will be aligned on a multiple of 8, as is recommended for an array of 8-byte elements.

Solution to Problem 3.50 (page 300)

This exercise requires that you step through the code, paying careful attention to which conversion and data movement instructions are used. We can see the values being retrieved and converted as follows:

- The value at dp is retrieved, converted to an int (line 4), and then stored at ip. We can therefore infer that val1 is d.
- The value at ip is retrieved, converted to a float (line 6), and then stored at fp. We can therefore infer that val2 is i.
- The value of l is converted to a double (line 8) and stored at dp. We can therefore infer that val3 is l.
- The value at fp is retrieved on line 3. The two instructions at lines 10–11 convert this to double precision as the value returned in register %xmm0. We can therefore infer that val4 is f.

Solution to Problem 3.51 (page 300)

These cases can be handled by selecting the appropriate entries from the tables in Figures 3.47 and 3.48, or using one of the code sequences for converting between floating-point formats.

T_x	T_y	Instruction(s)
long	double	vcvtsi2sdq %rdi, %xmm0, %xmm0
double	int	vcvttsd2si %xmm0, %eax
float	double	vunpcklpd %xmm0, %xmm0, %xmm0
		vcvtpd2ps %xmm0, %xmm0
long	float	vcvtsi2ssq %rdi, %xmm0, %xmm0
float	long	vcvttss2siq %xmm0, %rax

Solution to Problem 3.52 (page 301)

The basic rules for mapping arguments to registers are fairly simple (although they become much more complex with more and other types of arguments [77]).

A. double g1(double a, long b, float c, int d);

   Registers: a in %xmm0, b in %rdi c in %xmm1, d in %esi

B. double g2(int a, double *b, float *c, long d);

   Registers: a in %edi, b in %rsi, c in %rdx, d in %rcx

C. double g3(double *a, double b, int c, float d);

   Registers: a in %rdi, b in %xmm0, c in %esi, d in %xmm1

D. double g4(float a, int *b, float c, double d);

   Registers: a in %xmm0, b in %rdi, c in %xmm1, d in %xmm2

Solution to Problem 3.53 (page 303)

We can see from the assembly code that there are two integer arguments, passed in registers %rdi and %rsi. Let us name these i1 and i2. Similarly, there are two floating-point arguments, passed in registers %xmm0 and %xmm1, which we name f1 and f2.

We can then annotate the assembly code:

```
       Refer to arguments as i1 (%rdi), i2 (%esi)
                        f1 (%xmm0), and f2 (%xmm1)


       double funct1(arg1_t p, arg2_t q, arg3_t r, arg4_t s)
1    funct1:
2      vcvtsi2ssq        %rsi, %xmm2, %xmm2     Get i2 and convert from long to float
3      vaddss  %xmm0, %xmm2, %xmm0              Add f1 (type float)
4      vcvtsi2ss         %edi, %xmm2, %xmm2     Get i1 and convert from int to float
5      vdivss  %xmm0, %xmm2, %xmm0              Compute i1 / (i2 + f1)
6      vunpcklps         %xmm0, %xmm0, %xmm0
7      vcvtps2pd         %xmm0, %xmm0           Convert to double
8      vsubsd  %xmm1, %xmm0, %xmm0              Compute i1 / (i2 + f1) - f2 (double)
9      ret
```

From this we see that the code computes the value i1/(i2+f1)-f2. We can also see that i1 has type int, i2 has type long, f1 has type float, and f2 has type double. The only ambiguity in matching arguments to the named values stems from the commutativity of multiplication—yielding two possible results:

```
double funct1a(int p, float q, long r, double s);
double funct1b(int p, long q, float r, double s);
```

Solution to Problem 3.54 (page 303)

This problem can readily be solved by stepping through the assembly code and determining what is computed on each step, as shown with the annotations below:

```
       double funct2(double w, int x, float y, long z)
       w in %xmm0, x in %edi, y in %xmm1, z in %rsi
1    funct2:
2      vcvtsi2ss         %edi, %xmm2, %xmm2     Convert x to float
3      vmulss  %xmm1, %xmm2, %xmm1              Multiply by y
4      vunpcklps         %xmm1, %xmm1, %xmm1
5      vcvtps2pd         %xmm1, %xmm2           Convert x*y to double
6      vcvtsi2sdq        %rsi, %xmm1, %xmm1     Convert z to double
7      vdivsd  %xmm1, %xmm0, %xmm0              Compute w/z
8      vsubsd  %xmm0, %xmm2, %xmm0              Subtract from x*y
9      ret                                     Return
```

We can conclude from this analysis that the function computes $y * x - w/z$.

Solution to Problem 3.55 (page 305)

This problem involves the same reasoning as was required to see that numbers declared at label .LC2 encode 1.8, but with a simpler example.

We see that the two values are 0 and 1077936128 (0x40400000). From the high-order bytes, we can extract an exponent field of 0x404 (1028), from which we subtract a bias of 1023 to get an exponent of 5. Concatenating the fraction bits of the two values, we get a fraction field of 0, but with the implied leading value giving value 1.0. The constant is therefore $1.0 \times 2^5 = 32.0$.

Solution to Problem 3.56 (page 305)

A. We see here that the 16 bytes starting at address .LC1 form a mask, where the low-order 8 bytes contain all ones, except for the most significant bit, which is the sign bit of a double-precision value. When we compute the AND of this mask with %xmm0, it will clear the sign bit of x, yielding the absolute value. In fact, we generated this code by defining EXPR(x) to be fabs(x), where fabs is defined in <math.h>.

B. We see that the vxorpd instruction sets the entire register to zero, and so this is a way to generate floating-point constant 0.0.

C. We see that the 16 bytes starting at address .LC2 form a mask with a single 1 bit, at the position of the sign bit for the low-order value in the XMM register. When we compute the EXCLUSIVE-OR of this mask with %xmm0, we change the sign of x, computing the expression −x.

Solution to Problem 3.57 (page 308)

Again, we annotate the code, including dealing with the conditional branch:

```
double funct3(int *ap, double b, long c, float *dp)
ap in %rdi, b in %xmm0, c in %rsi, dp in %rdx
1   funct3:
2     vmovss    (%rdx), %xmm1              Get d = *dp
3     vcvtsi2sd         (%rdi), %xmm2, %xmm2   Get a = *ap and convert to double
4     vucomisd  %xmm2, %xmm0              Compare b:a
5     jbe    .L8                         If <=, goto lesseq
6     vcvtsi2ssq        %rsi, %xmm0, %xmm0   Convert c to float
7     vmulss  %xmm1, %xmm0, %xmm1        Multiply by d
8     vunpcklps        %xmm1, %xmm1, %xmm1
9     vcvtps2pd        %xmm1, %xmm0         Convert to double
10    ret                                Return
11  .L8:                                 lesseq:
12    vaddss  %xmm1, %xmm1, %xmm1        Compute d+d = 2.0 * d
13    vcvtsi2ssq        %rsi, %xmm0, %xmm0   Convert c to float
14    vaddss  %xmm1, %xmm0, %xmm0        Compute c + 2*d
15    vunpcklps        %xmm0, %xmm0, %xmm0
16    vcvtps2pd        %xmm0, %xmm0         Convert to double
17    ret                                Return
```

From this, we can write the following code for funct3:

```
double funct3(int *ap, double b, long c, float *dp) {
    int a = *ap;
    float d = *dp;
    if (a < b)
        return c*d;
    else
        return c+2*d;
}
```

CHAPTER

5

Optimizing Program Performance

The primary objective in writing a program must be to make it work correctly under all possible conditions. A program that runs fast but gives incorrect results serves no useful purpose. Programmers must write clear and concise code, not only so that they can make sense of it, but also so that others can read and understand the code during code reviews and when modifications are required later.

On the other hand, there are many occasions when making a program run fast is also an important consideration. If a program must process video frames or network packets in real time, then a slow-running program will not provide the needed functionality. When a computational task is so demanding that it requires days or weeks to execute, then making it run just 20% faster can have significant impact. In this chapter, we will explore how to make programs run faster via several different types of program optimization.

Writing an efficient program requires several types of activities. First, we must select an appropriate set of algorithms and data structures. Second, we must write source code that the compiler can effectively optimize to turn into efficient executable code. For this second part, it is important to understand the capabilities and limitations of optimizing compilers. Seemingly minor changes in how a program is written can make large differences in how well a compiler can optimize it. Some programming languages are more easily optimized than others. Some features of C, such as the ability to perform pointer arithmetic and casting, make it challenging for a compiler to optimize. Programmers can often write their programs in ways that make it easier for compilers to generate efficient code. A third technique for dealing with especially demanding computations is to divide a task into portions that can be computed in parallel, on some combination of multiple cores and multiple processors. We will defer this aspect of performance enhancement to Chapter 12. Even when exploiting parallelism, it is important that each parallel thread execute with maximum performance, and so the material of this chapter remains relevant in any case.

In approaching program development and optimization, we must consider how the code will be used and what critical factors affect it. In general, programmers must make a trade-off between how easy a program is to implement and maintain, and how fast it runs. At an algorithmic level, a simple insertion sort can be programmed in a matter of minutes, whereas a highly efficient sort routine may take a day or more to implement and optimize. At the coding level, many low-level optimizations tend to reduce code readability and modularity, making the programs more susceptible to bugs and more difficult to modify or extend. For code that will be executed repeatedly in a performance-critical environment, extensive optimization may be appropriate. One challenge is to maintain some degree of elegance and readability in the code despite extensive transformations.

We describe a number of techniques for improving code performance. Ideally, a compiler would be able to take whatever code we write and generate the most efficient possible machine-level program having the specified behavior. Modern compilers employ sophisticated forms of analysis and optimization, and they keep getting better. Even the best compilers, however, can be thwarted by *optimization blockers*—aspects of the program's behavior that depend strongly on the execution environment. Programmers must assist the compiler by writing code that can be optimized readily.

The first step in optimizing a program is to eliminate unnecessary work, making the code perform its intended task as efficiently as possible. This includes eliminating unnecessary function calls, conditional tests, and memory references. These optimizations do not depend on any specific properties of the target machine.

To maximize the performance of a program, both the programmer and the compiler require a model of the target machine, specifying how instructions are processed and the timing characteristics of the different operations. For example, the compiler must know timing information to be able to decide whether it should use a multiply instruction or some combination of shifts and adds. Modern computers use sophisticated techniques to process a machine-level program, executing many instructions in parallel and possibly in a different order than they appear in the program. Programmers must understand how these processors work to be able to tune their programs for maximum speed. We present a high-level model of such a machine based on recent designs of Intel and AMD processors. We also devise a graphical *data-flow* notation to visualize the execution of instructions by the processor, with which we can predict program performance.

With this understanding of processor operation, we can take a second step in program optimization, exploiting the capability of processors to provide *instruction-level parallelism*, executing multiple instructions simultaneously. We cover several program transformations that reduce the data dependencies between different parts of a computation, increasing the degree of parallelism with which they can be executed.

We conclude the chapter by discussing issues related to optimizing large programs. We describe the use of code *profilers*—tools that measure the performance of different parts of a program. This analysis can help find inefficiencies in the code and identify the parts of the program on which we should focus our optimization efforts.

In this presentation, we make code optimization look like a simple linear process of applying a series of transformations to the code in a particular order. In fact, the task is not nearly so straightforward. A fair amount of trial-and-error experimentation is required. This is especially true as we approach the later optimization stages, where seemingly small changes can cause major changes in performance and some very promising techniques prove ineffective. As we will see in the examples that follow, it can be difficult to explain exactly why a particular code sequence has a particular execution time. Performance can depend on many detailed features of the processor design for which we have relatively little documentation or understanding. This is another reason to try a number of different variations and combinations of techniques.

Studying the assembly-code representation of a program is one of the most effective means for gaining an understanding of the compiler and how the generated code will run. A good strategy is to start by looking carefully at the code for the inner loops, identifying performance-reducing attributes such as excessive memory references and poor use of registers. Starting with the assembly code, we can also predict what operations will be performed in parallel and how well they will use the processor resources. As we will see, we can often determine the time (or at least a lower bound on the time) required to execute a loop by identifying *critical paths*, chains of data dependencies that form during repeated executions of a loop. We can then go back and modify the source code to try to steer the compiler toward more efficient implementations.

Most major compilers, including GCC, are continually being updated and improved, especially in terms of their optimization abilities. One useful strategy is to do only as much rewriting of a program as is required to get it to the point where the compiler can then generate efficient code. By this means, we avoid compromising the readability, modularity, and portability of the code as much as if we had to work with a compiler of only minimal capabilities. Again, it helps to iteratively modify the code and analyze its performance both through measurements and by examining the generated assembly code.

To novice programmers, it might seem strange to keep modifying the source code in an attempt to coax the compiler into generating efficient code, but this is indeed how many high-performance programs are written. Compared to the alternative of writing code in assembly language, this indirect approach has the advantage that the resulting code will still run on other machines, although perhaps not with peak performance.

5.1 Capabilities and Limitations of Optimizing Compilers

Modern compilers employ sophisticated algorithms to determine what values are computed in a program and how they are used. They can then exploit opportunities to simplify expressions, to use a single computation in several different places, and to reduce the number of times a given computation must be performed. Most compilers, including GCC, provide users with some control over which optimizations they apply. As discussed in Chapter 3, the simplest control is to specify the *optimization level*. For example, invoking GCC with the command-line option -Og specifies that it should apply a basic set of optimizations.

Invoking GCC with option -O1 or higher (e.g., -O2 or -O3) will cause it to apply more extensive optimizations. These can further improve program performance, but they may expand the program size and they may make the program more difficult to debug using standard debugging tools. For our presentation, we will mostly consider code compiled with optimization level -O1, even though level -O2 has become the accepted standard for most software projects that use GCC. We purposely limit the level of optimization to demonstrate how different ways of writing a function in C can affect the efficiency of the code generated by a compiler. We will find that we can write C code that, when compiled just with option -O1, vastly outperforms a more naive version compiled with the highest possible optimization levels.

Compilers must be careful to apply only *safe* optimizations to a program, meaning that the resulting program will have the exact same behavior as would an unoptimized version for all possible cases the program may encounter, up to the limits of the guarantees provided by the C language standards. Constraining the compiler to perform only safe optimizations eliminates possible sources of undesired run-time behavior, but it also means that the programmer must make more of an effort to write programs in a way that the compiler can then transform into efficient machine-level code. To appreciate the challenges of deciding which program transformations are safe or not, consider the following two procedures:

```
1   void twiddle1(long *xp, long *yp)
2   {
3       *xp += *yp;
4       *xp += *yp;
5   }
6
7   void twiddle2(long *xp, long *yp)
8   {
9       *xp += 2* *yp;
10  }
```

At first glance, both procedures seem to have identical behavior. They both add twice the value stored at the location designated by pointer yp to that designated by pointer xp. On the other hand, function `twiddle2` is more efficient. It requires only three memory references (read *xp, read *yp, write *xp), whereas `twiddle1` requires six (two reads of *xp, two reads of *yp, and two writes of *xp). Hence, if a compiler is given procedure `twiddle1` to compile, one might think it could generate more efficient code based on the computations performed by `twiddle2`.

Consider, however, the case in which xp and yp are equal. Then function `twiddle1` will perform the following computations:

```
3       *xp += *xp;  /* Double value at xp */
4       *xp += *xp;  /* Double value at xp */
```

The result will be that the value at xp will be increased by a factor of 4. On the other hand, function `twiddle2` will perform the following computation:

```
9       *xp += 2* *xp;  /* Triple value at xp */
```

The result will be that the value at xp will be increased by a factor of 3. The compiler knows nothing about how `twiddle1` will be called, and so it must assume that arguments xp and yp can be equal. It therefore cannot generate code in the style of `twiddle2` as an optimized version of `twiddle1`.

The case where two pointers may designate the same memory location is known as *memory aliasing*. In performing only safe optimizations, the compiler must assume that different pointers may be aliased. As another example, for a program with pointer variables p and q, consider the following code sequence:

```
x = 1000; y = 3000;
*q = y;    /* 3000 */
*p = x;    /* 1000 */
t1 = *q;   /* 1000 or 3000 */
```

The value computed for t1 depends on whether or not pointers p and q are aliased—if not, it will equal 3,000, but if so it will equal 1,000. This leads to one of the major *optimization blockers*, aspects of programs that can severely limit the opportunities for a compiler to generate optimized code. If a compiler cannot determine whether or not two pointers may be aliased, it must assume that either case is possible, limiting the set of possible optimizations.

Practice Problem 5.1 (solution page 573)

The following problem illustrates the way memory aliasing can cause unexpected program behavior. Consider the following procedure to swap two values:

```
1    /* Swap value x at xp with value y at yp */
2    void swap(long *xp, long *yp)
3    {
4        *xp = *xp + *yp; /* x+y        */
5        *yp = *xp - *yp; /* x+y-y = x */
6        *xp = *xp - *yp; /* x+y-x = y */
7    }
```

If this procedure is called with xp equal to yp, what effect will it have?

A second optimization blocker is due to function calls. As an example, consider the following two procedures:

```
1    long f();
2
3    long func1() {
4        return f() + f() + f() + f();
5    }
6
7    long func2() {
8        return 4*f();
9    }
```

It might seem at first that both compute the same result, but with func2 calling f only once, whereas func1 calls it four times. It is tempting to generate code in the style of func2 when given func1 as the source.

Consider, however, the following code for f:

```
1    long counter = 0;
2
3    long f() {
4        return counter++;
5    }
```

This function has a *side effect*—it modifies some part of the global program state. Changing the number of times it gets called changes the program behavior. In

Aside   Optimizing function calls by inline substitution

Code involving function calls can be optimized by a process known as *inline substitution* (or simply "inlining"), where the function call is replaced by the code for the body of the function. For example, we can expand the code for func1 by substituting four instantiations of function f:

```
1   /* Result of inlining f in func1 */
2   long func1in() {
3       long t = counter++; /* +0 */
4       t += counter++;     /* +1 */
5       t += counter++;     /* +2 */
6       t += counter++;     /* +3 */
7       return t;
8   }
```

This transformation both reduces the overhead of the function calls and allows further optimization of the expanded code. For example, the compiler can consolidate the updates of global variable counter in func1in to generate an optimized version of the function:

```
1   /* Optimization of inlined code */
2   long func1opt() {
3       long t = 4 * counter + 6;
4       counter += 4;
5       return t;
6   }
```

This code faithfully reproduces the behavior of func1 for this particular definition of function f.

Recent versions of GCC attempt this form of optimization, either when directed to with the command-line option -finline or for optimization level -O1 and higher. Unfortunately, GCC only attempts inlining for functions defined within a single file. That means it will not be applied in the common case where a set of library functions is defined in one file but invoked by functions in other files.

There are times when it is best to prevent a compiler from performing inline substitution. One is when the code will be evaluated using a symbolic debugger, such as GDB, as described in Section 3.10.2. If a function call has been optimized away via inline substitution, then any attempt to trace or set a breakpoint for that call will fail. The second is when evaluating the performance of a program by profiling, as is discussed in Section 5.14.1. Calls to functions that have been eliminated by inline substitution will not be profiled correctly.

particular, a call to func1 would return $0 + 1 + 2 + 3 = 6$, whereas a call to func2 would return $4 \cdot 0 = 0$, assuming both started with global variable counter set to zero.

Most compilers do not try to determine whether a function is free of side effects and hence is a candidate for optimizations such as those attempted in func2. Instead, the compiler assumes the worst case and leaves function calls intact.

Among compilers, GCC is considered adequate, but not exceptional, in terms of its optimization capabilities. It performs basic optimizations, but it does not perform the radical transformations on programs that more "aggressive" compilers do. As a consequence, programmers using GCC must put more effort into writing programs in a way that simplifies the compiler's task of generating efficient code.

5.2 Expressing Program Performance

We introduce the metric *cycles per element*, abbreviated CPE, to express program performance in a way that can guide us in improving the code. CPE measurements help us understand the loop performance of an iterative program at a detailed level. It is appropriate for programs that perform a repetitive computation, such as processing the pixels in an image or computing the elements in a matrix product.

The sequencing of activities by a processor is controlled by a clock providing a regular signal of some frequency, usually expressed in *gigahertz* (GHz), billions of cycles per second. For example, when product literature characterizes a system as a "4 GHz" processor, it means that the processor clock runs at 4.0×10^9 cycles per second. The time required for each clock cycle is given by the reciprocal of the clock frequency. These typically are expressed in *nanoseconds* (1 nanosecond is 10^{-9} seconds) or *picoseconds* (1 picosecond is 10^{-12} seconds). For example, the period of a 4 GHz clock can be expressed as either 0.25 nanoseconds or 250 picoseconds. From a programmer's perspective, it is more instructive to express measurements in clock cycles rather than nanoseconds or picoseconds. That way, the measurements express how many instructions are being executed rather than how fast the clock runs.

Many procedures contain a loop that iterates over a set of elements. For example, functions psum1 and psum2 in Figure 5.1 both compute the *prefix sum* of a vector of length n. For a vector $\vec{a} = \langle a_0, a_1, \ldots, a_{n-1} \rangle$, the prefix sum $\vec{p} = \langle p_0, p_1, \ldots, p_{n-1} \rangle$ is defined as

$$
\begin{aligned}
p_0 &= a_0 \\
p_i &= p_{i-1} + a_i, \quad 1 \le i < n
\end{aligned}
\tag{5.1}
$$

Function psum1 computes one element of the result vector per iteration. Function psum2 uses a technique known as *loop unrolling* to compute two elements per iteration. We will explore the benefits of loop unrolling later in this chapter. (See Problems 5.11, 5.12, and 5.19 for more about analyzing and optimizing the prefix-sum computation.)

The time required by such a procedure can be characterized as a constant plus a factor proportional to the number of elements processed. For example, Figure 5.2 shows a plot of the number of clock cycles required by the two functions for a range of values of n. Using a *least squares fit*, we find that the run times (in clock cycles) for psum1 and psum2 can be approximated by the equations $368 + 9.0n$ and $368 + 6.0n$, respectively. These equations indicate an overhead of 368 cycles due to the timing code and to initiate the procedure, set up the loop, and complete the

```
1    /* Compute prefix sum of vector a */
2    void psum1(float a[], float p[], long n)
3    {
4        long i;
5        p[0] = a[0];
6        for (i = 1; i < n; i++)
7            p[i] = p[i-1] + a[i];
8    }
9
10   void psum2(float a[], float p[], long n)
11   {
12       long i;
13       p[0] = a[0];
14       for (i = 1; i < n-1; i+=2) {
15           float mid_val = p[i-1] + a[i];
16           p[i]     = mid_val;
17           p[i+1]   = mid_val + a[i+1];
18       }
19       /* For even n, finish remaining element */
20       if (i < n)
21           p[i] = p[i-1] + a[i];
22   }
```

Figure 5.1   Prefix-sum functions. These functions provide examples for how we express program performance.

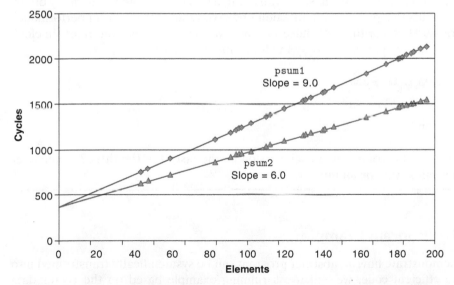

Figure 5.2   Performance of prefix-sum functions. The slope of the lines indicates the number of clock cycles per element (CPE).

Aside   What is a least squares fit?

For a set of data points $(x_1, y_1), \ldots (x_n, y_n)$, we often try to draw a line that best approximates the X–Y trend represented by these data. With a least squares fit, we look for a line of the form $y = mx + b$ that minimizes the following error measure:

$$E(m, b) = \sum_{i=1,n} (mx_i + b - y_i)^2$$

An algorithm for computing m and b can be derived by finding the derivatives of $E(m, b)$ with respect to m and b and setting them to 0.

procedure, plus a linear factor of 6.0 or 9.0 cycles per element. For large values of n (say, greater than 200), the run times will be dominated by the linear factors. We refer to the coefficients in these terms as the effective number of cycles per element. We prefer measuring the number of cycles per *element* rather than the number of cycles per *iteration*, because techniques such as loop unrolling allow us to use fewer iterations to complete the computation, but our ultimate concern is how fast the procedure will run for a given vector length. We focus our efforts on minimizing the CPE for our computations. By this measure, psum2, with a CPE of 6.0, is superior to psum1, with a CPE of 9.0.

Practice Problem 5.2 (solution page 573)

Later in this chapter we will start with a single function and generate many different variants that preserve the function's behavior, but with different performance characteristics. For three of these variants, we found that the run times (in clock cycles) can be approximated by the following functions:

Version 1: $60 + 35n$

Version 2: $136 + 4n$

Version 3: $157 + 1.25n$

For what values of n would each version be the fastest of the three? Remember that n will always be an integer.

5.3   Program Example

To demonstrate how an abstract program can be systematically transformed into more efficient code, we will use a running example based on the vector data structure shown in Figure 5.3. A vector is represented with two blocks of memory: the header and the data array. The header is a structure declared as follows:

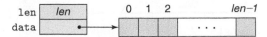

Figure 5.3 Vector abstract data type. A vector is represented by header information plus an array of designated length.

——— *code/opt/vec.h*

```
1   /* Create abstract data type for vector */
2   typedef struct {
3       long len;
4       data_t *data;
5   } vec_rec, *vec_ptr;
```

——— *code/opt/vec.h*

The declaration uses data_t to designate the data type of the underlying elements. In our evaluation, we measured the performance of our code for integer (C int and long), and floating-point (C float and double) data. We do this by compiling and running the program separately for different type declarations, such as the following for data type long:

```
typedef long data_t;
```

We allocate the data array block to store the vector elements as an array of len objects of type data_t.

Figure 5.4 shows some basic procedures for generating vectors, accessing vector elements, and determining the length of a vector. An important feature to note is that get_vec_element, the vector access routine, performs bounds checking for every vector reference. This code is similar to the array representations used in many other languages, including Java. Bounds checking reduces the chances of program error, but it can also slow down program execution.

As an optimization example, consider the code shown in Figure 5.5, which combines all of the elements in a vector into a single value according to some operation. By using different definitions of compile-time constants IDENT and OP, the code can be recompiled to perform different operations on the data. In particular, using the declarations

```
#define IDENT 0
#define OP   +
```

it sums the elements of the vector. Using the declarations

```
#define IDENT 1
#define OP   *
```

it computes the product of the vector elements.

In our presentation, we will proceed through a series of transformations of the code, writing different versions of the combining function. To gauge progress,

—————————————————————————— *code/opt/vec.c*

```
1    /* Create vector of specified length */
2    vec_ptr new_vec(long len)
3    {
4        /* Allocate header structure */
5        vec_ptr result = (vec_ptr) malloc(sizeof(vec_rec));
6        data_t *data = NULL;
7        if (!result)
8            return NULL;  /* Couldn't allocate storage */
9        result->len = len;
10       /* Allocate array */
11       if (len > 0) {
12           data = (data_t *)calloc(len, sizeof(data_t));
13           if (!data) {
14               free((void *) result);
15               return NULL; /* Couldn't allocate storage */
16           }
17       }
18       /* Data will either be NULL or allocated array */
19       result->data = data;
20       return result;
21   }
22
23   /*
24    * Retrieve vector element and store at dest.
25    * Return 0 (out of bounds) or 1 (successful)
26    */
27   int get_vec_element(vec_ptr v, long index, data_t *dest)
28   {
29       if (index < 0 || index >= v->len)
30           return 0;
31       *dest = v->data[index];
32       return 1;
33   }
34
35   /* Return length of vector */
36   long vec_length(vec_ptr v)
37   {
38       return v->len;
39   }
```

—————————————————————————— *code/opt/vec.c*

Figure 5.4 Implementation of vector abstract data type. In the actual program, data type `data_t` is declared to be `int`, `long`, `float`, or `double`.

```
1    /* Implementation with maximum use of data abstraction */
2    void combine1(vec_ptr v, data_t *dest)
3    {
4        long i;
5
6        *dest = IDENT;
7        for (i = 0; i < vec_length(v); i++) {
8            data_t val;
9            get_vec_element(v, i, &val);
10           *dest = *dest OP val;
11       }
12   }
```

Figure 5.5   Initial implementation of combining operation. Using different declarations of identity element IDENT and combining operation OP, we can measure the routine for different operations.

we measured the CPE performance of the functions on a machine with an Intel Core i7 Haswell processor, which we refer to as our *reference machine*. Some characteristics of this processor were given in Section 3.1. These measurements characterize performance in terms of how the programs run on just one particular machine, and so there is no guarantee of comparable performance on other combinations of machine and compiler. However, we have compared the results with those for a number of different compiler/processor combinations, and we have found them generally consistent with those presented here.

As we proceed through a set of transformations, we will find that many lead to only minimal performance gains, while others have more dramatic effects. Determining which combinations of transformations to apply is indeed part of the "black art" of writing fast code. Some combinations that do not provide measurable benefits are indeed ineffective, while others are important as ways to enable further optimizations by the compiler. In our experience, the best approach involves a combination of experimentation and analysis: repeatedly attempting different approaches, performing measurements, and examining the assembly-code representations to identify underlying performance bottlenecks.

As a starting point, the following table shows CPE measurements for combine1 running on our reference machine, with different combinations of operation (addition or multiplication) and data type (long integer and double-precision floating point). Our experiments with many different programs showed that operations on 32-bit and 64-bit integers have identical performance, with the exception of code involving division operations. Similarly, we found identical performance for programs operating on single- or double-precision floating-point data. In our tables, we will therefore show only separate results for integer data and for floating-point data.

Function	Page	Method	Integer		Floating point	
			+	*	+	*
combine1	507	Abstract unoptimized	22.68	20.02	19.98	20.18
combine1	507	Abstract -O1	10.12	10.12	10.17	11.14

We can see that our measurements are somewhat imprecise. The more likely CPE number for integer sum is 23.00, rather than 22.68, while the number for integer product is likely 20.0 instead of 20.02. Rather than "fudging" our numbers to make them look good, we will present the measurements we actually obtained. There are many factors that complicate the task of reliably measuring the precise number of clock cycles required by some code sequence. It helps when examining these numbers to mentally round the results up or down by a few hundredths of a clock cycle.

The unoptimized code provides a direct translation of the C code into machine code, often with obvious inefficiencies. By simply giving the command-line option -O1, we enable a basic set of optimizations. As can be seen, this significantly improves the program performance—more than a factor of 2—with no effort on behalf of the programmer. In general, it is good to get into the habit of enabling some level of optimization. (Similar performance results were obtained with optimization level -Og.) For the remainder of our measurements, we use optimization levels -O1 and -O2 when generating and measuring our programs.

5.4 Eliminating Loop Inefficiencies

Observe that procedure combine1, as shown in Figure 5.5, calls function vec_length as the test condition of the for loop. Recall from our discussion of how to translate code containing loops into machine-level programs (Section 3.6.7) that the test condition must be evaluated on every iteration of the loop. On the other hand, the length of the vector does not change as the loop proceeds. We could therefore compute the vector length only once and use this value in our test condition.

Figure 5.6 shows a modified version called combine2. It calls vec_length at the beginning and assigns the result to a local variable length. This transformation has noticeable effect on the overall performance for some data types and operations, and minimal or even none for others. In any case, this transformation is required to eliminate inefficiencies that would become bottlenecks as we attempt further optimizations.

Function	Page	Method	Integer		Floating point	
			+	*	+	*
combine1	507	Abstract -O1	10.12	10.12	10.17	11.14
combine2	509	Move vec_length	7.02	9.03	9.02	11.03

This optimization is an instance of a general class of optimizations known as *code motion*. They involve identifying a computation that is performed multiple

```
1    /* Move call to vec_length out of loop */
2    void combine2(vec_ptr v, data_t *dest)
3    {
4        long i;
5        long length = vec_length(v);
6
7        *dest = IDENT;
8        for (i = 0; i < length; i++) {
9            data_t val;
10           get_vec_element(v, i, &val);
11           *dest = *dest OP val;
12       }
13   }
```

Figure 5.6   Improving the efficiency of the loop test. By moving the call to vec_length out of the loop test, we eliminate the need to execute it on every iteration.

times, (e.g., within a loop), but such that the result of the computation will not change. We can therefore move the computation to an earlier section of the code that does not get evaluated as often. In this case, we moved the call to vec_length from within the loop to just before the loop.

Optimizing compilers attempt to perform code motion. Unfortunately, as discussed previously, they are typically very cautious about making transformations that change where or how many times a procedure is called. They cannot reliably detect whether or not a function will have side effects, and so they assume that it might. For example, if vec_length had some side effect, then combine1 and combine2 could have different behaviors. To improve the code, the programmer must often help the compiler by explicitly performing code motion.

As an extreme example of the loop inefficiency seen in combine1, consider the procedure lower1 shown in Figure 5.7. This procedure is styled after routines submitted by several students as part of a network programming project. Its purpose is to convert all of the uppercase letters in a string to lowercase. The procedure steps through the string, converting each uppercase character to lowercase. The case conversion involves shifting characters in the range 'A' to 'Z' to the range 'a' to 'z'.

The library function strlen is called as part of the loop test of lower1. Although strlen is typically implemented with special x86 string-processing instructions, its overall execution is similar to the simple version that is also shown in Figure 5.7. Since strings in C are null-terminated character sequences, strlen can only determine the length of a string by stepping through the sequence until it hits a null character. For a string of length n, strlen takes time proportional to n. Since strlen is called in each of the n iterations of lower1, the overall run time of lower1 is quadratic in the string length, proportional to n^2.

```
1    /* Convert string to lowercase: slow */
2    void lower1(char *s)
3    {
4        long i;
5
6        for (i = 0; i < strlen(s); i++)
7            if (s[i] >= 'A' && s[i] <= 'Z')
8                s[i] -= ('A' - 'a');
9    }
10
11   /* Convert string to lowercase: faster */
12   void lower2(char *s)
13   {
14       long i;
15       long len = strlen(s);
16
17       for (i = 0; i < len; i++)
18           if (s[i] >= 'A' && s[i] <= 'Z')
19               s[i] -= ('A' - 'a');
20   }
21
22   /* Sample implementation of library function strlen */
23   /* Compute length of string */
24   size_t strlen(const char *s)
25   {
26       long length = 0;
27       while (*s != '\0') {
28           s++;
29           length++;
30       }
31       return length;
32   }
```

Figure 5.7 Lowercase conversion routines. The two procedures have radically different performance.

This analysis is confirmed by actual measurements of the functions for different length strings, as shown in Figure 5.8 (and using the library version of `strlen`). The graph of the run time for `lower1` rises steeply as the string length increases (Figure 5.8(a)). Figure 5.8(b) shows the run times for seven different lengths (not the same as shown in the graph), each of which is a power of 2. Observe that for `lower1` each doubling of the string length causes a quadrupling of the run time. This is a clear indicator of a quadratic run time. For a string of length 1,048,576, `lower1` requires over 17 minutes of CPU time.

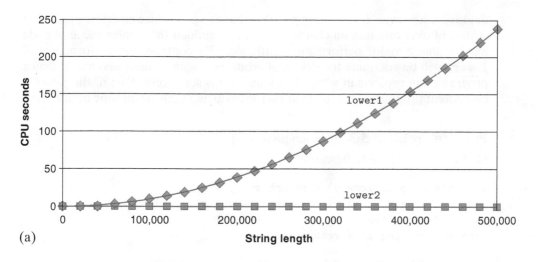

(a)

			String length			
Function	16,384	32,768	65,536	131,072	262,144	524,288	1,048,576
lower1	0.26	1.03	4.10	16.41	65.62	262.48	1,049.89
lower2	0.0000	0.0001	0.0001	0.0003	0.0005	0.0010	0.0020

(b)

Figure 5.8 Comparative performance of lowercase conversion routines. The original code `lower1` has a quadratic run time due to an inefficient loop structure. The modified code `lower2` has a linear run time.

Function `lower2` shown in Figure 5.7 is identical to that of `lower1`, except that we have moved the call to `strlen` out of the loop. The performance improves dramatically. For a string length of 1,048,576, the function requires just 2.0 milliseconds—over 500,000 times faster than `lower1`. Each doubling of the string length causes a doubling of the run time—a clear indicator of linear run time. For longer strings, the run-time improvement will be even greater.

In an ideal world, a compiler would recognize that each call to `strlen` in the loop test will return the same result, and thus the call could be moved out of the loop. This would require a very sophisticated analysis, since `strlen` checks the elements of the string and these values are changing as `lower1` proceeds. The compiler would need to detect that even though the characters within the string are changing, none are being set from nonzero to zero, or vice versa. Such an analysis is well beyond the ability of even the most sophisticated compilers, even if they employ inlining, and so programmers must do such transformations themselves.

This example illustrates a common problem in writing programs, in which a seemingly trivial piece of code has a hidden asymptotic inefficiency. One would not expect a lowercase conversion routine to be a limiting factor in a program's performance. Typically, programs are tested and analyzed on small data sets, for which the performance of `lower1` is adequate. When the program is ultimately deployed, however, it is entirely possible that the procedure could be applied to strings of over one million characters. All of a sudden this benign piece of code has become a major performance bottleneck. By contrast, the performance of lower2 will be adequate for strings of arbitrary length. Stories abound of major programming projects in which problems of this sort occur. Part of the job of a competent programmer is to avoid ever introducing such asymptotic inefficiency.

Practice Problem 5.3 (solution page 573)

Consider the following functions:

```
long min(long x, long y) { return x < y ? x : y; }
long max(long x, long y) { return x < y ? y : x; }
void incr(long *xp, long v) { *xp += v; }
long square(long x) { return x*x; }
```

The following three code fragments call these functions:

A.
```
for (i = min(x, y); i < max(x, y); incr(&i, 1))
    t += square(i);
```

B.
```
for (i = max(x, y) - 1; i >= min(x, y); incr(&i, -1))
    t += square(i);
```

C.
```
long low = min(x, y);
long high = max(x, y);

for (i = low; i < high; incr(&i, 1))
    t += square(i);
```

Assume x equals 10 and y equals 100. Fill in the following table indicating the number of times each of the four functions is called in code fragments A–C:

Code	min	max	incr	square
A.				
B.				
C.				

5.5 Reducing Procedure Calls

As we have seen, procedure calls can incur overhead and also block most forms of program optimization. We can see in the code for combine2 (Figure 5.6) that get_vec_element is called on every loop iteration to retrieve the next vector element. This function checks the vector index i against the loop bounds with every vector reference, a clear source of inefficiency. Bounds checking might be a useful feature when dealing with arbitrary array accesses, but a simple analysis of the code for combine2 shows that all references will be valid.

code/opt/vec.c

```
1   data_t *get_vec_start(vec_ptr v)
2   {
3       return v->data;
4   }
```

code/opt/vec.c

```
1   /* Direct access to vector data */
2   void combine3(vec_ptr v, data_t *dest)
3   {
4       long i;
5       long length = vec_length(v);
6       data_t *data = get_vec_start(v);
7
8       *dest = IDENT;
9       for (i = 0; i < length; i++) {
10          *dest = *dest OP data[i];
11      }
12  }
```

Figure 5.9 Eliminating function calls within the loop. The resulting code does not show a performance gain, but it enables additional optimizations.

Suppose instead that we add a function get_vec_start to our abstract data type. This function returns the starting address of the data array, as shown in Figure 5.9. We could then write the procedure shown as combine3 in this figure, having no function calls in the inner loop. Rather than making a function call to retrieve each vector element, it accesses the array directly. A purist might say that this transformation seriously impairs the program modularity. In principle, the user of the vector abstract data type should not even need to know that the vector contents are stored as an array, rather than as some other data structure such as a linked list. A more pragmatic programmer would argue that this transformation is a necessary step toward achieving high-performance results.

Function	Page	Method	Integer		Floating point	
			+	*	+	*
combine2	509	Move vec_length	7.02	9.03	9.02	11.03
combine3	513	Direct data access	7.17	9.02	9.02	11.03

Surprisingly, there is no apparent performance improvement. Indeed, the performance for integer sum has gotten slightly worse. Evidently, other operations in the inner loop are forming a bottleneck that limits the performance more than the call to get_vec_element. We will return to this function later (Section 5.11.2) and see why the repeated bounds checking by combine2 does not incur a performance penalty. For now, we can view this transformation as one of a series of steps that will ultimately lead to greatly improved performance.

5.6   Eliminating Unneeded Memory References

The code for combine3 accumulates the value being computed by the combining operation at the location designated by the pointer dest. This attribute can be seen by examining the assembly code generated for the inner loop of the compiled code. We show here the x86-64 code generated for data type double and with multiplication as the combining operation:

```
     Inner loop of combine3.  data_t = double, OP = *
     dest in %rbx, data+i in %rdx, data+length in %rax
1    .L17:                                 loop:
2       vmovsd  (%rbx), %xmm0              Read product from dest
3       vmulsd  (%rdx), %xmm0, %xmm0       Multiply product by data[i]
4       vmovsd  %xmm0, (%rbx)              Store product at dest
5       addq    $8, %rdx                   Increment data+i
6       cmpq    %rax, %rdx                 Compare to data+length
7       jne     .L17                       If !=, goto loop
```

We see in this loop code that the address corresponding to pointer dest is held in register %rbx. It has also transformed the code to maintain a pointer to the ith data element in register %rdx, shown in the annotations as data+i. This pointer is incremented by 8 on every iteration. The loop termination is detected by comparing this pointer to one stored in register %rax. We can see that the accumulated value is read from and written to memory on each iteration. This reading and writing is wasteful, since the value read from dest at the beginning of each iteration should simply be the value written at the end of the previous iteration.

We can eliminate this needless reading and writing of memory by rewriting the code in the style of combine4 in Figure 5.10. We introduce a temporary variable acc that is used in the loop to accumulate the computed value. The result is stored at dest only after the loop has been completed. As the assembly code that follows shows, the compiler can now use register %xmm0 to hold the accumulated value. Compared to the loop in combine3, we have reduced the memory operations per iteration from two reads and one write to just a single read.

```
     Inner loop of combine4.  data_t = double, OP = *
     acc in %xmm0, data+i in %rdx, data+length in %rax
1    .L25:                                 loop:
2       vmulsd  (%rdx), %xmm0, %xmm0       Multiply acc by data[i]
3       addq    $8, %rdx                   Increment data+i
4       cmpq    %rax, %rdx                 Compare to data+length
5       jne     .L25                       If !=, goto loop
```

We see a significant improvement in program performance, as shown in the following table:

```
1    /* Accumulate result in local variable */
2    void combine4(vec_ptr v, data_t *dest)
3    {
4        long i;
5        long length = vec_length(v);
6        data_t *data = get_vec_start(v);
7        data_t acc = IDENT;
8
9        for (i = 0; i < length; i++) {
10            acc = acc OP data[i];
11        }
12        *dest = acc;
13    }
```

Figure 5.10   Accumulating result in temporary. Holding the accumulated value in local variable acc (short for "accumulator") eliminates the need to retrieve it from memory and write back the updated value on every loop iteration.

Function	Page	Method	Integer +	Integer *	Floating point +	Floating point *
combine3	513	Direct data access	7.17	9.02	9.02	11.03
combine4	515	Accumulate in temporary	1.27	3.01	3.01	5.01

All of our times improve by factors ranging from 2.2× to 5.7×, with the integer addition case dropping to just 1.27 clock cycles per element.

Again, one might think that a compiler should be able to automatically transform the combine3 code shown in Figure 5.9 to accumulate the value in a register, as it does with the code for combine4 shown in Figure 5.10. In fact, however, the two functions can have different behaviors due to memory aliasing. Consider, for example, the case of integer data with multiplication as the operation and 1 as the identity element. Let $v = [2, 3, 5]$ be a vector of three elements and consider the following two function calls:

```
combine3(v, get_vec_start(v) + 2);
combine4(v, get_vec_start(v) + 2);
```

That is, we create an alias between the last element of the vector and the destination for storing the result. The two functions would then execute as follows:

Function	Initial	Before loop	i = 0	i = 1	i = 2	Final
combine3	[2, 3, 5]	[2, 3, 1]	[2, 3, 2]	[2, 3, 6]	[2, 3, 36]	[2, 3, 36]
combine4	[2, 3, 5]	[2, 3, 5]	[2, 3, 5]	[2, 3, 5]	[2, 3, 5]	[2, 3, 30]

As shown previously, combine3 accumulates its result at the destination, which in this case is the final vector element. This value is therefore set first to 1, then to $2 \cdot 1 = 2$, and then to $3 \cdot 2 = 6$. On the last iteration, this value is then multiplied by itself to yield a final value of 36. For the case of combine4, the vector remains unchanged until the end, when the final element is set to the computed result $1 \cdot 2 \cdot 3 \cdot 5 = 30$.

Of course, our example showing the distinction between combine3 and combine4 is highly contrived. One could argue that the behavior of combine4 more closely matches the intention of the function description. Unfortunately, a compiler cannot make a judgment about the conditions under which a function might be used and what the programmer's intentions might be. Instead, when given combine3 to compile, the conservative approach is to keep reading and writing memory, even though this is less efficient.

Practice Problem 5.4 (solution page 574)

When we use GCC to compile combine3 with command-line option -02, we get code with substantially better CPE performance than with -01:

Function	Page	Method	Integer +	Integer *	Floating point +	Floating point *
combine3	513	Compiled -O1	7.17	9.02	9.02	11.03
combine3	513	Compiled -O2	1.60	3.01	3.01	5.01
combine4	515	Accumulate in temporary	1.27	3.01	3.01	5.01

We achieve performance comparable to that for combine4, except for the case of integer sum, but even it improves significantly. On examining the assembly code generated by the compiler, we find an interesting variant for the inner loop:

```
        Inner loop of combine3.  data_t = double, OP = *.  Compiled -O2
        dest in %rbx, data+i in %rdx, data+length in %rax
        Accumulated product in %xmm0
1   .L22:                                loop:
2       vmulsd   (%rdx), %xmm0, %xmm0    Multiply product by data[i]
3       addq     $8, %rdx                Increment data+i
4       cmpq     %rax, %rdx              Compare to data+length
5       vmovsd   %xmm0, (%rbx)           Store product at dest
6       jne      .L22                    If !=, goto loop
```

We can compare this to the version created with optimization level 1:

```
        Inner loop of combine3.  data_t = double, OP = *.  Compiled -O1
        dest in %rbx, data+i in %rdx, data+length in %rax
1   .L17:                                loop:
2       vmovsd   (%rbx), %xmm0           Read product from dest
3       vmulsd   (%rdx), %xmm0, %xmm0    Multiply product by data[i]
4       vmovsd   %xmm0, (%rbx)           Store product at dest
```

```
5      addq    $8, %rdx              Increment data+i
6      cmpq    %rax, %rdx            Compare to data+length
7      jne     .L17                  If !=, goto loop
```

We see that, besides some reordering of instructions, the only difference is that the more optimized version does not contain the vmovsd implementing the read from the location designated by dest (line 2).

A. How does the role of register %xmm0 differ in these two loops?

B. Will the more optimized version faithfully implement the C code of combine3, including when there is memory aliasing between dest and the vector data?

C. Either explain why this optimization preserves the desired behavior, or give an example where it would produce different results than the less optimized code.

With this final transformation, we reached a point where we require just 1.25–5 clock cycles for each element to be computed. This is a considerable improvement over the original 9–11 cycles when we first enabled optimization. We would now like to see just what factors are constraining the performance of our code and how we can improve things even further.

5.7   Understanding Modern Processors

Up to this point, we have applied optimizations that did not rely on any features of the target machine. They simply reduced the overhead of procedure calls and eliminated some of the critical "optimization blockers" that cause difficulties for optimizing compilers. As we seek to push the performance further, we must consider optimizations that exploit the *microarchitecture* of the processor—that is, the underlying system design by which a processor executes instructions. Getting every last bit of performance requires a detailed analysis of the program as well as code generation tuned for the target processor. Nonetheless, we can apply some basic optimizations that will yield an overall performance improvement on a large class of processors. The detailed performance results we report here may not hold for other machines, but the general principles of operation and optimization apply to a wide variety of machines.

To understand ways to improve performance, we require a basic understanding of the microarchitectures of modern processors. Due to the large number of transistors that can be integrated onto a single chip, modern microprocessors employ complex hardware that attempts to maximize program performance. One result is that their actual operation is far different from the view that is perceived by looking at machine-level programs. At the code level, it appears as if instructions are executed one at a time, where each instruction involves fetching values from registers or memory, performing an operation, and storing results back to a register or memory location. In the actual processor, a number of instructions are evaluated simultaneously, a phenomenon referred to as *instruction-level parallelism*. In some designs, there can be 100 or more instructions "in flight." Elaborate mechanisms are employed to make sure the behavior of this parallel execution exactly captures the sequential semantic model required by the machine-level program. This is one of the remarkable feats of modern microprocessors: they employ complex and exotic microarchitectures, in which multiple instructions can be executed in parallel, while presenting an operational view of simple sequential instruction execution.

Although the detailed design of a modern microprocessor is well beyond the scope of this book, having a general idea of the principles by which they operate suffices to understand how they achieve instruction-level parallelism. We will find that two different lower bounds characterize the maximum performance of a program. The *latency bound* is encountered when a series of operations must be performed in strict sequence, because the result of one operation is required before the next one can begin. This bound can limit program performance when the data dependencies in the code limit the ability of the processor to exploit instruction-level parallelism. The *throughput bound* characterizes the raw computing capacity of the processor's functional units. This bound becomes the ultimate limit on program performance.

5.7.1 Overall Operation

Figure 5.11 shows a very simplified view of a modern microprocessor. Our hypothetical processor design is based loosely on the structure of recent Intel processors. These processors are described in the industry as being *superscalar*, which means they can perform multiple operations on every clock cycle and *out of order*, meaning that the order in which instructions execute need not correspond to their ordering in the machine-level program. The overall design has two main parts: the *instruction control unit* (ICU), which is responsible for reading a sequence of instructions from memory and generating from these a set of primitive operations to perform on program data, and the *execution unit* (EU), which then executes these operations. Compared to the simple *in-order* pipeline we studied in Chapter 4, out-of-order processors require far greater and more complex hardware, but they are better at achieving higher degrees of instruction-level parallelism.

The ICU reads the instructions from an *instruction cache*—a special high-speed memory containing the most recently accessed instructions. In general, the ICU fetches well ahead of the currently executing instructions, so that it has enough time to decode these and send operations down to the EU. One problem, however, is that when a program hits a branch,[1] there are two possible directions the program might go. The branch can be *taken*, with control passing to the branch target. Alternatively, the branch can be *not taken*, with control passing to the next

---

1. We use the term "branch" specifically to refer to conditional jump instructions. Other instructions that can transfer control to multiple destinations, such as procedure return and indirect jumps, provide similar challenges for the processor.

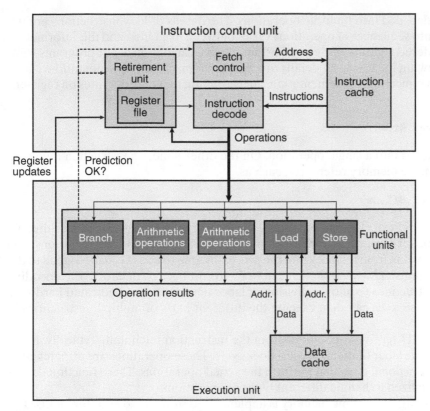

Figure 5.11 Block diagram of an out-of-order processor. The instruction control unit is responsible for reading instructions from memory and generating a sequence of primitive operations. The execution unit then performs the operations and indicates whether the branches were correctly predicted.

instruction in the instruction sequence. Modern processors employ a technique known as *branch prediction*, in which they guess whether or not a branch will be taken and also predict the target address for the branch. Using a technique known as *speculative execution*, the processor begins fetching and decoding instructions at where it predicts the branch will go, and even begins executing these operations before it has been determined whether or not the branch prediction was correct. If it later determines that the branch was predicted incorrectly, it resets the state to that at the branch point and begins fetching and executing instructions in the other direction. The block labeled "Fetch control" incorporates branch prediction to perform the task of determining which instructions to fetch.

The *instruction decoding* logic takes the actual program instructions and converts them into a set of primitive *operations* (sometimes referred to as *micro-operations*). Each of these operations performs some simple computational task such as adding two numbers, reading data from memory, or writing data to memory. For machines with complex instructions, such as x86 processors, an instruction can be decoded into multiple operations. The details of how instructions are decoded into sequences of operations varies between machines, and this information is considered highly proprietary. Fortunately, we can optimize our programs without knowing the low-level details of a particular machine implementation.

In a typical x86 implementation, an instruction that only operates on registers, such as

```
addq %rax,%rdx
```

is converted into a single operation. On the other hand, an instruction involving one or more memory references, such as

```
addq %rax,8(%rdx)
```

yields multiple operations, separating the memory references from the arithmetic operations. This particular instruction would be decoded as three operations: one to *load* a value from memory into the processor, one to add the loaded value to the value in register %eax, and one to *store* the result back to memory. The decoding splits instructions to allow a division of labor among a set of dedicated hardware units. These units can then execute the different parts of multiple instructions in parallel.

The EU receives operations from the instruction fetch unit. Typically, it can receive a number of them on each clock cycle. These operations are dispatched to a set of *functional units* that perform the actual operations. These functional units are specialized to handle different types of operations.

Reading and writing memory is implemented by the load and store units. The load unit handles operations that read data from the memory into the processor. This unit has an adder to perform address computations. Similarly, the store unit handles operations that write data from the processor to the memory. It also has an adder to perform address computations. As shown in the figure, the load and store units access memory via a *data cache*, a high-speed memory containing the most recently accessed data values.

With speculative execution, the operations are evaluated, but the final results are not stored in the program registers or data memory until the processor can be certain that these instructions should actually have been executed. Branch operations are sent to the EU, not to determine where the branch should go, but rather to determine whether or not they were predicted correctly. If the prediction was incorrect, the EU will discard the results that have been computed beyond the branch point. It will also signal the branch unit that the prediction was incorrect and indicate the correct branch destination. In this case, the branch unit begins fetching at the new location. As we saw in Section 3.6.6, such a *misprediction* incurs a significant cost in performance. It takes a while before the new instructions can be fetched, decoded, and sent to the functional units.

Figure 5.11 indicates that the different functional units are designed to perform different operations. Those labeled as performing "arithmetic operations" are typically specialized to perform different combinations of integer and floating-point operations. As the number of transistors that can be integrated onto a single microprocessor chip has grown over time, successive models of microprocessors have increased the total number of functional units, the combinations of operations each unit can perform, and the performance of each of these units. The arithmetic units are intentionally designed to be able to perform a variety of different operations, since the required operations vary widely across different programs. For example, some programs might involve many integer operations, while others require many floating-point operations. If one functional unit were specialized to perform integer operations while another could only perform floating-point operations, then none of these programs would get the full benefit of having multiple functional units.

For example, our Intel Core i7 Haswell reference machine has eight functional units, numbered 0–7. Here is a partial list of each one's capabilities:

0. Integer arithmetic, floating-point multiplication, integer and floating-point division, branches

1. Integer arithmetic, floating-point addition, integer multiplication, floating-point multiplication

2. Load, address computation

3. Load, address computation

4. Store

5. Integer arithmetic

6. Integer arithmetic, branches

7. Store address computation

In the above list, "integer arithmetic" refers to basic operations, such as addition, bitwise operations, and shifting. Multiplication and division require more specialized resources. We see that a store operation requires two functional units—one to compute the store address and one to actually store the data. We will discuss the mechanics of store (and load) operations in Section 5.12.

We can see that this combination of functional units has the potential to perform multiple operations of the same type simultaneously. It has four units capable of performing integer operations, two that can perform load operations, and two that can perform floating-point multiplication. We will later see the impact these resources have on the maximum performance our programs can achieve.

Within the ICU, the *retirement unit* keeps track of the ongoing processing and makes sure that it obeys the sequential semantics of the machine-level program. Our figure shows a *register file* containing the integer, floating-point, and, more recently, SSE and AVX registers as part of the retirement unit, because this unit controls the updating of these registers. As an instruction is decoded, information about it is placed into a first-in, first-out queue. This information remains in the queue until one of two outcomes occurs. First, once the operations for the instruction have completed and any branch points leading to this instruction are confirmed as having been correctly predicted, the instruction can be *retired*, with any updates to the program registers being made. If some branch point leading to this instruction was mispredicted, on the other hand, the instruction will be

Aside   The history of out-of-order processing

Out-of-order processing was first implemented in the Control Data Corporation 6600 processor in 1964. Instructions were processed by 10 different functional units, each of which could be operated independently. In its day, this machine, with a clock rate of 10 MHz, was considered the premium machine for scientific computing.

IBM first implemented out-of-order processing with the IBM 360/91 processor in 1966, but just to execute the floating-point instructions. For around 25 years, out-of-order processing was considered an exotic technology, found only in machines striving for the highest possible performance, until IBM reintroduced it in the RS/6000 line of workstations in 1990. This design became the basis for the IBM/Motorola PowerPC line, with the model 601, introduced in 1993, becoming the first single-chip microprocessor to use out-of-order processing. Intel introduced out-of-order processing with its PentiumPro model in 1995, with an underlying microarchitecture similar to that of our reference machine.

flushed, discarding any results that may have been computed. By this means, mispredictions will not alter the program state.

As we have described, any updates to the program registers occur only as instructions are being retired, and this takes place only after the processor can be certain that any branches leading to this instruction have been correctly predicted. To expedite the communication of results from one instruction to another, much of this information is exchanged among the execution units, shown in the figure as "Operation results." As the arrows in the figure show, the execution units can send results directly to each other. This is a more elaborate form of the data-forwarding techniques we incorporated into our simple processor design in Section 4.5.5.

The most common mechanism for controlling the communication of operands among the execution units is called *register renaming*. When an instruction that updates register r is decoded, a *tag t* is generated giving a unique identifier to the result of the operation. An entry (r, t) is added to a table maintaining the association between program register r and tag t for an operation that will update this register. When a subsequent instruction using register r as an operand is decoded, the operation sent to the execution unit will contain t as the source for the operand value. When some execution unit completes the first operation, it generates a result (v, t), indicating that the operation with tag t produced value v. Any operation waiting for t as a source will then use v as the source value, a form of data forwarding. By this mechanism, values can be forwarded directly from one operation to another, rather than being written to and read from the register file, enabling the second operation to begin as soon as the first has completed. The renaming table only contains entries for registers having pending write operations. When a decoded instruction requires a register r, and there is no tag associated with this register, the operand is retrieved directly from the register file. With register renaming, an entire sequence of operations can be performed speculatively, even though the registers are updated only after the processor is certain of the branch outcomes.

Operation	Integer			Floating point		
	Latency	Issue	Capacity	Latency	Issue	Capacity
Addition	1	1	4	3	1	1
Multiplication	3	1	1	5	1	2
Division	3–30	3–30	1	3–15	3–15	1

Figure 5.12   Latency, issue time, and capacity characteristics of reference machine operations. Latency indicates the total number of clock cycles required to perform the actual operations, while issue time indicates the minimum number of cycles between two independent operations. The capacity indicates how many of these operations can be issued simultaneously. The times for division depend on the data values.

5.7.2   Functional Unit Performance

Figure 5.12 documents the performance of some of the arithmetic operations for our Intel Core i7 Haswell reference machine, determined by both measurements and by reference to Intel literature [49]. These timings are typical for other processors as well. Each operation is characterized by its *latency*, meaning the total time required to perform the operation, the *issue time*, meaning the minimum number of clock cycles between two independent operations of the same type, and the *capacity*, indicating the number of functional units capable of performing that operation.

We see that the latencies increase in going from integer to floating-point operations. We see also that the addition and multiplication operations all have issue times of 1, meaning that on each clock cycle, the processor can start a new one of these operations. This short issue time is achieved through the use of *pipelining*. A pipelined function unit is implemented as a series of *stages*, each of which performs part of the operation. For example, a typical floating-point adder contains three stages (and hence the three-cycle latency): one to process the exponent values, one to add the fractions, and one to round the result. The arithmetic operations can proceed through the stages in close succession rather than waiting for one operation to complete before the next begins. This capability can be exploited only if there are successive, logically independent operations to be performed. Functional units with issue times of 1 cycle are said to be *fully pipelined:* they can start a new operation every clock cycle. Operations with capacity greater than 1 arise due to the capabilities of the multiple functional units, as was described earlier for the reference machine.

We see also that the divider (used for integer and floating-point division, as well as floating-point square root) is not pipelined—its issue time equals its latency. What this means is that the divider must perform a complete division before it can begin a new one. We also see that the latencies and issue times for division are given as ranges, because some combinations of dividend and divisor require more steps than others. The long latency and issue times of division make it a comparatively costly operation.

A more common way of expressing issue time is to specify the maximum *throughput* of the unit, defined as the reciprocal of the issue time. A fully pipelined functional unit has a maximum throughput of 1 operation per clock cycle, while units with higher issue times have lower maximum throughput. Having multiple functional units can increase throughput even further. For an operation with capacity C and issue time I, the processor can potentially achieve a throughput of C/I operations per clock cycle. For example, our reference machine is capable of performing floating-point multiplication operations at a rate of 2 per clock cycle. We will see how this capability can be exploited to increase program performance.

Circuit designers can create functional units with wide ranges of performance characteristics. Creating a unit with short latency or with pipelining requires more hardware, especially for more complex functions such as multiplication and floating-point operations. Since there is only a limited amount of space for these units on the microprocessor chip, CPU designers must carefully balance the number of functional units and their individual performance to achieve optimal overall performance. They evaluate many different benchmark programs and dedicate the most resources to the most critical operations. As Figure 5.12 indicates, integer multiplication and floating-point multiplication and addition were considered important operations in the design of the Core i7 Haswell processor, even though a significant amount of hardware is required to achieve the low latencies and high degree of pipelining shown. On the other hand, division is relatively infrequent and difficult to implement with either short latency or full pipelining.

The latencies, issue times, and capacities of these arithmetic operations can affect the performance of our combining functions. We can express these effects in terms of two fundamental bounds on the CPE values:

	Integer		Floating point	
Bound	+	*	+	*
Latency	1.00	3.00	3.00	5.00
Throughput	0.50	1.00	1.00	0.50

The *latency bound* gives a minimum value for the CPE for any function that must perform the combining operation in a strict sequence. The *throughput bound* gives a minimum bound for the CPE based on the maximum rate at which the functional units can produce results. For example, since there is only one integer multiplier, and it has an issue time of 1 clock cycle, the processor cannot possibly sustain a rate of more than 1 multiplication per clock cycle. On the other hand, with four functional units capable of performing integer addition, the processor can potentially sustain a rate of 4 operations per cycle. Unfortunately, the need to read elements from memory creates an additional throughput bound. The two load units limit the processor to reading at most 2 data values per clock cycle, yielding a throughput bound of 0.50. We will demonstrate the effect of both the latency and throughput bounds with different versions of the combining functions.

5.7.3   An Abstract Model of Processor Operation

As a tool for analyzing the performance of a machine-level program executing on a modern processor, we will use a *data-flow* representation of programs, a graphical notation showing how the data dependencies between the different operations constrain the order in which they are executed. These constraints then lead to *critical paths* in the graph, putting a lower bound on the number of clock cycles required to execute a set of machine instructions.

Before proceeding with the technical details, it is instructive to examine the CPE measurements obtained for function `combine4`, our fastest code up to this point:

Function	Page	Method	Integer +	Integer *	Floating point +	Floating point *
combine4	515	Accumulate in temporary	1.27	3.01	3.01	5.01
Latency bound			1.00	3.00	3.00	5.00
Throughput bound			0.50	1.00	1.00	0.50

We can see that these measurements match the latency bound for the processor, except for the case of integer addition. This is not a coincidence—it indicates that the performance of these functions is dictated by the latency of the sum or product computation being performed. Computing the product or sum of n elements requires around $L \cdot n + K$ clock cycles, where L is the latency of the combining operation and K represents the overhead of calling the function and initiating and terminating the loop. The CPE is therefore equal to the latency bound L.

From Machine-Level Code to Data-Flow Graphs

Our data-flow representation of programs is informal. We use it as a way to visualize how the data dependencies in a program dictate its performance. We present the data-flow notation by working with `combine4` (Figure 5.10) as an example. We focus just on the computation performed by the loop, since this is the dominating factor in performance for large vectors. We consider the case of data type `double` with multiplication as the combining operation. Other combinations of data type and operation yield similar code. The compiled code for this loop consists of four instructions, with registers `%rdx` holding a pointer to the ith element of array `data`, `%rax` holding a pointer to the end of the array, and `%xmm0` holding the accumulated value `acc`.

```
      Inner loop of combine4.  data_t = double, OP = *
      acc in %xmm0, data+i in %rdx, data+length in %rax
1   .L25:                             loop:
2       vmulsd  (%rdx), %xmm0, %xmm0     Multiply acc by data[i]
3       addq    $8, %rdx                 Increment data+i
4       cmpq    %rax, %rdx               Compare to data+length
5       jne     .L25                     If !=, goto loop
```

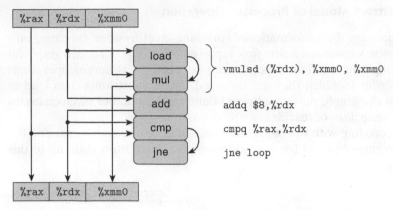

Figure 5.13 Graphical representation of inner-loop code for combine4. Instructions are dynamically translated into one or two operations, each of which receives values from other operations or from registers and produces values for other operations and for registers. We show the target of the final instruction as the label loop. It jumps to the first instruction shown.

As Figure 5.13 indicates, with our hypothetical processor design, the four instructions are expanded by the instruction decoder into a series of five *operations*, with the initial multiplication instruction being expanded into a load operation to read the source operand from memory, and a mul operation to perform the multiplication.

As a step toward generating a data-flow graph representation of the program, the boxes and lines along the left-hand side of Figure 5.13 show how the registers are used and updated by the different operations, with the boxes along the top representing the register values at the beginning of the loop, and those along the bottom representing the values at the end. For example, register %rax is only used as a source value by the cmp operation, and so the register has the same value at the end of the loop as at the beginning. Register %rdx, on the other hand, is both used and updated within the loop. Its initial value is used by the load and add operations; its new value is generated by the add operation, which is then used by the cmp operation. Register %xmm0 is also updated within the loop by the mul operation, which first uses the initial value as a source value.

Some of the operations in Figure 5.13 produce values that do not correspond to registers. We show these as arcs between operations on the right-hand side. The load operation reads a value from memory and passes it directly to the mul operation. Since these two operations arise from decoding a single vmulsd instruction, there is no register associated with the intermediate value passing between them. The cmp operation updates the condition codes, and these are then tested by the jne operation.

For a code segment forming a loop, we can classify the registers that are accessed into four categories:

Figure 5.14

Abstracting combine4 **operations as a data-flow graph.** We rearrange the operators of Figure 5.13 to more clearly show the data dependencies (a), and then further show only those operations that use values from one iteration to produce new values for the next (b).

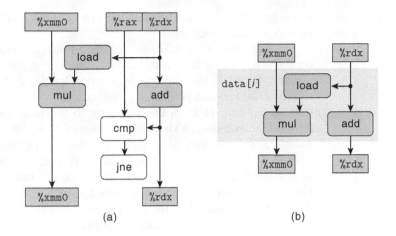

(a)   (b)

Read-only. These are used as source values, either as data or to compute memory addresses, but they are not modified within the loop. The only read-only register for the loop in combine4 is %rax.

Write-only. These are used as the destinations of data-movement operations. There are no such registers in this loop.

Local. These are updated and used within the loop, but there is no dependency from one iteration to another. The condition code registers are examples for this loop: they are updated by the cmp operation and used by the jne operation, but this dependency is contained within individual iterations.

Loop. These are used both as source values and as destinations for the loop, with the value generated in one iteration being used in another. We can see that %rdx and %xmm0 are loop registers for combine4, corresponding to program values data+i and acc.

As we will see, the chains of operations between loop registers determine the performance-limiting data dependencies.

Figure 5.14 shows further refinements of the graphical representation of Figure 5.13, with a goal of showing only those operations and data dependencies that affect the program execution time. We see in Figure 5.14(a) that we rearranged the operators to show more clearly the flow of data from the source registers at the top (both read-only and loop registers) and to the destination registers at the bottom (both write-only and loop registers).

In Figure 5.14(a), we also color operators white if they are not part of some chain of dependencies between loop registers. For this example, the comparison (cmp) and branch (jne) operations do not directly affect the flow of data in the program. We assume that the instruction control unit predicts that branch will be taken, and hence the program will continue looping. The purpose of the compare and branch operations is to test the branch condition and notify the ICU if it is not taken. We assume this checking can be done quickly enough that it does not slow down the processor.

In Figure 5.14(b), we have eliminated the operators that were colored white on the left, and we have retained only the loop registers. What we have left is an abstract template showing the data dependencies that form among loop registers due to one iteration of the loop. We can see in this diagram that there are two data dependencies from one iteration to the next. Along one side, we see the dependencies between successive values of program value acc, stored in register %xmm0. The loop computes a new value for acc by multiplying the old value by a data element, generated by the load operation. Along the other side, we see the dependencies between successive values of the pointer to the ith data element. On each iteration, the old value is used as the address for the load operation, and it is also incremented by the add operation to compute its new value.

Figure 5.15 shows the data-flow representation of n iterations by the inner loop of function combine4. This graph was obtained by simply replicating the template shown in Figure 5.14(b) n times. We can see that the program has two chains of data

Figure 5.15

Data-flow representation of computation by n iterations of the inner loop of combine4. The sequence of multiplication operations forms a critical path that limits program performance.

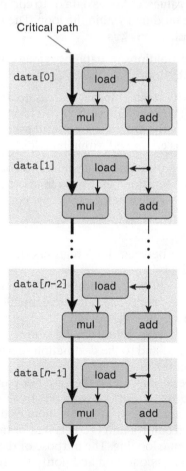

dependencies, corresponding to the updating of program values `acc` and `data+i` with operations mul and add, respectively. Given that floating-point multiplication has a latency of 5 cycles, while integer addition has a latency of 1 cycle, we can see that the chain on the left will form a *critical path*, requiring $5n$ cycles to execute. The chain on the right would require only n cycles to execute, and so it does not limit the program performance.

Figure 5.15 demonstrates why we achieved a CPE equal to the latency bound of 5 cycles for `combine4`, when performing floating-point multiplication. When executing the function, the floating-point multiplier becomes the limiting resource. The other operations required during the loop—manipulating and testing pointer value `data+i` and reading data from memory—proceed in parallel with the multiplication. As each successive value of `acc` is computed, it is fed back around to compute the next value, but this will not occur until 5 cycles later.

The flow for other combinations of data type and operation are identical to those shown in Figure 5.15, but with a different data operation forming the chain of data dependencies shown on the left. For all of the cases where the operation has a latency L greater than 1, we see that the measured CPE is simply L, indicating that this chain forms the performance-limiting critical path.

Other Performance Factors

For the case of integer addition, on the other hand, our measurements of `combine4` show a CPE of 1.27, slower than the CPE of 1.00 we would predict based on the chains of dependencies formed along either the left- or the right-hand side of the graph of Figure 5.15. This illustrates the principle that the critical paths in a data-flow representation provide only a *lower* bound on how many cycles a program will require. Other factors can also limit performance, including the total number of functional units available and the number of data values that can be passed among the functional units on any given step. For the case of integer addition as the combining operation, the data operation is sufficiently fast that the rest of the operations cannot supply data fast enough. Determining exactly why the program requires 1.27 cycles per element would require a much more detailed knowledge of the hardware design than is publicly available.

To summarize our performance analysis of `combine4`: our abstract data-flow representation of program operation showed that `combine4` has a critical path of length $L \cdot n$ caused by the successive updating of program value `acc`, and this path limits the CPE to at least L. This is indeed the CPE we measure for all cases except integer addition, which has a measured CPE of 1.27 rather than the CPE of 1.00 we would expect from the critical path length.

It may seem that the latency bound forms a fundamental limit on how fast our combining operations can be performed. Our next task will be to restructure the operations to enhance instruction-level parallelism. We want to transform the program in such a way that our only limitation becomes the throughput bound, yielding CPEs below or close to 1.00.

Practice Problem 5.5 (solution page 575)

Suppose we wish to write a function to evaluate a polynomial, where a polynomial of degree n is defined to have a set of coefficients $a_0, a_1, a_2, \ldots, a_n$. For a value x, we evaluate the polynomial by computing

$$a_0 + a_1 x + a_2 x^2 + \cdots + a_n x^n \tag{5.2}$$

This evaluation can be implemented by the following function, having as arguments an array of coefficients a, a value x, and the polynomial degree degree (the value n in Equation 5.2). In this function, we compute both the successive terms of the equation and the successive powers of x within a single loop:

```
1    double poly(double a[], double x, long degree)
2    {
3        long i;
4        double result = a[0];
5        double xpwr = x;   /* Equals x^i at start of loop */
6        for (i = 1; i <= degree; i++) {
7            result += a[i] * xpwr;
8            xpwr = x * xpwr;
9        }
10       return result;
11   }
```

A. For degree n, how many additions and how many multiplications does this code perform?

B. On our reference machine, with arithmetic operations having the latencies shown in Figure 5.12, we measure the CPE for this function to be 5.00. Explain how this CPE arises based on the data dependencies formed between iterations due to the operations implementing lines 7–8 of the function.

Practice Problem 5.6 (solution page 575)

Let us continue exploring ways to evaluate polynomials, as described in Practice Problem 5.5. We can reduce the number of multiplications in evaluating a polynomial by applying *Horner's method*, named after British mathematician William G. Horner (1786–1837). The idea is to repeatedly factor out the powers of x to get the following evaluation:

$$a_0 + x(a_1 + x(a_2 + \cdots + x(a_{n-1} + x a_n) \cdots)) \tag{5.3}$$

Using Horner's method, we can implement polynomial evaluation using the following code:

```
1    /* Apply Horner's method */
2    double polyh(double a[], double x, long degree)
3    {
```

```
4        long i;
5        double result = a[degree];
6        for (i = degree-1; i >= 0; i--)
7             result = a[i] + x*result;
8        return result;
9   }
```

A. For degree n, how many additions and how many multiplications does this code perform?

B. On our reference machine, with the arithmetic operations having the latencies shown in Figure 5.12, we measure the CPE for this function to be 8.00. Explain how this CPE arises based on the data dependencies formed between iterations due to the operations implementing line 7 of the function.

C. Explain how the function shown in Practice Problem 5.5 can run faster, even though it requires more operations.

5.8　Loop Unrolling

Loop unrolling is a program transformation that reduces the number of iterations for a loop by increasing the number of elements computed on each iteration. We saw an example of this with the function psum2 (Figure 5.1), where each iteration computes two elements of the prefix sum, thereby halving the total number of iterations required. Loop unrolling can improve performance in two ways. First, it reduces the number of operations that do not contribute directly to the program result, such as loop indexing and conditional branching. Second, it exposes ways in which we can further transform the code to reduce the number of operations in the critical paths of the overall computation. In this section, we will examine simple loop unrolling, without any further transformations.

Figure 5.16 shows a version of our combining code using what we will refer to as "2×1 loop unrolling." The first loop steps through the array two elements at a time. That is, the loop index i is incremented by 2 on each iteration, and the combining operation is applied to array elements i and $i + 1$ in a single iteration.

In general, the vector length will not be a multiple of 2. We want our code to work correctly for arbitrary vector lengths. We account for this requirement in two ways. First, we make sure the first loop does not overrun the array bounds. For a vector of length n, we set the loop limit to be $n - 1$. We are then assured that the loop will only be executed when the loop index i satisfies $i < n - 1$, and hence the maximum array index $i + 1$ will satisfy $i + 1 < (n - 1) + 1 = n$.

We can generalize this idea to unroll a loop by any factor k, yielding $k \times 1$ *loop unrolling*. To do so, we set the upper limit to be $n - k + 1$ and within the loop apply the combining operation to elements i through $i + k - 1$. Loop index i is incremented by k in each iteration. The maximum array index $i + k - 1$ will then be less than n. We include the second loop to step through the final few elements of the vector one at a time. The body of this loop will be executed between 0 and $k - 1$ times. For $k = 2$, we could use a simple conditional statement

```
1    /* 2 x 1 loop unrolling */
2    void combine5(vec_ptr v, data_t *dest)
3    {
4        long i;
5        long length = vec_length(v);
6        long limit = length-1;
7        data_t *data = get_vec_start(v);
8        data_t acc = IDENT;
9
10       /* Combine 2 elements at a time */
11       for (i = 0; i < limit; i+=2) {
12           acc = (acc OP data[i]) OP data[i+1];
13       }
14
15       /* Finish any remaining elements */
16       for (; i < length; i++) {
17           acc = acc OP data[i];
18       }
19       *dest = acc;
20   }
```

Figure 5.16 **Applying** 2×1 **loop unrolling.** This transformation can reduce the effect of loop overhead.

to optionally add a final iteration, as we did with the function psum2 (Figure 5.1). For $k > 2$, the finishing cases are better expressed with a loop, and so we adopt this programming convention for $k = 2$ as well. We refer to this transformation as "$k \times 1$ loop unrolling," since we unroll by a factor of k but accumulate values in a single variable acc.

Practice Problem 5.7 (solution page 575)

Modify the code for combine5 to unroll the loop by a factor $k = 5$.

When we measure the performance of unrolled code for unrolling factors $k = 2$ (combine5) and $k = 3$, we get the following results:

Function	Page	Method	Integer +	Integer *	Floating point +	Floating point *
combine4	515	No unrolling	1.27	3.01	3.01	5.01
combine5	532	2×1 unrolling	1.01	3.01	3.01	5.01
		3×1 unrolling	1.01	3.01	3.01	5.01
Latency bound			1.00	3.00	3.00	5.00
Throughput bound			0.50	1.00	1.00	0.50

Figure 5.17
CPE performance for different degrees of $k \times 1$ **loop unrolling.** Only integer addition improves with this transformation.

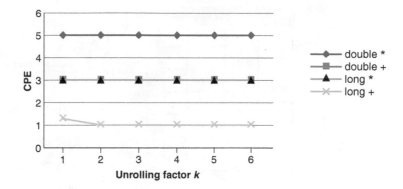

We see that the CPE for integer addition improves, achieving the latency bound of 1.00. This result can be attributed to the benefits of reducing loop overhead operations. By reducing the number of overhead operations relative to the number of additions required to compute the vector sum, we can reach the point where the 1-cycle latency of integer addition becomes the performance-limiting factor. On the other hand, none of the other cases improve—they are already at their latency bounds. Figure 5.17 shows CPE measurements when unrolling the loop by up to a factor of 10. We see that the trends we observed for unrolling by 2 and 3 continue—none go below their latency bounds.

To understand why $k \times 1$ unrolling cannot improve performance beyond the latency bound, let us examine the machine-level code for the inner loop of combine5, having $k = 2$. The following code gets generated when type data_t is double, and the operation is multiplication:

```
      Inner loop of combine5. data_t = double, OP = *
      i in %rdx, data %rax, limit in %rbx, acc in %xmm0
1   .L35:                                   loop:
2     vmulsd  (%rax,%rdx,8), %xmm0, %xmm0     Multiply acc by data[i]
3     vmulsd  8(%rax,%rdx,8), %xmm0, %xmm0    Multiply acc by data[i+1]
4     addq    $2, %rdx                        Increment i by 2
5     cmpq    %rdx, %rbp                      Compare to limit:i
6     jg      .L35                            If >, goto loop
```

We can see that GCC uses a more direct translation of the array referencing seen in the C code, compared to the pointer-based code generated for combine4.[2] Loop index i is held in register %rdx, and the address of data is held in register %rax. As before, the accumulated value acc is held in vector register %xmm0. The loop unrolling leads to two vmulsd instructions—one to add data[i] to acc, and

---

2. The GCC optimizer operates by generating multiple variants of a function and then choosing one that it predicts will yield the best performance and smallest code size. As a consequence, small changes in the source code can yield widely varying forms of machine code. We have found that the choice of pointer-based or array-based code has no impact on the performance of programs running on our reference machine.

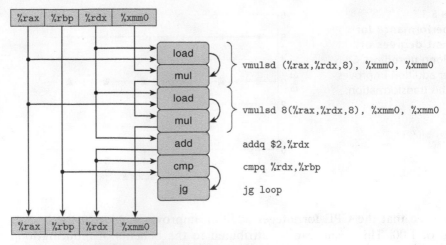

Figure 5.18 Graphical representation of inner-loop code for combine5. **Each iteration has two** vmulsd **instructions, each of which is translated into a load and a mul operation.**

Figure 5.19

Abstracting combine5 **operations as a data-flow graph.** We rearrange, simplify, and abstract the representation of Figure 5.18 to show the data dependencies between successive iterations (a). We see that each iteration must perform two multiplications in sequence (b).

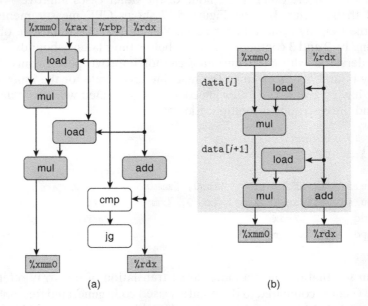

the second to add data[i+1] to acc. Figure 5.18 shows a graphical representation of this code. The vmulsd instructions each get translated into two operations: one to load an array element from memory and one to multiply this value by the accumulated value. We see here that register %xmm0 gets read and written twice in each execution of the loop. We can rearrange, simplify, and abstract this graph, following the process shown in Figure 5.19(a), to obtain the template shown in Figure 5.19(b). We then replicate this template $n/2$ times to show the computation for a vector of length n, obtaining the data-flow representation

Figure 5.20

Data-flow representation of combine5 **operating on a vector of length** n. Even though the loop has been unrolled by a factor of 2, there are still n mul operations along the critical path.

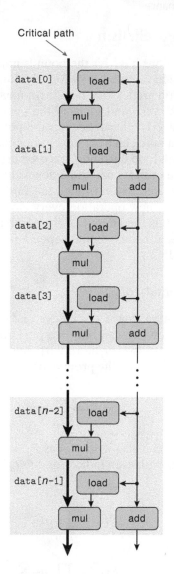

Critical path

shown in Figure 5.20. We see here that there is still a critical path of n mul operations in this graph—there are half as many iterations, but each iteration has two multiplication operations in sequence. Since the critical path was the limiting factor for the performance of the code without loop unrolling, it remains so with $k \times 1$ loop unrolling.

Aside   Getting the compiler to unroll loops

Loop unrolling can easily be performed by a compiler. Many compilers do this as part of their collection of optimizations. GCC will perform some forms of loop unrolling when invoked with optimization level 3 or higher.

5.9 Enhancing Parallelism

At this point, our functions have hit the bounds imposed by the latencies of the arithmetic units. As we have noted, however, the functional units performing addition and multiplication are all fully pipelined, meaning that they can start new operations every clock cycle, and some of the operations can be performed by multiple functional units. The hardware has the potential to perform multiplications and additions at a much higher rate, but our code cannot take advantage of this capability, even with loop unrolling, since we are accumulating the value as a single variable acc. We cannot compute a new value for acc until the preceding computation has completed. Even though the functional unit computing a new value for acc can start a new operation every clock cycle, it will only start one every L cycles, where L is the latency of the combining operation. We will now investigate ways to break this sequential dependency and get performance better than the latency bound.

5.9.1 Multiple Accumulators

For a combining operation that is associative and commutative, such as integer addition or multiplication, we can improve performance by splitting the set of combining operations into two or more parts and combining the results at the end. For example, let P_n denote the product of elements $a_0, a_1, \ldots, a_{n-1}$:

$$P_n = \prod_{i=0}^{n-1} a_i$$

Assuming n is even, we can also write this as $P_n = PE_n \times PO_n$, where PE_n is the product of the elements with even indices, and PO_n is the product of the elements with odd indices:

$$PE_n = \prod_{i=0}^{n/2-1} a_{2i}$$

$$PO_n = \prod_{i=0}^{n/2-1} a_{2i+1}$$

Figure 5.21 shows code that uses this method. It uses both two-way loop unrolling, to combine more elements per iteration, and two-way parallelism, accumulating elements with even indices in variable acc0 and elements with odd indices in variable acc1. We therefore refer to this as "2 × 2 loop unrolling." As before, we include a second loop to accumulate any remaining array elements for the case where the vector length is not a multiple of 2. We then apply the combining operation to acc0 and acc1 to compute the final result.

Comparing loop unrolling alone to loop unrolling with two-way parallelism, we obtain the following performance:

```
1    /* 2 x 2 loop unrolling */
2    void combine6(vec_ptr v, data_t *dest)
3    {
4        long i;
5        long length = vec_length(v);
6        long limit = length-1;
7        data_t *data = get_vec_start(v);
8        data_t acc0 = IDENT;
9        data_t acc1 = IDENT;
10
11       /* Combine 2 elements at a time */
12       for (i = 0; i < limit; i+=2) {
13           acc0 = acc0 OP data[i];
14           acc1 = acc1 OP data[i+1];
15       }
16
17       /* Finish any remaining elements */
18       for (; i < length; i++) {
19           acc0 = acc0 OP data[i];
20       }
21       *dest = acc0 OP acc1;
22   }
```

Figure 5.21   Applying 2×2 **loop unrolling.** By maintaining multiple accumulators, this approach can make better use of the multiple functional units and their pipelining capabilities.

Function	Page	Method	Integer		Floating point	
			+	*	+	*
combine4	515	Accumulate in temporary	1.27	3.01	3.01	5.01
combine5	532	2×1 unrolling	1.01	3.01	3.01	5.01
combine6	537	2×2 unrolling	0.81	1.51	1.51	2.51
Latency bound			1.00	3.00	3.00	5.00
Throughput bound			0.50	1.00	1.00	0.50

We see that we have improved the performance for all cases, with integer product, floating-point addition, and floating-point multiplication improving by a factor of around 2, and integer addition improving somewhat as well. Most significantly, we have broken through the barrier imposed by the latency bound. The processor no longer needs to delay the start of one sum or product operation until the previous one has completed.

To understand the performance of combine6, we start with the code and operation sequence shown in Figure 5.22. We can derive a template showing the

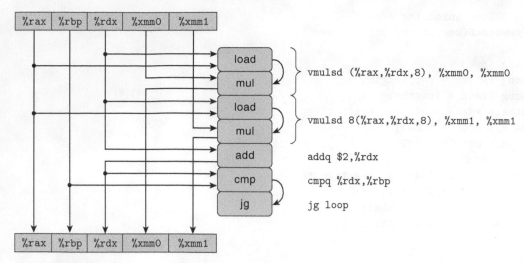

Figure 5.22 Graphical representation of inner-loop code for combine6. Each iteration has two vmulsd instructions, each of which is translated into a load and a mul operation.

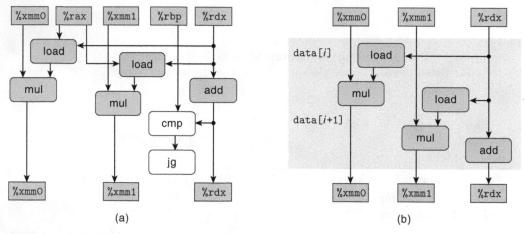

Figure 5.23 Abstracting combine6 **operations as a data-flow graph.** We rearrange, simplify, and abstract the representation of Figure 5.22 to show the data dependencies between successive iterations (a). We see that there is no dependency between the two mul operations (b).

data dependencies between iterations through the process shown in Figure 5.23. As with combine5, the inner loop contains two vmulsd operations, but these instructions translate into mul operations that read and write separate registers, with no data dependency between them (Figure 5.23(b)). We then replicate this template $n/2$ times (Figure 5.24), modeling the execution of the function on a vector of length n. We see that we now have two critical paths, one corresponding to computing the product of even-numbered elements (program value acc0) and

Figure 5.24
Data-flow representation of `combine6` **operating on a vector of length** n. We now have two critical paths, each containing $n/2$ operations.

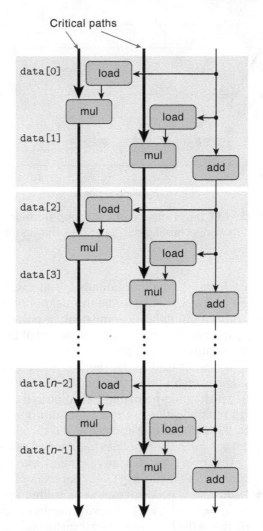

Critical paths

one for the odd-numbered elements (program value `acc1`). Each of these critical paths contains only $n/2$ operations, thus leading to a CPE of around $5.00/2 = 2.50$. A similar analysis explains our observed CPE of around $L/2$ for operations with latency L for the different combinations of data type and combining operation. Operationally, the programs are exploiting the capabilities of the functional units to increase their utilization by a factor of 2. The only exception is for integer addition. We have reduced the CPE to below 1.0, but there is still too much loop overhead to achieve the theoretical limit of 0.50.

We can generalize the multiple accumulator transformation to unroll the loop by a factor of k and accumulate k values in parallel, yielding $k \times k$ *loop unrolling*. Figure 5.25 demonstrates the effect of applying this transformation for values up to $k = 10$. We can see that, for sufficiently large values of k, the program can

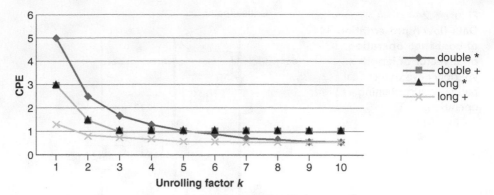

Figure 5.25 CPE performance of $k \times k$ loop unrolling. All of the CPEs improve with this transformation, achieving near or at their throughput bounds.

achieve nearly the throughput bounds for all cases. Integer addition achieves a CPE of 0.54 with $k = 7$, close to the throughput bound of 0.50 caused by the two load units. Integer multiplication and floating-point addition achieve CPEs of 1.01 when $k \geq 3$, approaching the throughput bound of 1.00 set by their functional units. Floating-point multiplication achieves a CPE of 0.51 for $k \geq 10$, approaching the throughput bound of 0.50 set by the two floating-point multipliers and the two load units. It is worth noting that our code is able to achieve nearly twice the throughput with floating-point multiplication as it can with floating-point addition, even though multiplication is a more complex operation.

In general, a program can achieve the throughput bound for an operation only when it can keep the pipelines filled for all of the functional units capable of performing that operation. For an operation with latency L and capacity C, this requires an unrolling factor $k \geq C \cdot L$. For example, floating-point multiplication has $C = 2$ and $L = 5$, necessitating an unrolling factor of $k \geq 10$. Floating-point addition has $C = 1$ and $L = 3$, achieving maximum throughput with $k \geq 3$.

In performing the $k \times k$ unrolling transformation, we must consider whether it preserves the functionality of the original function. We have seen in Chapter 2 that two's-complement arithmetic is commutative and associative, even when overflow occurs. Hence, for an integer data type, the result computed by `combine6` will be identical to that computed by `combine5` under all possible conditions. Thus, an optimizing compiler could potentially convert the code shown in `combine4` first to a two-way unrolled variant of `combine5` by loop unrolling, and then to that of `combine6` by introducing parallelism. Some compilers do either this or similar transformations to improve performance for integer data.

On the other hand, floating-point multiplication and addition are not associative. Thus, `combine5` and `combine6` could produce different results due to rounding or overflow. Imagine, for example, a product computation in which all of the elements with even indices are numbers with very large absolute values, while those with odd indices are very close to 0.0. In such a case, product PE_n might overflow, or PO_n might underflow, even though computing product P_n proceeds normally. In most real-life applications, however, such patterns are unlikely. Since most physical phenomena are continuous, numerical data tend to be reasonably smooth and well behaved. Even when there are discontinuities, they do not generally cause periodic patterns that lead to a condition such as that sketched earlier. It is unlikely that multiplying the elements in strict order gives fundamentally better accuracy than does multiplying two groups independently and then multiplying those products together. For most applications, achieving a performance gain of 2× outweighs the risk of generating different results for strange data patterns. Nevertheless, a program developer should check with potential users to see if there are particular conditions that may cause the revised algorithm to be unacceptable. Most compilers do not attempt such transformations with floating-point code, since they have no way to judge the risks of introducing transformations that can change the program behavior, no matter how small.

5.9.2   Reassociation Transformation

We now explore another way to break the sequential dependencies and thereby improve performance beyond the latency bound. We saw that the $k \times 1$ loop unrolling of combine5 did not change the set of operations performed in combining the vector elements to form their sum or product. By a very small change in the code, however, we can fundamentally change the way the combining is performed, and also greatly increase the program performance.

Figure 5.26 shows a function combine7 that differs from the unrolled code of combine5 (Figure 5.16) only in the way the elements are combined in the inner loop. In combine5, the combining is performed by the statement

```
12      acc = (acc OP data[i]) OP data[i+1];
```

while in combine7 it is performed by the statement

```
12      acc = acc OP (data[i] OP data[i+1]);
```

differing only in how two parentheses are placed. We call this a *reassociation transformation*, because the parentheses shift the order in which the vector elements are combined with the accumulated value acc, yielding a form of loop unrolling we refer to as "$2 \times 1a$."

To an untrained eye, the two statements may seem essentially the same, but when we measure the CPE, we get a surprising result:

			Integer		Floating point	
Function	Page	Method	+	*	+	*
combine4	515	Accumulate in temporary	1.27	3.01	3.01	5.01
combine5	532	2×1 unrolling	1.01	3.01	3.01	5.01
combine6	537	2×2 unrolling	0.81	1.51	1.51	2.51
combine7	542	$2 \times 1a$ unrolling	1.01	1.51	1.51	2.51
Latency bound			1.00	3.00	3.00	5.00
Throughput bound			0.50	1.00	1.00	0.50

```
1    /* 2 x 1a loop unrolling */
2    void combine7(vec_ptr v, data_t *dest)
3    {
4        long i;
5        long length = vec_length(v);
6        long limit = length-1;
7        data_t *data = get_vec_start(v);
8        data_t acc = IDENT;
9
10       /* Combine 2 elements at a time */
11       for (i = 0; i < limit; i+=2) {
12           acc = acc OP (data[i] OP data[i+1]);
13       }
14
15       /* Finish any remaining elements */
16       for (; i < length; i++) {
17           acc = acc OP data[i];
18       }
19       *dest = acc;
20   }
```

Figure 5.26 Applying $2 \times 1a$ **unrolling.** By reassociating the arithmetic, this approach increases the number of operations that can be performed in parallel.

The integer addition case matches the performance of $k \times 1$ unrolling (combine5), while the other three cases match the performance of the versions with parallel accumulators (combine6), doubling the performance relative to $k \times 1$ unrolling. These cases have broken through the barrier imposed by the latency bound.

Figure 5.27 illustrates how the code for the inner loop of combine7 (for the case of multiplication as the combining operation and double as data type) gets decoded into operations and the resulting data dependencies. We see that the load operations resulting from the vmovsd and the first vmulsd instructions load vector elements i and $i + 1$ from memory, and the first mul operation multiplies them together. The second mul operation then multiples this result by the accumulated value acc. Figure 5.28(a) shows how we rearrange, refine, and abstract the operations of Figure 5.27 to get a template representing the data dependencies for one iteration (Figure 5.28(b)). As with the templates for combine5 and combine7, we have two load and two mul operations, but only one of the mul operations forms a data-dependency chain between loop registers. When we then replicate this template $n/2$ times to show the computations performed in multiplying n vector elements (Figure 5.29), we see that we only have $n/2$ operations along the critical path. The first multiplication within each iteration can be performed without waiting for the accumulated value from the previous iteration. Thus, we reduce the minimum possible CPE by a factor of around 2.

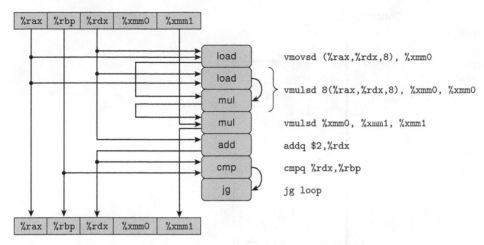

Figure 5.27   Graphical representation of inner-loop code for combine7. Each iteration gets decoded into similar operations as for combine5 or combine6, but with different data dependencies.

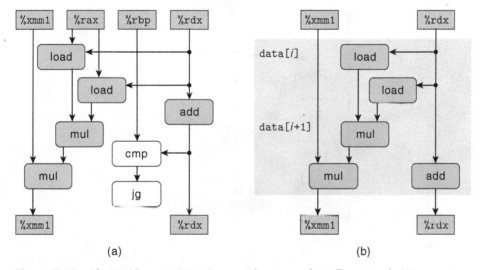

Figure 5.28   Abstracting combine7 **operations as a data-flow graph.** We rearrange, simplify, and abstract the representation of Figure 5.27 to show the data dependencies between successive iterations. The upper mul operation multiplies two 2-vector elements with each other, while the lower one multiplies the result by loop variable acc.

Figure 5.29

Data-flow representation of `combine7` operating on a vector of length n. We have a single critical path, but it contains only $n/2$ operations.

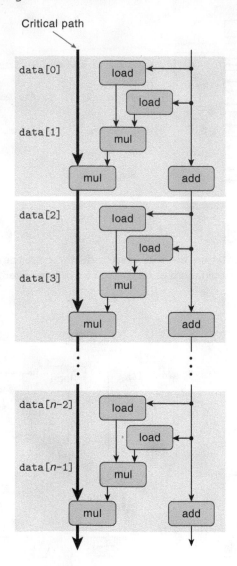

Figure 5.30 demonstrates the effect of applying the reassociation transformation to achieve what we refer to as $k \times 1a$ *loop unrolling* for values up to $k = 10$. We can see that this transformation yields performance results similar to what is achieved by maintaining k separate accumulators with $k \times k$ unrolling. In all cases, we come close to the throughput bounds imposed by the functional units.

In performing the reassociation transformation, we once again change the order in which the vector elements will be combined together. For integer addition and multiplication, the fact that these operations are associative implies that this reordering will have no effect on the result. For the floating-point cases, we must once again assess whether this reassociation is likely to significantly affect

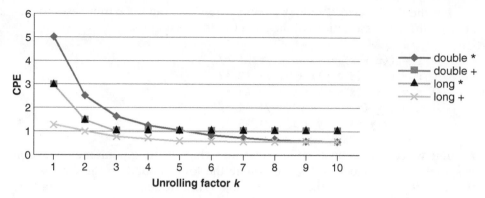

Figure 5.30   CPE performance for $k \times 1a$ loop unrolling. All of the CPEs improve with this transformation, nearly approaching their throughput bounds.

the outcome. We would argue that the difference would be immaterial for most applications.

In summary, a reassociation transformation can reduce the number of operations along the critical path in a computation, resulting in better performance by better utilizing the multiple functional units and their pipelining capabilities. Most compilers will not attempt any reassociations of floating-point operations, since these operations are not guaranteed to be associative. Current versions of GCC do perform reassociations of integer operations, but not always with good effects. In general, we have found that unrolling a loop and accumulating multiple values in parallel is a more reliable way to achieve improved program performance.

Practice Problem 5.8 (solution page 576)

Consider the following function for computing the product of an array of n double-precision numbers. We have unrolled the loop by a factor of 3.

```
double aprod(double a[], long n)
{
    long i;
    double x, y, z;
    double r = 1;
    for (i = 0; i < n-2; i+= 3) {
        x = a[i]; y = a[i+1]; z = a[i+2];
        r = r * x * y * z; /* Product computation */
    }
    for (; i < n; i++)
        r *= a[i];
    return r;
}
```

For the line labeled "Product computation," we can use parentheses to create five different associations of the computation, as follows:

```
r = ((r * x) * y) * z;  /* A1 */
r = (r * (x * y)) * z;  /* A2 */
r = r * ((x * y) * z);  /* A3 */
r = r * (x * (y * z));  /* A4 */
r = (r * x) * (y * z);  /* A5 */
```

Assume we run these functions on a machine where floating-point multiplication has a latency of 5 clock cycles. Determine the lower bound on the CPE set by the data dependencies of the multiplication. (*Hint:* It helps to draw a data-flow representation of how r is computed on every iteration.)

Web Aside OPT:SIMD   Achieving greater parallelism with vector instructions

As described in Section 3.1, Intel introduced the SSE instructions in 1999, where SSE is the acronym for "streaming SIMD extensions" and, in turn, SIMD (pronounced "sim-dee") is the acronym for "single instruction, multiple data." The SSE capability has gone through multiple generations, with more recent versions being named *advanced vector extensions*, or AVX. The SIMD execution model involves operating on entire vectors of data within single instructions. These vectors are held in a special set of *vector registers*, named %ymm0–%ymm15. Current AVX vector registers are 32 bytes long, and therefore each can hold eight 32-bit numbers or four 64-bit numbers, where the numbers can be either integer or floating-point values. AVX instructions can then perform vector operations on these registers, such as adding or multiplying eight or four sets of values in parallel. For example, if YMM register %ymm0 contains eight single-precision floating-point numbers, which we denote $a_0, \ldots, a_7$, and %rcx contains the memory address of a sequence of eight single-precision floating-point numbers, which we denote $b_0, \ldots, b_7$, then the instruction

```
vmulps  (%rcs), %ymm0, %ymm1
```

will read the eight values from memory and perform eight multiplications in parallel, computing $a_i \leftarrow a_i \cdot b_i$, for $0 \leq i \leq 7$ and storing the resulting eight products in vector register %ymm1. We see that a single instruction is able to generate a computation over multiple data values, hence the term "SIMD."

GCC supports extensions to the C language that let programmers express a program in terms of vector operations that can be compiled into the vector instructions of AVX (as well as code based on the earlier SSE instructions). This coding style is preferable to writing code directly in assembly language, since GCC can also generate code for the vector instructions found on other processors.

Using a combination of GCC instructions, loop unrolling, and multiple accumulators, we are able to achieve the following performance for our combining functions:

Web Aside OPT:SIMD   Achieving greater parallelism with vector instructions *(continued)*

Method	Integer				Floating point			
	int		long		int		long	
	+	*	+	*	+	*	+	*
Scalar 10 × 10	0.54	1.01	0.55	1.00	1.01	0.51	1.01	0.52
Scalar throughput bound	0.50	0.50	1.00	1.00	1.00	1.00	0.50	0.50
Vector 8 × 8	0.05	0.24	0.13	1.51	0.12	0.08	0.25	0.16
Vector throughput bound	0.06	0.12	0.12	—	0.12	0.06	0.25	0.12

In this chart, the first set of numbers is for conventional, *scalar* code written in the style of combine6, unrolling by a factor of 10 and maintaining 10 accumulators. The second set of numbers is for code written in a form that GCC can compile into AVX vector code. In addition to using vector operations, this version unrolls the main loop by a factor of 8 and maintains eight separate vector accumulators. We show results for both 32-bit and 64-bit numbers, since the vector instructions achieve 8-way parallelism in the first case, but only 4-way parallelism in the second.

We can see that the vector code achieves almost an eightfold improvement on the four 32-bit cases, and a fourfold improvement on three of the four 64-bit cases. Only the long integer multiplication code does not perform well when we attempt to express it in vector code. The AVX instruction set does not include one to do parallel multiplication of 64-bit integers, and so GCC cannot generate vector code for this case. Using vector instructions creates a new throughput bound for the combining operations. These are eight times lower for 32-bit operations and four times lower for 64-bit operations than the scalar limits. Our code comes close to achieving these bounds for several combinations of data type and operation.

5.10   Summary of Results for Optimizing Combining Code

Our efforts at maximizing the performance of a routine that adds or multiplies the elements of a vector have clearly paid off. The following summarizes the results we obtain with *scalar* code, not making use of the vector parallelism provided by AVX vector instructions:

Function	Page	Method	Integer		Floating point	
			+	*	+	*
combine1	507	Abstract -O1	10.12	10.12	10.17	11.14
combine6	537	2 × 2 unrolling	0.81	1.51	1.51	2.51
		10 × 10 unrolling	0.55	1.00	1.01	0.52
Latency bound			1.00	3.00	3.00	5.00
Throughput bound			0.50	1.00	1.00	0.50

By using multiple optimizations, we have been able to achieve CPEs close to the throughput bounds of 0.50 and 1.00, limited only by the capacities of the functional units. These represent 10–20× improvements on the original code. This has all been done using ordinary C code and a standard compiler. Rewriting the code to take advantage of the newer SIMD instructions yields additional performance gains of nearly 4× or 8×. For example, for single-precision multiplication, the CPE drops from the original value of 11.14 down to 0.06, an overall performance gain of over 180×. This example demonstrates that modern processors have considerable amounts of computing power, but we may need to coax this power out of them by writing our programs in very stylized ways.

5.11   Some Limiting Factors

We have seen that the critical path in a data-flow graph representation of a program indicates a fundamental lower bound on the time required to execute a program. That is, if there is some chain of data dependencies in a program where the sum of all of the latencies along that chain equals T, then the program will require at least T cycles to execute.

We have also seen that the throughput bounds of the functional units also impose a lower bound on the execution time for a program. That is, assume that a program requires a total of N computations of some operation, that the microprocessor has C functional units capable of performing that operation, and that these units have an issue time of I. Then the program will require at least $N \cdot I / C$ cycles to execute.

In this section, we will consider some other factors that limit the performance of programs on actual machines.

5.11.1   Register Spilling

The benefits of loop parallelism are limited by the ability to express the computation in assembly code. If a program has a degree of parallelism P that exceeds the number of available registers, then the compiler will resort to *spilling*, storing some of the temporary values in memory, typically by allocating space on the run-time stack. As an example, the following measurements compare the result of extending the multiple accumulator scheme of combine6 to the cases of $k = 10$ and $k = 20$:

Function	Page	Method	Integer		Floating point	
			+	*	+	*
combine6	537					
		10 × 10 unrolling	0.55	1.00	1.01	0.52
		20 × 20 unrolling	0.83	1.03	1.02	0.68
Throughput bound			0.50	1.00	1.00	0.50

We can see that none of the CPEs improve with this increased unrolling, and some even get worse. Modern x86-64 processors have 16 integer registers and can make use of the 16 YMM registers to store floating-point data. Once the number of loop variables exceeds the number of available registers, the program must allocate some on the stack.

As an example, the following snippet of code shows how accumulator acc0 is updated in the inner loop of the code with 10×10 unrolling:

```
Updating of accumulator acc0 in 10 x 10 urolling
vmulsd  (%rdx), %xmm0, %xmm0        acc0 *= data[i]
```

We can see that the accumulator is kept in register %xmm0, and so the program can simply read data[i] from memory and multiply it by this register.

The comparable part of the code for 20×20 unrolling has a much different form:

```
Updating of accumulator acc0 in 20 x 20 unrolling
vmovsd  40(%rsp), %xmm0
vmulsd  (%rdx), %xmm0, %xmm0
vmovsd  %xmm0, 40(%rsp)
```

The accumulator is kept as a local variable on the stack, at offset 40 from the stack pointer. The program must read both its value and the value of data[i] from memory, multiply them, and store the result back to memory.

Once a compiler must resort to register spilling, any advantage of maintaining multiple accumulators will most likely be lost. Fortunately, x86-64 has enough registers that most loops will become throughput limited before this occurs.

5.11.2 Branch Prediction and Misprediction Penalties

We demonstrated via experiments in Section 3.6.6 that a conditional branch can incur a significant *misprediction penalty* when the branch prediction logic does not correctly anticipate whether or not a branch will be taken. Now that we have learned something about how processors operate, we can understand where this penalty arises.

Modern processors work well ahead of the currently executing instructions, reading new instructions from memory and decoding them to determine what operations to perform on what operands. This *instruction pipelining* works well as long as the instructions follow in a simple sequence. When a branch is encountered, the processor must guess which way the branch will go. For the case of a conditional jump, this means predicting whether or not the branch will be taken. For an instruction such as an indirect jump (as we saw in the code to jump to an address specified by a jump table entry) or a procedure return, this means predicting the target address. In this discussion, we focus on conditional branches.

In a processor that employs *speculative execution*, the processor begins executing the instructions at the predicted branch target. It does this in a way that avoids modifying any actual register or memory locations until the actual outcome has been determined. If the prediction is correct, the processor can then "commit" the results of the speculatively executed instructions by storing them in registers or memory. If the prediction is incorrect, the processor must discard all of the speculatively executed results and restart the instruction fetch process at the correct location. The misprediction penalty is incurred in doing this, because the instruction pipeline must be refilled before useful results are generated.

We saw in Section 3.6.6 that recent versions of x86 processors, including all processors capable of executing x86-64 programs, have *conditional move* instructions. GCC can generate code that uses these instructions when compiling conditional statements and expressions, rather than the more traditional realizations based on conditional transfers of control. The basic idea for translating into conditional moves is to compute the values along both branches of a conditional expression or statement and then use conditional moves to select the desired value. We saw in Section 4.5.7 that conditional move instructions can be implemented as part of the pipelined processing of ordinary instructions. There is no need to guess whether or not the condition will hold, and hence no penalty for guessing incorrectly.

How, then, can a C programmer make sure that branch misprediction penalties do not hamper a program's efficiency? Given the 19-cycle misprediction penalty we measured for the reference machine, the stakes are very high. There is no simple answer to this question, but the following general principles apply.

Do Not Be Overly Concerned about Predictable Branches

We have seen that the effect of a mispredicted branch can be very high, but that does not mean that all program branches will slow a program down. In fact, the branch prediction logic found in modern processors is very good at discerning regular patterns and long-term trends for the different branch instructions. For example, the loop-closing branches in our combining routines would typically be predicted as being taken, and hence would only incur a misprediction penalty on the last time around.

As another example, consider the results we observed when shifting from `combine2` to `combine3`, when we took the function `get_vec_element` out of the inner loop of the function, as is reproduced below:

Function	Page	Method	Integer		Floating point	
			+	*	+	*
combine2	509	Move `vec_length`	7.02	9.03	9.02	11.03
combine3	513	Direct data access	7.17	9.02	9.02	11.03

The CPE did not improve, even though the transformation eliminated two conditionals on each iteration that check whether the vector index is within bounds. For this function, the checks always succeed, and hence they are highly predictable.

As a way to measure the performance impact of bounds checking, consider the following combining code, where we have modified the inner loop of `combine4` by replacing the access to the data element with the result of performing an inline substitution of the code for `get_vec_element`. We will call this new version combine4b. This code performs bounds checking and also references the vector elements through the vector data structure.

```
1   /* Include bounds check in loop */
2   void combine4b(vec_ptr v, data_t *dest)
3   {
4       long i;
5       long length = vec_length(v);
6       data_t acc = IDENT;
7
8       for (i = 0; i < length; i++) {
9           if (i >= 0 && i < v->len) {
10              acc = acc OP v->data[i];
11          }
12      }
13      *dest = acc;
14  }
```

We can then directly compare the CPE for the functions with and without bounds checking:

Function	Page	Method	Integer		Floating point	
			+	*	+	*
combine4	515	No bounds checking	1.27	3.01	3.01	5.01
combine4b	515	Bounds checking	2.02	3.01	3.01	5.01

The version with bounds checking is slightly slower for the case of integer addition, but it achieves the same performance for the other three cases. The performance of these cases is limited by the latencies of their respective combining operations. The additional computation required to perform bounds checking can take place in parallel with the combining operations. The processor is able to predict the outcomes of these branches, and so none of this evaluation has much effect on the fetching and processing of the instructions that form the critical path in the program execution.

Write Code Suitable for Implementation with Conditional Moves

Branch prediction is only reliable for regular patterns. Many tests in a program are completely unpredictable, dependent on arbitrary features of the data, such as whether a number is negative or positive. For these, the branch prediction logic will do very poorly. For inherently unpredictable cases, program performance can be greatly enhanced if the compiler is able to generate code using conditional data transfers rather than conditional control transfers. This cannot be controlled directly by the C programmer, but some ways of expressing conditional behavior can be more directly translated into conditional moves than others.

We have found that GCC is able to generate conditional moves for code written in a more "functional" style, where we use conditional operations to compute values and then update the program state with these values, as opposed to a more "imperative" style, where we use conditionals to selectively update program state.

There are no strict rules for these two styles, and so we illustrate with an example. Suppose we are given two arrays of integers a and b, and at each position i, we want to set a[i] to the minimum of a[i] and b[i], and b[i] to the maximum.

An imperative style of implementing this function is to check at each position i and swap the two elements if they are out of order:

```
1   /* Rearrange two vectors so that for each i, b[i] >= a[i] */
2   void minmax1(long a[], long b[], long n) {
3       long i;
4       for (i = 0; i < n; i++) {
5           if (a[i] > b[i]) {
6               long t = a[i];
7               a[i] = b[i];
8               b[i] = t;
9           }
10      }
11  }
```

Our measurements for this function show a CPE of around 13.5 for random data and 2.5–3.5 for predictable data, an indication of a misprediction penalty of around 20 cycles.

A functional style of implementing this function is to compute the minimum and maximum values at each position i and then assign these values to a[i] and b[i], respectively:

```
1   /* Rearrange two vectors so that for each i, b[i] >= a[i] */
2   void minmax2(long a[], long b[], long n) {
3       long i;
4       for (i = 0; i < n; i++) {
5           long min = a[i] < b[i] ? a[i] : b[i];
6           long max = a[i] < b[i] ? b[i] : a[i];
7           a[i] = min;
8           b[i] = max;
9       }
10  }
```

Our measurements for this function show a CPE of around 4.0 regardless of whether the data are arbitrary or predictable. (We also examined the generated assembly code to make sure that it indeed uses conditional moves.)

As discussed in Section 3.6.6, not all conditional behavior can be implemented with conditional data transfers, and so there are inevitably cases where programmers cannot avoid writing code that will lead to conditional branches for which the processor will do poorly with its branch prediction. But, as we have shown, a little cleverness on the part of the programmer can sometimes make code more amenable to translation into conditional data transfers. This requires some amount of experimentation, writing different versions of the function and then examining the generated assembly code and measuring performance.

Practice Problem 5.9 (solution page 576)

The traditional implementation of the merge step of mergesort requires three loops [98]:

```
1    void merge(long src1[], long src2[], long dest[], long n) {
2        long i1 = 0;
3        long i2 = 0;
4        long id = 0;
5        while (i1 < n && i2 < n) {
6            if (src1[i1] < src2[i2])
7                dest[id++] = src1[i1++];
8            else
9                dest[id++] = src2[i2++];
10       }
11       while (i1 < n)
12           dest[id++] = src1[i1++];
13       while (i2 < n)
14           dest[id++] = src2[i2++];
15   }
```

The branches caused by comparing variables i1 and i2 to n have good prediction performance—the only mispredictions occur when they first become false. The comparison between values src1[i1] and src2[i2] (line 6), on the other hand, is highly unpredictable for typical data. This comparison controls a conditional branch, yielding a CPE (where the number of elements is $2n$) of around 15.0 when run on random data.

Rewrite the code so that the effect of the conditional statement in the first loop (lines 6–9) can be implemented with a conditional move.

5.12 Understanding Memory Performance

All of the code we have written thus far, and all the tests we have run, access relatively small amounts of memory. For example, the combining routines were measured over vectors of length less than 1,000 elements, requiring no more than 8,000 bytes of data. All modern processors contain one or more *cache* memories to provide fast access to such small amounts of memory. In this section, we will further investigate the performance of programs that involve load (reading from memory into registers) and store (writing from registers to memory) operations, considering only the cases where all data are held in cache. In Chapter 6, we go into much more detail about how caches work, their performance characteristics, and how to write code that makes best use of caches.

As Figure 5.11 shows, modern processors have dedicated functional units to perform load and store operations, and these units have internal buffers to hold sets of outstanding requests for memory operations. For example, our reference machine has two load units, each of which can hold up to 72 pending read requests. It has a single store unit with a store buffer containing up to 42 write requests. Each of these units can initiate 1 operation every clock cycle.

5.12.1 Load Performance

The performance of a program containing load operations depends on both the pipelining capability and the latency of the load unit. In our experiments with combining operations using our reference machine, we saw that the CPE never got below 0.50 for any combination of data type and combining operation, except when using SIMD operations. One factor limiting the CPE for our examples is that they all require reading one value from memory for each element computed. With two load units, each able to initiate at most 1 load operation every clock cycle, the CPE cannot be less than 0.50. For applications where we must load k values for every element computed, we can never achieve a CPE lower than $k/2$ (see, for example, Problem 5.15).

In our examples so far, we have not seen any performance effects due to the latency of load operations. The addresses for our load operations depended only on the loop index i, and so the load operations did not form part of a performance-limiting critical path.

To determine the latency of the load operation on a machine, we can set up a computation with a sequence of load operations, where the outcome of one determines the address for the next. As an example, consider the function list_len in Figure 5.31, which computes the length of a linked list. In the loop of this function, each successive value of variable ls depends on the value read by the pointer reference ls->next. Our measurements show that function list_len has

```
1   typedef struct ELE {
2       struct ELE *next;
3       long data;
4   } list_ele, *list_ptr;
5
6   long list_len(list_ptr ls) {
7       long len = 0;
8       while (ls) {
9           len++;
10          ls = ls->next;
11      }
12      return len;
13  }
```

Figure 5.31 Linked list function. Its performance is limited by the latency of the load operation.

a CPE of 4.00, which we claim is a direct indication of the latency of the load operation. To see this, consider the assembly code for the loop:

```
      Inner loop of list_len
      ls in %rdi, len in %rax
1     .L3:                         loop:
2         addq    $1, %rax         Increment len
3         movq    (%rdi), %rdi     ls = ls->next
4         testq   %rdi, %rdi       Test ls
5         jne     .L3              If nonnull, goto loop
```

The movq instruction on line 3 forms the critical bottleneck in this loop. Each successive value of register %rdi depends on the result of a load operation having the value in %rdi as its address. Thus, the load operation for one iteration cannot begin until the one for the previous iteration has completed. The CPE of 4.00 for this function is determined by the latency of the load operation. Indeed, this measurement matches the documented access time of 4 cycles for the reference machine's L1 cache, as is discussed in Section 6.4.

5.12.2   Store Performance

In all of our examples thus far, we analyzed only functions that reference memory mostly with load operations, reading from a memory location into a register. Its counterpart, the *store* operation, writes a register value to memory. The performance of this operation, particularly in relation to its interactions with load operations, involves several subtle issues.

As with the load operation, in most cases, the store operation can operate in a fully pipelined mode, beginning a new store on every cycle. For example, consider the function shown in Figure 5.32 that sets the elements of an array dest of length n to zero. Our measurements show a CPE of 1.0. This is the best we can achieve on a machine with a single store functional unit.

Unlike the other operations we have considered so far, the store operation does not affect any register values. Thus, by their very nature, a series of store operations cannot create a data dependency. Only a load operation is affected by the result of a store operation, since only a load can read back the memory value that has been written by the store. The function write_read shown in Figure 5.33

```
1     /* Set elements of array to 0 */
2     void clear_array(long *dest, long n) {
3         long i;
4         for (i = 0; i < n; i++)
5             dest[i] = 0;
6     }
```

Figure 5.32   Function to set array elements to 0. This code achieves a CPE of 1.0.

```
1    /* Write to dest, read from src */
2    void write_read(long *src, long *dst, long n)
3    {
4        long cnt = n;
5        long val = 0;
6
7        while (cnt) {
8            *dst = val;
9            val = (*src)+1;
10           cnt--;
11       }
12   }
```

Example A: `write_read(&a[0],&a[1],3)`

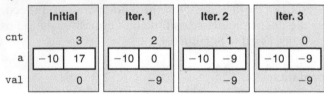

Example B: `write_read(&a[0],&a[0],3)`

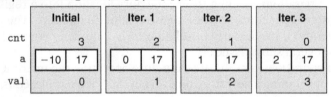

Figure 5.33 Code to write and read memory locations, along with illustrative executions. This function highlights the interactions between stores and loads when arguments src and dest are equal.

illustrates the potential interactions between loads and stores. This figure also shows two example executions of this function, when it is called for a two-element array a, with initial contents −10 and 17, and with argument cnt equal to 3. These executions illustrate some subtleties of the load and store operations.

In Example A of Figure 5.33, argument src is a pointer to array element a[0], while dest is a pointer to array element a[1]. In this case, each load by the pointer reference *src will yield the value −10. Hence, after two iterations, the array elements will remain fixed at −10 and −9, respectively. The result of the read from src is not affected by the write to dest. Measuring this example over a larger number of iterations gives a CPE of 1.3.

In Example B of Figure 5.33, both arguments src and dest are pointers to array element a[0]. In this case, each load by the pointer reference *src will yield the value stored by the previous execution of the pointer reference *dest.

Figure 5.34

Detail of load and store units. The store unit maintains a buffer of pending writes. The load unit must check its address with those in the store unit to detect a write/read dependency.

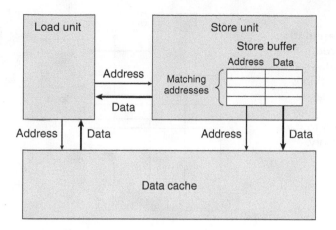

As a consequence, a series of ascending values will be stored in this location. In general, if function `write_read` is called with arguments `src` and `dest` pointing to the same memory location, and with argument `cnt` having some value $n > 0$, the net effect is to set the location to $n - 1$. This example illustrates a phenomenon we will call a *write/read dependency*—the outcome of a memory read depends on a recent memory write. Our performance measurements show that Example B has a CPE of 7.3. The write/read dependency causes a slowdown in the processing of around 6 clock cycles.

To see how the processor can distinguish between these two cases and why one runs slower than the other, we must take a more detailed look at the load and store execution units, as shown in Figure 5.34. The store unit includes a *store buffer* containing the addresses and data of the store operations that have been issued to the store unit, but have not yet been completed, where completion involves updating the data cache. This buffer is provided so that a series of store operations can be executed without having to wait for each one to update the cache. When a load operation occurs, it must check the entries in the store buffer for matching addresses. If it finds a match (meaning that any of the bytes being written have the same address as any of the bytes being read), it retrieves the corresponding data entry as the result of the load operation.

GCC generates the following code for the inner loop of `write_read`:

```
Inner loop of write_read
src in %rdi, dst in %rsi, val in %rax
.L3:                        loop:
    movq    %rax, (%rsi)      Write val to dst
    movq    (%rdi), %rax      t = *src
    addq    $1, %rax          val = t+1
    subq    $1, %rdx          cnt--
    jne     .L3               If != 0, goto loop
```

Figure 5.35

Graphical representation of inner-loop code for `write_read`**.** The first `movl` instruction is decoded into separate operations to compute the store address and to store the data to memory.

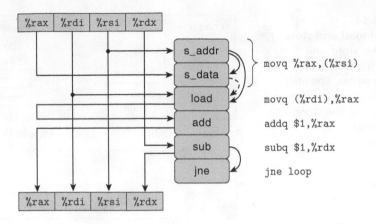

Figure 5.35 shows a data-flow representation of this loop code. The instruction `movq %rax,(%rsi)` is translated into two operations: The s_addr instruction computes the address for the store operation, creates an entry in the store buffer, and sets the address field for that entry. The s_data operation sets the data field for the entry. As we will see, the fact that these two computations are performed independently can be important to program performance. This motivates the separate functional units for these operations in the reference machine.

In addition to the data dependencies between the operations caused by the writing and reading of registers, the arcs on the right of the operators denote a set of implicit dependencies for these operations. In particular, the address computation of the s_addr operation must clearly precede the s_data operation. In addition, the load operation generated by decoding the instruction `movq (%rdi),` `%rax` must check the addresses of any pending store operations, creating a data dependency between it and the s_addr operation. The figure shows a dashed arc between the s_data and load operations. This dependency is conditional: if the two addresses match, the load operation must wait until the s_data has deposited its result into the store buffer, but if the two addresses differ, the two operations can proceed independently.

Figure 5.36 illustrates the data dependencies between the operations for the inner loop of `write_read`. In Figure 5.36(a), we have rearranged the operations to allow the dependencies to be seen more clearly. We have labeled the three dependencies involving the load and store operations for special attention. The arc labeled "1" represents the requirement that the store address must be computed before the data can be stored. The arc labeled "2" represents the need for the load operation to compare its address with that for any pending store operations. Finally, the dashed arc labeled "3" represents the conditional data dependency that arises when the load and store addresses match.

Figure 5.36(b) illustrates what happens when we take away those operations that do not directly affect the flow of data from one iteration to the next. The data-flow graph shows just two chains of dependencies: the one on the left, with data values being stored, loaded, and incremented (only for the case of matching addresses); and the one on the right, decrementing variable cnt.

Figure 5.36
Abstracting the operations for `write_read`. We first rearrange the operators of Figure 5.35(a) and then show only those operations that use values from one iteration to produce new values for the next (b).

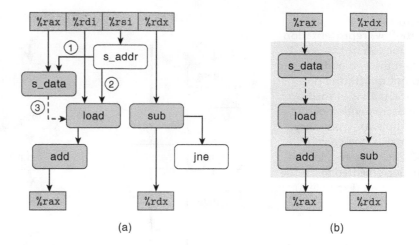

(a)   (b)

We can now understand the performance characteristics of function `write_read`. Figure 5.37 illustrates the data dependencies formed by multiple iterations of its inner loop. For the case of Example A in Figure 5.33, with differing source and destination addresses, the load and store operations can proceed independently, and hence the only critical path is formed by the decrementing of variable `cnt`, resulting in a CPE bound of 1.0. For the case of Example B with matching source and destination addresses, the data dependency between the `s_data` and `load` instructions causes a critical path to form involving data being stored, loaded, and incremented. We found that these three operations in sequence require a total of around 7 clock cycles.

As these two examples show, the implementation of memory operations involves many subtleties. With operations on registers, the processor can determine which instructions will affect which others as they are being decoded into operations. With memory operations, on the other hand, the processor cannot predict which will affect which others until the load and store addresses have been computed. Efficient handling of memory operations is critical to the performance of many programs. The memory subsystem makes use of many optimizations, such as the potential parallelism when operations can proceed independently.

Practice Problem 5.10 (solution page 577)

As another example of code with potential load-store interactions, consider the following function to copy the contents of one array to another:

```
1    void copy_array(long *src, long *dest, long n)
2    {
3        long i;
4        for (i = 0; i < n; i++)
5            dest[i] = src[i];
6    }
```

Figure 5.37
Data-flow representation of function `write_read`. When the two addresses do not match, the only critical path is formed by the decrementing of `cnt` (Example A). When they do match, the chain of data being stored, loaded, and incremented forms the critical path (Example B).

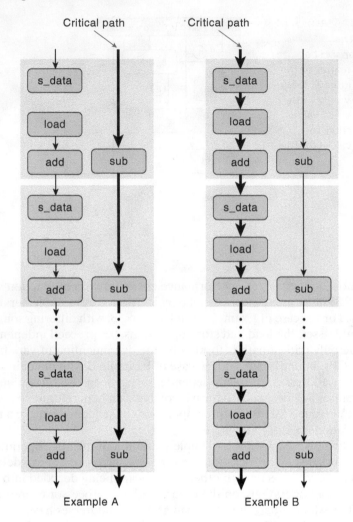

Suppose a is an array of length 1,000 initialized so that each element a[i] equals i.

A. What would be the effect of the call `copy_array(a+1,a,999)`?

B. What would be the effect of the call `copy_array(a,a+1,999)`?

C. Our performance measurements indicate that the call of part A has a CPE of 1.2 (which drops to 1.0 when the loop is unrolled by a factor of 4), while the call of part B has a CPE of 5.0. To what factor do you attribute this performance difference?

D. What performance would you expect for the call `copy_array(a,a,999)`?

Practice Problem 5.11 (solution page 577)

We saw that our measurements of the prefix-sum function psum1 (Figure 5.1) yield a CPE of 9.00 on a machine where the basic operation to be performed, floating-point addition, has a latency of just 3 clock cycles. Let us try to understand why our function performs so poorly.

The following is the assembly code for the inner loop of the function:

```
    Inner loop of psum1
    a in %rdi, i in %rax, cnt in %rdx
1   .L5:                                            loop:
2       vmovss  -4(%rsi,%rax,4), %xmm0              Get p[i-1]
3       vaddss  (%rdi,%rax,4), %xmm0, %xmm0         Add a[i]
4       vmovss  %xmm0, (%rsi,%rax,4)                Store at p[i]
5       addq    $1, %rax                            Increment i
6       cmpq    %rdx, %rax                          Compare i:cnt
7       jne     .L5                                 If !=, goto loop
```

Perform an analysis similar to those shown for combine3 (Figure 5.14) and for write_read (Figure 5.36) to diagram the data dependencies created by this loop, and hence the critical path that forms as the computation proceeds. Explain why the CPE is so high.

Practice Problem 5.12 (solution page 577)

Rewrite the code for psum1 (Figure 5.1) so that it does not need to repeatedly retrieve the value of p[i] from memory. You do not need to use loop unrolling. We measured the resulting code to have a CPE of 3.00, limited by the latency of floating-point addition.

5.13 Life in the Real World: Performance Improvement Techniques

Although we have only considered a limited set of applications, we can draw important lessons on how to write efficient code. We have described a number of basic strategies for optimizing program performance:

High-level design. Choose appropriate algorithms and data structures for the problem at hand. Be especially vigilant to avoid algorithms or coding techniques that yield asymptotically poor performance.

Basic coding principles. Avoid optimization blockers so that a compiler can generate efficient code.

  ■ Eliminate excessive function calls. Move computations out of loops when possible. Consider selective compromises of program modularity to gain greater efficiency.

- Eliminate unnecessary memory references. Introduce temporary variables to hold intermediate results. Store a result in an array or global variable only when the final value has been computed.

Low-level optimizations. Structure code to take advantage of the hardware capabilities.

- Unroll loops to reduce overhead and to enable further optimizations.
- Find ways to increase instruction-level parallelism by techniques such as multiple accumulators and reassociation.
- Rewrite conditional operations in a functional style to enable compilation via conditional data transfers.

A final word of advice to the reader is to be vigilant to avoid introducing errors as you rewrite programs in the interest of efficiency. It is very easy to make mistakes when introducing new variables, changing loop bounds, and making the code more complex overall. One useful technique is to use checking code to test each version of a function as it is being optimized, to ensure no bugs are introduced during this process. Checking code applies a series of tests to the new versions of a function and makes sure they yield the same results as the original. The set of test cases must become more extensive with highly optimized code, since there are more cases to consider. For example, checking code that uses loop unrolling requires testing for many different loop bounds to make sure it handles all of the different possible numbers of single-step iterations required at the end.

5.14 Identifying and Eliminating Performance Bottlenecks

Up to this point, we have only considered optimizing small programs, where there is some clear place in the program that limits its performance and therefore should be the focus of our optimization efforts. When working with large programs, even knowing where to focus our optimization efforts can be difficult. In this section, we describe how to use *code profilers*, analysis tools that collect performance data about a program as it executes. We also discuss some general principles of code optimization, including the implications of Amdahl's law, introduced in Section 1.9.1.

5.14.1 Program Profiling

Program *profiling* involves running a version of a program in which instrumentation code has been incorporated to determine how much time the different parts of the program require. It can be very useful for identifying the parts of a program we should focus on in our optimization efforts. One strength of profiling is that it can be performed while running the actual program on realistic benchmark data.

Unix systems provide the profiling program GPROF. This program generates two forms of information. First, it determines how much CPU time was spent for each of the functions in the program. Second, it computes a count of how many times each function gets called, categorized by which function performs the call. Both forms of information can be quite useful. The timings give a sense of the relative importance of the different functions in determining the overall run time. The calling information allows us to understand the dynamic behavior of the program.

Profiling with GPROF requires three steps, as shown for a C program `prog.c`, which runs with command-line argument `file.txt`:

1. The program must be compiled and linked for profiling. With GCC (and other C compilers), this involves simply including the run-time flag `-pg` on the command line. It is important to ensure that the compiler does not attempt to perform any optimizations via inline substitution, or else the calls to functions may not be tabulated accurately. We use optimization flag `-Og`, guaranteeing that function calls will be tracked properly.

   ```
   linux> gcc -Og -pg prog.c -o prog
   ```

2. The program is then executed as usual:

   ```
   linux> ./prog file.txt
   ```

   It runs slightly (around a factor of 2) slower than normal, but otherwise the only difference is that it generates a file `gmon.out`.

3. GPROF is invoked to analyze the data in `gmon.out`:

   ```
   linux> gprof prog
   ```

The first part of the profile report lists the times spent executing the different functions, sorted in descending order. As an example, the following listing shows this part of the report for the three most time-consuming functions in a program:

```
%     cumulative   self              self     total
time   seconds   seconds    calls  s/call   s/call  name
97.58    203.66   203.66        1  203.66   203.66  sort_words
 2.32    208.50     4.85   965027    0.00     0.00  find_ele_rec
 0.14    208.81     0.30 12511031    0.00     0.00  Strlen
```

Each row represents the time spent for all calls to some function. The first column indicates the percentage of the overall time spent on the function. The second shows the cumulative time spent by the functions up to and including the one on this row. The third shows the time spent on this particular function, and the fourth shows how many times it was called (not counting recursive calls). In our example, the function `sort_words` was called only once, but this single call required 203.66 seconds, while the function `find_ele_rec` was called 965,027 times (not including recursive calls), requiring a total of 4.85 seconds. Function `Strlen` computes the length of a string by calling the library function `strlen`. Library function calls are normally not shown in the results by GPROF. Their times are usually reported as part of the function calling them. By creating the "wrapper function" `Strlen`, we can reliably track the calls to `strlen`, showing that it was called 12,511,031 times but only requiring a total of 0.30 seconds.

The second part of the profile report shows the calling history of the functions. The following is the history for a recursive function find_ele_rec:

```
                               158655725                find_ele_rec [5]
                 4.85    0.10  965027/965027            insert_string [4]
   [5]     2.4   4.85    0.10  965027+158655725 find_ele_rec [5]
                 0.08    0.01  363039/363039            save_string [8]
                 0.00    0.01  363039/363039            new_ele [12]
                               158655725                find_ele_rec [5]
```

This history shows both the functions that called find_ele_rec, as well as the functions that it called. The first two lines show the calls to the function: 158,655,725 calls by itself recursively, and 965,027 calls by function insert_string (which is itself called 965,027 times). Function find_ele_rec, in turn, called two other functions, save_string and new_ele, each a total of 363,039 times.

From these call data, we can often infer useful information about the program behavior. For example, the function find_ele_rec is a recursive procedure that scans the linked list for a hash bucket looking for a particular string. For this function, comparing the number of recursive calls with the number of top-level calls provides statistical information about the lengths of the traversals through these lists. Given that their ratio is 164.4:1, we can infer that the program scanned an average of around 164 elements each time.

Some properties of GPROF are worth noting:

- The timing is not very precise. It is based on a simple *interval counting* scheme in which the compiled program maintains a counter for each function recording the time spent executing that function. The operating system causes the program to be interrupted at some regular time interval δ. Typical values of δ range between 1.0 and 10.0 milliseconds. It then determines what function the program was executing when the interrupt occurred and increments the counter for that function by δ. Of course, it may happen that this function just started executing and will shortly be completed, but it is assigned the full cost of the execution since the previous interrupt. Some other function may run between two interrupts and therefore not be charged any time at all.

  Over a long duration, this scheme works reasonably well. Statistically, every function should be charged according to the relative time spent executing it. For programs that run for less than around 1 second, however, the numbers should be viewed as only rough estimates.

- The calling information is quite reliable, assuming no inline substitutions have been performed. The compiled program maintains a counter for each combination of caller and callee. The appropriate counter is incremented every time a procedure is called.

- By default, the timings for library functions are not shown. Instead, these times are incorporated into the times for the calling functions.

5.14.2   Using a Profiler to Guide Optimization

As an example of using a profiler to guide program optimization, we created an application that involves several different tasks and data structures. This application analyzes the *n-gram* statistics of a text document, where an *n*-gram is a sequence of *n* words occurring in a document. For $n = 1$, we collect statistics on individual words, for $n = 2$ on pairs of words, and so on. For a given value of *n*, our program reads a text file, creates a table of unique *n*-grams and how many times each one occurs, then sorts the *n*-grams in descending order of occurrence.

As a benchmark, we ran it on a file consisting of the complete works of William Shakespeare, totaling 965,028 words, of which 23,706 are unique. We found that for $n = 1$, even a poorly written analysis program can readily process the entire file in under 1 second, and so we set $n = 2$ to make things more challenging. For the case of $n = 2$, *n*-grams are referred to as *bigrams* (pronounced "bye-grams"). We determined that Shakespeare's works contain 363,039 unique bigrams. The most common is "I am," occurring 1,892 times. Perhaps his most famous bigram, "to be," occurs 1,020 times. Fully 266,018 of the bigrams occur only once.

Our program consists of the following parts. We created multiple versions, starting with simple algorithms for the different parts and then replacing them with more sophisticated ones:

1. Each word is read from the file and converted to lowercase. Our initial version used the function `lower1` (Figure 5.7), which we know to have quadratic run time due to repeated calls to `strlen`.

2. A hash function is applied to the string to create a number between 0 and $s - 1$, for a hash table with *s* buckets. Our initial function simply summed the ASCII codes for the characters modulo *s*.

3. Each hash bucket is organized as a linked list. The program scans down this list looking for a matching entry. If one is found, the frequency for this *n*-gram is incremented. Otherwise, a new list element is created. Our initial version performed this operation recursively, inserting new elements at the end of the list.

4. Once the table has been generated, we sort all of the elements according to the frequencies. Our initial version used insertion sort.

Figure 5.38 shows the profile results for six different versions of our *n*-gram-frequency analysis program. For each version, we divide the time into the following categories:

Sort. Sorting *n*-grams by frequency

List. Scanning the linked list for a matching *n*-gram, inserting a new element if necessary

Lower. Converting strings to lowercase

Strlen. Computing string lengths

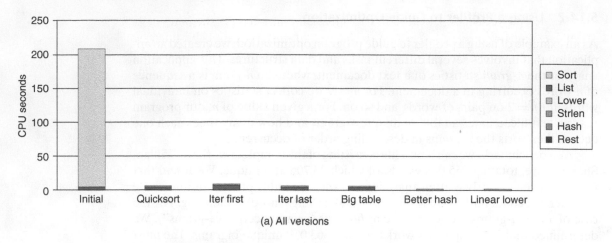

(a) All versions

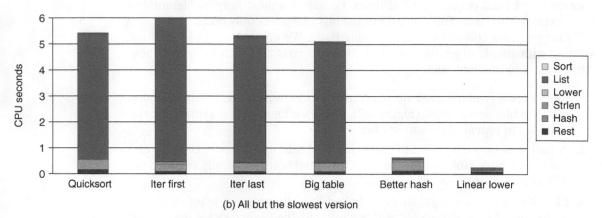

(b) All but the slowest version

Figure 5.38 Profile results for different versions of bigram-frequency counting program. Time is divided according to the different major operations in the program.

Hash. Computing the hash function

Rest. The sum of all other functions

As part (a) of the figure shows, our initial version required 3.5 minutes, with most of the time spent sorting. This is not surprising, since insertion sort has quadratic run time and the program sorted 363,039 values.

In our next version, we performed sorting using the library function qsort, which is based on the quicksort algorithm [98]. It has an expected run time of $O(n \log n)$. This version is labeled "Quicksort" in the figure. The more efficient sorting algorithm reduces the time spent sorting to become negligible, and the overall run time to around 5.4 seconds. Part (b) of the figure shows the times for the remaining version on a scale where we can see them more clearly.

With improved sorting, we now find that list scanning becomes the bottleneck. Thinking that the inefficiency is due to the recursive structure of the function, we replaced it by an iterative one, shown as "Iter first." Surprisingly, the run time increases to around 7.5 seconds. On closer study, we find a subtle difference between the two list functions. The recursive version inserted new elements at the end of the list, while the iterative one inserted them at the front. To maximize performance, we want the most frequent n-grams to occur near the beginning of the lists. That way, the function will quickly locate the common cases. Assuming that n-grams are spread uniformly throughout the document, we would expect the first occurrence of a frequent one to come before that of a less frequent one. By inserting new n-grams at the end, the first function tended to order n-grams in descending order of frequency, while the second function tended to do just the opposite. We therefore created a third list-scanning function that uses iteration but inserts new elements at the end of this list. With this version, shown as "Iter last," the time dropped to around 5.3 seconds, slightly better than with the recursive version. These measurements demonstrate the importance of running experiments on a program as part of an optimization effort. We initially assumed that converting recursive code to iterative code would improve its performance and did not consider the distinction between adding to the end or to the beginning of a list.

Next, we consider the hash table structure. The initial version had only 1,021 buckets (typically, the number of buckets is chosen to be a prime number to enhance the ability of the hash function to distribute keys uniformly among the buckets). For a table with 363,039 entries, this would imply an average *load* of $363,039/1,021 = 355.6$. That explains why so much of the time is spent performing list operations—the searches involve testing a significant number of candidate n-grams. It also explains why the performance is so sensitive to the list ordering. We then increased the number of buckets to 199,999, reducing the average load to 1.8. Oddly enough, however, our overall run time only drops to 5.1 seconds, a difference of only 0.2 seconds.

On further inspection, we can see that the minimal performance gain with a larger table was due to a poor choice of hash function. Simply summing the character codes for a string does not produce a very wide range of values. In particular, the maximum code value for a letter is 122, and so a string of n characters will generate a sum of at most $122n$. The longest bigram in our document, "honorificabilitudinitatibus thou" sums to just 3,371, and so most of the buckets in our hash table will go unused. In addition, a commutative hash function, such as addition, does not differentiate among the different possible orderings of characters with a string. For example, the words "rat" and "tar" will generate the same sums.

We switched to a hash function that uses shift and EXCLUSIVE-OR operations. With this version, shown as "Better hash," the time drops to 0.6 seconds. A more systematic approach would be to study the distribution of keys among the buckets more carefully, making sure that it comes close to what one would expect if the hash function had a uniform output distribution.

Finally, we have reduced the run time to the point where most of the time is spent in `strlen`, and most of the calls to `strlen` occur as part of the lowercase conversion. We have already seen that function `lower1` has quadratic performance, especially for long strings. The words in this document are short enough to avoid the disastrous consequences of quadratic performance; the longest bigram is just 32 characters. Still, switching to `lower2`, shown as "Linear lower," yields a significant improvement, with the overall time dropping to around 0.2 seconds.

With this exercise, we have shown that code profiling can help drop the time required for a simple application from 3.5 minutes down to 0.2 seconds, yielding a performance gain of around 1,000×. The profiler helps us focus our attention on the most time-consuming parts of the program and also provides useful information about the procedure call structure. Some of the bottlenecks in our code, such as using a quadratic sort routine, are easy to anticipate, while others, such as whether to append to the beginning or end of a list, emerge only through a careful analysis.

We can see that profiling is a useful tool to have in the toolbox, but it should not be the only one. The timing measurements are imperfect, especially for shorter (less than 1 second) run times. More significantly, the results apply only to the particular data tested. For example, if we had run the original function on data consisting of a smaller number of longer strings, we would have found that the lowercase conversion routine was the major performance bottleneck. Even worse, if it only profiled documents with short words, we might never detect hidden bottlenecks such as the quadratic performance of `lower1`. In general, profiling can help us optimize for *typical* cases, assuming we run the program on representative data, but we should also make sure the program will have respectable performance for all possible cases. This mainly involves avoiding algorithms (such as insertion sort) and bad programming practices (such as `lower1`) that yield poor asymptotic performance.

Amdahl's law, described in Section 1.9.1, provides some additional insights into the performance gains that can be obtained by targeted optimizations. For our n-gram code, we saw the total execution time drop from 209.0 to 5.4 seconds when we replaced insertion sort by quicksort. The initial version spent 203.7 of its 209.0 seconds performing insertion sort, giving $\alpha = 0.974$, the fraction of time subject to speedup. With quicksort, the time spent sorting becomes negligible, giving a predicted speedup of $209/\alpha = 39.0$, close to the measured speedup of 38.5. We were able to gain a large speedup because sorting constituted a very large fraction of the overall execution time. However, when one bottleneck is eliminated, a new one arises, and so gaining additional speedup required focusing on other parts of the program.

5.15 Summary

Although most presentations on code optimization describe how compilers can generate efficient code, much can be done by an application programmer to assist the compiler in this task. No compiler can replace an inefficient algorithm or data structure by a good one, and so these aspects of program design should remain a primary concern for programmers. We also have seen that optimization blockers, such as memory aliasing and procedure calls, seriously restrict the ability of compilers to perform extensive optimizations. Again, the programmer must take primary responsibility for eliminating these. These should simply be considered parts of good programming practice, since they serve to eliminate unneeded work.

Tuning performance beyond a basic level requires some understanding of the processor's microarchitecture, describing the underlying mechanisms by which the processor implements its instruction set architecture. For the case of out-of-order processors, just knowing something about the operations, capabilities, latencies, and issue times of the functional units establishes a baseline for predicting program performance.

We have studied a series of techniques—including loop unrolling, creating multiple accumulators, and reassociation—that can exploit the instruction-level parallelism provided by modern processors. As we get deeper into the optimization, it becomes important to study the generated assembly code and to try to understand how the computation is being performed by the machine. Much can be gained by identifying the critical paths determined by the data dependencies in the program, especially between the different iterations of a loop. We can also compute a throughput bound for a computation, based on the number of operations that must be computed and the number and issue times of the units that perform those operations.

Programs that involve conditional branches or complex interactions with the memory system are more difficult to analyze and optimize than the simple loop programs we first considered. The basic strategy is to try to make branches more predictable or make them amenable to implementation using conditional data transfers. We must also watch out for the interactions between store and load operations. Keeping values in local variables, allowing them to be stored in registers, can often be helpful.

When working with large programs, it becomes important to focus our optimization efforts on the parts that consume the most time. Code profilers and related tools can help us systematically evaluate and improve program performance. We described GPROF, a standard Unix profiling tool. More sophisticated profilers are available, such as the VTUNE program development system from Intel, and VALGRIND, commonly available on Linux systems. These tools can break down the execution time below the procedure level to estimate the performance of each *basic block* of the program. (A basic block is a sequence of instructions that has no transfers of control out of its middle, and so the block is always executed in its entirety.)

Bibliographic Notes

Our focus has been to describe code optimization from the programmer's perspective, demonstrating how to write code that will make it easier for compilers to generate efficient code. An extended paper by Chellappa, Franchetti, and Püschel [19] takes a similar approach but goes into more detail with respect to the processor's characteristics.

Many publications describe code optimization from a compiler's perspective, formulating ways that compilers can generate more efficient code. Muchnick's book is considered the most comprehensive [80]. Wadleigh and Crawford's book on software optimization [115] covers some of the material we have presented, but it also describes the process of getting high performance on parallel machines. An early paper by Mahlke et al. [75] describes how several techniques developed for compilers that map programs onto parallel machines can be adapted to exploit the instruction-level parallelism of modern processors. This paper covers the code transformations we presented, including loop unrolling, multiple accumulators (which they refer to as *accumulator variable expansion*), and reassociation (which they refer to as *tree height reduction*).

Our presentation of the operation of an out-of-order processor is fairly brief and abstract. More complete descriptions of the general principles can be found in advanced computer architecture textbooks, such as the one by Hennessy and Patterson [46, Ch. 2–3]. Shen and Lipasti's book [100] provides an in-depth treatment of modern processor design.

Homework Problems

5.13 ◆◆

Suppose we wish to write a procedure that computes the inner product of two vectors u and v. An abstract version of the function has a CPE of 14–18 with x86-64 for different types of integer and floating-point data. By doing the same sort of transformations we did to transform the abstract program combine1 into the more efficient combine4, we get the following code:

```
1    /* Inner product.  Accumulate in temporary */
2    void inner4(vec_ptr u, vec_ptr v, data_t *dest)
3    {
4        long i;
5        long length = vec_length(u);
6        data_t *udata = get_vec_start(u);
7        data_t *vdata = get_vec_start(v);
8        data_t sum = (data_t) 0;
9
10       for (i = 0; i < length; i++) {
11           sum = sum + udata[i] * vdata[i];
12       }
13       *dest = sum;
14   }
```

Our measurements show that this function has CPEs of 1.50 for integer data and 3.00 for floating-point data. For data type double, the x86-64 assembly code for the inner loop is as follows:

```
     Inner loop of inner4.  data_t = double, OP = *
     udata in %rbp, vdata in %rax, sum in %xmm0
     i in %rcx, limit in %rbx
1    .L15:                                        loop:
2      vmovsd  0(%rbp,%rcx,8), %xmm1                Get udata[i]
3      vmulsd  (%rax,%rcx,8), %xmm1, %xmm1          Multiply by vdata[i]
4      vaddsd  %xmm1, %xmm0, %xmm0                  Add to sum
5      addq    $1, %rcx                             Increment i
6      cmpq    %rbx, %rcx                           Compare i:limit
7      jne     .L15                                 If !=, goto loop
```

Assume that the functional units have the characteristics listed in Figure 5.12.

A. Diagram how this instruction sequence would be decoded into operations and show how the data dependencies between them would create a critical path of operations, in the style of Figures 5.13 and 5.14.

B. For data type double, what lower bound on the CPE is determined by the critical path?

C. Assuming similar instruction sequences for the integer code as well, what lower bound on the CPE is determined by the critical path for integer data?

D. Explain how the floating-point versions can have CPEs of 3.00, even though the multiplication operation requires 5 clock cycles.

5.14 ◆
Write a version of the inner product procedure described in Problem 5.13 that uses 6 × 1 loop unrolling. For x86-64, our measurements of the unrolled version give a CPE of 1.07 for integer data but still 3.01 for both floating-point data.

A. Explain why any (scalar) version of an inner product procedure running on an Intel Core i7 Haswell processor cannot achieve a CPE less than 1.00.

B. Explain why the performance for floating-point data did not improve with loop unrolling.

5.15 ◆
Write a version of the inner product procedure described in Problem 5.13 that uses 6 × 6 loop unrolling. Our measurements for this function with x86-64 give a CPE of 1.06 for integer data and 1.01 for floating-point data.
    What factor limits the performance to a CPE of 1.00?

5.16 ◆
Write a version of the inner product procedure described in Problem 5.13 that uses 6 × 1a loop unrolling to enable greater parallelism. Our measurements for this function give a CPE of 1.10 for integer data and 1.05 for floating-point data.

5.17 ◆◆
The library function memset has the following prototype:

```
void *memset(void *s, int c, size_t n);
```

This function fills n bytes of the memory area starting at s with copies of the low-order byte of c. For example, it can be used to zero out a region of memory by giving argument 0 for c, but other values are possible.

The following is a straightforward implementation of memset:

```
1   /* Basic implementation of memset */
2   void *basic_memset(void *s, int c, size_t n)
3   {
4       size_t cnt = 0;
5       unsigned char *schar = s;
6       while (cnt < n) {
7           *schar++ = (unsigned char) c;
8           cnt++;
9       }
10      return s;
11  }
```

Implement a more efficient version of the function by using a word of data type unsigned long to pack eight copies of c, and then step through the region using word-level writes. You might find it helpful to do additional loop unrolling as well. On our reference machine, we were able to reduce the CPE from 1.00 for the straightforward implementation to 0.127. That is, the program is able to write 8 bytes every clock cycle.

Here are some additional guidelines. To ensure portability, let K denote the value of sizeof(unsigned long) for the machine on which you run your program.

- You may not call any library functions.
- Your code should work for arbitrary values of n, including when it is not a multiple of K. You can do this in a manner similar to the way we finish the last few iterations with loop unrolling.
- You should write your code so that it will compile and run correctly on any machine regardless of the value of K. Make use of the operation sizeof to do this.
- On some machines, unaligned writes can be much slower than aligned ones. (On some non-x86 machines, they can even cause segmentation faults.) Write your code so that it starts with byte-level writes until the destination address is a multiple of K, then do word-level writes, and then (if necessary) finish with byte-level writes.
- Beware of the case where cnt is small enough that the upper bounds on some of the loops become negative. With expressions involving the sizeof operator, the testing may be performed with unsigned arithmetic. (See Section 2.2.8 and Problem 2.72.)

5.18 ◆◆◆

We considered the task of polynomial evaluation in Practice Problems 5.5 and 5.6, with both a direct evaluation and an evaluation by Horner's method. Try to write faster versions of the function using the optimization techniques we have explored, including loop unrolling, parallel accumulation, and reassociation. You will find many different ways of mixing together Horner's scheme and direct evaluation with these optimization techniques.

Ideally, you should be able to reach a CPE close to the throughput limit of your machine. Our best version achieves a CPE of 1.07 on our reference machine.

5.19 ◆◆◆

In Problem 5.12, we were able to reduce the CPE for the prefix-sum computation to 3.00, limited by the latency of floating-point addition on this machine. Simple loop unrolling does not improve things.

Using a combination of loop unrolling and reassociation, write code for a prefix sum that achieves a CPE less than the latency of floating-point addition on your machine. Doing this requires actually increasing the number of additions performed. For example, our version with two-way unrolling requires three additions per iteration, while our version with four-way unrolling requires five. Our best implementation achieves a CPE of 1.67 on our reference machine.

Determine how the throughput and latency limits of your machine limit the minimum CPE you can achieve for the prefix-sum operation.

Solutions to Practice Problems

Solution to Problem 5.1 (page 500)

This problem illustrates some of the subtle effects of memory aliasing.

As the following commented code shows, the effect will be to set the value at xp to zero:

```
4        *xp = *xp + *xp; /* 2x */
5        *xp = *xp - *xp; /* 2x-2x = 0 */
6        *xp = *xp - *xp; /* 0-0 = 0 */
```

This example illustrates that our intuition about program behavior can often be wrong. We naturally think of the case where xp and yp are distinct but overlook the possibility that they might be equal. Bugs often arise due to conditions the programmer does not anticipate.

Solution to Problem 5.2 (page 504)

This problem illustrates the relationship between CPE and absolute performance. It can be solved using elementary algebra. We find that for $n \leq 2$, version 1 is the fastest. Version 2 is fastest for $3 \leq n \leq 7$, and version 3 is fastest for $n \geq 8$.

Solution to Problem 5.3 (page 512)

This is a simple exercise, but it is important to recognize that the four statements of a for loop—initial, test, update, and body—get executed different numbers of times.

Code	min	max	incr	square
A.	1	91	90	90
B.	91	1	90	90
C.	1	1	90	90

Solution to Problem 5.4 (page 516)

This assembly code demonstrates a clever optimization opportunity detected by GCC. It is worth studying this code carefully to better understand the subtleties of code optimization.

A. In the less optimized code, register %xmm0 is simply used as a temporary value, both set and used on each loop iteration. In the more optimized code, it is used more in the manner of variable acc in combine4, accumulating the product of the vector elements. The difference with combine4, however, is that location dest is updated on each iteration by the second vmovsd instruction.

   We can see that this optimized version operates much like the following C code:

```
1    /* Make sure dest updated on each iteration */
2    void combine3w(vec_ptr v, data_t *dest)
3    {
4        long i;
5        long length = vec_length(v);
6        data_t *data = get_vec_start(v);
7        data_t acc = IDENT;
8
9        /* Initialize in event length <= 0 */
10       *dest = acc;
11
12       for (i = 0; i < length; i++) {
13           acc = acc OP data[i];
14           *dest = acc;
15       }
16   }
```

B. The two versions of combine3 will have identical functionality, even with memory aliasing.

C. This transformation can be made without changing the program behavior, because, with the exception of the first iteration, the value read from dest at the beginning of each iteration will be the same value written to this register at the end of the previous iteration. Therefore, the combining instruction can simply use the value already in %xmm0 at the beginning of the loop.

Solution to Problem 5.5 (page 530)

Polynomial evaluation is a core technique for solving many problems. For example, polynomial functions are commonly used to approximate trigonometric functions in math libraries.

A. The function performs $2n$ multiplications and n additions.

B. We can see that the performance-limiting computation here is the repeated computation of the expression xpwr = x * xpwr. This requires a floating-point multiplication (5 clock cycles), and the computation for one iteration cannot begin until the one for the previous iteration has completed. The updating of result only requires a floating-point addition (3 clock cycles) between successive iterations.

Solution to Problem 5.6 (page 530)

This problem demonstrates that minimizing the number of operations in a computation may not improve its performance.

A. The function performs n multiplications and n additions, half the number of multiplications as the original function poly.

B. We can see that the performance-limiting computation here is the repeated computation of the expression result = a[i] + x*result. Starting from the value of result from the previous iteration, we must first multiply it by x (5 clock cycles) and then add it to a[i] (3 cycles) before we have the value for this iteration. Thus, each iteration imposes a minimum latency of 8 cycles, exactly our measured CPE.

C. Although each iteration in function poly requires two multiplications rather than one, only a single multiplication occurs along the critical path per iteration.

Solution to Problem 5.7 (page 532)

The following code directly follows the rules we have stated for unrolling a loop by some factor k:

```
1    void unroll5(vec_ptr v, data_t *dest)
2    {
3        long i;
4        long length = vec_length(v);
5        long limit = length-4;
6        data_t *data = get_vec_start(v);
7        data_t acc = IDENT;
8
```

```
 9          /* Combine 5 elements at a time */
10          for (i = 0; i < limit; i+=5) {
11              acc = acc OP data[i]   OP data[i+1];
12              acc = acc OP data[i+2] OP data[i+3];
13              acc = acc OP data[i+4];
14          }
15
16          /* Finish any remaining elements */
17          for (; i < length; i++) {
18              acc = acc OP data[i];
19          }
20          *dest = acc;
21      }
```

Solution to Problem 5.8 (page 545)

This problem demonstrates how small changes in a program can yield dramatic performance differences, especially on a machine with out-of-order execution. Figure 5.39 diagrams the three multiplication operations for a single iteration of the function. In this figure, the operations shown as blue boxes are along the critical path—they need to be computed in sequence to compute a new value for loop variable r. The operations shown as light boxes can be computed in parallel with the critical path operations. For a loop with P operations along the critical path, each iteration will require a minimum of $5P$ clock cycles and will compute the product for three elements, giving a lower bound on the CPE of $5P/3$. This implies lower bounds of 5.00 for A1, 3.33 for A2 and A5, and 1.67 for A3 and A4. We ran these functions on an Intel Core i7 Haswell processor and found that it could achieve these CPE values.

Solution to Problem 5.9 (page 553)

This is another demonstration that a slight change in coding style can make it much easier for the compiler to detect opportunities to use conditional moves:

```
while (i1 < n && i2 < n) {
    long v1 = src1[i1];
```

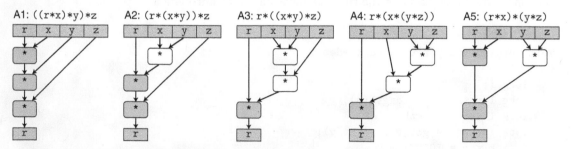

Figure 5.39 Data dependencies among multiplication operations for cases in Problem 5.8. The operations shown as blue boxes form the critical paths for the iterations.

```
        long v2 = src2[i2];
        long take1 = v1 < v2;
        dest[id++] = take1 ? v1 : v2;
        i1 += take1;
        i2 += (1-take1);
    }
```

We measured a CPE of around 12.0 for this version of the code, a modest improvement over the original CPE of 15.0.

Solution to Problem 5.10 (page 559)

This problem requires you to analyze the potential load-store interactions in a program.

A. It will set each element $a[i]$ to $i + 1$, for $0 \leq i \leq 998$.

B. It will set each element $a[i]$ to 0, for $1 \leq i \leq 999$.

C. In the second case, the load of one iteration depends on the result of the store from the previous iteration. Thus, there is a write/read dependency between successive iterations.

D. It will give a CPE of 1.2, the same as for Example A, since there are no dependencies between stores and subsequent loads.

Solution to Problem 5.11 (page 561)

We can see that this function has a write/read dependency between successive iterations—the destination value p[i] on one iteration matches the source value p[i-1] on the next. A critical path is therefore formed for each iteration consisting of a store (from the previous iteration), a load, and a floating-point addition. The CPE measurement of 9.0 is consistent with our measurement of 7.3 for the CPE of write_read when there is a data dependency, since write_read involves an integer addition (1 clock-cycle latency), while psum1 involves a floating-point addition (3 clock-cycle latency).

Solution to Problem 5.12 (page 561)

Here is a revised version of the function:

```
1   void psum1a(float a[], float p[], long n)
2   {
3       long i;
4       /* last_val holds p[i-1]; val holds p[i] */
5       float last_val, val;
6       last_val = p[0] = a[0];
7       for (i = 1; i < n; i++) {
8           val  = last_val + a[i];
9           p[i] = val;
10          last_val = val;
11      }
12  }
```

We introduce a local variable last_val. At the start of iteration i, it holds the value of p[i-1]. We then compute val to be the value of p[i] and to be the new value for last_val.

This version compiles to the following assembly code:

```
Inner loop of psum1a
a in %rdi, i in %rax, cnt in %rdx, last_val in %xmm0
1   .L16:                                      loop:
2     vaddss   (%rdi,%rax,4), %xmm0, %xmm0     last_val = val = last_val + a[i]
3     vmovss   %xmm0, (%rsi,%rax,4)            Store val in p[i]
4     addq     $1, %rax                        Increment i
5     cmpq     %rdx, %rax                      Compare i:cnt
6     jne      .L16                            If !=, goto loop
```

This code holds last_val in %xmm0, avoiding the need to read p[i-1] from memory and thus eliminating the write/read dependency seen in psum1.

CHAPTER 6

The Memory Hierarchy

To this point in our study of systems, we have relied on a simple model of a computer system as a CPU that executes instructions and a memory system that holds instructions and data for the CPU. In our simple model, the memory system is a linear array of bytes, and the CPU can access each memory location in a constant amount of time. While this is an effective model up to a point, it does not reflect the way that modern systems really work.

In practice, a *memory system* is a hierarchy of storage devices with different capacities, costs, and access times. CPU registers hold the most frequently used data. Small, fast *cache memories* nearby the CPU act as staging areas for a subset of the data and instructions stored in the relatively slow main memory. The main memory stages data stored on large, slow disks, which in turn often serve as staging areas for data stored on the disks or tapes of other machines connected by networks.

Memory hierarchies work because well-written programs tend to access the storage at any particular level more frequently than they access the storage at the next lower level. So the storage at the next level can be slower, and thus larger and cheaper per bit. The overall effect is a large pool of memory that costs as much as the cheap storage near the bottom of the hierarchy but that serves data to programs at the rate of the fast storage near the top of the hierarchy.

As a programmer, you need to understand the memory hierarchy because it has a big impact on the performance of your applications. If the data your program needs are stored in a CPU register, then they can be accessed in 0 cycles during the execution of the instruction. If stored in a cache, 4 to 75 cycles. If stored in main memory, hundreds of cycles. And if stored in disk, tens of millions of cycles!

Here, then, is a fundamental and enduring idea in computer systems: if you understand how the system moves data up and down the memory hierarchy, then you can write your application programs so that their data items are stored higher in the hierarchy, where the CPU can access them more quickly.

This idea centers around a fundamental property of computer programs known as *locality*. Programs with good locality tend to access the same set of data items over and over again, or they tend to access sets of nearby data items. Programs with good locality tend to access more data items from the upper levels of the memory hierarchy than programs with poor locality, and thus run faster. For example, on our Core i7 system, the running times of different matrix multiplication kernels that perform the same number of arithmetic operations, but have different degrees of locality, can vary by a factor of almost 40!

In this chapter, we will look at the basic storage technologies—SRAM memory, DRAM memory, ROM memory, and rotating and solid state disks—and describe how they are organized into hierarchies. In particular, we focus on the cache memories that act as staging areas between the CPU and main memory, because they have the most impact on application program performance. We show you how to analyze your C programs for locality, and we introduce techniques for improving the locality in your programs. You will also learn an interesting way to characterize the performance of the memory hierarchy on a particular machine as a "memory mountain" that shows read access times as a function of locality.

6.1   Storage Technologies

Much of the success of computer technology stems from the tremendous progress in storage technology. Early computers had a few kilobytes of random access memory. The earliest IBM PCs didn't even have a hard disk. That changed with the introduction of the IBM PC-XT in 1982, with its 10-megabyte disk. By the year 2015, typical machines had 300,000 times as much disk storage, and the amount of storage was increasing by a factor of 2 every couple of years.

6.1.1   Random Access Memory

Random access memory (RAM) comes in two varieties—static and dynamic. *Static RAM (SRAM)* is faster and significantly more expensive than *dynamic RAM (DRAM)*. SRAM is used for cache memories, both on and off the CPU chip. DRAM is used for the main memory plus the frame buffer of a graphics system. Typically, a desktop system will have no more than a few tens of megabytes of SRAM, but hundreds or thousands of megabytes of DRAM.

Static RAM

SRAM stores each bit in a *bistable* memory cell. Each cell is implemented with a six-transistor circuit. This circuit has the property that it can stay indefinitely in either of two different voltage configurations, or *states*. Any other state will be unstable—starting from there, the circuit will quickly move toward one of the stable states. Such a memory cell is analogous to the inverted pendulum illustrated in Figure 6.1.

The pendulum is stable when it is tilted either all the way to the left or all the way to the right. From any other position, the pendulum will fall to one side or the other. In principle, the pendulum could also remain balanced in a vertical position indefinitely, but this state is *metastable*—the smallest disturbance would make it start to fall, and once it fell it would never return to the vertical position.

Due to its bistable nature, an SRAM memory cell will retain its value indefinitely, as long as it is kept powered. Even when a disturbance, such as electrical noise, perturbs the voltages, the circuit will return to the stable value when the disturbance is removed.

Figure 6.1
Inverted pendulum.
Like an SRAM cell, the pendulum has only two stable configurations, or *states*.

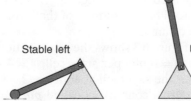
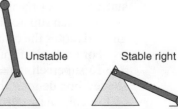

Stable left   Unstable   Stable right

	Transistors per bit	Relative access time	Persistent?	Sensitive?	Relative cost	Applications
SRAM	6	1×	Yes	No	1,000×	Cache memory
DRAM	1	10×	No	Yes	1×	Main memory, frame buffers

Figure 6.2   Characteristics of DRAM and SRAM memory.

Dynamic RAM

DRAM stores each bit as charge on a capacitor. This capacitor is very small—typically around 30 femtofarads—that is, 30×10^{-15} farads. Recall, however, that a farad is a very large unit of measure. DRAM storage can be made very dense—each cell consists of a capacitor and a single access transistor. Unlike SRAM, however, a DRAM memory cell is very sensitive to any disturbance. When the capacitor voltage is disturbed, it will never recover. Exposure to light rays will cause the capacitor voltages to change. In fact, the sensors in digital cameras and camcorders are essentially arrays of DRAM cells.

Various sources of leakage current cause a DRAM cell to lose its charge within a time period of around 10 to 100 milliseconds. Fortunately, for computers operating with clock cycle times measured in nanoseconds, this retention time is quite long. The memory system must periodically refresh every bit of memory by reading it out and then rewriting it. Some systems also use error-correcting codes, where the computer words are encoded using a few more bits (e.g., a 64-bit word might be encoded using 72 bits), such that circuitry can detect and correct any single erroneous bit within a word.

Figure 6.2 summarizes the characteristics of SRAM and DRAM memory. SRAM is persistent as long as power is applied. Unlike DRAM, no refresh is necessary. SRAM can be accessed faster than DRAM. SRAM is not sensitive to disturbances such as light and electrical noise. The trade-off is that SRAM cells use more transistors than DRAM cells and thus have lower densities, are more expensive, and consume more power.

Conventional DRAMs

The cells (bits) in a DRAM chip are partitioned into d *supercells*, each consisting of w DRAM cells. A $d \times w$ DRAM stores a total of dw bits of information. The supercells are organized as a rectangular array with r rows and c columns, where $rc = d$. Each supercell has an address of the form (i, j), where i denotes the row and j denotes the column.

For example, Figure 6.3 shows the organization of a 16×8 DRAM chip with $d = 16$ supercells, $w = 8$ bits per supercell, $r = 4$ rows, and $c = 4$ columns. The shaded box denotes the supercell at address $(2, 1)$. Information flows in and out of the chip via external connectors called *pins*. Each pin carries a 1-bit signal. Figure 6.3 shows two of these sets of pins: eight data pins that can transfer 1 byte

Aside   A note on terminology

The storage community has never settled on a standard name for a DRAM array element. Computer architects tend to refer to it as a "cell," overloading the term with the DRAM storage cell. Circuit designers tend to refer to it as a "word," overloading the term with a word of main memory. To avoid confusion, we have adopted the unambiguous term "supercell."

Figure 6.3

High-level view of a 128-bit 16 × 8 DRAM chip.

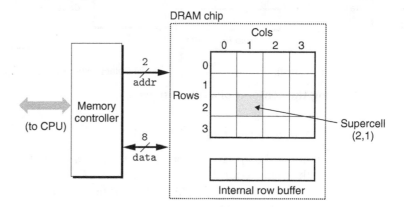

in or out of the chip, and two `addr` pins that carry two-bit row and column supercell addresses. Other pins that carry control information are not shown.

Each DRAM chip is connected to some circuitry, known as the *memory controller*, that can transfer w bits at a time to and from each DRAM chip. To read the contents of supercell (i, j), the memory controller sends the row address i to the DRAM, followed by the column address j. The DRAM responds by sending the contents of supercell (i, j) back to the controller. The row address i is called a *RAS (row access strobe) request*. The column address j is called a *CAS (column access strobe) request*. Notice that the RAS and CAS requests share the same DRAM address pins.

For example, to read supercell $(2, 1)$ from the 16×8 DRAM in Figure 6.3, the memory controller sends row address 2, as shown in Figure 6.4(a). The DRAM responds by copying the entire contents of row 2 into an internal row buffer. Next, the memory controller sends column address 1, as shown in Figure 6.4(b). The DRAM responds by copying the 8 bits in supercell $(2, 1)$ from the row buffer and sending them to the memory controller.

One reason circuit designers organize DRAMs as two-dimensional arrays instead of linear arrays is to reduce the number of address pins on the chip. For example, if our example 128-bit DRAM were organized as a linear array of 16 supercells with addresses 0 to 15, then the chip would need four address pins instead of two. The disadvantage of the two-dimensional array organization is that addresses must be sent in two distinct steps, which increases the access time.

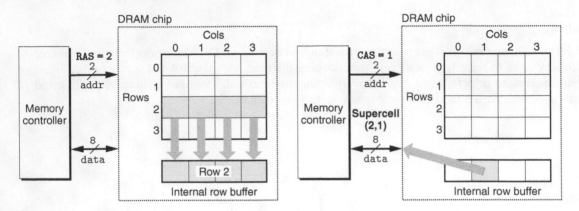

(a) Select row 2 (RAS request). (b) Select column 1 (CAS request).

Figure 6.4 Reading the contents of a DRAM supercell.

Memory Modules

DRAM chips are packaged in *memory modules* that plug into expansion slots on the main system board (motherboard). Core i7 systems use the 240-pin *dual inline memory module (DIMM)*, which transfers data to and from the memory controller in 64-bit chunks.

Figure 6.5 shows the basic idea of a memory module. The example module stores a total of 64 MB (megabytes) using eight 64-Mbit 8M × 8 DRAM chips, numbered 0 to 7. Each supercell stores 1 byte of *main memory*, and each 64-bit word at byte address A in main memory is represented by the eight supercells whose corresponding supercell address is (i, j). In the example in Figure 6.5, DRAM 0 stores the first (lower-order) byte, DRAM 1 stores the next byte, and so on.

To retrieve the word at memory address A, the memory controller converts A to a supercell address (i, j) and sends it to the memory module, which then broadcasts i and j to each DRAM. In response, each DRAM outputs the 8-bit contents of its (i, j) supercell. Circuitry in the module collects these outputs and forms them into a 64-bit word, which it returns to the memory controller.

Main memory can be aggregated by connecting multiple memory modules to the memory controller. In this case, when the controller receives an address A, the controller selects the module k that contains A, converts A to its (i, j) form, and sends (i, j) to module k.

Practice Problem 6.1 (solution page 660)

In the following, let r be the number of rows in a DRAM array, c the number of columns, b_r the number of bits needed to address the rows, and b_c the number of bits needed to address the columns. For each of the following DRAMs, determine the power-of-2 array dimensions that minimize $\max(b_r, b_c)$, the maximum number of bits needed to address the rows or columns of the array.

Figure 6.5
Reading the contents of a memory module.

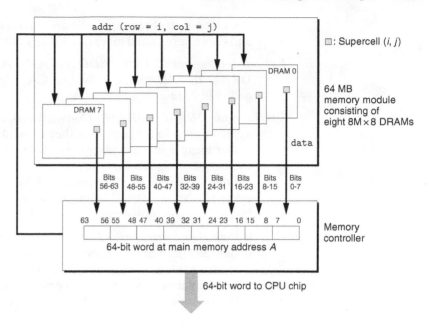

Organization	r	c	b_r	b_c	$\max(b_r, b_c)$
16×1					
16×4					
128×8					
512×4					
$1{,}024 \times 4$					

Enhanced DRAMs

There are many kinds of DRAM memories, and new kinds appear on the market with regularity as manufacturers attempt to keep up with rapidly increasing processor speeds. Each is based on the conventional DRAM cell, with optimizations that improve the speed with which the basic DRAM cells can be accessed.

Fast page mode DRAM (FPM DRAM). A conventional DRAM copies an entire row of supercells into its internal row buffer, uses one, and then discards the rest. FPM DRAM improves on this by allowing consecutive accesses to the same row to be served directly from the row buffer. For example, to read four supercells from row i of a conventional DRAM, the memory controller must send four RAS/CAS requests, even though the row address i is identical in each case. To read supercells from the same row of an FPM DRAM, the memory controller sends an initial RAS/CAS request, followed by three CAS requests. The initial RAS/CAS request copies row i into the row buffer and returns the supercell addressed by the

CAS. The next three supercells are served directly from the row buffer, and thus are returned more quickly than the initial supercell.

Extended data out DRAM (EDO DRAM). An enhanced form of FPM DRAM that allows the individual CAS signals to be spaced closer together in time.

Synchronous DRAM (SDRAM). Conventional, FPM, and EDO DRAMs are asynchronous in the sense that they communicate with the memory controller using a set of explicit control signals. SDRAM replaces many of these control signals with the rising edges of the same external clock signal that drives the memory controller. Without going into detail, the net effect is that an SDRAM can output the contents of its supercells at a faster rate than its asynchronous counterparts.

Double Data-Rate Synchronous DRAM (DDR SDRAM). DDR SDRAM is an enhancement of SDRAM that doubles the speed of the DRAM by using both clock edges as control signals. Different types of DDR SDRAMs are characterized by the size of a small prefetch buffer that increases the effective bandwidth: DDR (2 bits), DDR2 (4 bits), and DDR3 (8 bits).

Video RAM (VRAM). Used in the frame buffers of graphics systems. VRAM is similar in spirit to FPM DRAM. Two major differences are that (1) VRAM output is produced by shifting the entire contents of the internal buffer in sequence and (2) VRAM allows concurrent reads and writes to the memory. Thus, the system can be painting the screen with the pixels in the frame buffer (reads) while concurrently writing new values for the next update (writes).

Nonvolatile Memory

DRAMs and SRAMs are *volatile* in the sense that they lose their information if the supply voltage is turned off. *Nonvolatile memories*, on the other hand, retain their information even when they are powered off. There are a variety of nonvolatile memories. For historical reasons, they are referred to collectively as *read-only memories* (ROMs), even though some types of ROMs can be written to as well as read. ROMs are distinguished by the number of times they can be reprogrammed (written to) and by the mechanism for reprogramming them.

Aside Historical popularity of DRAM technologies

Until 1995, most PCs were built with FPM DRAMs. From 1996 to 1999, EDO DRAMs dominated the market, while FPM DRAMs all but disappeared. SDRAMs first appeared in 1995 in high-end systems, and by 2002 most PCs were built with SDRAMs and DDR SDRAMs. By 2010, most server and desktop systems were built with DDR3 SDRAMs. In fact, the Intel Core i7 supports only DDR3 SDRAM.

A *programmable ROM (PROM)* can be programmed exactly once. PROMs include a sort of fuse with each memory cell that can be blown once by zapping it with a high current.

An *erasable programmable ROM (EPROM)* has a transparent quartz window that permits light to reach the storage cells. The EPROM cells are cleared to zeros by shining ultraviolet light through the window. Programming an EPROM is done by using a special device to write ones into the EPROM. An EPROM can be erased and reprogrammed on the order of 1,000 times. An *electrically erasable PROM (EEPROM)* is akin to an EPROM, but it does not require a physically separate programming device, and thus can be reprogrammed in-place on printed circuit cards. An EEPROM can be reprogrammed on the order of 10^5 times before it wears out.

Flash memory is a type of nonvolatile memory, based on EEPROMs, that has become an important storage technology. Flash memories are everywhere, providing fast and durable nonvolatile storage for a slew of electronic devices, including digital cameras, cell phones, and music players, as well as laptop, desktop, and server computer systems. In Section 6.1.3, we will look in detail at a new form of flash-based disk drive, known as a *solid state disk (SSD)*, that provides a faster, sturdier, and less power-hungry alternative to conventional rotating disks.

Programs stored in ROM devices are often referred to as *firmware*. When a computer system is powered up, it runs firmware stored in a ROM. Some systems provide a small set of primitive input and output functions in firmware—for example, a PC's BIOS (basic input/output system) routines. Complicated devices such as graphics cards and disk drive controllers also rely on firmware to translate I/O (input/output) requests from the CPU.

Accessing Main Memory

Data flows back and forth between the processor and the DRAM main memory over shared electrical conduits called *buses*. Each transfer of data between the CPU and memory is accomplished with a series of steps called a *bus transaction*. A *read transaction* transfers data from the main memory to the CPU. A *write transaction* transfers data from the CPU to the main memory.

A *bus* is a collection of parallel wires that carry address, data, and control signals. Depending on the particular bus design, data and address signals can share the same set of wires or can use different sets. Also, more than two devices can share the same bus. The control wires carry signals that synchronize the transaction and identify what kind of transaction is currently being performed. For example, is this transaction of interest to the main memory, or to some other I/O device such as a disk controller? Is the transaction a read or a write? Is the information on the bus an address or a data item?

Figure 6.6 shows the configuration of an example computer system. The main components are the CPU chip, a chipset that we will call an *I/O bridge* (which includes the memory controller), and the DRAM memory modules that make up main memory. These components are connected by a pair of buses: a *system bus* that connects the CPU to the I/O bridge, and a *memory bus* that connects the I/O

Aside A note on bus designs

Bus design is a complex and rapidly changing aspect of computer systems. Different vendors develop different bus architectures as a way to differentiate their products. For example, some Intel systems use chipsets known as the *northbridge* and the *southbridge* to connect the CPU to memory and I/O devices, respectively. In older Pentium and Core 2 systems, a *front side bus* (FSB) connects the CPU to the northbridge. Systems from AMD replace the FSB with the *HyperTransport* interconnect, while newer Intel Core i7 systems use the *QuickPath* interconnect. The details of these different bus architectures are beyond the scope of this text. Instead, we will use the high-level bus architecture from Figure 6.6 as a running example throughout. It is a simple but useful abstraction that allows us to be concrete. It captures the main ideas without being tied too closely to the detail of any proprietary designs.

Figure 6.6

Example bus structure that connects the CPU and main memory.

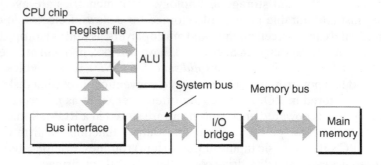

bridge to the main memory. The I/O bridge translates the electrical signals of the system bus into the electrical signals of the memory bus. As we will see, the I/O bridge also connects the system bus and memory bus to an *I/O bus* that is shared by I/O devices such as disks and graphics cards. For now, though, we will focus on the memory bus.

Consider what happens when the CPU performs a load operation such as

```
movq A,%rax
```

where the contents of address *A* are loaded into register %rax. Circuitry on the CPU chip called the *bus interface* initiates a read transaction on the bus. The read transaction consists of three steps. First, the CPU places the address *A* on the system bus. The I/O bridge passes the signal along to the memory bus (Figure 6.7(a)). Next, the main memory senses the address signal on the memory bus, reads the address from the memory bus, fetches the data from the DRAM, and writes the data to the memory bus. The I/O bridge translates the memory bus signal into a system bus signal and passes it along to the system bus (Figure 6.7(b)). Finally, the CPU senses the data on the system bus, reads the data from the bus, and copies the data to register %rax (Figure 6.7(c)).

Conversely, when the CPU performs a store operation such as

```
movq %rax,A
```

Figure 6.7
Memory read transaction for a load operation: `movq A,%rax`.

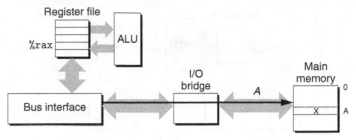

(a) CPU places address *A* on the memory bus.

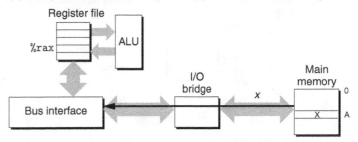

(b) Main memory reads *A* from the bus, retrieves word *x*, and places it on the bus.

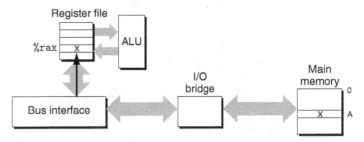

(c) CPU reads word *x* from the bus, and copies it into register `%rax`.

where the contents of register `%rax` are written to address *A*, the CPU initiates a write transaction. Again, there are three basic steps. First, the CPU places the address on the system bus. The memory reads the address from the memory bus and waits for the data to arrive (Figure 6.8(a)). Next, the CPU copies the data in `%rax` to the system bus (Figure 6.8(b)). Finally, the main memory reads the data from the memory bus and stores the bits in the DRAM (Figure 6.8(c)).

6.1.2   Disk Storage

Disks are workhorse storage devices that hold enormous amounts of data, on the order of hundreds to thousands of gigabytes, as opposed to the hundreds or thousands of megabytes in a RAM-based memory. However, it takes on the order of milliseconds to read information from a disk, a hundred thousand times longer than from DRAM and a million times longer than from SRAM.

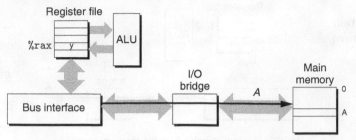

(a) CPU places address *A* on the memory bus. Main memory reads it and waits for the data word.

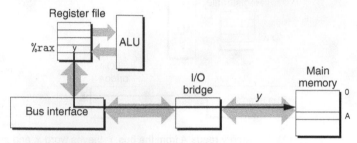

(b) CPU places data word *y* on the bus.

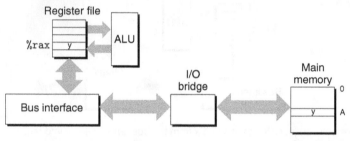

(c) Main memory reads data word *y* from the bus and stores it at address *A*.

Figure 6.8   Memory write transaction for a store operation: movq %rax, A.

Disk Geometry

Disks are constructed from *platters*. Each platter consists of two sides, or *surfaces*, that are coated with magnetic recording material. A rotating *spindle* in the center of the platter spins the platter at a fixed *rotational rate*, typically between 5,400 and 15,000 *revolutions per minute (RPM)*. A disk will typically contain one or more of these platters encased in a sealed container.

Figure 6.9(a) shows the geometry of a typical disk surface. Each surface consists of a collection of concentric rings called *tracks*. Each track is partitioned into a collection of *sectors*. Each sector contains an equal number of data bits (typically 512 bytes) encoded in the magnetic material on the sector. Sectors are separated by *gaps* where no data bits are stored. Gaps store formatting bits that identify sectors.

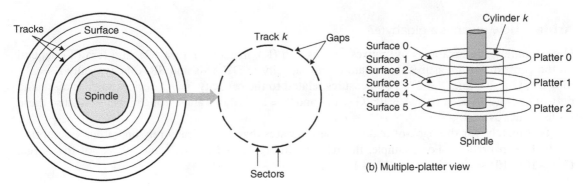

(a) Single-platter view

Figure 6.9   Disk geometry.

A disk consists of one or more platters stacked on top of each other and encased in a sealed package, as shown in Figure 6.9(b). The entire assembly is often referred to as a *disk drive*, although we will usually refer to it as simply a *disk*. We will sometimes refer to disks as *rotating disks* to distinguish them from flash-based solid state disks (SSDs), which have no moving parts.

Disk manufacturers describe the geometry of multiple-platter drives in terms of *cylinders*, where a cylinder is the collection of tracks on all the surfaces that are equidistant from the center of the spindle. For example, if a drive has three platters and six surfaces, and the tracks on each surface are numbered consistently, then cylinder k is the collection of the six instances of track k.

Disk Capacity

The maximum number of bits that can be recorded by a disk is known as its *maximum capacity*, or simply *capacity*. Disk capacity is determined by the following technology factors:

Recording density (bits/in). The number of bits that can be squeezed into a 1-inch segment of a track.

Track density (tracks/in). The number of tracks that can be squeezed into a 1-inch segment of the radius extending from the center of the platter.

Areal density (bits/in^2). The product of the recording density and the track density.

Disk manufacturers work tirelessly to increase areal density (and thus capacity), and this is doubling every couple of years. The original disks, designed in an age of low areal density, partitioned every track into the same number of sectors, which was determined by the number of sectors that could be recorded on the innermost track. To maintain a fixed number of sectors per track, the sectors were spaced farther apart on the outer tracks. This was a reasonable approach

Aside   How much is a gigabyte?

Unfortunately, the meanings of prefixes such as kilo (K), mega (M), giga (G), and tera (T) depend on the context. For measures that relate to the capacity of DRAMs and SRAMs, typically $K = 2^{10}$, $M = 2^{20}$, $G = 2^{30}$, and $T = 2^{40}$. For measures related to the capacity of I/O devices such as disks and networks, typically $K = 10^3$, $M = 10^6$, $G = 10^9$, and $T = 10^{12}$. Rates and throughputs usually use these prefix values as well.

Fortunately, for the back-of-the-envelope estimates that we typically rely on, either assumption works fine in practice. For example, the relative difference between 2^{30} and 10^9 is not that large: $(2^{30} - 10^9)/10^9 \approx 7\%$. Similarly, $(2^{40} - 10^{12})/10^{12} \approx 10\%$.

when areal densities were relatively low. However, as areal densities increased, the gaps between sectors (where no data bits were stored) became unacceptably large. Thus, modern high-capacity disks use a technique known as *multiple zone recording*, where the set of cylinders is partitioned into disjoint subsets known as *recording zones*. Each zone consists of a contiguous collection of cylinders. Each track in each cylinder in a zone has the same number of sectors, which is determined by the number of sectors that can be packed into the innermost track of the zone.

The capacity of a disk is given by the following formula:

$$\text{Capacity} = \frac{\text{\# bytes}}{\text{sector}} \times \frac{\text{average \# sectors}}{\text{track}} \times \frac{\text{\# tracks}}{\text{surface}} \times \frac{\text{\# surfaces}}{\text{platter}} \times \frac{\text{\# platters}}{\text{disk}}$$

For example, suppose we have a disk with five platters, 512 bytes per sector, 20,000 tracks per surface, and an average of 300 sectors per track. Then the capacity of the disk is

$$\text{Capacity} = \frac{512 \text{ bytes}}{\text{sector}} \times \frac{300 \text{ sectors}}{\text{track}} \times \frac{20{,}000 \text{ tracks}}{\text{surface}} \times \frac{2 \text{ surfaces}}{\text{platter}} \times \frac{5 \text{ platters}}{\text{disk}}$$

$$= 30{,}720{,}000{,}000 \text{ bytes}$$

$$= 30.72 \text{ GB}$$

Notice that manufacturers express disk capacity in units of gigabytes (GB) or terabytes (TB), where $1 \text{ GB} = 10^9$ bytes and $1 \text{ TB} = 10^{12}$ bytes.

Practice Problem 6.2 (solution page 661)

What is the capacity of a disk with 2 platters, 10,000 cylinders, an average of 400 sectors per track, and 512 bytes per sector?

Disk Operation

Disks read and write bits stored on the magnetic surface using a *read/write head* connected to the end of an *actuator arm*, as shown in Figure 6.10(a). By moving

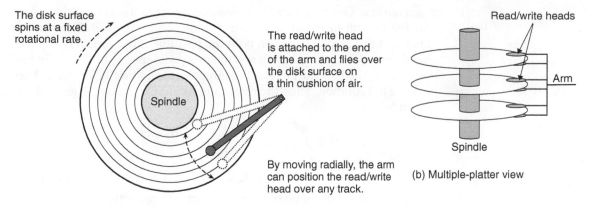

The disk surface spins at a fixed rotational rate.

The read/write head is attached to the end of the arm and flies over the disk surface on a thin cushion of air.

Spindle

By moving radially, the arm can position the read/write head over any track.

Read/write heads

Arm

Spindle

(b) Multiple-platter view

(a) Single-platter view

Figure 6.10   Disk dynamics.

the arm back and forth along its radial axis, the drive can position the head over any track on the surface. This mechanical motion is known as a *seek*. Once the head is positioned over the desired track, then, as each bit on the track passes underneath, the head can either sense the value of the bit (read the bit) or alter the value of the bit (write the bit). Disks with multiple platters have a separate read/write head for each surface, as shown in Figure 6.10(b). The heads are lined up vertically and move in unison. At any point in time, all heads are positioned on the same cylinder.

The read/write head at the end of the arm flies (literally) on a thin cushion of air over the disk surface at a height of about 0.1 microns and a speed of about 80 km/h. This is analogous to placing a skyscraper on its side and flying it around the world at a height of 2.5 cm (1 inch) above the ground, with each orbit of the earth taking only 8 seconds! At these tolerances, a tiny piece of dust on the surface is like a huge boulder. If the head were to strike one of these boulders, the head would cease flying and crash into the surface (a so-called head crash). For this reason, disks are always sealed in airtight packages.

Disks read and write data in sector-size blocks. The *access time* for a sector has three main components: *seek time*, *rotational latency*, and *transfer time:*

Seek time. To read the contents of some target sector, the arm first positions the head over the track that contains the target sector. The time required to move the arm is called the *seek time*. The seek time, T_{seek}, depends on the previous position of the head and the speed that the arm moves across the surface. The average seek time in modern drives, $T_{\text{avg seek}}$, measured by taking the mean of several thousand seeks to random sectors, is typically on the order of 3 to 9 ms. The maximum time for a single seek, $T_{\text{max seek}}$, can be as high as 20 ms.

Rotational latency. Once the head is in position over the track, the drive waits for the first bit of the target sector to pass under the head. The performance of this step depends on both the position of the surface when the head arrives at the target track and the rotational speed of the disk. In the worst case, the head just misses the target sector and waits for the disk to make a full rotation. Thus, the maximum rotational latency, in seconds, is given by

$$T_{\text{max rotation}} = \frac{1}{\text{RPM}} \times \frac{60 \text{ secs}}{1 \text{ min}}$$

The average rotational latency, $T_{\text{avg rotation}}$, is simply half of $T_{\text{max rotation}}$.

Transfer time. When the first bit of the target sector is under the head, the drive can begin to read or write the contents of the sector. The transfer time for one sector depends on the rotational speed and the number of sectors per track. Thus, we can roughly estimate the average transfer time for one sector in seconds as

$$T_{\text{avg transfer}} = \frac{1}{\text{RPM}} \times \frac{1}{(\text{average \# sectors/track})} \times \frac{60 \text{ secs}}{1 \text{ min}}$$

We can estimate the average time to access the contents of a disk sector as the sum of the average seek time, the average rotational latency, and the average transfer time. For example, consider a disk with the following parameters:

Parameter	Value
Rotational rate	7,200 RPM
$T_{\text{avg seek}}$	9 ms
Average number of sectors/track	400

For this disk, the average rotational latency (in ms) is

$$T_{\text{avg rotation}} = 1/2 \times T_{\text{max rotation}}$$
$$= 1/2 \times (60 \text{ secs}/7{,}200 \text{ RPM}) \times 1{,}000 \text{ ms/sec}$$
$$\approx 4 \text{ ms}$$

The average transfer time is

$$T_{\text{avg transfer}} = 60/7{,}200 \text{ RPM} \times 1/400 \text{ sectors/track} \times 1{,}000 \text{ ms/sec}$$
$$\approx 0.02 \text{ ms}$$

Putting it all together, the total estimated access time is

$$T_{\text{access}} = T_{\text{avg seek}} + T_{\text{avg rotation}} + T_{\text{avg transfer}}$$
$$= 9 \text{ ms} + 4 \text{ ms} + 0.02 \text{ ms}$$
$$= 13.02 \text{ ms}$$

This example illustrates some important points:

- The time to access the 512 bytes in a disk sector is dominated by the seek time and the rotational latency. Accessing the first byte in the sector takes a long time, but the remaining bytes are essentially free.
- Since the seek time and rotational latency are roughly the same, twice the seek time is a simple and reasonable rule for estimating disk access time.
- The access time for a 64-bit word stored in SRAM is roughly 4 ns, and 60 ns for DRAM. Thus, the time to read a 512-byte sector-size block from memory is roughly 256 ns for SRAM and 4,000 ns for DRAM. The disk access time, roughly 10 ms, is about 40,000 times greater than SRAM, and about 2,500 times greater than DRAM.

Practice Problem 6.3 (solution page 661)

Estimate the average time (in ms) to access a sector on the following disk:

Parameter	Value
Rotational rate	15,000 RPM
$T_{avg\ seek}$	8 ms
Average number of sectors/track	500

Logical Disk Blocks

As we have seen, modern disks have complex geometries, with multiple surfaces and different recording zones on those surfaces. To hide this complexity from the operating system, modern disks present a simpler view of their geometry as a sequence of B sector-size *logical blocks*, numbered $0, 1, \ldots, B - 1$. A small hardware/firmware device in the disk package, called the *disk controller*, maintains the mapping between logical block numbers and actual (physical) disk sectors.

When the operating system wants to perform an I/O operation such as reading a disk sector into main memory, it sends a command to the disk controller asking it to read a particular logical block number. Firmware on the controller performs a fast table lookup that translates the logical block number into a *(surface, track, sector)* triple that uniquely identifies the corresponding physical sector. Hardware on the controller interprets this triple to move the heads to the appropriate cylinder, waits for the sector to pass under the head, gathers up the bits sensed by the head into a small memory buffer on the controller, and copies them into main memory.

Practice Problem 6.4 (solution page 661)

Suppose that a 1 MB file consisting of 512-byte logical blocks is stored on a disk drive with the following characteristics:

Aside Formatted disk capacity

Before a disk can be used to store data, it must be *formatted* by the disk controller. This involves filling in the gaps between sectors with information that identifies the sectors, identifying any cylinders with surface defects and taking them out of action, and setting aside a set of cylinders in each zone as spares that can be called into action if one or more cylinders in the zone goes bad during the lifetime of the disk. The *formatted capacity* quoted by disk manufacturers is less than the maximum capacity because of the existence of these spare cylinders.

Parameter	Value
Rotational rate	10,000 RPM
$T_{\text{avg seek}}$	5 ms
Average number of sectors/track	1,000
Surfaces	4
Sector size	512 bytes

For each case below, suppose that a program reads the logical blocks of the file sequentially, one after the other, and that the time to position the head over the first block is $T_{\text{avg seek}} + T_{\text{avg rotation}}$.

A. *Best case:* Estimate the optimal time (in ms) required to read the file given the best possible mapping of logical blocks to disk sectors (i.e., sequential).

B. *Random case:* Estimate the time (in ms) required to read the file if blocks are mapped randomly to disk sectors.

Connecting I/O Devices

Input/output (I/O) devices such as graphics cards, monitors, mice, keyboards, and disks are connected to the CPU and main memory using an *I/O bus*. Unlike the system bus and memory buses, which are CPU-specific, I/O buses are designed to be independent of the underlying CPU. Figure 6.11 shows a representative I/O bus structure that connects the CPU, main memory, and I/O devices.

Although the I/O bus is slower than the system and memory buses, it can accommodate a wide variety of third-party I/O devices. For example, the bus in Figure 6.11 has three different types of devices attached to it.

- A *Universal Serial Bus (USB)* controller is a conduit for devices attached to a USB bus, which is a wildly popular standard for connecting a variety of peripheral I/O devices, including keyboards, mice, modems, digital cameras, game controllers, printers, external disk drives, and solid state disks. USB 3.0 buses have a maximum bandwidth of 625 MB/s. USB 3.1 buses have a maximum bandwidth of 1,250 MB/s.

Figure 6.11

Example bus structure that connects the CPU, main memory, and I/O devices.

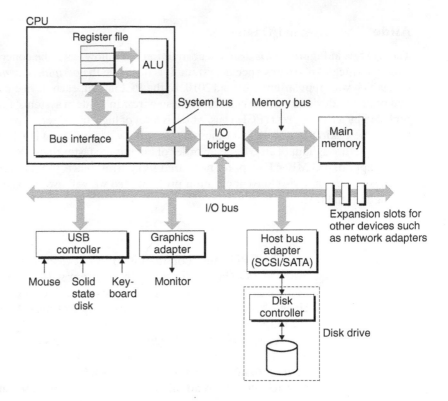

- A *graphics card* (or *adapter*) contains hardware and software logic that is responsible for painting the pixels on the display monitor on behalf of the CPU.
- A *host bus adapter* that connects one or more disks to the I/O bus using a communication protocol defined by a particular *host bus interface*. The two most popular such interfaces for disks are *SCSI* (pronounced "scuzzy") and *SATA* (pronounced "sat-uh"). SCSI disks are typically faster and more expensive than SATA drives. A SCSI host bus adapter (often called a *SCSI controller*) can support multiple disk drives, as opposed to SATA adapters, which can only support one drive.

Additional devices such as *network adapters* can be attached to the I/O bus by plugging the adapter into empty *expansion slots* on the motherboard that provide a direct electrical connection to the bus.

Accessing Disks

While a detailed description of how I/O devices work and how they are programmed is outside our scope here, we can give you a general idea. For example, Figure 6.12 summarizes the steps that take place when a CPU reads data from a disk.

Aside Advances in I/O bus designs

The I/O bus in Figure 6.11 is a simple abstraction that allows us to be concrete, without being tied too closely to the details of any specific system. It is based on the *peripheral component interconnect (PCI)* bus, which was popular until around 2010. In the PCI model, each device in the system shares the bus, and only one device at a time can access these wires. In modern systems, the shared PCI bus has been replaced by a *PCI express* (PCIe) bus, which is a set of high-speed serial, point-to-point links connected by switches, akin to the switched Ethernets that you will learn about in Chapter 11. A PCIe bus, with a maximum throughput of 16 GB/s, is an order of magnitude faster than a PCI bus, which has a maximum throughput of 533 MB/s. Except for measured I/O performance, the differences between the different bus designs are not visible to application programs, so we will use the simple shared bus abstraction throughout the text.

The CPU issues commands to I/O devices using a technique called *memory-mapped I/O* (Figure 6.12(a)). In a system with memory-mapped I/O, a block of addresses in the address space is reserved for communicating with I/O devices. Each of these addresses is known as an *I/O port*. Each device is associated with (or mapped to) one or more ports when it is attached to the bus.

As a simple example, suppose that the disk controller is mapped to port 0xa0. Then the CPU might initiate a disk read by executing three store instructions to address 0xa0: The first of these instructions sends a command word that tells the disk to initiate a read, along with other parameters such as whether to interrupt the CPU when the read is finished. (We will discuss interrupts in Section 8.1.) The second instruction indicates the logical block number that should be read. The third instruction indicates the main memory address where the contents of the disk sector should be stored.

After it issues the request, the CPU will typically do other work while the disk is performing the read. Recall that a 1 GHz processor with a 1 ns clock cycle can potentially execute 16 million instructions in the 16 ms it takes to read the disk. Simply waiting and doing nothing while the transfer is taking place would be enormously wasteful.

After the disk controller receives the read command from the CPU, it translates the logical block number to a sector address, reads the contents of the sector, and transfers the contents directly to main memory, without any intervention from the CPU (Figure 6.12(b)). This process, whereby a device performs a read or write bus transaction on its own, without any involvement of the CPU, is known as *direct memory access* (DMA). The transfer of data is known as a *DMA transfer*.

After the DMA transfer is complete and the contents of the disk sector are safely stored in main memory, the disk controller notifies the CPU by sending an interrupt signal to the CPU (Figure 6.12(c)). The basic idea is that an interrupt signals an external pin on the CPU chip. This causes the CPU to stop what it is currently working on and jump to an operating system routine. The routine records the fact that the I/O has finished and then returns control to the point where the CPU was interrupted.

Figure 6.12
Reading a disk sector.

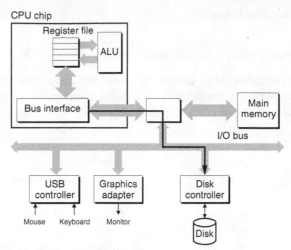

(a) The CPU initiates a disk read by writing a command, logical block number, and destination memory address to the memory-mapped address associated with the disk.

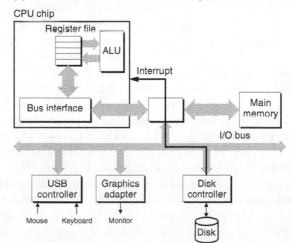

(b) The disk controller reads the sector and performs a DMA transfer into main memory.

(c) When the DMA transfer is complete, the disk controller notifies the CPU with an interrupt.

Aside Characteristics of a commercial disk drive

Disk manufacturers publish a lot of useful high-level technical information on their Web sites. For example, the Seagate Web site contains the following information (and much more!) about one of their popular drives, the Barracuda 7400. (Seagate.com)

Geometry characteristic	Value	Geometry characteristic	Value
Surface diameter	3.5 in	Rotational rate	7,200 RPM
Formatted capacity	3 TB	Average rotational latency	4.16 ms
Platters	3	Average seek time	8.5 ms
Surfaces	6	Track-to-track seek time	1.0 ms
Logical blocks	5,860,533,168	Average transfer rate	156 MB/s
Logical block size	512 bytes	Maximum sustained transfer rate	210 MB/s

Figure 6.13
Solid state disk (SSD).

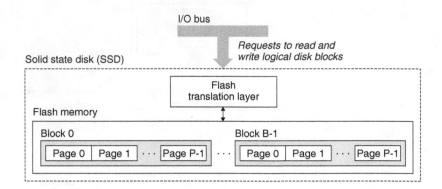

6.1.3 Solid State Disks

A solid state disk (SSD) is a storage technology, based on flash memory (Section 6.1.1), that in some situations is an attractive alternative to the conventional rotating disk. Figure 6.13 shows the basic idea. An SSD package plugs into a standard disk slot on the I/O bus (typically USB or SATA) and behaves like any other disk, processing requests from the CPU to read and write logical disk blocks. An SSD package consists of one or more flash memory chips, which replace the mechanical drive in a conventional rotating disk, and a *flash translation layer*, which is a hardware/firmware device that plays the same role as a disk controller, translating requests for logical blocks into accesses of the underlying physical device.

Figure 6.14 shows the performance characteristics of a typical SSD. Notice that reading from SSDs is faster than writing. The difference between random reading and writing performance is caused by a fundamental property of the underlying flash memory. As shown in Figure 6.13, a flash memory consists of a sequence of B *blocks*, where each block consists of P pages. Typically, pages are 512 bytes to 4 KB in size, and a block consists of 32–128 pages, with total block sizes ranging from 16

Reads		Writes	
Sequential read throughput	550 MB/s	Sequential write throughput	470 MB/s
Random read throughput (IOPS)	89,000 IOPS	Random write throughput (IOPS)	74,000 IOPS
Random read throughput (MB/s)	365 MB/s	Random write throughput (MB/s)	303 MB/s
Avg. sequential read access time	50 μs	Avg. sequential write access time	60 μs

Figure 6.14   Performance characteristics of a commercial solid state disk. Source: Intel SSD 730 product specification [53]. *IOPS* is I/O operations per second. Throughput numbers are based on reads and writes of 4 KB blocks. (Intel SSD 730 product specification. Intel Corporation. 52.)

KB to 512 KB. Data are read and written in units of pages. A page can be written only after the entire block to which it belongs has been *erased* (typically, this means that all bits in the block are set to 1). However, once a block is erased, each page in the block can be written once with no further erasing. A block wears out after roughly 100,000 repeated writes. Once a block wears out, it can no longer be used.

Random writes are slower for two reasons. First, erasing a block takes a relatively long time, on the order of 1 ms, which is more than an order of magnitude longer than it takes to access a page. Second, if a write operation attempts to modify a page p that contains existing data (i.e., not all ones), then any pages in the same block with useful data must be copied to a new (erased) block before the write to page p can occur. Manufacturers have developed sophisticated logic in the flash translation layer that attempts to amortize the high cost of erasing blocks and to minimize the number of internal copies on writes, but it is unlikely that random writing will ever perform as well as reading.

SSDs have a number of advantages over rotating disks. They are built of semiconductor memory, with no moving parts, and thus have much faster random access times than rotating disks, use less power, and are more rugged. However, there are some disadvantages. First, because flash blocks wear out after repeated writes, SSDs have the potential to wear out as well. *Wear-leveling* logic in the flash translation layer attempts to maximize the lifetime of each block by spreading erasures evenly across all blocks. In practice, the wear-leveling logic is so good that it takes many years for SSDs to wear out (see Practice Problem 6.5). Second, SSDs are about 30 times more expensive per byte than rotating disks, and thus the typical storage capacities are significantly less than rotating disks. However, SSD prices are decreasing rapidly as they become more popular, and the gap between the two is decreasing.

SSDs have completely replaced rotating disks in portable music devices, are popular as disk replacements in laptops, and have even begun to appear in desktops and servers. While rotating disks are here to stay, it is clear that SSDs are an important alternative.

Practice Problem 6.5 (solution page 662)

As we have seen, a potential drawback of SSDs is that the underlying flash memory can wear out. For example, for the SSD in Figure 6.14, Intel guarantees about

128 petabytes (128×10^{15} bytes) of writes before the drive wears out. Given this assumption, estimate the lifetime (in years) of this SSD for the following workloads:

A. *Worst case for sequential writes:* The SSD is written to continuously at a rate of 470 MB/s (the average sequential write throughput of the device).

B. *Worst case for random writes:* The SSD is written to continuously at a rate of 303 MB/s (the average random write throughput of the device).

C. *Average case:* The SSD is written to at a rate of 20 GB/day (the average daily write rate assumed by some computer manufacturers in their mobile computer workload simulations).

6.1.4 Storage Technology Trends

There are several important concepts to take away from our discussion of storage technologies.

Different storage technologies have different price and performance trade-offs. SRAM is somewhat faster than DRAM, and DRAM is much faster than disk. On the other hand, fast storage is always more expensive than slower storage. SRAM costs more per byte than DRAM. DRAM costs much more than disk. SSDs split the difference between DRAM and rotating disk.

The price and performance properties of different storage technologies are changing at dramatically different rates. Figure 6.15 summarizes the price and performance properties of storage technologies since 1985, shortly after the first PCs were introduced. The numbers were culled from back issues of trade magazines and the Web. Although they were collected in an informal survey, the numbers reveal some interesting trends.

Since 1985, both the cost and performance of SRAM technology have improved at roughly the same rate. Access times and cost per megabyte have decreased by a factor of about 100 (Figure 6.15(a)). However, the trends for DRAM and disk are much more dramatic and divergent. While the cost per megabyte of DRAM has decreased by a factor of 44,000 (more than four orders of magnitude!), DRAM access times have decreased by only a factor of 10 (Figure 6.15(b)). Disk technology has followed the same trend as DRAM and in even more dramatic fashion. While the cost of a megabyte of disk storage has plummeted by a factor of more than 3,000,000 (more than six orders of magnitude!) since 1980, access times have improved much more slowly, by only a factor of 25 (Figure 6.15(c)). These startling long-term trends highlight a basic truth of memory and disk technology: it is much easier to increase density (and thereby reduce cost) than to decrease access time.

DRAM and disk performance are lagging behind CPU performance. As we see in Figure 6.15(d), CPU cycle times improved by a factor of 500 between 1985 and 2010. If we look at the *effective cycle time* —which we define to be the cycle time of an individual CPU (processor) divided by the number of its processor cores— then the improvement between 1985 and 2010 is even greater, a factor of 2,000.

Metric	1985	1990	1995	2000	2005	2010	2015	2015:1985
$/MB	2,900	320	256	100	75	60	25	116
Access (ns)	150	35	15	3	2	1.5	1.3	115

(a) SRAM trends

Metric	1985	1990	1995	2000	2005	2010	2015	2015:1985
$/MB	880	100	30	1	0.1	0.06	0.02	44,000
Access (ns)	200	100	70	60	50	40	20	10
Typical size (MB)	0.256	4	16	64	2,000	8,000	16,000	62,500

(b) DRAM trends

Metric	1985	1990	1995	2000	2005	2010	2015	2015:1985
$/GB	100,000	8,000	300	10	5	0.3	0.03	3,333,333
Min. seek time (ms)	75	28	10	8	5	3	3	25
Typical size (GB)	0.01	0.16	1	20	160	1,500	3,000	300,000

(c) Rotating disk trends

Metric	1985	1990	1995	2000	2003	2005	2010	2015	2015:1985
Intel CPU	80286	80386	Pent.	P-III	Pent. 4	Core 2	Core i7 (n)	Core i7 (h)	—
Clock rate (MHz)	6	20	150	600	3,300	2,000	2,500	3,000	500
Cycle time (ns)	166	50	6	1.6	0.3	0.5	0.4	0.33	500
Cores	1	1	1	1	1	2	4	4	4
Effective cycle time (ns)	166	50	6	1.6	0.30	0.25	0.10	0.08	2,075

(d) CPU trends

Figure 6.15 Storage and processing technology trends. The Core i7 circa 2010 uses the Nehalem processor core. The Core i7 circa 2015 uses the Haswell core.

The split in the CPU performance curve around 2003 reflects the introduction of multi-core processors (see aside on page 605). After this split, cycle times of individual cores actually increased a bit before starting to decrease again, albeit at a slower rate than before.

Note that while SRAM performance lags, it is roughly keeping up. However, the gap between DRAM and disk performance and CPU performance is actually widening. Until the advent of multi-core processors around 2003, this performance gap was a function of latency, with DRAM and disk access times decreasing more slowly than the cycle time of an individual processor. However, with the introduction of multiple cores, this performance gap is increasingly a function of

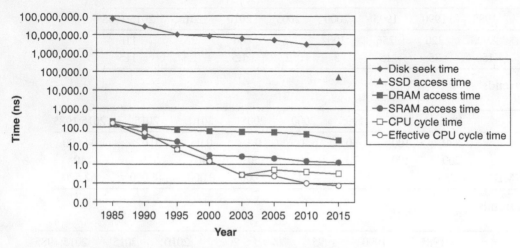

Figure 6.16 The gap between disk, DRAM, and CPU speeds.

throughput, with multiple processor cores issuing requests to the DRAM and disk in parallel.

The various trends are shown quite clearly in Figure 6.16, which plots the access and cycle times from Figure 6.15 on a semi-log scale.

As we will see in Section 6.4, modern computers make heavy use of SRAM-based caches to try to bridge the processor–memory gap. This approach works because of a fundamental property of application programs known as *locality*, which we discuss next.

Practice Problem 6.6 (solution page 662)

Using the data from the years 2005 to 2015 in Figure 6.15(c), estimate the year when you will be able to buy a petabyte (10^{15} bytes) of rotating disk storage for $500. Assume actual dollars (no inflation).

6.2 Locality

Well-written computer programs tend to exhibit good *locality*. That is, they tend to reference data items that are near other recently referenced data items or that were recently referenced themselves. This tendency, known as the *principle of locality*, is an enduring concept that has enormous impact on the design and performance of hardware and software systems.

Locality is typically described as having two distinct forms: *temporal locality* and *spatial locality*. In a program with good temporal locality, a memory location that is referenced once is likely to be referenced again multiple times in the near future. In a program with good spatial locality, if a memory location is referenced

Aside   When cycle time stood still: The advent of multi-core processors

The history of computers is marked by some singular events that caused profound changes in the industry and the world. Interestingly, these inflection points tend to occur about once per decade: the development of Fortran in the 1950s, the introduction of the IBM 360 in the early 1960s, the dawn of the Internet (then called ARPANET) in the early 1970s, the introduction of the IBM PC in the early 1980s, and the creation of the World Wide Web in the early 1990s.

The most recent such event occurred early in the 21st century, when computer manufacturers ran headlong into the so-called power wall, discovering that they could no longer increase CPU clock frequencies as quickly because the chips would then consume too much power. The solution was to improve performance by replacing a single large processor with multiple smaller processor *cores*, each a complete processor capable of executing programs independently and in parallel with the other cores. This *multi-core* approach works in part because the power consumed by a processor is proportional to $P = fCV^2$, where f is the clock frequency, C is the capacitance, and V is the voltage. The capacitance C is roughly proportional to the area, so the power drawn by multiple cores can be held constant as long as the total area of the cores is constant. As long as feature sizes continue to shrink at the exponential Moore's Law rate, the number of cores in each processor, and thus its effective performance, will continue to increase.

From this point forward, computers will get faster not because the clock frequency increases but because the number of cores in each processor increases, and because architectural innovations increase the efficiency of programs running on those cores. We can see this trend clearly in Figure 6.16. CPU cycle time reached its lowest point in 2003 and then actually started to rise before leveling off and starting to decline again at a slower rate than before. However, because of the advent of multi-core processors (dual-core in 2004 and quad-core in 2007), the effective cycle time continues to decrease at close to its previous rate.

once, then the program is likely to reference a nearby memory location in the near future.

Programmers should understand the principle of locality because, in general, *programs with good locality run faster than programs with poor locality*. All levels of modern computer systems, from the hardware, to the operating system, to application programs, are designed to exploit locality. At the hardware level, the principle of locality allows computer designers to speed up main memory accesses by introducing small fast memories known as *cache memories* that hold blocks of the most recently referenced instructions and data items. At the operating system level, the principle of locality allows the system to use the main memory as a cache of the most recently referenced chunks of the virtual address space. Similarly, the operating system uses main memory to cache the most recently used disk blocks in the disk file system. The principle of locality also plays a crucial role in the design of application programs. For example, Web browsers exploit temporal locality by caching recently referenced documents on a local disk. High-volume Web servers hold recently requested documents in front-end disk caches that satisfy requests for these documents without requiring any intervention from the server.

```
1    int sumvec(int v[N])
2    {
3        int i, sum = 0;
4
5        for (i = 0; i < N; i++)
6            sum += v[i];
7        return sum;
8    }
```

(a)

Address	0	4	8	12	16	20	24	28
Contents	v_0	v_1	v_2	v_3	v_4	v_5	v_6	v_7
Access order	1	2	3	4	5	6	7	8

(b)

Figure 6.17 **(a) A function with good locality. (b) Reference pattern for vector** v ($N = 8$). Notice how the vector elements are accessed in the same order that they are stored in memory.

6.2.1 Locality of References to Program Data

Consider the simple function in Figure 6.17(a) that sums the elements of a vector. Does this function have good locality? To answer this question, we look at the reference pattern for each variable. In this example, the sum variable is referenced once in each loop iteration, and thus there is good temporal locality with respect to sum. On the other hand, since sum is a scalar, there is no spatial locality with respect to sum.

As we see in Figure 6.17(b), the elements of vector v are read sequentially, one after the other, in the order they are stored in memory (we assume for convenience that the array starts at address 0). Thus, with respect to variable v, the function has good spatial locality but poor temporal locality since each vector element is accessed exactly once. Since the function has either good spatial or temporal locality with respect to each variable in the loop body, we can conclude that the sumvec function enjoys good locality.

A function such as sumvec that visits each element of a vector sequentially is said to have a *stride-1 reference pattern* (with respect to the element size). We will sometimes refer to stride-1 reference patterns as *sequential reference patterns*. Visiting every kth element of a contiguous vector is called a *stride-k reference pattern*. Stride-1 reference patterns are a common and important source of spatial locality in programs. In general, as the stride increases, the spatial locality decreases.

Stride is also an important issue for programs that reference multidimensional arrays. For example, consider the sumarrayrows function in Figure 6.18(a) that sums the elements of a two-dimensional array.

The doubly nested loop reads the elements of the array in *row-major order*. That is, the inner loop reads the elements of the first row, then the second row, and so on. The sumarrayrows function enjoys good spatial locality because it references the array in the same row-major order that the array is stored (Figure 6.18(b)). The result is a nice stride-1 reference pattern with excellent spatial locality.

```
1    int sumarrayrows(int a[M][N])
2    {
3        int i, j, sum = 0;
4
5        for (i = 0; i < M; i++)
6            for (j = 0; j < N; j++)
7                sum += a[i][j];
8        return sum;
9    }
```

(a)

Address	0	4	8	12	16	20
Contents	a_{00}	a_{01}	a_{02}	a_{10}	a_{11}	a_{12}
Access order	1	2	3	4	5	6

(b)

Figure 6.18   **(a) Another function with good locality. (b) Reference pattern for array** a ($M = 2$, $N = 3$). There is good spatial locality because the array is accessed in the same row-major order in which it is stored in memory.

```
1    int sumarraycols(int a[M][N])
2    {
3        int i, j, sum = 0;
4
5        for (j = 0; j < N; j++)
6            for (i = 0; i < M; i++)
7                sum += a[i][j];
8        return sum;
9    }
```

(a)

Address	0	4	8	12	16	20
Contents	a_{00}	a_{01}	a_{02}	a_{10}	a_{11}	a_{12}
Access order	1	3	5	2	4	6

(b)

Figure 6.19   **(a) A function with poor spatial locality. (b) Reference pattern for array** a ($M = 2$, $N = 3$). The function has poor spatial locality because it scans memory with a stride-N reference pattern.

Seemingly trivial changes to a program can have a big impact on its locality. For example, the sumarraycols function in Figure 6.19(a) computes the same result as the sumarrayrows function in Figure 6.18(a). The only difference is that we have interchanged the i and j loops. What impact does interchanging the loops have on its locality?

The sumarraycols function suffers from poor spatial locality because it scans the array column-wise instead of row-wise. Since C arrays are laid out in memory row-wise, the result is a stride-N reference pattern, as shown in Figure 6.19(b).

6.2.2   Locality of Instruction Fetches

Since program instructions are stored in memory and must be fetched (read) by the CPU, we can also evaluate the locality of a program with respect to its instruction fetches. For example, in Figure 6.17 the instructions in the body of the for loop are executed in sequential memory order, and thus the loop enjoys good spatial locality. Since the loop body is executed multiple times, it also enjoys good temporal locality.

An important property of code that distinguishes it from program data is that it is rarely modified at run time. While a program is executing, the CPU reads its instructions from memory. The CPU rarely overwrites or modifies these instructions.

6.2.3 Summary of Locality

In this section, we have introduced the fundamental idea of locality and have identified some simple rules for qualitatively evaluating the locality in a program:

- Programs that repeatedly reference the same variables enjoy good temporal locality.
- For programs with stride-k reference patterns, the smaller the stride, the better the spatial locality. Programs with stride-1 reference patterns have good spatial locality. Programs that hop around memory with large strides have poor spatial locality.
- Loops have good temporal and spatial locality with respect to instruction fetches. The smaller the loop body and the greater the number of loop iterations, the better the locality.

Later in this chapter, after we have learned about cache memories and how they work, we will show you how to quantify the idea of locality in terms of cache hits and misses. It will also become clear to you why programs with good locality typically run faster than programs with poor locality. Nonetheless, knowing how to glance at a source code and getting a high-level feel for the locality in the program is a useful and important skill for a programmer to master.

Practice Problem 6.7 (solution page 662)

Permute the loops in the following function so that it scans the three-dimensional array a with a stride-1 reference pattern.

```
1    int sumarray3d(int a[N][N][N])
2    {
3        int i, j, k, sum = 0;
4
5        for (i = 0; i < N; i++) {
6            for (j = 0; j < N; j++) {
7                for (k = 0; k < N; k++) {
8                    sum += a[k][i][j];
9                }
10            }
11        }
12        return sum;
13    }
```

(a) An array of structs

```
1    #define N 1000
2
3    typedef struct {
4        int vel[3];
5        int acc[3];
6    } point;
7
8    point p[N];
```

(b) The clear1 function

```
1    void clear1(point *p, int n)
2    {
3        int i, j;
4
5        for (i = 0; i < n; i++) {
6            for (j = 0; j < 3; j++)
7                p[i].vel[j] = 0;
8            for (j = 0; j < 3; j++)
9                p[i].acc[j] = 0;
10       }
11   }
```

(c) The clear2 function

```
1    void clear2(point *p, int n)
2    {
3        int i, j;
4
5        for (i = 0; i < n; i++) {
6            for (j = 0; j < 3; j++) {
7                p[i].vel[j] = 0;
8                p[i].acc[j] = 0;
9            }
10       }
11   }
```

(d) The clear3 function

```
1    void clear3(point *p, int n)
2    {
3        int i, j;
4
5        for (j = 0; j < 3; j++) {
6            for (i = 0; i < n; i++)
7                p[i].vel[j] = 0;
8            for (i = 0; i < n; i++)
9                p[i].acc[j] = 0;
10       }
11   }
```

Figure 6.20 Code examples for Practice Problem 6.8.

Practice Problem 6.8 (solution page 663)

The three functions in Figure 6.20 perform the same operation with varying degrees of spatial locality. Rank-order the functions with respect to the spatial locality enjoyed by each. Explain how you arrived at your ranking.

6.3 The Memory Hierarchy

Sections 6.1 and 6.2 described some fundamental and enduring properties of storage technology and computer software:

Storage technology. Different storage technologies have widely different access times. Faster technologies cost more per byte than slower ones and have less capacity. The gap between CPU and main memory speed is widening.

Computer software. Well-written programs tend to exhibit good locality.

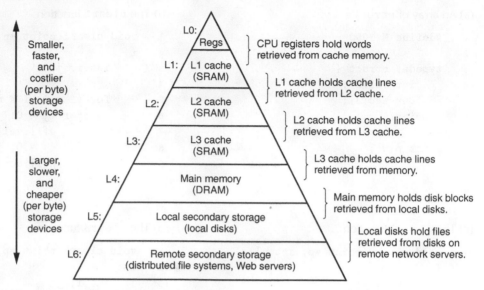

Figure 6.21 The memory hierarchy.

In one of the happier coincidences of computing, these fundamental properties of hardware and software complement each other beautifully. Their complementary nature suggests an approach for organizing memory systems, known as the *memory hierarchy*, that is used in all modern computer systems. Figure 6.21 shows a typical memory hierarchy.

In general, the storage devices get slower, cheaper, and larger as we move from higher to lower *levels*. At the highest level (L0) are a small number of fast CPU registers that the CPU can access in a single clock cycle. Next are one or more small to moderate-size SRAM-based cache memories that can be accessed in a few CPU clock cycles. These are followed by a large DRAM-based main memory that can be accessed in tens to hundreds of clock cycles. Next are slow but enormous local disks. Finally, some systems even include an additional level of disks on remote servers that can be accessed over a network. For example, distributed file systems such as the Andrew File System (AFS) or the Network File System (NFS) allow a program to access files that are stored on remote network-connected servers. Similarly, the World Wide Web allows programs to access remote files stored on Web servers anywhere in the world.

6.3.1 Caching in the Memory Hierarchy

In general, a *cache* (pronounced "cash") is a small, fast storage device that acts as a staging area for the data objects stored in a larger, slower device. The process of using a cache is known as *caching* (pronounced "cashing").

The central idea of a memory hierarchy is that for each k, the faster and smaller storage device at level k serves as a cache for the larger and slower storage device

Aside Other memory hierarchies

We have shown you one example of a memory hierarchy, but other combinations are possible, and indeed common. For example, many sites, including Google datacenters, back up local disks onto archival magnetic tapes. At some of these sites, human operators manually mount the tapes onto tape drives as needed. At other sites, tape robots handle this task automatically. In either case, the collection of tapes represents a level in the memory hierarchy, below the local disk level, and the same general principles apply. Tapes are cheaper per byte than disks, which allows sites to archive multiple snapshots of their local disks. The trade-off is that tapes take longer to access than disks. As another example, solid state disks are playing an increasingly important role in the memory hierarchy, bridging the gulf between DRAM and rotating disk.

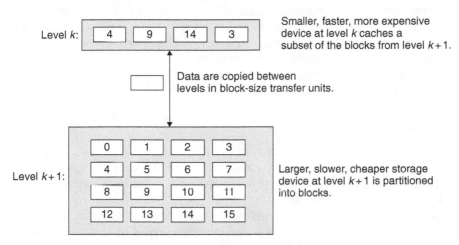

Figure 6.22 The basic principle of caching in a memory hierarchy.

at level $k + 1$. In other words, each level in the hierarchy caches data objects from the next lower level. For example, the local disk serves as a cache for files (such as Web pages) retrieved from remote disks over the network, the main memory serves as a cache for data on the local disks, and so on, until we get to the smallest cache of all, the set of CPU registers.

Figure 6.22 shows the general concept of caching in a memory hierarchy. The storage at level $k + 1$ is partitioned into contiguous chunks of data objects called *blocks*. Each block has a unique address or name that distinguishes it from other blocks. Blocks can be either fixed size (the usual case) or variable size (e.g., the remote HTML files stored on Web servers). For example, the level $k + 1$ storage in Figure 6.22 is partitioned into 16 fixed-size blocks, numbered 0 to 15.

Similarly, the storage at level k is partitioned into a smaller set of blocks that are the same size as the blocks at level $k + 1$. At any point in time, the cache at level k contains copies of a subset of the blocks from level $k + 1$. For example, in

Figure 6.22, the cache at level k has room for four blocks and currently contains copies of blocks 4, 9, 14, and 3.

Data are always copied back and forth between level k and level $k + 1$ in block-size *transfer units*. It is important to realize that while the block size is fixed between any particular pair of adjacent levels in the hierarchy, other pairs of levels can have different block sizes. For example, in Figure 6.21, transfers between L1 and L0 typically use word-size blocks. Transfers between L2 and L1 (and L3 and L2, and L4 and L3) typically use blocks of tens of bytes. And transfers between L5 and L4 use blocks with hundreds or thousands of bytes. In general, devices lower in the hierarchy (further from the CPU) have longer access times, and thus tend to use larger block sizes in order to amortize these longer access times.

Cache Hits

When a program needs a particular data object d from level $k + 1$, it first looks for d in one of the blocks currently stored at level k. If d happens to be cached at level k, then we have what is called a *cache hit*. The program reads d directly from level k, which by the nature of the memory hierarchy is faster than reading d from level $k + 1$. For example, a program with good temporal locality might read a data object from block 14, resulting in a cache hit from level k.

Cache Misses

If, on the other hand, the data object d is not cached at level k, then we have what is called a *cache miss*. When there is a miss, the cache at level k fetches the block containing d from the cache at level $k + 1$, possibly overwriting an existing block if the level k cache is already full.

This process of overwriting an existing block is known as *replacing* or *evicting* the block. The block that is evicted is sometimes referred to as a *victim block*. The decision about which block to replace is governed by the cache's *replacement policy*. For example, a cache with a *random replacement policy* would choose a random victim block. A cache with a *least recently used (LRU)* replacement policy would choose the block that was last accessed the furthest in the past.

After the cache at level k has fetched the block from level $k + 1$, the program can read d from level k as before. For example, in Figure 6.22, reading a data object from block 12 in the level k cache would result in a cache miss because block 12 is not currently stored in the level k cache. Once it has been copied from level $k + 1$ to level k, block 12 will remain there in expectation of later accesses.

Kinds of Cache Misses

It is sometimes helpful to distinguish between different kinds of cache misses. If the cache at level k is empty, then any access of any data object will miss. An empty cache is sometimes referred to as a *cold cache*, and misses of this kind are called *compulsory misses* or *cold misses*. Cold misses are important because they are often transient events that might not occur in steady state, after the cache has been *warmed up* by repeated memory accesses.

Whenever there is a miss, the cache at level k must implement some *placement policy* that determines where to place the block it has retrieved from level $k + 1$. The most flexible placement policy is to allow any block from level $k + 1$ to be stored in any block at level k. For caches high in the memory hierarchy (close to the CPU) that are implemented in hardware and where speed is at a premium, this policy is usually too expensive to implement because randomly placed blocks are expensive to locate.

Thus, hardware caches typically implement a simpler placement policy that restricts a particular block at level $k + 1$ to a small subset (sometimes a singleton) of the blocks at level k. For example, in Figure 6.22, we might decide that a block i at level $k + 1$ must be placed in block (i mod 4) at level k. For example, blocks 0, 4, 8, and 12 at level $k + 1$ would map to block 0 at level k; blocks 1, 5, 9, and 13 would map to block 1; and so on. Notice that our example cache in Figure 6.22 uses this policy.

Restrictive placement policies of this kind lead to a type of miss known as a *conflict miss*, in which the cache is large enough to hold the referenced data objects, but because they map to the same cache block, the cache keeps missing. For example, in Figure 6.22, if the program requests block 0, then block 8, then block 0, then block 8, and so on, each of the references to these two blocks would miss in the cache at level k, even though this cache can hold a total of four blocks.

Programs often run as a sequence of phases (e.g., loops) where each phase accesses some reasonably constant set of cache blocks. For example, a nested loop might access the elements of the same array over and over again. This set of blocks is called the *working set* of the phase. When the size of the working set exceeds the size of the cache, the cache will experience what are known as *capacity misses*. In other words, the cache is just too small to handle this particular working set.

Cache Management

As we have noted, the essence of the memory hierarchy is that the storage device at each level is a cache for the next lower level. At each level, some form of logic must *manage* the cache. By this we mean that something has to partition the cache storage into blocks, transfer blocks between different levels, decide when there are hits and misses, and then deal with them. The logic that manages the cache can be hardware, software, or a combination of the two.

For example, the compiler manages the register file, the highest level of the cache hierarchy. It decides when to issue loads when there are misses, and determines which register to store the data in. The caches at levels L1, L2, and L3 are managed entirely by hardware logic built into the caches. In a system with virtual memory, the DRAM main memory serves as a cache for data blocks stored on disk, and is managed by a combination of operating system software and address translation hardware on the CPU. For a machine with a distributed file system such as AFS, the local disk serves as a cache that is managed by the AFS client process running on the local machine. In most cases, caches operate automatically and do not require any specific or explicit actions from the program.

Type	What cached	Where cached	Latency (cycles)	Managed by
CPU registers	4-byte or 8-byte words	On-chip CPU registers	0	Compiler
TLB	Address translations	On-chip TLB	0	Hardware MMU
L1 cache	64-byte blocks	On-chip L1 cache	4	Hardware
L2 cache	64-byte blocks	On-chip L2 cache	10	Hardware
L3 cache	64-byte blocks	On-chip L3 cache	50	Hardware
Virtual memory	4-KB pages	Main memory	200	Hardware + OS
Buffer cache	Parts of files	Main memory	200	OS
Disk cache	Disk sectors	Disk controller	100,000	Controller firmware
Network cache	Parts of files	Local disk	10,000,000	NFS client
Browser cache	Web pages	Local disk	10,000,000	Web browser
Web cache	Web pages	Remote server disks	1,000,000,000	Web proxy server

Figure 6.23 The ubiquity of caching in modern computer systems. Acronyms: TLB: translation lookaside buffer; MMU: memory management unit; OS: operating system; NFS: network file system.

6.3.2 Summary of Memory Hierarchy Concepts

To summarize, memory hierarchies based on caching work because slower storage is cheaper than faster storage and because programs tend to exhibit locality:

Exploiting temporal locality. Because of temporal locality, the same data objects are likely to be reused multiple times. Once a data object has been copied into the cache on the first miss, we can expect a number of subsequent hits on that object. Since the cache is faster than the storage at the next lower level, these subsequent hits can be served much faster than the original miss.

Exploiting spatial locality. Blocks usually contain multiple data objects. Because of spatial locality, we can expect that the cost of copying a block after a miss will be amortized by subsequent references to other objects within that block.

Caches are used everywhere in modern systems. As you can see from Figure 6.23, caches are used in CPU chips, operating systems, distributed file systems, and on the World Wide Web. They are built from and managed by various combinations of hardware and software. Note that there are a number of terms and acronyms in Figure 6.23 that we haven't covered yet. We include them here to demonstrate how common caches are.

6.4 Cache Memories

The memory hierarchies of early computer systems consisted of only three levels: CPU registers, main memory, and disk storage. However, because of the increasing gap between CPU and main memory, system designers were compelled to insert

Figure 6.24
Typical bus structure for cache memories.

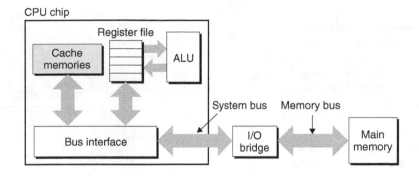

a small SRAM *cache memory*, called an *L1 cache* (level 1 cache) between the CPU register file and main memory, as shown in Figure 6.24. The L1 cache can be accessed nearly as fast as the registers, typically in about 4 clock cycles.

As the performance gap between the CPU and main memory continued to increase, system designers responded by inserting an additional larger cache, called an *L2 cache*, between the L1 cache and main memory, that can be accessed in about 10 clock cycles. Many modern systems include an even larger cache, called an *L3 cache*, which sits between the L2 cache and main memory in the memory hierarchy and can be accessed in about 50 cycles. While there is considerable variety in the arrangements, the general principles are the same. For our discussion in the next section, we will assume a simple memory hierarchy with a single L1 cache between the CPU and main memory.

6.4.1 Generic Cache Memory Organization

Consider a computer system where each memory address has m bits that form $M = 2^m$ unique addresses. As illustrated in Figure 6.25(a), a cache for such a machine is organized as an array of $S = 2^s$ *cache sets*. Each set consists of E *cache lines*. Each line consists of a data *block* of $B = 2^b$ bytes, a *valid bit* that indicates whether or not the line contains meaningful information, and $t = m - (b + s)$ *tag bits* (a subset of the bits from the current block's memory address) that uniquely identify the block stored in the cache line.

In general, a cache's organization can be characterized by the tuple (S, E, B, m). The size (or capacity) of a cache, C, is stated in terms of the aggregate size of all the blocks. The tag bits and valid bit are not included. Thus, $C = S \times E \times B$.

When the CPU is instructed by a load instruction to read a word from address A of main memory, it sends address A to the cache. If the cache is holding a copy of the word at address A, it sends the word immediately back to the CPU. So how does the cache know whether it contains a copy of the word at address A? The cache is organized so that it can find the requested word by simply inspecting the bits of the address, similar to a hash table with an extremely simple hash function. Here is how it works:

The parameters S and B induce a partitioning of the m address bits into the three fields shown in Figure 6.25(b). The s *set index bits* in A form an index into

Figure 6.25
General organization of cache (S, E, B, m). (a) A cache is an array of sets. Each set contains one or more lines. Each line contains a valid bit, some tag bits, and a block of data. (b) The cache organization induces a partition of the m address bits into t tag bits, s set index bits, and b block offset bits.

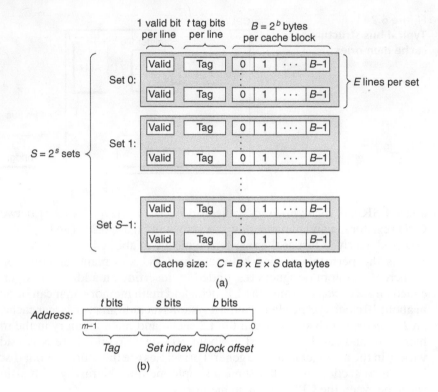

the array of S sets. The first set is set 0, the second set is set 1, and so on. When interpreted as an unsigned integer, the set index bits tell us which set the word must be stored in. Once we know which set the word must be contained in, the t tag bits in A tell us which line (if any) in the set contains the word. A line in the set contains the word if and only if the valid bit is set and the tag bits in the line match the tag bits in the address A. Once we have located the line identified by the tag in the set identified by the set index, then the b *block offset bits* give us the offset of the word in the B-byte data block.

As you may have noticed, descriptions of caches use a lot of symbols. Figure 6.26 summarizes these symbols for your reference.

Practice Problem 6.9 (solution page 663)

The following table gives the parameters for a number of different caches. For each cache, determine the number of cache sets (S), tag bits (t), set index bits (s), and block offset bits (b).

Cache	m	C	B	E	S	t	s	b
1.	32	1,024	4	1	___	___	___	___
2.	32	1,024	8	4	___	___	___	___
3.	32	1,024	32	32	___	___	___	___

Parameter	Description
Fundamental parameters	
$S = 2^s$	Number of sets
E	Number of lines per set
$B = 2^b$	Block size (bytes)
$m = \log_2(M)$	Number of physical (main memory) address bits
Derived quantities	
$M = 2^m$	Maximum number of unique memory addresses
$s = \log_2(S)$	Number of *set index bits*
$b = \log_2(B)$	Number of *block offset bits*
$t = m - (s + b)$	Number of *tag bits*
$C = B \times E \times S$	Cache size (bytes), not including overhead such as the valid and tag bits

Figure 6.26   Summary of cache parameters.

Figure 6.27
Direct-mapped cache
($E = 1$). There is exactly
one line per set.

6.4.2   Direct-Mapped Caches

Caches are grouped into different classes based on E, the number of cache lines per set. A cache with exactly one line per set ($E = 1$) is known as a *direct-mapped* cache (see Figure 6.27). Direct-mapped caches are the simplest both to implement and to understand, so we will use them to illustrate some general concepts about how caches work.

Suppose we have a system with a CPU, a register file, an L1 cache, and a main memory. When the CPU executes an instruction that reads a memory word w, it requests the word from the L1 cache. If the L1 cache has a cached copy of w, then we have an L1 cache hit, and the cache quickly extracts w and returns it to the CPU. Otherwise, we have a cache miss, and the CPU must wait while the L1 cache requests a copy of the block containing w from the main memory. When the requested block finally arrives from memory, the L1 cache stores the block in one of its cache lines, extracts word w from the stored block, and returns it to the CPU. The process that a cache goes through of determining whether a request is a hit or a miss and then extracting the requested word consists of three steps: (1) *set selection*, (2) *line matching*, and (3) *word extraction*.

Figure 6.28
Set selection in a direct-mapped cache.

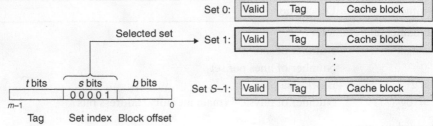

Figure 6.29
Line matching and word selection in a direct-mapped cache. Within the cache block, w_0 denotes the low-order byte of the word w, w_1 the next byte, and so on.

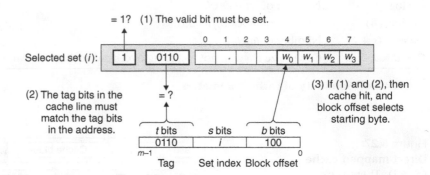

Set Selection in Direct-Mapped Caches

In this step, the cache extracts the s set index bits from the middle of the address for w. These bits are interpreted as an unsigned integer that corresponds to a set number. In other words, if we think of the cache as a one-dimensional array of sets, then the set index bits form an index into this array. Figure 6.28 shows how set selection works for a direct-mapped cache. In this example, the set index bits 00001_2 are interpreted as an integer index that selects set 1.

Line Matching in Direct-Mapped Caches

Now that we have selected some set i in the previous step, the next step is to determine if a copy of the word w is stored in one of the cache lines contained in set i. In a direct-mapped cache, this is easy and fast because there is exactly one line per set. A copy of w is contained in the line if and only if the valid bit is set and the tag in the cache line matches the tag in the address of w.

Figure 6.29 shows how line matching works in a direct-mapped cache. In this example, there is exactly one cache line in the selected set. The valid bit for this line is set, so we know that the bits in the tag and block are meaningful. Since the tag bits in the cache line match the tag bits in the address, we know that a copy of the word we want is indeed stored in the line. In other words, we have a cache hit. On the other hand, if either the valid bit were not set or the tags did not match, then we would have had a cache miss.

Word Selection in Direct-Mapped Caches

Once we have a hit, we know that w is somewhere in the block. This last step determines where the desired word starts in the block. As shown in Figure 6.29, the block offset bits provide us with the offset of the first byte in the desired word. Similar to our view of a cache as an array of lines, we can think of a block as an array of bytes, and the byte offset as an index into that array. In the example, the block offset bits of 100_2 indicate that the copy of w starts at byte 4 in the block. (We are assuming that words are 4 bytes long.)

Line Replacement on Misses in Direct-Mapped Caches

If the cache misses, then it needs to retrieve the requested block from the next level in the memory hierarchy and store the new block in one of the cache lines of the set indicated by the set index bits. In general, if the set is full of valid cache lines, then one of the existing lines must be evicted. For a direct-mapped cache, where each set contains exactly one line, the replacement policy is trivial: the current line is replaced by the newly fetched line.

Putting It Together: A Direct-Mapped Cache in Action

The mechanisms that a cache uses to select sets and identify lines are extremely simple. They have to be, because the hardware must perform them in a few nanoseconds. However, manipulating bits in this way can be confusing to us humans. A concrete example will help clarify the process. Suppose we have a direct-mapped cache described by

$$(S, E, B, m) = (4, 1, 2, 4)$$

In other words, the cache has four sets, one line per set, 2 bytes per block, and 4-bit addresses. We will also assume that each word is a single byte. Of course, these assumptions are totally unrealistic, but they will help us keep the example simple.

When you are first learning about caches, it can be very instructive to enumerate the entire address space and partition the bits, as we've done in Figure 6.30 for our 4-bit example. There are some interesting things to notice about this enumerated space:

- The concatenation of the tag and index bits uniquely identifies each block in memory. For example, block 0 consists of addresses 0 and 1, block 1 consists of addresses 2 and 3, block 2 consists of addresses 4 and 5, and so on.
- Since there are eight memory blocks but only four cache sets, multiple blocks map to the same cache set (i.e., they have the same set index). For example, blocks 0 and 4 both map to set 0, blocks 1 and 5 both map to set 1, and so on.
- Blocks that map to the same cache set are uniquely identified by the tag. For example, block 0 has a tag bit of 0 while block 4 has a tag bit of 1, block 1 has a tag bit of 0 while block 5 has a tag bit of 1, and so on.

Address (decimal)	Address bits			Block number (decimal)
	Tag bits $(t = 1)$	Index bits $(s = 2)$	Offset bits $(b = 1)$	
0	0	00	0	0
1	0	00	1	0
2	0	01	0	1
3	0	01	1	1
4	0	10	0	2
5	0	10	1	2
6	0	11	0	3
7	0	11	1	3
8	1	00	0	4
9	1	00	1	4
10	1	01	0	5
11	1	01	1	5
12	1	10	0	6
13	1	10	1	6
14	1	11	0	7
15	1	11	1	7

Figure 6.30 **4-bit address space for example direct-mapped cache.**

Let us simulate the cache in action as the CPU performs a sequence of reads. Remember that for this example we are assuming that the CPU reads 1-byte words. While this kind of manual simulation is tedious and you may be tempted to skip it, in our experience students do not really understand how caches work until they work their way through a few of them.

Initially, the cache is empty (i.e., each valid bit is 0):

Set	Valid	Tag	block[0]	block[1]
0	0			
1	0			
2	0			
3	0			

Each row in the table represents a cache line. The first column indicates the set that the line belongs to, but keep in mind that this is provided for convenience and is not really part of the cache. The next four columns represent the actual bits in each cache line. Now, let's see what happens when the CPU performs a sequence of reads:

1. **Read word at address 0.** Since the valid bit for set 0 is 0, this is a cache miss. The cache fetches block 0 from memory (or a lower-level cache) and stores the

block in set 0. Then the cache returns m[0] (the contents of memory location 0) from block[0] of the newly fetched cache line.

Set	Valid	Tag	block[0]	block[1]
0	1	0	m[0]	m[1]
1	0			
2	0			
3	0			

2. **Read word at address 1.** This is a cache hit. The cache immediately returns m[1] from block[1] of the cache line. The state of the cache does not change.

3. **Read word at address 13.** Since the cache line in set 2 is not valid, this is a cache miss. The cache loads block 6 into set 2 and returns m[13] from block[1] of the new cache line.

Set	Valid	Tag	block[0]	block[1]
0	1	0	m[0]	m[1]
1	0			
2	1	1	m[12]	m[13]
3	0			

4. **Read word at address 8.** This is a miss. The cache line in set 0 is indeed valid, but the tags do not match. The cache loads block 4 into set 0 (replacing the line that was there from the read of address 0) and returns m[8] from block[0] of the new cache line.

Set	Valid	Tag	block[0]	block[1]
0	1	1	m[8]	m[9]
1	0			
2	1	1	m[12]	m[13]
3	0			

5. **Read word at address 0.** This is another miss, due to the unfortunate fact that we just replaced block 0 during the previous reference to address 8. This kind of miss, where we have plenty of room in the cache but keep alternating references to blocks that map to the same set, is an example of a conflict miss.

Set	Valid	Tag	block[0]	block[1]
0	1	0	m[0]	m[1]
1	0			
2	1	1	m[12]	m[13]
3	0			

Conflict Misses in Direct-Mapped Caches

Conflict misses are common in real programs and can cause baffling performance problems. Conflict misses in direct-mapped caches typically occur when programs access arrays whose sizes are a power of 2. For example, consider a function that computes the dot product of two vectors:

```
1   float dotprod(float x[8], float y[8])
2   {
3       float sum = 0.0;
4       int i;
5
6       for (i = 0; i < 8; i++)
7           sum += x[i] * y[i];
8       return sum;
9   }
```

This function has good spatial locality with respect to x and y, and so we might expect it to enjoy a good number of cache hits. Unfortunately, this is not always true.

Suppose that floats are 4 bytes, that x is loaded into the 32 bytes of contiguous memory starting at address 0, and that y starts immediately after x at address 32. For simplicity, suppose that a block is 16 bytes (big enough to hold four floats) and that the cache consists of two sets, for a total cache size of 32 bytes. We will assume that the variable sum is actually stored in a CPU register and thus does not require a memory reference. Given these assumptions, each x[i] and y[i] will map to the identical cache set:

Element	Address	Set index	Element	Address	Set index
x[0]	0	0	y[0]	32	0
x[1]	4	0	y[1]	36	0
x[2]	8	0	y[2]	40	0
x[3]	12	0	y[3]	44	0
x[4]	16	1	y[4]	48	1
x[5]	20	1	y[5]	52	1
x[6]	24	1	y[6]	56	1
x[7]	28	1	y[7]	60	1

At run time, the first iteration of the loop references x[0], a miss that causes the block containing x[0]–x[3] to be loaded into set 0. The next reference is to y[0], another miss that causes the block containing y[0]–y[3] to be copied into set 0, overwriting the values of x that were copied in by the previous reference. During the next iteration, the reference to x[1] misses, which causes the x[0]–x[3] block to be loaded back into set 0, overwriting the y[0]–y[3] block. So now we have a conflict miss, and in fact each subsequent reference to x and y will result in a conflict miss as we thrash back and forth between blocks of x and y. The term *thrashing* describes any situation where a cache is repeatedly loading and evicting the same sets of cache blocks.

Aside   Why index with the middle bits?

You may be wondering why caches use the middle bits for the set index instead of the high-order bits. There is a good reason why the middle bits are better. Figure 6.31 shows why. If the high-order bits are used as an index, then some contiguous memory blocks will map to the same cache set. For example, in the figure, the first four blocks map to the first cache set, the second four blocks map to the second set, and so on. If a program has good spatial locality and scans the elements of an array sequentially, then the cache can only hold a block-size chunk of the array at any point in time. This is an inefficient use of the cache. Contrast this with middle-bit indexing, where adjacent blocks always map to different cache sets. In this case, the cache can hold an entire C-size chunk of the array, where C is the cache size.

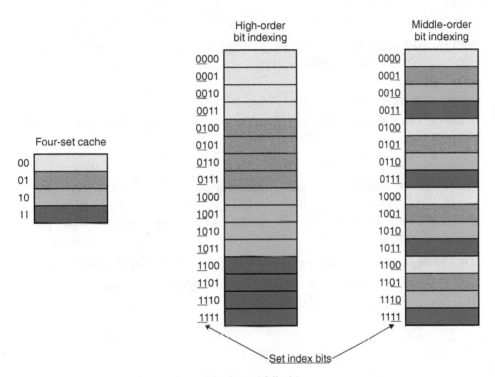

Figure 6.31   Why caches index with the middle bits.

The bottom line is that even though the program has good spatial locality and we have room in the cache to hold the blocks for both x[i] and y[i], each reference results in a conflict miss because the blocks map to the same cache set. It is not unusual for this kind of thrashing to result in a slowdown by a factor of 2 or 3. Also, be aware that even though our example is extremely simple, the problem is real for larger and more realistic direct-mapped caches.

Luckily, thrashing is easy for programmers to fix once they recognize what is going on. One easy solution is to put B bytes of padding at the end of each array.

For example, instead of defining x to be float x[8], we define it to be float x[12]. Assuming y starts immediately after x in memory, we have the following mapping of array elements to sets:

Element	Address	Set index	Element	Address	Set index
x[0]	0	0	y[0]	48	1
x[1]	4	0	y[1]	52	1
x[2]	8	0	y[2]	56	1
x[3]	12	0	y[3]	60	1
x[4]	16	1	y[4]	64	0
x[5]	20	1	y[5]	68	0
x[6]	24	1	y[6]	72	0
x[7]	28	1	y[7]	76	0

With the padding at the end of x, x[i] and y[i] now map to different sets, which eliminates the thrashing conflict misses.

Practice Problem 6.10 (solution page 663)

In the previous dotprod example, what fraction of the total references to x and y will be hits once we have padded array x?

Practice Problem 6.11 (solution page 663)

Imagine a hypothetical cache that uses the high-order s bits of an address as the set index. For such a cache, contiguous chunks of memory blocks are mapped to the same cache set.

A. How many blocks are in each of these contiguous array chunks?

B. Consider the following code that runs on a system with a cache of the form $(S, E, B, m) = (512, 1, 32, 32)$:

```
int array[4096];

for (i = 0; i < 4096; i++)
    sum += array[i];
```

What is the maximum number of array blocks that are stored in the cache at any point in time?

6.4.3 Set Associative Caches

The problem with conflict misses in direct-mapped caches stems from the constraint that each set has exactly one line (or in our terminology, $E = 1$). A *set associative cache* relaxes this constraint so that each set holds more than one cache line. A cache with $1 < E < C/B$ is often called an E-way set associative cache. We

Figure 6.32

Set associative cache
$(1 < E < C/B)$. In a set
associative cache, each
set contains more than
one line. This particular
example shows a two-way
set associative cache.

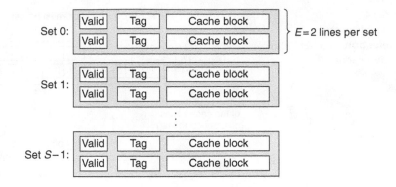

Figure 6.33

**Set selection in a set
associative cache.**

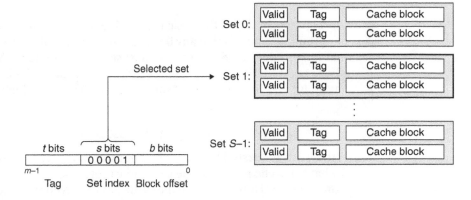

will discuss the special case, where $E = C/B$, in the next section. Figure 6.32 shows
the organization of a two-way set associative cache.

Set Selection in Set Associative Caches

Set selection is identical to a direct-mapped cache, with the set index bits identifying the set. Figure 6.33 summarizes this principle.

Line Matching and Word Selection in Set Associative Caches

Line matching is more involved in a set associative cache than in a direct-mapped
cache because it must check the tags and valid bits of multiple lines in order to
determine if the requested word is in the set. A conventional memory is an array of
values that takes an address as input and returns the value stored at that address.
An *associative memory*, on the other hand, is an array of (key, value) pairs that
takes as input the key and returns a value from one of the (key, value) pairs that
matches the input key. Thus, we can think of each set in a set associative cache as
a small associative memory where the keys are the concatenation of the tag and
valid bits, and the values are the contents of a block.

Figure 6.34
Line matching and word selection in a set associative cache.

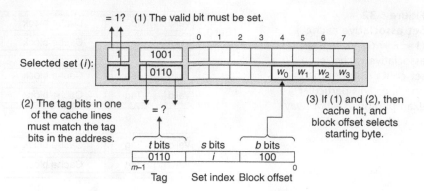

Figure 6.34 shows the basic idea of line matching in an associative cache. An important idea here is that any line in the set can contain any of the memory blocks that map to that set. So the cache must search each line in the set for a valid line whose tag matches the tag in the address. If the cache finds such a line, then we have a hit and the block offset selects a word from the block, as before.

Line Replacement on Misses in Set Associative Caches

If the word requested by the CPU is not stored in any of the lines in the set, then we have a cache miss, and the cache must fetch the block that contains the word from memory. However, once the cache has retrieved the block, which line should it replace? Of course, if there is an empty line, then it would be a good candidate. But if there are no empty lines in the set, then we must choose one of the nonempty lines and hope that the CPU does not reference the replaced line anytime soon.

It is very difficult for programmers to exploit knowledge of the cache replacement policy in their codes, so we will not go into much detail about it here. The simplest replacement policy is to choose the line to replace at random. Other more sophisticated policies draw on the principle of locality to try to minimize the probability that the replaced line will be referenced in the near future. For example, a *least frequently used (LFU)* policy will replace the line that has been referenced the fewest times over some past time window. A *least recently used (LRU)* policy will replace the line that was last accessed the furthest in the past. All of these policies require additional time and hardware. But as we move further down the memory hierarchy, away from the CPU, the cost of a miss becomes more expensive and it becomes more worthwhile to minimize misses with good replacement policies.

6.4.4 Fully Associative Caches

A *fully associative cache* consists of a single set (i.e., $E = C/B$) that contains all of the cache lines. Figure 6.35 shows the basic organization.

Figure 6.35

Fully associative cache $(E = C/B)$. In a fully associative cache, a single set contains all of the lines.

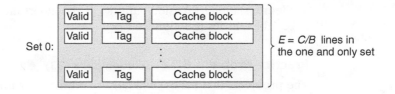

Figure 6.36

Set selection in a fully associative cache. Notice that there are no set index bits.

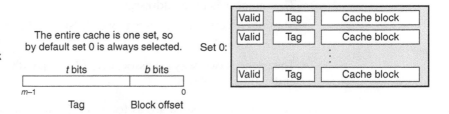

Figure 6.37

Line matching and word selection in a fully associative cache.

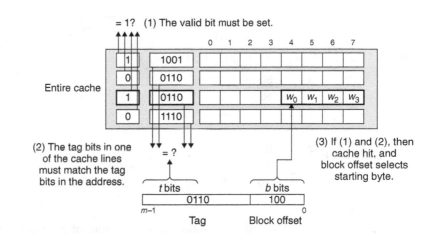

Set Selection in Fully Associative Caches

Set selection in a fully associative cache is trivial because there is only one set, summarized in Figure 6.36. Notice that there are no set index bits in the address, which is partitioned into only a tag and a block offset.

Line Matching and Word Selection in Fully Associative Caches

Line matching and word selection in a fully associative cache work the same as with a set associative cache, as we show in Figure 6.37. The difference is mainly a question of scale.

Because the cache circuitry must search for many matching tags in parallel, it is difficult and expensive to build an associative cache that is both large and fast. As a result, fully associative caches are only appropriate for small caches, such as the translation lookaside buffers (TLBs) in virtual memory systems that cache page table entries (Section 9.6.2).

Practice Problem 6.12 (solution page 663)

The problems that follow will help reinforce your understanding of how caches work. Assume the following:

- The memory is byte addressable.
- Memory accesses are to 1-byte words (not to 4-byte words).
- Addresses are 13 bits wide.
- The cache is two-way set associative ($E = 2$), with a 4-byte block size ($B = 4$) and eight sets ($S = 8$).

The contents of the cache are as follows, with all numbers given in hexadecimal notation.

2-way set associative cache

Set index	Line 0						Line 1					
	Tag	Valid	Byte 0	Byte 1	Byte 2	Byte 3	Tag	Valid	Byte 0	Byte 1	Byte 2	Byte 3
0	09	1	86	30	3F	10	00	0	—	—	—	—
1	45	1	60	4F	E0	23	38	1	00	BC	0B	37
2	EB	0	—	—	—	—	0B	0	—	—	—	—
3	06	0	—	—	—	—	32	1	12	08	7B	AD
4	C7	1	06	78	07	C5	05	1	40	67	C2	3B
5	71	1	0B	DE	18	4B	6E	0	—	—	—	—
6	91	1	A0	B7	26	2D	F0	0	—	—	—	—
7	46	0	—	—	—	—	DE	1	12	C0	88	37

The following figure shows the format of an address (1 bit per box). Indicate (by labeling the diagram) the fields that would be used to determine the following:

CO. The cache block offset

CI. The cache set index

CT. The cache tag

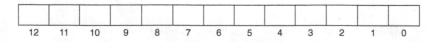

Practice Problem 6.13 (solution page 664)

Suppose a program running on the machine in Problem 6.12 references the 1-byte word at address 0x0E34. Indicate the cache entry accessed and the cache byte value returned in hexadecimal notation. Indicate whether a cache miss occurs. If there is a cache miss, enter "—" for "Cache byte returned."

A. Address format (1 bit per box):

12	11	10	9	8	7	6	5	4	3	2	1	0

B. Memory reference:

Parameter	Value
Cache block offset (CO)	0x____
Cache set index (CI)	0x____
Cache tag (CT)	0x____
Cache hit? (Y/N)	____
Cache byte returned	0x____

Practice Problem 6.14 (solution page 664)

Repeat Problem 6.13 for memory address 0x0DD5.

A. Address format (1 bit per box):

12	11	10	9	8	7	6	5	4	3	2	1	0

B. Memory reference:

Parameter	Value
Cache block offset (CO)	0x____
Cache set index (CI)	0x____
Cache tag (CT)	0x____
Cache hit? (Y/N)	____
Cache byte returned	0x____

Practice Problem 6.15 (solution page 664)

Repeat Problem 6.13 for memory address 0x1FE4.

A. Address format (1 bit per box):

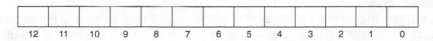

12	11	10	9	8	7	6	5	4	3	2	1	0

B.   Memory reference:

Parameter	Value
Cache block offset (CO)	0x_____
Cache set index (CI)	0x_____
Cache tag (CT)	0x_____
Cache hit? (Y/N)	_____
Cache byte returned	0x_____

Practice Problem 6.16 (solution page 665)

For the cache in Problem 6.12, list all of the hexadecimal memory addresses that will hit in set 3.

6.4.5   Issues with Writes

As we have seen, the operation of a cache with respect to reads is straightforward. First, look for a copy of the desired word w in the cache. If there is a hit, return w immediately. If there is a miss, fetch the block that contains w from the next lower level of the memory hierarchy, store the block in some cache line (possibly evicting a valid line), and then return w.

The situation for writes is a little more complicated. Suppose we write a word w that is already cached (a *write hit*). After the cache updates its copy of w, what does it do about updating the copy of w in the next lower level of the hierarchy? The simplest approach, known as *write-through*, is to immediately write w's cache block to the next lower level. While simple, write-through has the disadvantage of causing bus traffic with every write. Another approach, known as *write-back*, defers the update as long as possible by writing the updated block to the next lower level only when it is evicted from the cache by the replacement algorithm. Because of locality, write-back can significantly reduce the amount of bus traffic, but it has the disadvantage of additional complexity. The cache must maintain an additional *dirty bit* for each cache line that indicates whether or not the cache block has been modified.

Another issue is how to deal with write misses. One approach, known as *write-allocate*, loads the corresponding block from the next lower level into the cache and then updates the cache block. Write-allocate tries to exploit spatial locality of writes, but it has the disadvantage that every miss results in a block transfer from the next lower level to the cache. The alternative, known as *no-write-allocate*, bypasses the cache and writes the word directly to the next lower level. Write-through caches are typically no-write-allocate. Write-back caches are typically write-allocate.

Optimizing caches for writes is a subtle and difficult issue, and we are only scratching the surface here. The details vary from system to system and are often proprietary and poorly documented. To the programmer trying to write reasonably cache-friendly programs, we suggest adopting a mental model that assumes write-back, write-allocate caches. There are several reasons for this suggestion: As a rule, caches at lower levels of the memory hierarchy are more likely to use write-back instead of write-through because of the larger transfer times. For example, virtual memory systems (which use main memory as a cache for the blocks stored on disk) use write-back exclusively. But as logic densities increase, the increased complexity of write-back is becoming less of an impediment and we are seeing write-back caches at all levels of modern systems. So this assumption matches current trends. Another reason for assuming a write-back, write-allocate approach is that it is symmetric to the way reads are handled, in that write-back write-allocate tries to exploit locality. Thus, we can develop our programs at a high level to exhibit good spatial and temporal locality rather than trying to optimize for a particular memory system.

6.4.6   Anatomy of a Real Cache Hierarchy

So far, we have assumed that caches hold only program data. But, in fact, caches can hold instructions as well as data. A cache that holds instructions only is called an *i-cache*. A cache that holds program data only is called a *d-cache*. A cache that holds both instructions and data is known as a *unified cache*. Modern processors include separate i-caches and d-caches. There are a number of reasons for this. With two separate caches, the processor can read an instruction word and a data word at the same time. I-caches are typically read-only, and thus simpler. The two caches are often optimized to different access patterns and can have different block sizes, associativities, and capacities. Also, having separate caches ensures that data accesses do not create conflict misses with instruction accesses, and vice versa, at the cost of a potential increase in capacity misses.

Figure 6.38 shows the cache hierarchy for the Intel Core i7 processor. Each CPU chip has four cores. Each core has its own private L1 i-cache, L1 d-cache, and L2 unified cache. All of the cores share an on-chip L3 unified cache. An interesting feature of this hierarchy is that all of the SRAM cache memories are contained in the CPU chip.

Figure 6.39 summarizes the basic characteristics of the Core i7 caches.

6.4.7   Performance Impact of Cache Parameters

Cache performance is evaluated with a number of metrics:

Miss rate. The fraction of memory references during the execution of a program, or a part of a program, that miss. It is computed as # *misses/* # *references*.

Hit rate. The fraction of memory references that hit. It is computed as $1 - miss\ rate$.

Hit time. The time to deliver a word in the cache to the CPU, including the time for set selection, line identification, and word selection. Hit time is on the order of several clock cycles for L1 caches.

Figure 6.38
Intel Core i7 cache hierarchy.

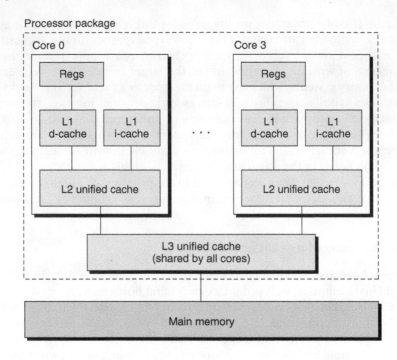

Cache type	Access time (cycles)	Cache size (C)	Assoc. (E)	Block size (B)	Sets (S)
L1 i-cache	4	32 KB	8	64 B	64
L1 d-cache	4	32 KB	8	64 B	64
L2 unified cache	10	256 KB	8	64 B	512
L3 unified cache	40–75	8 MB	16	64 B	8,192

Figure 6.39 Characteristics of the Intel Core i7 cache hierarchy.

Miss penalty. Any additional time required because of a miss. The penalty for
L1 misses served from L2 is on the order of 10 cycles; from L3, 50 cycles;
and from main memory, 200 cycles.

Optimizing the cost and performance trade-offs of cache memories is a subtle
exercise that requires extensive simulation on realistic benchmark codes and thus
is beyond our scope. However, it is possible to identify some of the qualitative
trade-offs.

Impact of Cache Size

On the one hand, a larger cache will tend to increase the hit rate. On the other
hand, it is always harder to make large memories run faster. As a result, larger
caches tend to increase the hit time. This explains why an L1 cache is smaller than
an L2 cache, and an L2 cache is smaller than an L3 cache.

Impact of Block Size

Large blocks are a mixed blessing. On the one hand, larger blocks can help increase the hit rate by exploiting any spatial locality that might exist in a program. However, for a given cache size, larger blocks imply a smaller number of cache lines, which can hurt the hit rate in programs with more temporal locality than spatial locality. Larger blocks also have a negative impact on the miss penalty, since larger blocks cause larger transfer times. Modern systems such as the Core i7 compromise with cache blocks that contain 64 bytes.

Impact of Associativity

The issue here is the impact of the choice of the parameter E, the number of cache lines per set. The advantage of higher associativity (i.e., larger values of E) is that it decreases the vulnerability of the cache to thrashing due to conflict misses. However, higher associativity comes at a significant cost. Higher associativity is expensive to implement and hard to make fast. It requires more tag bits per line, additional LRU state bits per line, and additional control logic. Higher associativity can increase hit time, because of the increased complexity, and it can also increase the miss penalty because of the increased complexity of choosing a victim line.

The choice of associativity ultimately boils down to a trade-off between the hit time and the miss penalty. Traditionally, high-performance systems that pushed the clock rates would opt for smaller associativity for L1 caches (where the miss penalty is only a few cycles) and a higher degree of associativity for the lower levels, where the miss penalty is higher. For example, in Intel Core i7 systems, the L1 and L2 caches are 8-way associative, and the L3 cache is 16-way.

Impact of Write Strategy

Write-through caches are simpler to implement and can use a *write buffer* that works independently of the cache to update memory. Furthermore, read misses are less expensive because they do not trigger a memory write. On the other hand, write-back caches result in fewer transfers, which allows more bandwidth to memory for I/O devices that perform DMA. Further, reducing the number of transfers becomes increasingly important as we move down the hierarchy and the transfer times increase. In general, caches further down the hierarchy are more likely to use write-back than write-through.

6.5 Writing Cache-Friendly Code

In Section 6.2, we introduced the idea of locality and talked in qualitative terms about what constitutes good locality. Now that we understand how cache memories work, we can be more precise. Programs with better locality will tend to have lower miss rates, and programs with lower miss rates will tend to run faster than programs with higher miss rates. Thus, good programmers should always try to

Aside Cache lines, sets, and blocks: What's the difference?

It is easy to confuse the distinction between cache lines, sets, and blocks. Let's review these ideas and make sure they are clear:

- A *block* is a fixed-size packet of information that moves back and forth between a cache and main memory (or a lower-level cache).
- A *line* is a container in a cache that stores a block, as well as other information such as the valid bit and the tag bits.
- A *set* is a collection of one or more lines. Sets in direct-mapped caches consist of a single line. Sets in set associative and fully associative caches consist of multiple lines.

In direct-mapped caches, sets and lines are indeed equivalent. However, in associative caches, sets and lines are very different things and the terms cannot be used interchangeably.

Since a line always stores a single block, the terms "line" and "block" are often used interchangeably. For example, systems professionals usually refer to the "line size" of a cache, when what they really mean is the block size. This usage is very common and shouldn't cause any confusion as long as you understand the distinction between blocks and lines.

write code that is *cache friendly*, in the sense that it has good locality. Here is the basic approach we use to try to ensure that our code is cache friendly.

1. *Make the common case go fast.* Programs often spend most of their time in a few core functions. These functions often spend most of their time in a few loops. So focus on the inner loops of the core functions and ignore the rest.

2. *Minimize the number of cache misses in each inner loop.* All other things being equal, such as the total number of loads and stores, loops with better miss rates will run faster.

To see how this works in practice, consider the sumvec function from Section 6.2:

```
1    int sumvec(int v[N])
2    {
3        int i, sum = 0;
4
5        for (i = 0; i < N; i++)
6            sum += v[i];
7        return sum;
8    }
```

Is this function cache friendly? First, notice that there is good temporal locality in the loop body with respect to the local variables i and sum. In fact, because these are local variables, any reasonable optimizing compiler will cache them in the register file, the highest level of the memory hierarchy. Now consider the stride-1 references to vector v. In general, if a cache has a block size of B bytes, then a stride-k reference pattern (where k is expressed in words) results in an average of min $(1, (word\ size \times k)/B)$ misses per loop iteration. This is minimized for $k = 1$, so the stride-1 references to v are indeed cache friendly. For example, suppose that v is block aligned, words are 4 bytes, cache blocks are 4 words, and the cache is initially empty (a cold cache). Then, regardless of the cache organization, the references to v will result in the following pattern of hits and misses:

v[i]	$i = 0$	$i = 1$	$i = 2$	$i = 3$	$i = 4$	$i = 5$	$i = 6$	$i = 7$
Access order, [h]it or [m]iss	1 **[m]**	2 [h]	3 [h]	4 [h]	5 **[m]**	6 [h]	7 [h]	8 [h]

In this example, the reference to v[0] misses and the corresponding block, which contains v[0]–v[3], is loaded into the cache from memory. Thus, the next three references are all hits. The reference to v[4] causes another miss as a new block is loaded into the cache, the next three references are hits, and so on. In general, three out of four references will hit, which is the best we can do in this case with a cold cache.

To summarize, our simple sumvec example illustrates two important points about writing cache-friendly code:

- Repeated references to local variables are good because the compiler can cache them in the register file (temporal locality).

- Stride-1 reference patterns are good because caches at all levels of the memory hierarchy store data as contiguous blocks (spatial locality).

Spatial locality is especially important in programs that operate on multi-dimensional arrays. For example, consider the sumarrayrows function from Section 6.2, which sums the elements of a two-dimensional array in row-major order:

```
1    int sumarrayrows(int a[M][N])
2    {
3        int i, j, sum = 0;
4
5        for (i = 0; i < M; i++)
6            for (j = 0; j < N; j++)
7                sum += a[i][j];
8        return sum;
9    }
```

Since C stores arrays in row-major order, the inner loop of this function has the same desirable stride-1 access pattern as sumvec. For example, suppose we make the same assumptions about the cache as for sumvec. Then the references to the array a will result in the following pattern of hits and misses:

a[i][j]	$j = 0$	$j = 1$	$j = 2$	$j = 3$	$j = 4$	$j = 5$	$j = 6$	$j = 7$
$i = 0$	1 **[m]**	2 [h]	3 [h]	4 [h]	5 **[m]**	6 [h]	7 [h]	8 [h]
$i = 1$	9 **[m]**	10 [h]	11 [h]	12 [h]	13 **[m]**	14 [h]	15 [h]	16 [h]
$i = 2$	17 **[m]**	18 [h]	19 [h]	20 [h]	21 **[m]**	22 [h]	23 [h]	24 [h]
$i = 3$	25 **[m]**	26 [h]	27 [h]	28 [h]	29 **[m]**	30 [h]	31 [h]	32 [h]

But consider what happens if we make the seemingly innocuous change of permuting the loops:

```
1    int sumarraycols(int a[M][N])
2    {
3        int i, j, sum = 0;
4
5        for (j = 0; j < N; j++)
6            for (i = 0; i < M; i++)
7                sum += a[i][j];
8        return sum;
9    }
```

In this case, we are scanning the array column by column instead of row by row. If we are lucky and the entire array fits in the cache, then we will enjoy the same miss rate of 1/4. However, if the array is larger than the cache (the more likely case), then each and every access of a[i][j] will miss!

a[i][j]	$j=0$	$j=1$	$j=2$	$j=3$	$j=4$	$j=5$	$j=6$	$j=7$
$i=0$	1 [m]	5 [m]	9 [m]	13 [m]	17 [m]	21 [m]	25 [m]	29 [m]
$i=1$	2 [m]	6 [m]	10 [m]	14 [m]	18 [m]	22 [m]	26 [m]	30 [m]
$i=2$	3 [m]	7 [m]	11 [m]	15 [m]	19 [m]	23 [m]	27 [m]	31 [m]
$i=3$	4 [m]	8 [m]	12 [m]	16 [m]	20 [m]	24 [m]	28 [m]	32 [m]

Higher miss rates can have a significant impact on running time. For example, on our desktop machine, sumarrayrows runs 25 times faster than sumarraycols for large array sizes. To summarize, programmers should be aware of locality in their programs and try to write programs that exploit it.

Practice Problem 6.17 (solution page 665)

Transposing the rows and columns of a matrix is an important problem in signal processing and scientific computing applications. It is also interesting from a locality point of view because its reference pattern is both row-wise and column-wise. For example, consider the following transpose routine:

```
1    typedef int array[2][2];
2
3    void transpose1(array dst, array src)
4    {
5        int i, j;
6
7        for (i = 0; i < 2; i++) {
8            for (j = 0; j < 2; j++) {
9                dst[j][i] = src[i][j];
10           }
11       }
12   }
```

Assume this code runs on a machine with the following properties:

- `sizeof(int) = 4`.
- The `src` array starts at address 0 and the `dst` array starts at address 16 (decimal).
- There is a single L1 data cache that is direct-mapped, write-through, and write-allocate, with a block size of 8 bytes.
- The cache has a total size of 16 data bytes and the cache is initially empty.
- Accesses to the `src` and `dst` arrays are the only sources of read and write misses, respectively.

A. For each `row` and `col`, indicate whether the access to `src[row][col]` and `dst[row][col]` is a hit (h) or a miss (m). For example, reading `src[0][0]` is a miss and writing `dst[0][0]` is also a miss.

dst array	Col. 0	Col. 1		src array	Col. 0	Col. 1
Row 0	m	_____		Row0	m	_____
Row 1	_____	_____		Row 1	_____	_____

B. Repeat the problem for a cache with 32 data bytes.

Practice Problem 6.18 (solution page 666)

The heart of the recent hit game *SimAquarium* is a tight loop that calculates the average position of 256 algae. You are evaluating its cache performance on a machine with a 1,024-byte direct-mapped data cache with 16-byte blocks ($B = 16$). You are given the following definitions:

```
1    struct algae_position {
2        int x;
3        int y;
4    };
5
6    struct algae_position grid[16][16];
7    int total_x = 0, total_y = 0;
8    int i, j;
```

You should also assume the following:

- `sizeof(int) = 4`.
- `grid` begins at memory address 0.
- The cache is initially empty.
- The only memory accesses are to the entries of the array `grid`. Variables `i`, `j`, `total_x`, and `total_y` are stored in registers.

Determine the cache performance for the following code:

```
1        for (i = 0; i < 16; i++) {
2            for (j = 0; j < 16; j++) {
3                total_x += grid[i][j].x;
4            }
5        }
6
7        for (i = 0; i < 16; i++) {
8            for (j = 0; j < 16; j++) {
9                total_y += grid[i][j].y;
10           }
11       }
```

A. What is the total number of reads?

B. What is the total number of reads that miss in the cache?

C. What is the miss rate?

Practice Problem 6.19 (solution page 666)

Given the assumptions of Practice Problem 6.18, determine the cache performance of the following code:

```
1        for (i = 0; i < 16; i++){
2            for (j = 0; j < 16; j++) {
3                total_x += grid[j][i].x;
4                total_y += grid[j][i].y;
5            }
6        }
```

A. What is the total number of reads?

B. What is the total number of reads that miss in the cache?

C. What is the miss rate?

D. What would the miss rate be if the cache were twice as big?

Practice Problem 6.20 (solution page 666)

Given the assumptions of Practice Problem 6.18, determine the cache performance of the following code:

```
1        for (i = 0; i < 16; i++){
2            for (j = 0; j < 16; j++) {
3                total_x += grid[i][j].x;
4                total_y += grid[i][j].y;
5            }
6        }
```

A. What is the total number of reads?

B. What is the total number of reads that miss in the cache?

C. What is the miss rate?

D. What would the miss rate be if the cache were twice as big?

6.6   Putting It Together: The Impact of Caches on Program Performance

This section wraps up our discussion of the memory hierarchy by studying the impact that caches have on the performance of programs running on real machines.

6.6.1   The Memory Mountain

The rate that a program reads data from the memory system is called the *read throughput*, or sometimes the *read bandwidth*. If a program reads n bytes over a period of s seconds, then the read throughput over that period is n/s, typically expressed in units of megabytes per second (MB/s).

If we were to write a program that issued a sequence of read requests from a tight program loop, then the measured read throughput would give us some insight into the performance of the memory system for that particular sequence of reads. Figure 6.40 shows a pair of functions that measure the read throughput for a particular read sequence.

The `test` function generates the read sequence by scanning the first `elems` elements of an array with a stride of `stride`. To increase the available parallelism in the inner loop, it uses 4×4 unrolling (Section 5.9). The `run` function is a wrapper that calls the `test` function and returns the measured read throughput. The call to the `test` function in line 37 warms the cache. The `fcyc2` function in line 38 calls the `test` function with arguments `elems` and estimates the running time of the `test` function in CPU cycles. Notice that the `size` argument to the `run` function is in units of bytes, while the corresponding `elems` argument to the `test` function is in units of array elements. Also, notice that line 39 computes MB/s as 10^6 bytes/s, as opposed to 2^{20} bytes/s.

The `size` and `stride` arguments to the `run` function allow us to control the degree of temporal and spatial locality in the resulting read sequence. Smaller values of `size` result in a smaller working set size, and thus better temporal locality. Smaller values of `stride` result in better spatial locality. If we call the `run` function repeatedly with different values of `size` and `stride`, then we can recover a fascinating two-dimensional function of read throughput versus temporal and spatial locality. This function is called a *memory mountain* [112].

Every computer has a unique memory mountain that characterizes the capabilities of its memory system. For example, Figure 6.41 shows the memory mountain for an Intel Core i7 Haswell system. In this example, the `size` varies from 16 KB to 128 MB, and the `stride` varies from 1 to 12 elements, where each element is an 8-byte `long int`.

—————————————————————————— code/mem/mountain/mountain.c

```
1    long data[MAXELEMS];        /* The global array we'll be traversing */
2
3    /* test - Iterate over first "elems" elements of array "data" with
4     *         stride of "stride", using 4 x 4 loop unrolling.
5     */
6    int test(int elems, int stride)
7    {
8        long i, sx2 = stride*2, sx3 = stride*3, sx4 = stride*4;
9        long acc0 = 0, acc1 = 0, acc2 = 0, acc3 = 0;
10       long length = elems;
11       long limit = length - sx4;
12
13       /* Combine 4 elements at a time */
14       for (i = 0; i < limit; i += sx4) {
15           acc0 = acc0 + data[i];
16           acc1 = acc1 + data[i+stride];
17           acc2 = acc2 + data[i+sx2];
18           acc3 = acc3 + data[i+sx3];
19       }
20
21       /* Finish any remaining elements */
22       for (; i < length; i++) {
23           acc0 = acc0 + data[i];
24       }
25       return ((acc0 + acc1) + (acc2 + acc3));
26   }
27
28   /* run - Run test(elems, stride) and return read throughput (MB/s).
29    *        "size" is in bytes, "stride" is in array elements, and Mhz is
30    *        CPU clock frequency in Mhz.
31    */
32   double run(int size, int stride, double Mhz)
33   {
34       double cycles;
35       int elems = size / sizeof(double);
36
37       test(elems, stride);                    /* Warm up the cache */
38       cycles = fcyc2(test, elems, stride, 0); /* Call test(elems,stride) */
39       return (size / stride) / (cycles / Mhz); /* Convert cycles to MB/s */
40   }
```

—————————————————————————— code/mem/mountain/mountain.c

Figure 6.40 Functions that measure and compute read throughput. We can generate a memory mountain for a particular computer by calling the run function with different values of size (which corresponds to temporal locality) and stride (which corresponds to spatial locality).

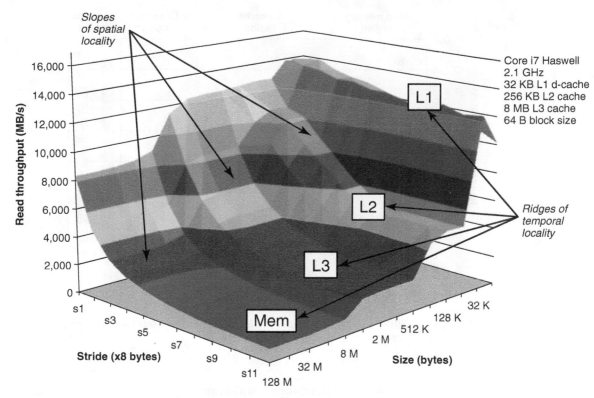

Figure 6.41   A memory mountain. Shows read throughput as a function of temporal and spatial locality.

The geography of the Core i7 mountain reveals a rich structure. Perpendicular to the `size` axis are four *ridges* that correspond to the regions of temporal locality where the working set fits entirely in the L1 cache, L2 cache, L3 cache, and main memory, respectively. Notice that there is more than an order of magnitude difference between the highest peak of the L1 ridge, where the CPU reads at a rate of over 14 GB/s, and the lowest point of the main memory ridge, where the CPU reads at a rate of 900 MB/s.

On each of the L2, L3, and main memory ridges, there is a slope of spatial locality that falls downhill as the stride increases and spatial locality decreases. Notice that even when the working set is too large to fit in any of the caches, the highest point on the main memory ridge is a factor of 8 higher than its lowest point. So even when a program has poor temporal locality, spatial locality can still come to the rescue and make a significant difference.

There is a particularly interesting flat ridge line that extends perpendicular to the stride axis for a stride of 1, where the read throughput is a relatively flat 12 GB/s, even though the working set exceeds the capacities of L1 and L2. This is apparently due to a hardware *prefetching* mechanism in the Core i7 memory system that automatically identifies sequential stride-1 reference patterns and attempts to fetch those blocks into the cache before they are accessed. While the

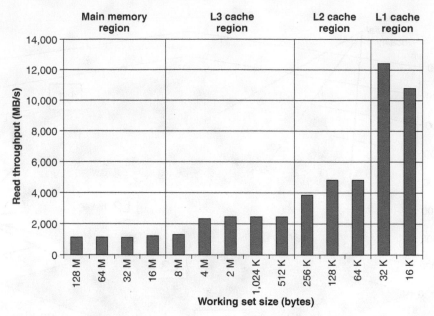

Figure 6.42 Ridges of temporal locality in the memory mountain. The graph shows a slice through Figure 6.41 with `stride = 8`.

details of the particular prefetching algorithm are not documented, it is clear from the memory mountain that the algorithm works best for small strides—yet another reason to favor sequential stride-1 accesses in your code.

If we take a slice through the mountain, holding the stride constant as in Figure 6.42, we can see the impact of cache size and temporal locality on performance. For sizes up to 32 KB, the working set fits entirely in the L1 d-cache, and thus reads are served from L1 at throughput of about 12 GB/s. For sizes up to 256 KB, the working set fits entirely in the unified L2 cache, and for sizes up to 8 MB, the working set fits entirely in the unified L3 cache. Larger working set sizes are served primarily from main memory.

The dips in read throughputs at the leftmost edges of the L2 and L3 cache regions—where the working set sizes of 256 KB and 8 MB are equal to their respective cache sizes—are interesting. It is not entirely clear why these dips occur. The only way to be sure is to perform a detailed cache simulation, but it is likely that the drops are caused by conflicts with other code and data lines.

Slicing through the memory mountain in the opposite direction, holding the working set size constant, gives us some insight into the impact of spatial locality on the read throughput. For example, Figure 6.43 shows the slice for a fixed working set size of 4 MB. This slice cuts along the L3 ridge in Figure 6.41, where the working set fits entirely in the L3 cache but is too large for the L2 cache.

Notice how the read throughput decreases steadily as the stride increases from one to eight words. In this region of the mountain, a read miss in L2 causes a block to be transferred from L3 to L2. This is followed by some number of hits

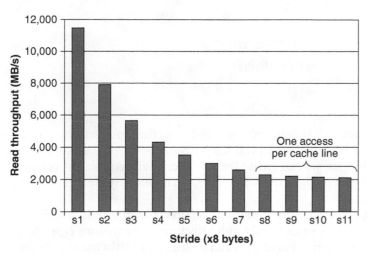

Figure 6.43   A slope of spatial locality. The graph shows a slice through Figure 6.41 with `size = 4 MB`.

on the block in L2, depending on the stride. As the stride increases, the ratio of L2 misses to L2 hits increases. Since misses are served more slowly than hits, the read throughput decreases. Once the stride reaches eight 8-byte words, which on this system equals the block size of 64 bytes, every read request misses in L2 and must be served from L3. Thus, the read throughput for strides of at least eight is a constant rate determined by the rate that cache blocks can be transferred from L3 into L2.

To summarize our discussion of the memory mountain, the performance of the memory system is not characterized by a single number. Instead, it is a mountain of temporal and spatial locality whose elevations can vary by over an order of magnitude. Wise programmers try to structure their programs so that they run in the peaks instead of the valleys. The aim is to exploit temporal locality so that heavily used words are fetched from the L1 cache, and to exploit spatial locality so that as many words as possible are accessed from a single L1 cache line.

Practice Problem 6.21 (solution page 666)

Use the memory mountain in Figure 6.41 to estimate the time, in CPU cycles, to read an 8-byte word from the L1 d-cache.

6.6.2   Rearranging Loops to Increase Spatial Locality

Consider the problem of multiplying a pair of $n \times n$ matrices: $C = AB$. For example, if $n = 2$, then

$$\begin{bmatrix} c_{11} & c_{12} \\ c_{21} & c_{22} \end{bmatrix} = \begin{bmatrix} a_{11} & a_{12} \\ a_{21} & a_{22} \end{bmatrix} \begin{bmatrix} b_{11} & b_{12} \\ b_{21} & b_{22} \end{bmatrix}$$

where

$$c_{11} = a_{11}b_{11} + a_{12}b_{21}$$
$$c_{12} = a_{11}b_{12} + a_{12}b_{22}$$
$$c_{21} = a_{21}b_{11} + a_{22}b_{21}$$
$$c_{22} = a_{21}b_{12} + a_{22}b_{22}$$

A matrix multiply function is usually implemented using three nested loops, which are identified by their indices i, j, and k. If we permute the loops and make some other minor code changes, we can create the six functionally equivalent versions of matrix multiply shown in Figure 6.44. Each version is uniquely identified by the ordering of its loops.

At a high level, the six versions are quite similar. If addition is associative, then each version computes an identical result.[1] Each version performs $O(n^3)$ total operations and an identical number of adds and multiplies. Each of the n^2 elements of A and B is read n times. Each of the n^2 elements of C is computed by summing n values. However, if we analyze the behavior of the innermost loop iterations, we find that there are differences in the number of accesses and the locality. For the purposes of this analysis, we make the following assumptions:

- Each array is an $n \times n$ array of double, with sizeof(double) $= 8$.
- There is a single cache with a 32-byte block size ($B = 32$).
- The array size n is so large that a single matrix row does not fit in the L1 cache.
- The compiler stores local variables in registers, and thus references to local variables inside loops do not require any load or store instructions.

Figure 6.45 summarizes the results of our inner-loop analysis. Notice that the six versions pair up into three equivalence classes, which we denote by the pair of matrices that are accessed in the inner loop. For example, versions ijk and jik are members of class AB because they reference arrays A and B (but not C) in their innermost loop. For each class, we have counted the number of loads (reads) and stores (writes) in each inner-loop iteration, the number of references to A, B, and C that will miss in the cache in each loop iteration, and the total number of cache misses per iteration.

The inner loops of the class AB routines (Figure 6.44(a) and (b)) scan a row of array A with a stride of 1. Since each cache block holds four 8-byte words, the miss rate for A is 0.25 misses per iteration. On the other hand, the inner loop scans a column of B with a stride of n. Since n is large, each access of array B results in a miss, for a total of 1.25 misses per iteration.

The inner loops in the class AC routines (Figure 6.44(c) and (d)) have some problems. Each iteration performs two loads and a store (as opposed to the

---

1. As we learned in Chapter 2, floating-point addition is commutative, but in general not associative. In practice, if the matrices do not mix extremely large values with extremely small ones, as often is true when the matrices store physical properties, then the assumption of associativity is reasonable.

(a) Version *ijk*

———————————————— *code/mem/matmult/mm.c*

```
1   for (i = 0; i < n; i++)
2       for (j = 0; j < n; j++) {
3           sum = 0.0;
4           for (k = 0; k < n; k++)
5               sum += A[i][k]*B[k][j];
6           C[i][j] += sum;
7       }
```

———————————————— *code/mem/matmult/mm.c*

(b) Version *jik*

———————————————— *code/mem/matmult/mm.c*

```
1   for (j = 0; j < n; j++)
2       for (i = 0; i < n; i++) {
3           sum = 0.0;
4           for (k = 0; k < n; k++)
5               sum += A[i][k]*B[k][j];
6           C[i][j] += sum;
7       }
```

———————————————— *code/mem/matmult/mm.c*

(c) Version *jki*

———————————————— *code/mem/matmult/mm.c*

```
1   for (j = 0; j < n; j++)
2       for (k = 0; k < n; k++) {
3           r = B[k][j];
4           for (i = 0; i < n; i++)
5               C[i][j] += A[i][k]*r;
6       }
```

———————————————— *code/mem/matmult/mm.c*

(d) Version *kji*

———————————————— *code/mem/matmult/mm.c*

```
1   for (k = 0; k < n; k++)
2       for (j = 0; j < n; j++) {
3           r = B[k][j];
4           for (i = 0; i < n; i++)
5               C[i][j] += A[i][k]*r;
6       }
```

———————————————— *code/mem/matmult/mm.c*

(e) Version *kij*

———————————————— *code/mem/matmult/mm.c*

```
1   for (k = 0; k < n; k++)
2       for (i = 0; i < n; i++) {
3           r = A[i][k];
4           for (j = 0; j < n; j++)
5               C[i][j] += r*B[k][j];
6       }
```

———————————————— *code/mem/matmult/mm.c*

(f) Version *ikj*

———————————————— *code/mem/matmult/mm.c*

```
1   for (i = 0; i < n; i++)
2       for (k = 0; k < n; k++) {
3           r = A[i][k];
4           for (j = 0; j < n; j++)
5               C[i][j] += r*B[k][j];
6       }
```

———————————————— *code/mem/matmult/mm.c*

Figure 6.44   Six versions of matrix multiply. Each version is uniquely identified by the ordering of its loops.

Matrix multiply version (class)	Per iteration					
	Loads	Stores	*A* misses	*B* misses	*C* misses	Total misses
ijk & *jik* (*AB*)	2	0	0.25	1.00	0.00	1.25
jki & *kji* (*AC*)	2	1	1.00	0.00	1.00	2.00
kij & *ikj* (*BC*)	2	1	0.00	0.25	0.25	0.50

Figure 6.45   Analysis of matrix multiply inner loops. The six versions partition into three equivalence classes, denoted by the pair of arrays that are accessed in the inner loop.

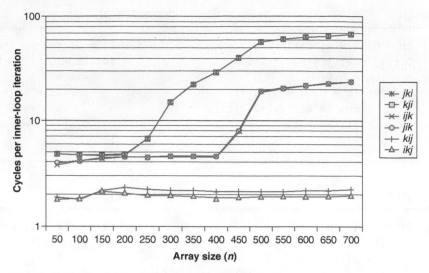

Figure 6.46 Core i7 matrix multiply performance.

class AB routines, which perform two loads and no stores). Second, the inner loop scans the columns of A and C with a stride of n. The result is a miss on each load, for a total of two misses per iteration. Notice that interchanging the loops has decreased the amount of spatial locality compared to the class AB routines.

The BC routines (Figure 6.44(e) and (f)) present an interesting trade-off: With two loads and a store, they require one more memory operation than the AB routines. On the other hand, since the inner loop scans both B and C row-wise with a stride-1 access pattern, the miss rate on each array is only 0.25 misses per iteration, for a total of 0.50 misses per iteration.

Figure 6.46 summarizes the performance of different versions of matrix multiply on a Core i7 system. The graph plots the measured number of CPU cycles per inner-loop iteration as a function of array size (n).

There are a number of interesting points to notice about this graph:

- For large values of n, the fastest version runs almost 40 times faster than the slowest version, even though each performs the same number of floating-point arithmetic operations.

- Pairs of versions with the same number of memory references and misses per iteration have almost identical measured performance.

- The two versions with the worst memory behavior, in terms of the number of accesses and misses per iteration, run significantly slower than the other four versions, which have fewer misses or fewer accesses, or both.

- Miss rate, in this case, is a better predictor of performance than the total number of memory accesses. For example, the class BC routines, with 0.5 misses per iteration, perform much better than the class AB routines, with 1.25 misses per iteration, even though the class BC routines perform more

Web Aside MEM:BLOCKING   Using blocking to increase temporal locality

There is an interesting technique called *blocking* that can improve the temporal locality of inner loops. The general idea of blocking is to organize the data structures in a program into large chunks called *blocks*. (In this context, "block" refers to an application-level chunk of data, *not* to a cache block.) The program is structured so that it loads a chunk into the L1 cache, does all the reads and writes that it needs to on that chunk, then discards the chunk, loads in the next chunk, and so on.

Unlike the simple loop transformations for improving spatial locality, blocking makes the code harder to read and understand. For this reason, it is best suited for optimizing compilers or frequently executed library routines. Blocking does not improve the performance of matrix multiply on the Core i7, because of its sophisticated prefetching hardware. Still, the technique is interesting to study and understand because it is a general concept that can produce big performance gains on systems that don't prefetch.

memory references in the inner loop (two loads and one store) than the class AB routines (two loads).

- For large values of n, the performance of the fastest pair of versions (kij and ikj) is constant. Even though the array is much larger than any of the SRAM cache memories, the prefetching hardware is smart enough to recognize the stride-1 access pattern, and fast enough to keep up with memory accesses in the tight inner loop. This is a stunning accomplishment by the Intel engineers who designed this memory system, providing even more incentive for programmers to develop programs with good spatial locality.

6.6.3   Exploiting Locality in Your Programs

As we have seen, the memory system is organized as a hierarchy of storage devices, with smaller, faster devices toward the top and larger, slower devices toward the bottom. Because of this hierarchy, the effective rate that a program can access memory locations is not characterized by a single number. Rather, it is a wildly varying function of program locality (what we have dubbed the memory mountain) that can vary by orders of magnitude. Programs with good locality access most of their data from fast cache memories. Programs with poor locality access most of their data from the relatively slow DRAM main memory.

Programmers who understand the nature of the memory hierarchy can exploit this understanding to write more efficient programs, regardless of the specific memory system organization. In particular, we recommend the following techniques:

- Focus your attention on the inner loops, where the bulk of the computations and memory accesses occur.
- Try to maximize the spatial locality in your programs by reading data objects sequentially, with stride 1, in the order they are stored in memory.
- Try to maximize the temporal locality in your programs by using a data object as often as possible once it has been read from memory.

6.7 Summary

The basic storage technologies are random access memories (RAMs), nonvolatile memories (ROMs), and disks. RAM comes in two basic forms. Static RAM (SRAM) is faster and more expensive and is used for cache memories. Dynamic RAM (DRAM) is slower and less expensive and is used for the main memory and graphics frame buffers. ROMs retain their information even if the supply voltage is turned off. They are used to store firmware. Rotating disks are mechanical nonvolatile storage devices that hold enormous amounts of data at a low cost per bit, but with much longer access times than DRAM. Solid state disks (SSDs) based on nonvolatile flash memory are becoming increasingly attractive alternatives to rotating disks for some applications.

In general, faster storage technologies are more expensive per bit and have smaller capacities. The price and performance properties of these technologies are changing at dramatically different rates. In particular, DRAM and disk access times are much larger than CPU cycle times. Systems bridge these gaps by organizing memory as a hierarchy of storage devices, with smaller, faster devices at the top and larger, slower devices at the bottom. Because well-written programs have good locality, most data are served from the higher levels, and the effect is a memory system that runs at the rate of the higher levels, but at the cost and capacity of the lower levels.

Programmers can dramatically improve the running times of their programs by writing programs with good spatial and temporal locality. Exploiting SRAM-based cache memories is especially important. Programs that fetch data primarily from cache memories can run much faster than programs that fetch data primarily from memory.

Bibliographic Notes

Memory and disk technologies change rapidly. In our experience, the best sources of technical information are the Web pages maintained by the manufacturers. Companies such as Micron, Toshiba, and Samsung provide a wealth of current technical information on memory devices. The pages for Seagate and Western Digital provide similarly useful information about disks.

Textbooks on circuit and logic design provide detailed information about memory technology [58, 89]. *IEEE Spectrum* published a series of survey articles on DRAM [55]. The International Symposiums on Computer Architecture (ISCA) and High Performance Computer Architecture (HPCA) are common forums for characterizations of DRAM memory performance [28, 29, 18].

Wilkes wrote the first paper on cache memories [117]. Smith wrote a classic survey [104]. Przybylski wrote an authoritative book on cache design [86]. Hennessy and Patterson provide a comprehensive discussion of cache design issues [46]. Levinthal wrote a comprehensive performance guide for the Intel Core i7 [70].

Stricker introduced the idea of the memory mountain as a comprehensive characterization of the memory system in [112] and suggested the term "memory mountain" informally in later presentations of the work. Compiler researchers work to increase locality by automatically performing the kinds of manual code transformations we discussed in Section 6.6 [22, 32, 66, 72, 79, 87, 119]. Carter and colleagues have proposed a cache-aware memory controller [17]. Other researchers have developed *cache-oblivious* algorithms that are designed to run well without any explicit knowledge of the structure of the underlying cache memory [30, 38, 39, 9].

There is a large body of literature on building and using disk storage. Many storage researchers look for ways to aggregate individual disks into larger, more robust, and more secure storage pools [20, 40, 41, 83, 121]. Others look for ways to use caches and locality to improve the performance of disk accesses [12, 21]. Systems such as Exokernel provide increased user-level control of disk and memory resources [57]. Systems such as the Andrew File System [78] and Coda [94] extend the memory hierarchy across computer networks and mobile notebook computers. Schindler and Ganger developed an interesting tool that automatically characterizes the geometry and performance of SCSI disk drives [95]. Researchers have investigated techniques for building and using flash-based SSDs [8, 81].

Homework Problems

6.22 ♦♦
Suppose you are asked to design a rotating disk where the number of bits per track is constant. You know that the number of bits per track is determined by the circumference of the innermost track, which you can assume is also the circumference of the hole. Thus, if you make the hole in the center of the disk larger, the number of bits per track increases, but the total number of tracks decreases. If you let r denote the radius of the platter, and $x \cdot r$ the radius of the hole, what value of x maximizes the capacity of the disk?

6.23 ♦
Estimate the average time (in ms) to access a sector on the following disk:

Parameter	Value
Rotational rate	15,000 RPM
$T_{avg\ seek}$	4 ms
Average number of sectors/track	800

6.24 ♦♦
Suppose that a 2 MB file consisting of 512-byte logical blocks is stored on a disk drive with the following characteristics:

Parameter	Value
Rotational rate	15,000 RPM
$T_{avg\ seek}$	4 ms
Average number of sectors/track	1,000
Surfaces	8
Sector size	512 bytes

For each case below, suppose that a program reads the logical blocks of the file sequentially, one after the other, and that the time to position the head over the first block is $T_{\text{avg seek}} + T_{\text{avg rotation}}$.

A. *Best case:* Estimate the optimal time (in ms) required to read the file over all possible mappings of logical blocks to disk sectors.

B. *Random case:* Estimate the time (in ms) required to read the file if blocks are mapped randomly to disk sectors.

6.25 ◆
The following table gives the parameters for a number of different caches. For each cache, fill in the missing fields in the table. Recall that m is the number of physical address bits, C is the cache size (number of data bytes), B is the block size in bytes, E is the associativity, S is the number of cache sets, t is the number of tag bits, s is the number of set index bits, and b is the number of block offset bits.

Cache	m	C	B	E	S	t	s	b
1.	32	1,024	4	4	_____	_____	_____	_____
2.	32	1,024	4	256	_____	_____	_____	_____
3.	32	1,024	8	1	_____	_____	_____	_____
4.	32	1,024	8	128	_____	_____	_____	_____
5.	32	1,024	32	1	_____	_____	_____	_____
6.	32	1,024	32	4	_____	_____	_____	_____

6.26 ◆
The following table gives the parameters for a number of different caches. Your task is to fill in the missing fields in the table. Recall that m is the number of physical address bits, C is the cache size (number of data bytes), B is the block size in bytes, E is the associativity, S is the number of cache sets, t is the number of tag bits, s is the number of set index bits, and b is the number of block offset bits.

Cache	m	C	B	E	S	t	s	b
1.	32	_____	8	1	_____	21	8	3
2.	32	2,048	_____	_____	128	23	7	2
3.	32	1,024	2	8	64	_____	_____	1
4.	32	1,024	_____	2	16	23	4	_____

6.27 ◆
This problem concerns the cache in Practice Problem 6.12.

A. List all of the hex memory addresses that will hit in set 1.

B. List all of the hex memory addresses that will hit in set 6.

6.28 ◆◆
This problem concerns the cache in Practice Problem 6.12.

A. List all of the hex memory addresses that will hit in set 2.

B. List all of the hex memory addresses that will hit in set 4.

C. List all of the hex memory addresses that will hit in set 5.

D. List all of the hex memory addresses that will hit in set 7.

6.29 ◆◆

Suppose we have a system with the following properties:

- The memory is byte addressable.
- Memory accesses are to 1-byte words (not to 4-byte words).
- Addresses are 12 bits wide.
- The cache is two-way set associative ($E = 2$), with a 4-byte block size ($B = 4$) and four sets ($S = 4$).

The contents of the cache are as follows, with all addresses, tags, and values given in hexadecimal notation:

Set index	Tag	Valid	Byte 0	Byte 1	Byte 2	Byte 3
0	00	1	40	41	42	43
	83	1	FE	97	CC	D0
1	00	1	44	45	46	47
	83	0	—	—	—	—
2	00	1	48	49	4A	4B
	40	0	—	—	—	—
3	FF	1	9A	C0	03	FF
	00	0	—	—	—	—

A. The following diagram shows the format of an address (1 bit per box). Indicate (by labeling the diagram) the fields that would be used to determine the following:

    CO. The cache block offset

    CI. The cache set index

    CT. The cache tag

12	11	10	9	8	7	6	5	4	3	2	1	0

B. For each of the following memory accesses, indicate if it will be a cache hit or miss when *carried out in sequence* as listed. Also give the value of a read if it can be inferred from the information in the cache.

Operation	Address	Hit?	Read value (or unknown)
Read	0x834	_____	_____
Write	0x836	_____	_____
Read	0xFFD	_____	_____

6.30 ◆

Suppose we have a system with the following properties:

- The memory is byte addressable.
- Memory accesses are to 1-byte words (not to 4-byte words).
- Addresses are 13 bits wide.
- The cache is 4-way set associative ($E = 4$), with a 4-byte block size ($B = 4$) and eight sets ($S = 8$).

Consider the following cache state. All addresses, tags, and values are given in hexadecimal format. The Index column contains the set index for each set of four lines. The Tag columns contain the tag value for each line. The V columns contain the valid bit for each line. The Bytes 0–3 columns contain the data for each line, numbered left to right starting with byte 0 on the left.

4-way set associative cache

Index	Tag	V	Bytes 0–3	Tag	V	Bytes 0–3	Tag	V	Bytes 0–3	Tag	V	Bytes 0–3
0	F0	1	ED 32 0A A2	8A	1	BF 80 1D FC	14	1	EF 09 86 2A	BC	0	25 44 6F 1A
1	BC	0	03 3E CD 38	A0	0	16 7B ED 5A	BC	1	8E 4C DF 18	E4	1	FB B7 12 02
2	BC	1	54 9E 1E FA	B6	1	DC 81 B2 14	00	0	B6 1F 7B 44	74	0	10 F5 B8 2E
3	BE	0	2F 7E 3D A8	C0	1	27 95 A4 74	C4	0	07 11 6B D8	BC	0	C7 B7 AF C2
4	7E	1	32 21 1C 2C	8A	1	22 C2 DC 34	BC	1	BA DD 37 D8	DC	0	E7 A2 39 BA
5	98	0	A9 76 2B EE	54	0	BC 91 D5 92	98	1	80 BA 9B F6	BC	1	48 16 81 0A
6	38	0	5D 4D F7 DA	BC	1	69 C2 8C 74	8A	1	A8 CE 7F DA	38	1	FA 93 EB 48
7	8A	1	04 2A 32 6A	9E	0	B1 86 56 0E	CC	1	96 30 47 F2	BC	1	F8 1D 42 30

A. What is the size (C) of this cache in bytes?

B. The box that follows shows the format of an address (1 bit per box). Indicate (by labeling the diagram) the fields that would be used to determine the following:

    CO. The cache block offset

    CI. The cache set index

    CT. The cache tag

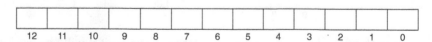

12	11	10	9	8	7	6	5	4	3	2	1	0

6.31 ◆◆

Suppose that a program using the cache in Problem 6.30 references the 1-byte word at address 0x071A. Indicate the cache entry accessed and the cache byte value returned *in hex*. Indicate whether a cache miss occurs. If there is a cache miss, enter "—" for "Cache byte returned." *Hint:* Pay attention to those valid bits!

A. Address format (1 bit per box):

12	11	10	9	8	7	6	5	4	3	2	1	0

B. Memory reference:

Parameter	Value
Block offset (CO)	0x_____
Index (CI)	0x_____
Cache tag (CT)	0x_____
Cache hit? (Y/N)	_____
Cache byte returned	0x_____

6.32 ◆◆

Repeat Problem 6.31 for memory address 0x16E8.

A. Address format (1 bit per box):

12	11	10	9	8	7	6	5	4	3	2	1	0

B. Memory reference:

Parameter	Value
Cache offset (CO)	0x_____
Cache index (CI)	0x_____
Cache tag (CT)	0x_____
Cache hit? (Y/N)	_____
Cache byte returned	0x_____

6.33 ◆◆

For the cache in Problem 6.30, list the eight memory addresses (in hex) that will hit in set 2.

6.34 ◆◆

Consider the following matrix transpose routine:

```
1   typedef int array[4][4];
2
3   void transpose2(array dst, array src)
4   {
5       int i, j;
6
```

```
7        for (i = 0; i < 4; i++) {
8            for (j = 0; j < 4; j++) {
9                dst[j][i] = src[i][j];
10           }
11       }
12   }
```

Assume this code runs on a machine with the following properties:

- sizeof(int) = 4.
- The src array starts at address 0 and the dst array starts at address 64 (decimal).
- There is a single L1 data cache that is direct-mapped, write-through, write-allocate, with a block size of 16 bytes.
- The cache has a total size of 32 data bytes, and the cache is initially empty.
- Accesses to the src and dst arrays are the only sources of read and write misses, respectively.

A. For each row and col, indicate whether the access to src[row][col] and dst[row][col] is a hit (h) or a miss (m). For example, reading src[0][0] is a miss and writing dst[0][0] is also a miss.

	dst array					src array			
	Col. 0	Col. 1	Col. 2	Col. 3		Col. 0	Col. 1	Col. 2	Col. 3
Row 0	m	___	___	___	Row 0	m	___	___	___
Row 1	___	___	___	___	Row 1	___	___	___	___
Row 2	___	___	___	___	Row 2	___	___	___	___
Row 3	___	___	___	___	Row 3	___	___	___	___

6.35 ◆◆
Repeat Problem 6.34 for a cache with a total size of 128 data bytes.

	dst array					src array			
	Col. 0	Col. 1	Col. 2	Col. 3		Col. 0	Col. 1	Col. 2	Col. 3
Row 0	___	___	___	___	Row 0	___	___	___	___
Row 1	___	___	___	___	Row 1	___	___	___	___
Row 2	___	___	___	___	Row 2	___	___	___	___
Row 3	___	___	___	___	Row 3	___	___	___	___

6.36 ◆◆
This problem tests your ability to predict the cache behavior of C code. You are given the following code to analyze:

```
1        int x[2][128];
2        int i;
```

```
3        int sum = 0;
4
5        for (i = 0; i < 128; i++) {
6            sum += x[0][i] * x[1][i];
7        }
```

Assume we execute this under the following conditions:

- $sizeof(int) = 4$.
- Array x begins at memory address 0x0 and is stored in row-major order.
- In each case below, the cache is initially empty.
- The only memory accesses are to the entries of the array x. All other variables are stored in registers.

Given these assumptions, estimate the miss rates for the following cases:

A. Case 1: Assume the cache is 512 bytes, direct-mapped, with 16-byte cache blocks. What is the miss rate?

B. Case 2: What is the miss rate if we double the cache size to 1,024 bytes?

C. Case 3: Now assume the cache is 512 bytes, two-way set associative using an LRU replacement policy, with 16-byte cache blocks. What is the cache miss rate?

D. For case 3, will a larger cache size help to reduce the miss rate? Why or why not?

E. For case 3, will a larger block size help to reduce the miss rate? Why or why not?

6.37 ◆◆

This is another problem that tests your ability to analyze the cache behavior of C code. Assume we execute the three summation functions in Figure 6.47 under the following conditions:

- $sizeof(int) = 4$.
- The machine has a 4 KB direct-mapped cache with a 16-byte block size.
- Within the two loops, the code uses memory accesses only for the array data. The loop indices and the value sum are held in registers.
- Array a is stored starting at memory address 0x08000000.

Fill in the table for the approximate cache miss rate for the two cases $N = 64$ and $N = 60$.

Function	$N = 64$	$N = 60$
sumA	___	___
sumB	___	___
sumC	___	___

```
1      typedef int array_t[N][N];
2
3      int sumA(array_t a)
4      {
5          int i, j;
6          int sum = 0;
7          for (i = 0; i < N; i++)
8              for (j = 0; j < N; j++) {
9                  sum += a[i][j];
10             }
11         return sum;
12     }
13
14     int sumB(array_t a)
15     {
16         int i, j;
17         int sum = 0;
18         for (j = 0; j < N; j++)
19             for (i = 0; i < N; i++) {
20                 sum += a[i][j];
21             }
22         return sum;
23     }
24
25     int sumC(array_t a)
26     {
27         int i, j;
28         int sum = 0;
29         for (j = 0; j < N; j+=2)
30             for (i = 0; i < N; i+=2) {
31                 sum += (a[i][j] + a[i+1][j]
32                         + a[i][j+1] + a[i+1][j+1]);
33             }
34         return sum;
35     }
```

Figure 6.47 Functions referenced in Problem 6.37.

6.38 ◆

3M decides to make Post-its by printing yellow squares on white pieces of paper. As part of the printing process, they need to set the CMYK (cyan, magenta, yellow, black) value for every point in the square. 3M hires you to determine the efficiency of the following algorithms on a machine with a 2,048-byte direct-mapped data cache with 32-byte blocks. You are given the following definitions:

```
1    struct point_color {
2        int c;
3        int m;
4        int y;
5        int k;
6    };
7
8    struct point_color square[16][16];
9    int i, j;
```

Assume the following:

- sizeof(int) = 4.
- square begins at memory address 0.
- The cache is initially empty.
- The only memory accesses are to the entries of the array square. Variables i and j are stored in registers.

Determine the cache performance of the following code:

```
1        for (i = 0; i < 16; i++){
2            for (j = 0; j < 16; j++) {
3                square[i][j].c = 0;
4                square[i][j].m = 0;
5                square[i][j].y = 1;
6                square[i][j].k = 0;
7            }
8        }
```

A. What is the total number of writes?

B. What is the total number of writes that miss in the cache?

C. What is the miss rate?

6.39 ◆
Given the assumptions in Problem 6.38, determine the cache performance of the following code:

```
1        for (i = 0; i < 16; i++){
2            for (j = 0; j < 16; j++) {
3                square[j][i].c = 0;
4                square[j][i].m = 0;
5                square[j][i].y = 1;
6                square[j][i].k = 0;
7            }
8        }
```

A. What is the total number of writes?

B. What is the total number of writes that miss in the cache?

C. What is the miss rate?

6.40 ◆

Given the assumptions in Problem 6.38, determine the cache performance of the following code:

```
1       for (i = 0; i < 16; i++) {
2           for (j = 0; j < 16; j++) {
3               square[i][j].y = 1;
4           }
5       }
6       for (i = 0; i < 16; i++) {
7           for (j = 0; j < 16; j++) {
8               square[i][j].c = 0;
9               square[i][j].m = 0;
10              square[i][j].k = 0;
11          }
12      }
```

A. What is the total number of writes?

B. What is the total number of writes that miss in the cache?

C. What is the miss rate?

6.41 ◆◆

You are writing a new 3D game that you hope will earn you fame and fortune. You are currently working on a function to blank the screen buffer before drawing the next frame. The screen you are working with is a 640 × 480 array of pixels. The machine you are working on has a 64 KB direct-mapped cache with 4-byte lines. The C structures you are using are as follows:

```
1       struct pixel {
2           char r;
3           char g;
4           char b;
5           char a;
6       };
7
8       struct pixel buffer[480][640];
9       int i, j;
10      char *cptr;
11      int *iptr;
```

Assume the following:

• sizeof(char) = 1 and sizeof(int) = 4.

- `buffer` begins at memory address 0.
- The cache is initially empty.
- The only memory accesses are to the entries of the array `buffer`. Variables `i`, `j`, `cptr`, and `iptr` are stored in registers.

What percentage of writes in the following code will miss in the cache?

```
1    for (j = 0; j < 640; j++) {
2        for (i = 0; i < 480; i++){
3            buffer[i][j].r = 0;
4            buffer[i][j].g = 0;
5            buffer[i][j].b = 0;
6            buffer[i][j].a = 0;
7        }
8    }
```

6.42 ◆◆
Given the assumptions in Problem 6.41, what percentage of writes in the following code will miss in the cache?

```
1    char *cptr = (char *) buffer;
2    for (; cptr < (((char *) buffer) + 640 * 480 * 4); cptr++)
3        *cptr = 0;
```

6.43 ◆◆
Given the assumptions in Problem 6.41, what percentage of writes in the following code will miss in the cache?

```
1    int *iptr = (int *)buffer;
2    for (; iptr < ((int *)buffer + 640*480); iptr++)
3        *iptr = 0;
```

6.44 ◆◆◆
Download the `mountain` program from the CS:APP Web site and run it on your favorite PC/Linux system. Use the results to estimate the sizes of the caches on your system.

6.45 ◆◆◆◆
In this assignment, you will apply the concepts you learned in Chapters 5 and 6 to the problem of optimizing code for a memory-intensive application. Consider a procedure to copy and transpose the elements of an $N \times N$ matrix of type int. That is, for source matrix S and destination matrix D, we want to copy each element $s_{i,j}$ to $d_{j,i}$. This code can be written with a simple loop,

```
1    void transpose(int *dst, int *src, int dim)
2    {
3        int i, j;
4
```

```
5          for (i = 0; i < dim; i++)
6              for (j = 0; j < dim; j++)
7                  dst[j*dim + i] = src[i*dim + j];
8      }
```

where the arguments to the procedure are pointers to the destination (dst) and source (src) matrices, as well as the matrix size N (dim). Your job is to devise a transpose routine that runs as fast as possible.

6.46 ◆◆◆◆

This assignment is an intriguing variation of Problem 6.45. Consider the problem of converting a directed graph g into its undirected counterpart g'. The graph g' has an edge from vertex u to vertex v if and only if there is an edge from u to v or from v to u in the original graph g. The graph g is represented by its *adjacency matrix G* as follows. If N is the number of vertices in g, then G is an $N \times N$ matrix and its entries are all either 0 or 1. Suppose the vertices of g are named $v_0, v_1, v_2, \ldots, v_{N-1}$. Then $G[i][j]$ is 1 if there is an edge from v_i to v_j and is 0 otherwise. Observe that the elements on the diagonal of an adjacency matrix are always 1 and that the adjacency matrix of an undirected graph is symmetric. This code can be written with a simple loop:

```
1      void col_convert(int *G, int dim) {
2          int i, j;
3
4          for (i = 0; i < dim; i++)
5              for (j = 0; j < dim; j++)
6                  G[j*dim + i] = G[j*dim + i] || G[i*dim + j];
7      }
```

Your job is to devise a conversion routine that runs as fast as possible. As before, you will need to apply concepts you learned in Chapters 5 and 6 to come up with a good solution.

Solutions to Practice Problems

Solution to Problem 6.1 (page 584)

The idea here is to minimize the number of address bits by minimizing the aspect ratio $\max(r, c)/\min(r, c)$. In other words, the squarer the array, the fewer the address bits.

Organization	r	c	b_r	b_c	$\max(b_r, b_c)$
16×1	4	4	2	2	2
16×4	4	4	2	2	2
128×8	16	8	4	3	4
512×4	32	16	5	4	5
$1,024 \times 4$	32	32	5	5	5

Solution to Problem 6.2 (page 592)

The point of this little drill is to make sure you understand the relationship between cylinders and tracks. Once you have that straight, just plug and chug:

$$\text{Disk capacity} = \frac{512 \text{ bytes}}{\text{sector}} \times \frac{400 \text{ sectors}}{\text{track}} \times \frac{10{,}000 \text{ tracks}}{\text{surface}} \times \frac{2 \text{ surfaces}}{\text{platter}} \times \frac{2 \text{ platters}}{\text{disk}}$$

$$= 8{,}192{,}000{,}000 \text{ bytes}$$

$$= 8.192 \text{ GB}$$

Solution to Problem 6.3 (page 595)

The solution to this problem is a straightforward application of the formula for disk access time. The average rotational latency (in ms) is

$$T_{\text{avg rotation}} = 1/2 \times T_{\text{max rotation}}$$

$$= 1/2 \times (60 \text{ secs}/15{,}000 \text{ RPM}) \times 1{,}000 \text{ ms/sec}$$

$$\approx 2 \text{ ms}$$

The average transfer time is

$$T_{\text{avg transfer}} = (60 \text{ secs}/15{,}000 \text{ RPM}) \times 1/500 \text{ sectors/track} \times 1{,}000 \text{ ms/sec}$$

$$\approx 0.008 \text{ ms}$$

Putting it all together, the total estimated access time is

$$T_{\text{access}} = T_{\text{avg seek}} + T_{\text{avg rotation}} + T_{\text{avg transfer}}$$

$$= 8 \text{ ms} + 2 \text{ ms} + 0.008 \text{ ms}$$

$$\approx 10 \text{ ms}$$

Solution to Problem 6.4 (page 595)

This is a good check of your understanding of the factors that affect disk performance. First we need to determine a few basic properties of the file and the disk. The file consists of 2,000 512-byte logical blocks. For the disk, $T_{\text{avg seek}} = 5$ ms, $T_{\text{max rotation}} = 6$ ms, and $T_{\text{avg rotation}} = 3$ ms.

A. *Best case:* In the optimal case, the blocks are mapped to contiguous sectors, on the same cylinder, that can be read one after the other without moving the head. Once the head is positioned over the first sector it takes two full rotations (1,000 sectors per rotation) of the disk to read all 2,000 blocks. So the total time to read the file is $T_{\text{avg seek}} + T_{\text{avg rotation}} + 2 \times T_{\text{max rotation}} = 5 + 3 + 12 = 20$ ms.

B. *Random case:* In this case, where blocks are mapped randomly to sectors, reading each of the 2,000 blocks requires $T_{\text{avg seek}} + T_{\text{avg rotation}}$ ms, so the total time to read the file is $(T_{\text{avg seek}} + T_{\text{avg rotation}}) \times 2{,}000 = 16{,}000$ ms (16 seconds!).

You can see now why it's often a good idea to defragment your disk drive!

Solution to Problem 6.5 (page 601)

This is a simple problem that will give you some interesting insights into the feasibility of SSDs. Recall that for disks, $1\,\text{PB} = 10^9\,\text{MB}$. Then the following straightforward translation of units yields the following predicted times for each case:

A. Worst-case sequential writes (470 MB/s):

$$(10^9 \times 128) \times (1/470) \times (1/(86{,}400 \times 365)) \approx 8 \text{ years}$$

B. Worst-case random writes (303 MB/s):

$$(10^9 \times 128) \times (1/303) \times (1/(86{,}400 \times 365)) \approx 13 \text{ years}$$

C. Average case (20 GB/day):

$$(10^9 \times 128) \times (1/20{,}000) \times (1/365) \approx 140 \text{ years}$$

So even if the SSD operates continuously, it should last for at least 8 years, which is longer than the expected lifetime of most computers.

Solution to Problem 6.6 (page 604)

In the 10-year period between 2005 and 2015, the unit price of rotating disks dropped by a factor of 166, which means the price is dropping by roughly a factor of 2 every 18 months or so. Assuming this trend continues, a petabyte of storage, which costs about $30,000 in 2015, will drop below $500 after about seven of these factor-of-2 reductions. Since these are occurring every 18 months, we might expect a petabyte of storage to be available for $500 around the year 2025.

Solution to Problem 6.7 (page 608)

To create a stride-1 reference pattern, the loops must be permuted so that the rightmost indices change most rapidly.

```
1    int sumarray3d(int a[N][N][N])
2    {
3        int i, j, k, sum = 0;
4
5        for (k = 0; k < N; k++) {
6            for (i = 0; i < N; i++) {
7                for (j = 0; j < N; j++) {
8                    sum += a[k][i][j];
9                }
10           }
11       }
12       return sum;
13   }
```

This is an important idea. Make sure you understand why this particular loop permutation results in a stride-1 access pattern.

Solution to Problem 6.8 (page 609)

The key to solving this problem is to visualize how the array is laid out in memory and then analyze the reference patterns. Function `clear1` accesses the array using a stride-1 reference pattern and thus clearly has the best spatial locality. Function `clear2` scans each of the N structs in order, which is good, but within each struct it hops around in a non-stride-1 pattern at the following offsets from the beginning of the struct: 0, 12, 4, 16, 8, 20. So `clear2` has worse spatial locality than `clear1`. Function `clear3` not only hops around within each struct, but also hops from struct to struct. So `clear3` exhibits worse spatial locality than `clear2` and `clear1`.

Solution to Problem 6.9 (page 616)

The solution is a straightforward application of the definitions of the various cache parameters in Figure 6.26. Not very exciting, but you need to understand how the cache organization induces these partitions in the address bits before you can really understand how caches work.

Cache	m	C	B	E	S	t	s	b
1.	32	1,024	4	1	256	22	8	2
2.	32	1,024	8	4	32	24	5	3
3.	32	1,024	32	32	1	27	0	5

Solution to Problem 6.10 (page 624)

The padding eliminates the conflict misses. Thus, three-fourths of the references are hits.

Solution to Problem 6.11 (page 624)

Sometimes, understanding why something is a bad idea helps you understand why the alternative is a good idea. Here, the bad idea we are looking at is indexing the cache with the high-order bits instead of the middle bits.

A. With high-order bit indexing, each contiguous array chunk consists of 2^t blocks, where t is the number of tag bits. Thus, the first 2^t contiguous blocks of the array would map to set 0, the next 2^t blocks would map to set 1, and so on.

B. For a direct-mapped cache where $(S, E, B, m) = (512, 1, 32, 32)$, the cache capacity is 512 32-byte blocks with $t = 18$ tag bits in each cache line. Thus, the first 2^{18} blocks in the array would map to set 0, the next 2^{18} blocks to set 1. Since our array consists of only $(4,096 \times 4)/32 = 512$ blocks, all of the blocks in the array map to set 0. Thus, the cache will hold at most 1 array block at any point in time, even though the array is small enough to fit entirely in the cache. Clearly, using high-order bit indexing makes poor use of the cache.

Solution to Problem 6.12 (page 628)

The 2 low-order bits are the block offset (CO), followed by 3 bits of set index (CI), with the remaining bits serving as the tag (CT):

CT	CT	CT	CT	CT	CT	CT	CT	CI	CI	CI	CO	CO
12	11	10	9	8	7	6	5	4	3	2	1	0

Solution to Problem 6.13 (page 628)

Address: 0x0E34

A. Address format (1 bit per box):

CT	CT	CT	CT	CT	CT	CT	CT	CI	CI	CI	CO	CO
0	1	1	1	0	0	0	1	1	0	1	0	0
12	11	10	9	8	7	6	5	4	3	2	1	0

B. Memory reference:

Parameter	Value
Cache block offset (CO)	0x0
Cache set index (CI)	0x5
Cache tag (CT)	0x71
Cache hit? (Y/N)	Y
Cache byte returned	0xB

Solution to Problem 6.14 (page 629)

Address: 0x0DD5

A. Address format (1 bit per box):

CT	CT	CT	CT	CT	CT	CT	CT	CI	CI	CI	CO	CO
0	1	1	0	1	1	1	0	1	0	1	0	1
12	11	10	9	8	7	6	5	4	3	2	1	0

B. Memory reference:

Parameter	Value
Cache block offset (CO)	0x1
Cache set index (CI)	0x5
Cache tag (CT)	0x6E
Cache hit? (Y/N)	N
Cache byte returned	—

Solution to Problem 6.15 (page 629)

Address: 0x1FE4

A. Address format (1 bit per box):

CT	CT	CT	CT	CT	CT	CT	CT	CI	CI	CI	CO	CO
1	1	1	1	1	1	1	1	0	0	1	0	0
12	11	10	9	8	7	6	5	4	3	2	1	0

B. Memory reference:

Parameter	Value
Cache block offset	0x0
Cache set index	0x1
Cache tag	0xFF
Cache hit? (Y/N)	N
Cache byte returned	—

Solution to Problem 6.16 (page 630)

This problem is a sort of inverse version of Practice Problems 6.12–6.15 that requires you to work backward from the contents of the cache to derive the addresses that will hit in a particular set. In this case, set 3 contains one valid line with a tag of 0x32. Since there is only one valid line in the set, four addresses will hit. These addresses have the binary form 0 0110 0100 11xx. Thus, the four hex addresses that hit in set 3 are

$$0x064C, \ 0x064D, \ 0x064E, \ \text{and } 0x064F$$

Solution to Problem 6.17 (page 636)

A. The key to solving this problem is to visualize the picture in Figure 6.48. Notice that each cache line holds exactly one row of the array, that the cache is exactly large enough to hold one array, and that for all i, row i of src and dst maps to the same cache line. Because the cache is too small to hold both arrays, references to one array keep evicting useful lines from the other array. For example, the write to dst[0][0] evicts the line that was loaded when we read src[0][0]. So when we next read src[0][1], we have a miss.

dst array	Col. 0	Col. 1		src array	Col. 0	Col. 1
Row 0	m	m		Row 0	m	m
Row 1	m	m		Row 1	m	h

B. When the cache is 32 bytes, it is large enough to hold both arrays. Thus, the only misses are the initial cold misses.

dst array	Col. 0	Col. 1		src array	Col. 0	Col. 1
Row 0	m	h		Row 0	m	h
Row 1	m	h		Row 1	m	h

Figure 6.48

Figure for solution to Problem 6.17.

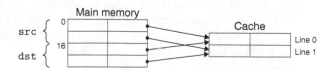

Solution to Problem 6.18 (page 637)

Each 16-byte cache line holds two contiguous `algae_position` structures. Each loop visits these structures in memory order, reading one integer element each time. So the pattern for each loop is miss, hit, miss, hit, and so on. Notice that for this problem we could have predicted the miss rate without actually enumerating the total number of reads and misses.

A. What is the total number of read accesses? 512 reads.

B. What is the total number of read accesses that miss in the cache? 256 misses.

C. What is the miss rate? $256/512 = 50\%$.

Solution to Problem 6.19 (page 638)

The key to this problem is noticing that the cache can only hold 1/2 of the array. So the column-wise scan of the second half of the array evicts the lines that were loaded during the scan of the first half. For example, reading the first element of `grid[8][0]` evicts the line that was loaded when we read elements from `grid[0][0]`. This line also contained `grid[0][1]`. So when we begin scanning the next column, the reference to the first element of `grid[0][1]` misses.

A. What is the total number of read accesses? 512 reads.

B. What is the total number of read accesses that miss in the cache? 256 misses.

C. What is the miss rate? $256/512 = 50\%$.

D. What would the miss rate be if the cache were twice as big? If the cache were twice as big, it could hold the entire `grid` array. The only misses would be the initial cold misses, and the miss rate would be $1/4 = 25\%$.

Solution to Problem 6.20 (page 638)

This loop has a nice stride-1 reference pattern, and thus the only misses are the initial cold misses.

A. What is the total number of read accesses? 512 reads.

B. What is the total number of read accesses that miss in the cache? 128 misses.

C. What is the miss rate? $128/512 = 25\%$.

D. What would the miss rate be if the cache were twice as big? Increasing the cache size by any amount would not change the miss rate, since cold misses are unavoidable.

Solution to Problem 6.21 (page 643)

The sustained throughput using large strides from L1 is about 12,000 MB/s, the clock frequency is 2,100 MHz, and the individual read accesses are in units of 8-byte `longs`. Thus, from this graph we can estimate that it takes roughly $2,100/12,000 \times 8 = 1.4 \approx 1.5$ cycles to access a word from L1 on this machine, which is roughly 2.5 times faster than the nominal 4-cycle latency from L1. This is due to the parallelism of the 4×4 unrolled loop, which allows multiple loads to be in flight at the same time.

Part II
Running Programs on a System

Our exploration of computer systems continues with a closer look at the systems software that builds and runs application programs. The linker combines different parts of our programs into a single file that can be loaded into memory and executed by the processor. Modern operating systems cooperate with the hardware to provide each program with the illusion that it has exclusive use of a processor and the main memory, when in reality multiple programs are running on the system at any point in time.

In the first part of this book, you developed a good understanding of the interaction between your programs and the hardware. Part II of the book will broaden your view of systems by giving you a solid understanding of the interactions between your programs and the operating system. You will learn how to use services provided by the operating system to build system-level programs such as Unix shells and dynamic memory allocation packages.

CHAPTER 7

Linking

Linking is the process of collecting and combining various pieces of code and data into a single file that can be *loaded* (copied) into memory and executed. Linking can be performed at *compile time*, when the source code is translated into machine code; at *load time*, when the program is loaded into memory and executed by the *loader*; and even at *run time*, by application programs. On early computer systems, linking was performed manually. On modern systems, linking is performed automatically by programs called *linkers*.

Linkers play a crucial role in software development because they enable *separate compilation*. Instead of organizing a large application as one monolithic source file, we can decompose it into smaller, more manageable modules that can be modified and compiled separately. When we change one of these modules, we simply recompile it and relink the application, without having to recompile the other files.

Linking is usually handled quietly by the linker and is not an important issue for students who are building small programs in introductory programming classes. So why bother learning about linking?

- *Understanding linkers will help you build large programs.* Programmers who build large programs often encounter linker errors caused by missing modules, missing libraries, or incompatible library versions. Unless you understand how a linker resolves references, what a library is, and how a linker uses a library to resolve references, these kinds of errors will be baffling and frustrating.

- *Understanding linkers will help you avoid dangerous programming errors.* The decisions that Linux linkers make when they resolve symbol references can silently affect the correctness of your programs. Programs that incorrectly define multiple global variables can pass through the linker without any warnings in the default case. The resulting programs can exhibit baffling run-time behavior and are extremely difficult to debug. We will show you how this happens and how to avoid it.

- *Understanding linking will help you understand how language scoping rules are implemented.* For example, what is the difference between global and local variables? What does it really mean when you define a variable or function with the static attribute?

- *Understanding linking will help you understand other important systems concepts.* The executable object files produced by linkers play key roles in important systems functions such as loading and running programs, virtual memory, paging, and memory mapping.

- *Understanding linking will enable you to exploit shared libraries.* For many years, linking was considered to be fairly straightforward and uninteresting. However, with the increased importance of shared libraries and dynamic linking in modern operating systems, linking is a sophisticated process that provides the knowledgeable programmer with significant power. For example, many software products use shared libraries to upgrade shrink-wrapped binaries at run time. Also, many Web servers rely on dynamic linking of shared libraries to serve dynamic content.

(a) main.c

——————————————————— *code/link/main.c*

```
1    int sum(int *a, int n);
2
3    int array[2] = {1, 2};
4
5    int main()
6    {
7        int val = sum(array, 2);
8        return val;
9    }
```

——————————————————— *code/link/main.c*

(b) sum.c

——————————————————— *code/link/sum.c*

```
1    int sum(int *a, int n)
2    {
3        int i, s = 0;
4
5        for (i = 0; i < n; i++) {
6            s += a[i];
7        }
8        return s;
9    }
```

——————————————————— *code/link/sum.c*

Figure 7.1 Example program 1. The example program consists of two source files, main.c and sum.c. The main function initializes an array of ints, and then calls the sum function to sum the array elements.

This chapter provides a thorough discussion of all aspects of linking, from traditional static linking, to dynamic linking of shared libraries at load time, to dynamic linking of shared libraries at run time. We will describe the basic mechanisms using real examples, and we will identify situations in which linking issues can affect the performance and correctness of your programs. To keep things concrete and understandable, we will couch our discussion in the context of an x86-64 system running Linux and using the standard ELF-64 (hereafter referred to as ELF) object file format. However, it is important to realize that the basic concepts of linking are universal, regardless of the operating system, the ISA, or the object file format. Details may vary, but the concepts are the same.

7.1 Compiler Drivers

Consider the C program in Figure 7.1. It will serve as a simple running example throughout this chapter that will allow us to make some important points about how linkers work.

Most compilation systems provide a *compiler driver* that invokes the language preprocessor, compiler, assembler, and linker, as needed on behalf of the user. For example, to build the example program using the GNU compilation system, we might invoke the GCC driver by typing the following command to the shell:

```
linux> gcc -Og -o prog main.c sum.c
```

Figure 7.2 summarizes the activities of the driver as it translates the example program from an ASCII source file into an executable object file. (If you want to see these steps for yourself, run GCC with the −v option.) The driver first runs the C preprocessor (cpp),[1] which translates the C source file main.c into an ASCII intermediate file main.i:

---

1. In some versions of GCC, the preprocessor is integrated into the compiler driver.

Figure 7.2
Static linking. The linker combines relocatable object files to form an executable object file prog.

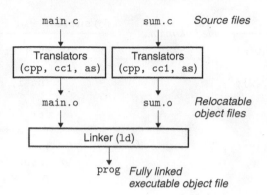

cpp [*other arguments*] main.c /tmp/main.i

Next, the driver runs the C compiler (cc1), which translates main.i into an ASCII assembly-language file main.s:

cc1 /tmp/main.i -Og [*other arguments*] -o /tmp/main.s

Then, the driver runs the assembler (as), which translates main.s into a binary *relocatable object file* main.o:

as [*other arguments*] -o /tmp/main.o /tmp/main.s

The driver goes through the same process to generate sum.o. Finally, it runs the linker program ld, which combines main.o and sum.o, along with the necessary system object files, to create the binary *executable object file* prog:

ld -o prog [*system object files and args*] /tmp/main.o /tmp/sum.o

To run the executable prog, we type its name on the Linux shell's command line:

linux> *./prog*

The shell invokes a function in the operating system called the *loader*, which copies the code and data in the executable file prog into memory, and then transfers control to the beginning of the program.

7.2 Static Linking

Static linkers such as the Linux LD program take as input a collection of relocatable object files and command-line arguments and generate as output a fully linked executable object file that can be loaded and run. The input relocatable object files consist of various code and data sections, where each section is a contiguous sequence of bytes. Instructions are in one section, initialized global variables are in another section, and uninitialized variables are in yet another section.

To build the executable, the linker must perform two main tasks:

Step 1. Symbol resolution.   Object files define and reference *symbols*, where each symbol corresponds to a function, a global variable, or a *static variable* (i.e., any C variable declared with the `static` attribute). The purpose of symbol resolution is to associate each symbol *reference* with exactly one symbol *definition*.

Step 2. Relocation.   Compilers and assemblers generate code and data sections that start at address 0. The linker *relocates* these sections by associating a memory location with each symbol definition, and then modifying all of the references to those symbols so that they point to this memory location. The linker blindly performs these relocations using detailed instructions, generated by the assembler, called *relocation entries*.

The sections that follow describe these tasks in more detail. As you read, keep in mind some basic facts about linkers: Object files are merely collections of blocks of bytes. Some of these blocks contain program code, others contain program data, and others contain data structures that guide the linker and loader. A linker concatenates blocks together, decides on run-time locations for the concatenated blocks, and modifies various locations within the code and data blocks. Linkers have minimal understanding of the target machine. The compilers and assemblers that generate the object files have already done most of the work.

7.3   Object Files

Object files come in three forms:

Relocatable object file.   Contains binary code and data in a form that can be combined with other relocatable object files at compile time to create an executable object file.

Executable object file.   Contains binary code and data in a form that can be copied directly into memory and executed.

Shared object file.   A special type of relocatable object file that can be loaded into memory and linked dynamically, at either load time or run time.

Compilers and assemblers generate relocatable object files (including shared object files). Linkers generate executable object files. Technically, an *object module* is a sequence of bytes, and an *object file* is an object module stored on disk in a file. However, we will use these terms interchangeably.

Object files are organized according to specific *object file formats*, which vary from system to system. The first Unix systems from Bell Labs used the `a.out` format. (To this day, executables are still referred to as `a.out` files.) Windows uses the Portable Executable (PE) format. Mac OS-X uses the Mach-O format. Modern x86-64 Linux and Unix systems use *Executable and Linkable Format (ELF)*. Although our discussion will focus on ELF, the basic concepts are similar, regardless of the particular format.

Figure 7.3
Typical ELF relocatable object file.

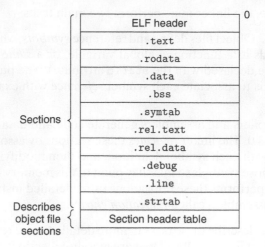

7.4 Relocatable Object Files

Figure 7.3 shows the format of a typical ELF relocatable object file. The *ELF header* begins with a 16-byte sequence that describes the word size and byte ordering of the system that generated the file. The rest of the ELF header contains information that allows a linker to parse and interpret the object file. This includes the size of the ELF header, the object file type (e.g., relocatable, executable, or shared), the machine type (e.g., x86-64), the file offset of the section header table, and the size and number of entries in the section header table. The locations and sizes of the various sections are described by the *section header table*, which contains a fixed-size entry for each section in the object file.

Sandwiched between the ELF header and the section header table are the sections themselves. A typical ELF relocatable object file contains the following sections:

.text The machine code of the compiled program.

.rodata Read-only data such as the format strings in printf statements, and jump tables for switch statements.

.data *Initialized* global and static C variables. Local C variables are maintained at run time on the stack and do *not* appear in either the .data or .bss sections.

.bss *Uninitialized* global and static C variables, along with any global or static variables that are initialized to zero. This section occupies no actual space in the object file; it is merely a placeholder. Object file formats distinguish between initialized and uninitialized variables for space efficiency: uninitialized variables do not have to occupy any actual disk space in the object file. At run time, these variables are allocated in memory with an initial value of zero.

Aside   Why is uninitialized data called .bss?

The use of the term .bss to denote uninitialized data is universal. It was originally an acronym for the "block started by symbol" directive from the IBM 704 assembly language (circa 1957) and the acronym has stuck. A simple way to remember the difference between the .data and .bss sections is to think of "bss" as an abbreviation for "Better Save Space!"

.symtab A *symbol table* with information about functions and global variables that are defined and referenced in the program. Some programmers mistakenly believe that a program must be compiled with the -g option to get symbol table information. In fact, every relocatable object file has a symbol table in .symtab (unless the programmer has specifically removed it with the STRIP command). However, unlike the symbol table inside a compiler, the .symtab symbol table does not contain entries for local variables.

.rel.text A list of locations in the .text section that will need to be modified when the linker combines this object file with others. In general, any instruction that calls an external function or references a global variable will need to be modified. On the other hand, instructions that call local functions do not need to be modified. Note that relocation information is not needed in executable object files, and is usually omitted unless the user explicitly instructs the linker to include it.

.rel.data Relocation information for any global variables that are referenced or defined by the module. In general, any initialized global variable whose initial value is the address of a global variable or externally defined function will need to be modified.

.debug A debugging symbol table with entries for local variables and typedefs defined in the program, global variables defined and referenced in the program, and the original C source file. It is only present if the compiler driver is invoked with the -g option.

.line A mapping between line numbers in the original C source program and machine code instructions in the .text section. It is only present if the compiler driver is invoked with the -g option.

.strtab A string table for the symbol tables in the .symtab and .debug sections and for the section names in the section headers. A string table is a sequence of null-terminated character strings.

7.5   Symbols and Symbol Tables

Each relocatable object module, *m*, has a symbol table that contains information about the symbols that are defined and referenced by *m*. In the context of a linker, there are three different kinds of symbols:

- *Global symbols* that are defined by module *m* and that can be referenced by other modules. Global linker symbols correspond to *nonstatic* C functions and global variables.

- Global symbols that are referenced by module *m* but defined by some other module. Such symbols are called *externals* and correspond to nonstatic C functions and global variables that are defined in other modules.

- *Local symbols* that are defined and referenced exclusively by module *m*. These correspond to static C functions and global variables that are defined with the `static` attribute. These symbols are visible anywhere within module *m*, but cannot be referenced by other modules.

It is important to realize that local linker symbols are not the same as local program variables. The symbol table in `.symtab` does not contain any symbols that correspond to local nonstatic program variables. These are managed at run time on the stack and are not of interest to the linker.

Interestingly, local procedure variables that are defined with the C `static` attribute are not managed on the stack. Instead, the compiler allocates space in `.data` or `.bss` for each definition and creates a local linker symbol in the symbol table with a unique name. For example, suppose a pair of functions in the same module define a static local variable x:

```
1    int f()
2    {
3        static int x = 0;
4        return x;
5    }
6
7    int g()
8    {
9        static int x = 1;
10       return x;
11   }
```

In this case, the compiler exports a pair of local linker symbols with different names to the assembler. For example, it might use `x.1` for the definition in function `f` and `x.2` for the definition in function g.

Symbol tables are built by assemblers, using symbols exported by the compiler into the assembly-language `.s` file. An ELF symbol table is contained in the `.symtab` section. It contains an array of entries. Figure 7.4 shows the format of each entry.

The `name` is a byte offset into the string table that points to the null-terminated string name of the symbol. The `value` is the symbol's address. For relocatable modules, the `value` is an offset from the beginning of the section where the object is defined. For executable object files, the `value` is an absolute run-time address. The `size` is the size (in bytes) of the object. The `type` is usually either `data` or `function`. The symbol table can also contain entries for the individual sections

New to C?   Hiding variable and function names with `static`

C programmers use the `static` attribute to hide variable and function declarations inside modules, much as you would use *public* and *private* declarations in Java and C++. In C, source files play the role of modules. Any global variable or function declared with the `static` attribute is private to that module. Similarly, any global variable or function declared without the `static` attribute is public and can be accessed by any other module. It is good programming practice to protect your variables and functions with the `static` attribute wherever possible.

--- *code/link/elfstructs.c*

```
1    typedef struct {
2        int    name;      /* String table offset */
3        char   type:4,    /* Function or data (4 bits) */
4               binding:4; /* Local or global (4 bits) */
5        char   reserved;  /* Unused */
6        short  section;   /* Section header index */
7        long   value;     /* Section offset or absolute address */
8        long   size;      /* Object size in bytes */
9    } Elf64_Symbol;
```

--- *code/link/elfstructs.c*

Figure 7.4 ELF symbol table entry. The `type` and `binding` fields are 4 bits each.

and for the path name of the original source file. So there are distinct types for these objects as well. The `binding` field indicates whether the symbol is local or global.

Each symbol is assigned to some section of the object file, denoted by the `section` field, which is an index into the section header table. There are three special pseudosections that don't have entries in the section header table: ABS is for symbols that should not be relocated. UNDEF is for undefined symbols—that is, symbols that are referenced in this object module but defined elsewhere. COMMON is for uninitialized data objects that are not yet allocated. For COMMON symbols, the `value` field gives the alignment requirement, and `size` gives the minimum size. Note that these pseudosections exist only in relocatable object files; they do not exist in executable object files.

The distinction between COMMON and `.bss` is subtle. Modern versions of GCC assign symbols in relocatable object files to COMMON and `.bss` using the following convention:

COMMON   Uninitialized global variables
`.bss`   Uninitialized static variables, and global or static variables that are initialized to zero

The reason for this seemingly arbitrary distinction stems from the way the linker performs symbol resolution, which we will explain in Section 7.6.

The GNU READELF program is a handy tool for viewing the contents of object files. For example, here are the last three symbol table entries for the relocatable object file main.o, from the example program in Figure 7.1. The first eight entries, which are not shown, are local symbols that the linker uses internally.

```
Num:    Value             Size Type     Bind    Vis      Ndx Name
  8: 0000000000000000       24 FUNC     GLOBAL  DEFAULT    1 main
  9: 0000000000000000        8 OBJECT   GLOBAL  DEFAULT    3 array
 10: 0000000000000000        0 NOTYPE   GLOBAL  DEFAULT  UND sum
```

In this example, we see an entry for the definition of global symbol main, a 24-byte function located at an offset (i.e., value) of zero in the .text section. This is followed by the definition of the global symbol array, an 8-byte object located at an offset of zero in the .data section. The last entry comes from the reference to the external symbol sum. READELF identifies each section by an integer index. Ndx=1 denotes the .text section, and Ndx=3 denotes the .data section.

Practice Problem 7.1 (solution page 717)

This problem concerns the m.o and swap.o modules from Figure 7.5. For each symbol that is defined or referenced in swap.o, indicate whether or not it will have a symbol table entry in the .symtab section in module swap.o. If so, indicate the module that defines the symbol (swap.o or m.o), the symbol type (local, global, or extern), and the section (.text, .data, .bss, or COMMON) it is assigned to in the module.

(a) m.c ————————————————— code/link/m.c

```
1   void swap();
2
3   int buf[2] = {1, 2};
4
5   int main()
6   {
7       swap();
8       return 0;
9   }
```

————————————————————— code/link/m.c

(b) swap.c ————————————————— code/link/swap.c

```
1    extern int buf[];
2
3    int *bufp0 = &buf[0];
4    int *bufp1;
5
6    void swap()
7    {
8        int temp;
9
10       bufp1 = &buf[1];
11       temp = *bufp0;
12       *bufp0 = *bufp1;
13       *bufp1 = temp;
14   }
```

————————————————————— code/link/swap.c

Figure 7.5 **Example program for Practice Problem 7.1.**

Symbol	.symtab entry?	Symbol type	Module where defined	Section
buf	_____	_____	_____	_____
bufp0	_____	_____	_____	_____
bufp1	_____	_____	_____	_____
swap	_____	_____	_____	_____
temp	_____	_____	_____	_____

7.6   Symbol Resolution

The linker resolves symbol references by associating each reference with exactly one symbol definition from the symbol tables of its input relocatable object files. Symbol resolution is straightforward for references to local symbols that are defined in the same module as the reference. The compiler allows only one definition of each local symbol per module. The compiler also ensures that static local variables, which get local linker symbols, have unique names.

Resolving references to global symbols, however, is trickier. When the compiler encounters a symbol (either a variable or function name) that is not defined in the current module, it assumes that it is defined in some other module, generates a linker symbol table entry, and leaves it for the linker to handle. If the linker is unable to find a definition for the referenced symbol in any of its input modules, it prints an (often cryptic) error message and terminates. For example, if we try to compile and link the following source file on a Linux machine,

```
1    void foo(void);
2
3    int main() {
4        foo();
5        return 0;
6    }
```

then the compiler runs without a hitch, but the linker terminates when it cannot resolve the reference to foo:

```
linux> gcc -Wall -Og -o linkerror linkerror.c
/tmp/ccSz5uti.o: In function 'main':
/tmp/ccSz5uti.o(.text+0x7): undefined reference to 'foo'
```

Symbol resolution for global symbols is also tricky because multiple object modules might define global symbols with the same name. In this case, the linker must either flag an error or somehow choose one of the definitions and discard the rest. The approach adopted by Linux systems involves cooperation between the compiler, assembler, and linker and can introduce some baffling bugs to the unwary programmer.

Aside Mangling of linker symbols in C++ and Java

Both C++ and Java allow overloaded methods that have the same name in the source code but different parameter lists. So how does the linker tell the difference between these different overloaded functions? Overloaded functions in C++ and Java work because the compiler encodes each unique method and parameter list combination into a unique name for the linker. This encoding process is called *mangling*, and the inverse process is known as *demangling*.

Happily, C++ and Java use compatible mangling schemes. A mangled class name consists of the integer number of characters in the name followed by the original name. For example, the class Foo is encoded as 3Foo. A method is encoded as the original method name, followed by __, followed by the mangled class name, followed by single letter encodings of each argument. For example, Foo::bar(int, long) is encoded as bar__3Fooil. Similar schemes are used to mangle global variable and template names.

7.6.1 How Linkers Resolve Duplicate Symbol Names

The input to the linker is a collection of relocatable object modules. Each of these modules defines a set of symbols, some of which are local (visible only to the module that defines it), and some of which are global (visible to other modules). What happens if multiple modules define global symbols with the same name? Here is the approach that Linux compilation systems use.

At compile time, the compiler exports each global symbol to the assembler as either *strong* or *weak*, and the assembler encodes this information implicitly in the symbol table of the relocatable object file. Functions and initialized global variables get strong symbols. Uninitialized global variables get weak symbols.

Given this notion of strong and weak symbols, Linux linkers use the following rules for dealing with duplicate symbol names:

Rule 1. Multiple strong symbols with the same name are not allowed.

Rule 2. Given a strong symbol and multiple weak symbols with the same name, choose the strong symbol.

Rule 3. Given multiple weak symbols with the same name, choose any of the weak symbols.

For example, suppose we attempt to compile and link the following two C modules:

```
1   /* foo1.c */
2   int main()
3   {
4       return 0;
5   }
```

```
1   /* bar1.c */
2   int main()
3   {
4       return 0;
5   }
```

In this case, the linker will generate an error message because the strong symbol main is defined multiple times (rule 1):

```
linux> gcc foo1.c bar1.c
/tmp/ccq2Uxnd.o: In function 'main':
bar1.c:(.text+0x0): multiple definition of 'main'
```

Similarly, the linker will generate an error message for the following modules because the strong symbol x is defined twice (rule 1):

```
1   /* foo2.c */
2   int x = 15213;
3
4   int main()
5   {
6       return 0;
7   }
```

```
1   /* bar2.c */
2   int x = 15213;
3
4   void f()
5   {
6   }
```

However, if x is uninitialized in one module, then the linker will quietly choose the strong symbol defined in the other (rule 2):

```
1    /* foo3.c */
2    #include <stdio.h>
3    void f(void);
4
5    int x = 15213;
6
7    int main()
8    {
9        f();
10       printf("x = %d\n", x);
11       return 0;
12   }
```

```
1    /* bar3.c */
2    int x;
3
4    void f()
5    {
6        x = 15212;
7    }
```

At run time, function f changes the value of x from 15213 to 15212, which might come as an unwelcome surprise to the author of function main! Notice that the linker normally gives no indication that it has detected multiple definitions of x:

```
linux> gcc -o foobar3 foo3.c bar3.c
linux> ./foobar3
x = 15212
```

The same thing can happen if there are two weak definitions of x (rule 3):

```
1   /* foo4.c */
2   #include <stdio.h>
3   void f(void);
4
5   int x;
6
7   int main()
8   {
9       x = 15213;
10      f();
11      printf("x = %d\n", x);
12      return 0;
13  }
```

```
1   /* bar4.c */
2   int x;
3
4   void f()
5   {
6       x = 15212;
7   }
```

The application of rules 2 and 3 can introduce some insidious run-time bugs that are incomprehensible to the unwary programmer, especially if the duplicate symbol definitions have different types. Consider the following example, in which x is inadvertently defined as an int in one module and a double in another:

```
1   /* foo5.c */
2   #include <stdio.h>
3   void f(void);
4
5   int y = 15212;
6   int x = 15213;
7
8   int main()
9   {
10      f();
```

```
11          printf("x = 0x%x y = 0x%x \n",
12                  x, y);
13          return 0;
14      }
```

```
1   /* bar5.c */
2   double x;
3
4   void f()
5   {
6       x = -0.0;
7   }
```

On an x86-64/Linux machine, doubles are 8 bytes and ints are 4 bytes. On our system, the address of x is 0x601020 and the address of y is 0x601024. Thus, the assignment x = -0.0 in line 6 of bar5.c will overwrite the memory locations for x and y (lines 5 and 6 in foo5.c) with the double-precision floating-point representation of negative zero!

```
linux> gcc -Wall -Og -o foobar5 foo5.c bar5.c
/usr/bin/ld: Warning: alignment 4 of symbol 'x' in /tmp/cclUFK5g.o
is smaller than 8 in /tmp/ccbTLcb9.o
linux> ./foobar5
x = 0x0 y = 0x80000000
```

This is a subtle and nasty bug, especially because it triggers only a warning from the linker, and because it typically manifests itself much later in the execution of the program, far away from where the error occurred. In a large system with hundreds of modules, a bug of this kind is extremely hard to fix, especially because many programmers are not aware of how linkers work, and because they often ignore compiler warnings. When in doubt, invoke the linker with a flag such as the GCC -fno-common flag, which triggers an error if it encounters multiply-defined global symbols. Or use the -Werror option, which turns all warnings into errors.

In Section 7.5, we saw how the compiler assigns symbols to COMMON and .bss using a seemingly arbitrary convention. Actually, this convention is due to the fact that in some cases the linker allows multiple modules to define global symbols with the same name. When the compiler is translating some module and encounters a weak global symbol, say, x, it does not know if other modules also define x, and if so, it cannot predict which of the multiple instances of x the linker might choose. So the compiler defers the decision to the linker by assigning x to COMMON. On the other hand, if x is initialized to zero, then it is a strong symbol (and thus must be unique by rule 2), so the compiler can confidently assign it to .bss. Similarly, static symbols are unique by construction, so the compiler can confidently assign them to either .data or .bss.

Practice Problem 7.2 (solution page 718)

In this problem, let REF(x.i) → DEF(x.k) denote that the linker will associate an arbitrary reference to symbol x in module i to the definition of x in module k. For each example that follows, use this notation to indicate how the linker would resolve references to the multiply-defined symbol in each module. If there is a link-time error (rule 1), write "ERROR". If the linker arbitrarily chooses one of the definitions (rule 3), write "UNKNOWN".

A.
```
/* Module 1 */          /* Module 2 */
int main()              int main;
{                       int p2()
}                       {
                        }
```

    (a) REF(main.1) → DEF(_____._____)

    (b) REF(main.2) → DEF(_____._____)

B.
```
/* Module 1 */          /* Module 2 */
void main()             int main = 1;
{                       int p2()
}                       {
                        }
```

    (a) REF(main.1) → DEF(_____._____)

    (b) REF(main.2) → DEF(_____._____)

C.
```
/* Module 1 */          /* Module 2 */
int x;                  double x = 1.0;
void main()             int p2()
{                       {
}                       }
```

    (a) REF(x.1) → DEF(_____._____)

    (b) REF(x.2) → DEF(_____._____)

7.6.2 Linking with Static Libraries

So far, we have assumed that the linker reads a collection of relocatable object files and links them together into an output executable file. In practice, all compilation systems provide a mechanism for packaging related object modules into a single file called a *static library*, which can then be supplied as input to the linker. When it builds the output executable, the linker copies only the object modules in the library that are referenced by the application program.

Why do systems support the notion of libraries? Consider ISO C99, which defines an extensive collection of standard I/O, string manipulation, and integer math functions such as atoi, printf, scanf, strcpy, and rand. They are available to every C program in the `libc.a` library. ISO C99 also defines an extensive collection of floating-point math functions such as `sin`, `cos`, and `sqrt` in the `libm.a` library.

Consider the different approaches that compiler developers might use to provide these functions to users without the benefit of static libraries. One approach would be to have the compiler recognize calls to the standard functions and to generate the appropriate code directly. Pascal, which provides a small set of standard functions, takes this approach, but it is not feasible for C, because of the large number of standard functions defined by the C standard. It would add significant complexity to the compiler and would require a new compiler version each time a function was added, deleted, or modified. To application programmers, however, this approach would be quite convenient because the standard functions would always be available.

Another approach would be to put all of the standard C functions in a single relocatable object module, say, `libc.o`, that application programmers could link into their executables:

```
linux> gcc main.c /usr/lib/libc.o
```

This approach has the advantage that it would decouple the implementation of the standard functions from the implementation of the compiler, and would still be reasonably convenient for programmers. However, a big disadvantage is that every executable file in a system would now contain a complete copy of the collection of standard functions, which would be extremely wasteful of disk space. (On our system, `libc.a` is about 5 MB and `libm.a` is about 2 MB.) Worse, each running program would now contain its own copy of these functions in memory, which would be extremely wasteful of memory. Another big disadvantage is that any change to any standard function, no matter how small, would require the library developer to recompile the entire source file, a time-consuming operation that would complicate the development and maintenance of the standard functions.

We could address some of these problems by creating a separate relocatable file for each standard function and storing them in a well-known directory. However, this approach would require application programmers to explicitly link the appropriate object modules into their executables, a process that would be error prone and time consuming:

```
linux> gcc main.c /usr/lib/printf.o /usr/lib/scanf.o ...
```

The notion of a static library was developed to resolve the disadvantages of these various approaches. Related functions can be compiled into separate object modules and then packaged in a single static library file. Application programs can then use any of the functions defined in the library by specifying a single filename on the command line. For example, a program that uses functions from the C standard library and the math library could be compiled and linked with a command of the form

```
linux> gcc main.c /usr/lib/libm.a /usr/lib/libc.a
```

(a) addvec.o ——————————————————— *code/link/addvec.c*

```
1    int addcnt = 0;
2
3    void addvec(int *x, int *y,
4                int *z, int n)
5    {
6        int i;
7
8        addcnt++;
9
10       for (i = 0; i < n; i++)
11           z[i] = x[i] + y[i];
12   }
```

———————————————————————— *code/link/addvec.c*

(b) multvec.o ——————————————————— *code/link/multvec.c*

```
1    int multcnt = 0;
2
3    void multvec(int *x, int *y,
4                 int *z, int n)
5    {
6        int i;
7
8        multcnt++;
9
10       for (i = 0; i < n; i++)
11           z[i] = x[i] * y[i];
12   }
```

———————————————————————— *code/link/multvec.c*

Figure 7.6 Member object files in the `libvector` **library.**

At link time, the linker will only copy the object modules that are referenced by the program, which reduces the size of the executable on disk and in memory. On the other hand, the application programmer only needs to include the names of a few library files. (In fact, C compiler drivers always pass `libc.a` to the linker, so the reference to `libc.a` mentioned previously is unnecessary.)

On Linux systems, static libraries are stored on disk in a particular file format known as an *archive*. An archive is a collection of concatenated relocatable object files, with a header that describes the size and location of each member object file. Archive filenames are denoted with the `.a` suffix.

To make our discussion of libraries concrete, consider the pair of vector routines in Figure 7.6. Each routine, defined in its own object module, performs a vector operation on a pair of input vectors and stores the result in an output vector. As a side effect, each routine records the number of times it has been called by incrementing a global variable. (This will be useful when we explain the idea of position-independent code in Section 7.12.)

To create a static library of these functions, we would use the AR tool as follows:

```
linux> gcc -c addvec.c multvec.c
linux> ar rcs libvector.a addvec.o multvec.o
```

To use the library, we might write an application such as `main2.c` in Figure 7.7, which invokes the `addvec` library routine. The include (or header) file `vector.h` defines the function prototypes for the routines in `libvector.a`,

To build the executable, we would compile and link the input files `main2.o` and `libvector.a`:

```
linux> gcc -c main2.c
linux> gcc -static -o prog2c main2.o ./libvector.a
```

code/link/main2.c

```
1    #include <stdio.h>
2    #include "vector.h"
3
4    int x[2] = {1, 2};
5    int y[2] = {3, 4};
6    int z[2];
7
8    int main()
9    {
10       addvec(x, y, z, 2);
11       printf("z = [%d %d]\n", z[0], z[1]);
12       return 0;
13   }
```

code/link/main2.c

Figure 7.7 Example program 2. This program invokes a function in the `libvector` library.

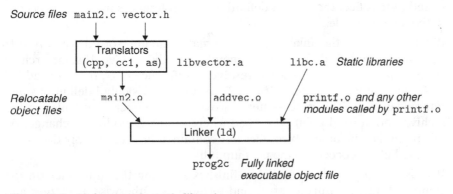

Figure 7.8 Linking with static libraries.

or equivalently,

```
linux> gcc -c main2.c
linux> gcc -static -o prog2c main2.o -L. -lvector
```

Figure 7.8 summarizes the activity of the linker. The `-static` argument tells the compiler driver that the linker should build a fully linked executable object file that can be loaded into memory and run without any further linking at load time. The `-lvector` argument is a shorthand for `libvector.a`, and the `-L.` argument tells the linker to look for `libvector.a` in the current directory.

When the linker runs, it determines that the `addvec` symbol defined by `addvec.o` is referenced by `main2.o`, so it copies `addvec.o` into the executable.

Since the program doesn't reference any symbols defined by `multvec.o`, the linker does *not* copy this module into the executable. The linker also copies the `printf.o` module from `libc.a`, along with a number of other modules from the C run-time system.

7.6.3 How Linkers Use Static Libraries to Resolve References

While static libraries are useful, they are also a source of confusion to programmers because of the way the Linux linker uses them to resolve external references. During the symbol resolution phase, the linker scans the relocatable object files and archives left to right in the same sequential order that they appear on the compiler driver's command line. (The driver automatically translates any `.c` files on the command line into `.o` files.) During this scan, the linker maintains a set E of relocatable object files that will be merged to form the executable, a set U of unresolved symbols (i.e., symbols referred to but not yet defined), and a set D of symbols that have been defined in previous input files. Initially, E, U, and D are empty.

- For each input file f on the command line, the linker determines if f is an object file or an archive. If f is an object file, the linker adds f to E, updates U and D to reflect the symbol definitions and references in f, and proceeds to the next input file.

- If f is an archive, the linker attempts to match the unresolved symbols in U against the symbols defined by the members of the archive. If some archive member m defines a symbol that resolves a reference in U, then m is added to E, and the linker updates U and D to reflect the symbol definitions and references in m. This process iterates over the member object files in the archive until a fixed point is reached where U and D no longer change. At this point, any member object files not contained in E are simply discarded and the linker proceeds to the next input file.

- If U is nonempty when the linker finishes scanning the input files on the command line, it prints an error and terminates. Otherwise, it merges and relocates the object files in E to build the output executable file.

Unfortunately, this algorithm can result in some baffling link-time errors because the ordering of libraries and object files on the command line is significant. If the library that defines a symbol appears on the command line before the object file that references that symbol, then the reference will not be resolved and linking will fail. For example, consider the following:

```
linux> gcc -static ./libvector.a main2.c
/tmp/cc9XH6Rp.o: In function 'main':
/tmp/cc9XH6Rp.o(.text+0x18): undefined reference to 'addvec'
```

What happened? When `libvector.a` is processed, U is empty, so no member object files from `libvector.a` are added to E. Thus, the reference to `addvec` is never resolved and the linker emits an error message and terminates.

The general rule for libraries is to place them at the end of the command line. If the members of the different libraries are independent, in that no member references a symbol defined by another member, then the libraries can be placed at the end of the command line in any order. If, on the other hand, the libraries are not independent, then they must be ordered so that for each symbol *s* that is referenced externally by a member of an archive, at least one definition of *s* follows a reference to *s* on the command line. For example, suppose foo.c calls functions in libx.a and libz.a that call functions in liby.a. Then libx.a and libz.a must precede liby.a on the command line:

```
linux> gcc foo.c libx.a libz.a liby.a
```

Libraries can be repeated on the command line if necessary to satisfy the dependence requirements. For example, suppose foo.c calls a function in libx.a that calls a function in liby.a that calls a function in libx.a. Then libx.a must be repeated on the command line:

```
linux> gcc foo.c libx.a liby.a libx.a
```

Alternatively, we could combine libx.a and liby.a into a single archive.

Practice Problem 7.3 (solution page 718)

Let a and b denote object modules or static libraries in the current directory, and let a→b denote that a depends on b, in the sense that b defines a symbol that is referenced by a. For each of the following scenarios, show the minimal command line (i.e., one with the least number of object file and library arguments) that will allow the static linker to resolve all symbol references.

A. p.o → libx.a

B. p.o → libx.a → liby.a

C. p.o → libx.a → liby.a *and* liby.a → libx.a → p.o

7.7 Relocation

Once the linker has completed the symbol resolution step, it has associated each symbol reference in the code with exactly one symbol definition (i.e., a symbol table entry in one of its input object modules). At this point, the linker knows the exact sizes of the code and data sections in its input object modules. It is now ready to begin the relocation step, where it merges the input modules and assigns run-time addresses to each symbol. Relocation consists of two steps:

1. *Relocating sections and symbol definitions.* In this step, the linker merges all sections of the same type into a new aggregate section of the same type. For example, the .data sections from the input modules are all merged into one section that will become the .data section for the output executable object

file. The linker then assigns run-time memory addresses to the new aggregate sections, to each section defined by the input modules, and to each symbol defined by the input modules. When this step is complete, each instruction and global variable in the program has a unique run-time memory address.

2. *Relocating symbol references within sections.* In this step, the linker modifies every symbol reference in the bodies of the code and data sections so that they point to the correct run-time addresses. To perform this step, the linker relies on data structures in the relocatable object modules known as relocation entries, which we describe next.

7.7.1 Relocation Entries

When an assembler generates an object module, it does not know where the code and data will ultimately be stored in memory. Nor does it know the locations of any externally defined functions or global variables that are referenced by the module. So whenever the assembler encounters a reference to an object whose ultimate location is unknown, it generates a *relocation entry* that tells the linker how to modify the reference when it merges the object file into an executable. Relocation entries for code are placed in .rel.text. Relocation entries for data are placed in .rel.data.

Figure 7.9 shows the format of an ELF relocation entry. The offset is the section offset of the reference that will need to be modified. The symbol identifies the symbol that the modified reference should point to. The type tells the linker how to modify the new reference. The addend is a signed constant that is used by some types of relocations to bias the value of the modified reference.

ELF defines 32 different relocation types, many quite arcane. We are concerned with only the two most basic relocation types:

R_X86_64_PC32. Relocate a reference that uses a 32-bit PC-relative address. Recall from Section 3.6.3 that a PC-relative address is an offset from the current run-time value of the program counter (PC). When the CPU executes an instruction using PC-relative addressing, it forms the *effective address* (e.g., the target of the call instruction) by adding the 32-bit value

---

—— code/link/elfstructs.c

```
1   typedef struct {
2       long offset;      /* Offset of the reference to relocate */
3       long type:32,     /* Relocation type */
4            symbol:32;   /* Symbol table index */
5       long addend;      /* Constant part of relocation expression */
6   } Elf64_Rela;
```

—— code/link/elfstructs.c

Figure 7.9 **ELF relocation entry.** Each entry identifies a reference that must be relocated and specifies how to compute the modified reference.

encoded in the instruction to the current run-time value of the PC, which is always the address of the next instruction in memory.

R_X86_64_32. Relocate a reference that uses a 32-bit absolute address. With absolute addressing, the CPU directly uses the 32-bit value encoded in the instruction as the effective address, without further modifications.

These two relocation types support the x86-64 *small code model*, which assumes that the total size of the code and data in the executable object file is smaller than 2 GB, and thus can be accessed at run-time using 32-bit PC-relative addresses. The small code model is the default for GCC. Programs larger than 2 GB can be compiled using the −mcmodel=medium (*medium code model*) and −mcmodel=large (*large code model*) flags, but we won't discuss those.

7.7.2   Relocating Symbol References

Figure 7.10 shows the pseudocode for the linker's relocation algorithm. Lines 1 and 2 iterate over each section s and each relocation entry r associated with each section. For concreteness, assume that each section s is an array of bytes and that each relocation entry r is a struct of type Elf64_Rela, as defined in Figure 7.9. Also, assume that when the algorithm runs, the linker has already chosen run-time addresses for each section (denoted ADDR(s)) and each symbol (denoted ADDR(r.symbol)). Line 3 computes the address in the s array of the 4-byte reference that needs to be relocated. If this reference uses PC-relative addressing, then it is relocated by lines 5–9. If the reference uses absolute addressing, then it is relocated by lines 11–13.

```
1   foreach section s {
2       foreach relocation entry r {
3           refptr = s + r.offset;  /* ptr to reference to be relocated */
4
5           /* Relocate a PC-relative reference */
6           if (r.type == R_X86_64_PC32) {
7               refaddr = ADDR(s) + r.offset; /* ref's run-time address */
8               *refptr = (unsigned) (ADDR(r.symbol) + r.addend - refaddr);
9           }
10
11          /* Relocate an absolute reference */
12          if (r.type == R_X86_64_32)
13              *refptr = (unsigned) (ADDR(r.symbol) + r.addend);
14      }
15  }
```

Figure 7.10   Relocation algorithm.

code/link/main-relo.d

```
1   0000000000000000 <main>:
2      0:   48 83 ec 08            sub    $0x8,%rsp
3      4:   be 02 00 00 00         mov    $0x2,%esi
4      9:   bf 00 00 00 00         mov    $0x0,%edi        %edi = &array
5                         a: R_X86_64_32 array             Relocation entry

6      e:   e8 00 00 00 00         callq  13 <main+0x13>   sum()
7                         f: R_X86_64_PC32 sum-0x4         Relocation entry
8     13:   48 83 c4 08            add    $0x8,%rsp
9     17:   c3                     retq
```

code/link/main-relo.d

Figure 7.11 Code and relocation entries from `main.o`. The original C code is in Figure 7.1.

Let's see how the linker uses this algorithm to relocate the references in our example program in Figure 7.1. Figure 7.11 shows the disassembled code from `main.o`, as generated by the GNU OBJDUMP tool (objdump -dx main.o).

The `main` function references two global symbols, `array` and `sum`. For each reference, the assembler has generated a relocation entry, which is displayed on the following line.[2] The relocation entries tell the linker that the reference to `sum` should be relocated using a 32-bit PC-relative address, and the reference to `array` should be relocated using a 32-bit absolute address. The next two sections detail how the linker relocates these references.

Relocating PC-Relative References

In line 6 in Figure 7.11, function `main` calls the `sum` function, which is defined in module `sum.o`. The `call` instruction begins at section offset 0xe and consists of the 1-byte opcode 0xe8, followed by a placeholder for the 32-bit PC-relative reference to the target `sum`.

The corresponding relocation entry r consists of four fields:

```
r.offset = 0xf
r.symbol = sum
r.type   = R_X86_64_PC32
r.addend = -4
```

These fields tell the linker to modify the 32-bit PC-relative reference starting at offset 0xf so that it will point to the `sum` routine at run time. Now, suppose that the linker has determined that

```
ADDR(s) = ADDR(.text) = 0x4004d0
```

---

2. Recall that relocation entries and instructions are actually stored in different sections of the object file. The OBJDUMP tool displays them together for convenience.

and

```
ADDR(r.symbol) = ADDR(sum) = 0x4004e8
```

Using the algorithm in Figure 7.10, the linker first computes the run-time address of the reference (line 7):

```
refaddr = ADDR(s)  + r.offset
        = 0x4004d0 + 0xf
        = 0x4004df
```

It then updates the reference so that it will point to the sum routine at run time (line 8):

```
*refptr = (unsigned) (ADDR(r.symbol) + r.addend - refaddr)
        = (unsigned) (0x4004e8      + (-4)    - 0x4004df)
        = (unsigned) (0x5)
```

In the resulting executable object file, the call instruction has the following relocated form:

```
4004de:  e8 05 00 00 00          callq  4004e8 <sum>        sum()
```

At run time, the call instruction will be located at address 0x4004de. When the CPU executes the call instruction, the PC has a value of 0x4004e3, which is the address of the instruction immediately following the call instruction. To execute the call instruction, the CPU performs the following steps:

1. Push PC onto stack
2. PC $\leftarrow$ PC + 0x5 = 0x4004e3 + 0x5 = 0x4004e8

Thus, the next instruction to execute is the first instruction of the sum routine, which of course is what we want!

Relocating Absolute References

Relocating absolute references is straightforward. For example, in line 4 in Figure 7.11, the mov instruction copies the address of array (a 32-bit immediate value) into register %edi. The mov instruction begins at section offset 0x9 and consists of the 1-byte opcode 0xbf, followed by a placeholder for the 32-bit absolute reference to array.

The corresponding relocation entry r consists of four fields:

```
r.offset = 0xa
r.symbol = array
r.type   = R_X86_64_32
r.addend = 0
```

These fields tell the linker to modify the absolute reference starting at offset 0xa so that it will point to the first byte of array at run time. Now, suppose that the linker has determined that

(a) Relocated .text section

```
1    00000000004004d0 <main>:
2      4004d0:  48 83 ec 08              sub    $0x8,%rsp
3      4004d4:  be 02 00 00 00           mov    $0x2,%esi
4      4004d9:  bf 18 10 60 00           mov    $0x601018,%edi    %edi = &array
5      4004de:  e8 05 00 00 00           callq  4004e8 <sum>       sum()
6      4004e3:  48 83 c4 08              add    $0x8,%rsp
7      4004e7:  c3                       retq

8    00000000004004e8 <sum>:
9      4004e8:  b8 00 00 00 00           mov    $0x0,%eax
10     4004ed:  ba 00 00 00 00           mov    $0x0,%edx
11     4004f2:  eb 09                    jmp    4004fd <sum+0x15>
12     4004f4:  48 63 ca                 movslq %edx,%rcx
13     4004f7:  03 04 8f                 add    (%rdi,%rcx,4),%eax
14     4004fa:  83 c2 01                 add    $0x1,%edx
15     4004fd:  39 f2                    cmp    %esi,%edx
16     4004ff:  7c f3                    jl     4004f4 <sum+0xc>
17     400501:  f3 c3                    repz retq
```

(b) Relocated .data section

```
1    0000000000601018 <array>:
2      601018:  01 00 00 00 02 00 00 00
```

Figure 7.12 Relocated .text and .data sections for the executable file prog. The original C code is in Figure 7.1.

$$ADDR(r.symbol) = ADDR(array) = 0x601018$$

The linker updates the reference using line 13 of the algorithm in Figure 7.10:

```
*refptr = (unsigned) (ADDR(r.symbol) + r.addend)
        = (unsigned) (0x601018       + 0)
        = (unsigned) (0x601018)
```

In the resulting executable object file, the reference has the following relocated form:

```
  4004d9:  bf 18 10 60 00           mov    $0x601018,%edi    %edi = &array
```

Putting it all together, Figure 7.12 shows the relocated .text and .data sections in the final executable object file. At load time, the loader can copy the bytes from these sections directly into memory and execute the instructions without any further modifications.

Practice Problem 7.4 (solution page 718)

This problem concerns the relocated program in Figure 7.12(a).

A. What is the hex address of the relocated reference to sum in line 5?

B. What is the hex value of the relocated reference to sum in line 5?

Practice Problem 7.5 (solution page 718)

Consider the call to function swap in object file m.o (Figure 7.5).

```
9:    e8 00 00 00 00              callq  e <main+0xe>      swap()
```

with the following relocation entry:

```
r.offset = 0xa
r.symbol = swap
r.type   = R_X86_64_PC32
r.addend = -4
```

Now suppose that the linker relocates .text in m.o to address 0x4004d0 and swap to address 0x4004e8. Then what is the value of the relocated reference to swap in the callq instruction?

7.8   Executable Object Files

We have seen how the linker merges multiple object files into a single executable object file. Our example C program, which began life as a collection of ASCII text files, has been transformed into a single binary file that contains all of the information needed to load the program into memory and run it. Figure 7.13 summarizes the kinds of information in a typical ELF executable file.

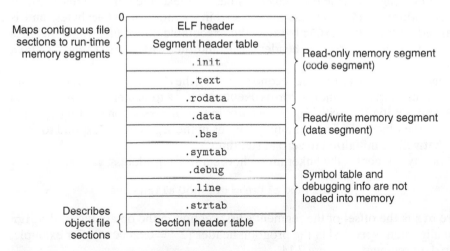

Figure 7.13   Typical ELF executable object file.

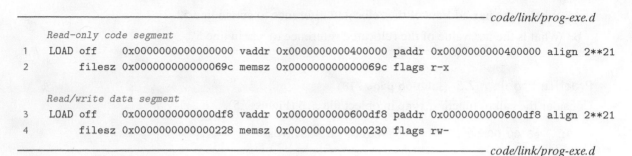

code/link/prog-exe.d

```
     Read-only code segment
1    LOAD off    0x0000000000000000 vaddr 0x0000000000400000 paddr 0x0000000000400000 align 2**21
2         filesz 0x000000000000069c memsz 0x000000000000069c flags r-x

     Read/write data segment
3    LOAD off    0x0000000000000df8 vaddr 0x0000000000600df8 paddr 0x0000000000600df8 align 2**21
4         filesz 0x0000000000000228 memsz 0x0000000000000230 flags rw-
```

code/link/prog-exe.d

Figure 7.14 Program header table for the example executable prog. off: offset in object file; vaddr/paddr: memory address; align: alignment requirement; filesz: segment size in object file; memsz: segment size in memory; flags: run-time permissions.

The format of an executable object file is similar to that of a relocatable object file. The ELF header describes the overall format of the file. It also includes the program's *entry point*, which is the address of the first instruction to execute when the program runs. The .text, .rodata, and .data sections are similar to those in a relocatable object file, except that these sections have been relocated to their eventual run-time memory addresses. The .init section defines a small function, called _init, that will be called by the program's initialization code. Since the executable is *fully linked* (relocated), it needs no .rel sections.

ELF executables are designed to be easy to load into memory, with contiguous chunks of the executable file mapped to contiguous memory segments. This mapping is described by the *program header table*. Figure 7.14 shows part of the program header table for our example executable prog, as displayed by OBJDUMP.

From the program header table, we see that two memory segments will be initialized with the contents of the executable object file. Lines 1 and 2 tell us that the first segment (the *code segment*) has read/execute permissions, starts at memory address 0x400000, has a total size in memory of 0x69c bytes, and is initialized with the first 0x69c bytes of the executable object file, which includes the ELF header, the program header table, and the .init, .text, and .rodata sections.

Lines 3 and 4 tell us that the second segment (the *data segment*) has read/write permissions, starts at memory address 0x600df8, has a total memory size of 0x230 bytes, and is initialized with the 0x228 bytes in the .data section starting at offset 0xdf8 in the object file. The remaining 8 bytes in the segment correspond to .bss data that will be initialized to zero at run time.

For any segment s, the linker must choose a starting address, vaddr, such that

$$\text{vaddr mod align} = \text{off mod align}$$

where off is the offset of the segment's first section in the object file, and align is the alignment specified in the program header ($2^{21} = $ 0x200000). For example, in the data segment in Figure 7.14,

$$\texttt{vaddr mod align} = \texttt{0x600df8 mod 0x200000} = \texttt{0xdf8}$$

and

$$\texttt{off mod align} = \texttt{0xdf8 mod 0x200000} = \texttt{0xdf8}$$

This alignment requirement is an optimization that enables segments in the object file to be transferred efficiently to memory when the program executes. The reason is somewhat subtle and is due to the way that virtual memory is organized as large contiguous power-of-2 chunks of bytes. You will learn all about virtual memory in Chapter 9.

7.9   Loading Executable Object Files

To run an executable object file `prog`, we can type its name to the Linux shell's command line:

```
linux> ./prog
```

Since `prog` does not correspond to a built-in shell command, the shell assumes that `prog` is an executable object file, which it runs for us by invoking some memory-resident operating system code known as the `loader`. Any Linux program can invoke the loader by calling the `execve` function, which we will describe in detail in Section 8.4.6. The loader copies the code and data in the executable object file from disk into memory and then runs the program by jumping to its first instruction, or *entry point*. This process of copying the program into memory and then running it is known as *loading*.

Every running Linux program has a run-time memory image similar to the one in Figure 7.15. On Linux x86-64 systems, the code segment starts at address 0x400000, followed by the data segment. The run-time *heap* follows the data segment and grows upward via calls to the `malloc` library. (We will describe `malloc` and the heap in detail in Section 9.9.) This is followed by a region that is reserved for shared modules. The user stack starts below the largest legal user address $(2^{48} - 1)$ and grows down, toward smaller memory addresses. The region above the stack, starting at address 2^{48}, is reserved for the code and data in the *kernel*, which is the memory-resident part of the operating system.

For simplicity, we've drawn the heap, data, and code segments as abutting each other, and we've placed the top of the stack at the largest legal user address. In practice, there is a gap between the code and data segments due to the alignment requirement on the `.data` segment (Section 7.8). Also, the linker uses address-space layout randomization (ASLR, Section 3.10.4) when it assigns run-time addresses to the stack, shared library, and heap segments. Even though the locations of these regions change each time the program is run, their relative positions are the same.

When the loader runs, it creates a memory image similar to the one shown in Figure 7.15. Guided by the program header table, it copies chunks of the

Figure 7.15

Linux x86-64 run-time memory image. Gaps due to segment alignment requirements and address-space layout randomization (ASLR) are not shown. Not to scale.

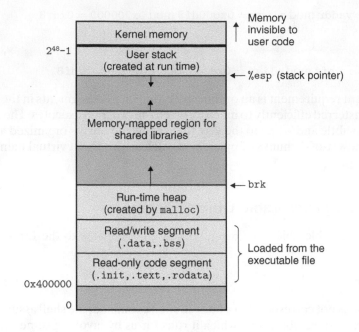

executable object file into the code and data segments. Next, the loader jumps to the program's entry point, which is always the address of the `_start` function. This function is defined in the system object file `crt1.o` and is the same for all C programs. The `_start` function calls the *system startup function*, `__libc_start_main`, which is defined in `libc.so`. It initializes the execution environment, calls the user-level `main` function, handles its return value, and if necessary returns control to the kernel.

7.10 Dynamic Linking with Shared Libraries

The static libraries that we studied in Section 7.6.2 address many of the issues associated with making large collections of related functions available to application programs. However, static libraries still have some significant disadvantages. Static libraries, like all software, need to be maintained and updated periodically. If application programmers want to use the most recent version of a library, they must somehow become aware that the library has changed and then explicitly relink their programs against the updated library.

Another issue is that almost every C program uses standard I/O functions such as `printf` and `scanf`. At run time, the code for these functions is duplicated in the text segment of each running process. On a typical system that is running hundreds of processes, this can be a significant waste of scarce memory system resources. (An interesting property of memory is that it is *always* a scarce resource, regardless

Aside How do loaders really work?

Our description of loading is conceptually correct but intentionally not entirely accurate. To understand how loading really works, you must understand the concepts of *processes*, *virtual memory*, and *memory mapping*, which we haven't discussed yet. As we encounter these concepts later in Chapters 8 and 9, we will revisit loading and gradually reveal the mystery to you.

For the impatient reader, here is a preview of how loading really works: Each program in a Linux system runs in the context of a process with its own virtual address space. When the shell runs a program, the parent shell process forks a child process that is a duplicate of the parent. The child process invokes the loader via the `execve` system call. The loader deletes the child's existing virtual memory segments and creates a new set of code, data, heap, and stack segments. The new stack and heap segments are initialized to zero. The new code and data segments are initialized to the contents of the executable file by mapping pages in the virtual address space to page-size chunks of the executable file. Finally, the loader jumps to the `_start` address, which eventually calls the application's `main` routine. Aside from some header information, there is no copying of data from disk to memory during loading. The copying is deferred until the CPU references a mapped virtual page, at which point the operating system automatically transfers the page from disk to memory using its paging mechanism.

of how much there is in a system. Disk space and kitchen trash cans share this same property.)

Shared libraries are modern innovations that address the disadvantages of static libraries. A shared library is an object module that, at either run time or load time, can be loaded at an arbitrary memory address and linked with a program in memory. This process is known as *dynamic linking* and is performed by a program called a *dynamic linker*. Shared libraries are also referred to as *shared objects*, and on Linux systems they are indicated by the `.so` suffix. Microsoft operating systems make heavy use of shared libraries, which they refer to as DLLs (dynamic link libraries).

Shared libraries are "shared" in two different ways. First, in any given file system, there is exactly one `.so` file for a particular library. The code and data in this `.so` file are shared by all of the executable object files that reference the library, as opposed to the contents of static libraries, which are copied and embedded in the executables that reference them. Second, a single copy of the `.text` section of a shared library in memory can be shared by different running processes. We will explore this in more detail when we study virtual memory in Chapter 9.

Figure 7.16 summarizes the dynamic linking process for the example program in Figure 7.7. To build a shared library `libvector.so` of our example vector routines in Figure 7.6, we invoke the compiler driver with some special directives to the compiler and linker:

```
linux> gcc -shared -fpic -o libvector.so addvec.c multvec.c
```

The `-fpic` flag directs the compiler to generate *position-independent code* (more on this in the next section). The `-shared` flag directs the linker to create a shared

Figure 7.16
Dynamic linking with shared libraries.

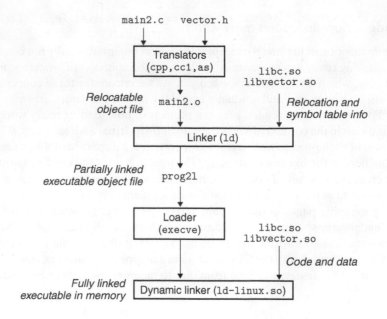

object file. Once we have created the library, we would then link it into our example program in Figure 7.7:

```
linux> gcc -o prog21 main2.c ./libvector.so
```

This creates an executable object file `prog21` in a form that can be linked with `libvector.so` at run time. The basic idea is to do some of the linking statically when the executable file is created, and then complete the linking process dynamically when the program is loaded. It is important to realize that none of the code or data sections from `libvector.so` are actually copied into the executable `prog21` at this point. Instead, the linker copies some relocation and symbol table information that will allow references to code and data in `libvector.so` to be resolved at load time.

When the loader loads and runs the executable `prog21`, it loads the partially linked executable `prog21`, using the techniques discussed in Section 7.9. Next, it notices that `prog21` contains a `.interp` section, which contains the path name of the dynamic linker, which is itself a shared object (e.g., `ld-linux.so` on Linux systems). Instead of passing control to the application, as it would normally do, the loader loads and runs the dynamic linker. The dynamic linker then finishes the linking task by performing the following relocations:

- Relocating the text and data of `libc.so` into some memory segment
- Relocating the text and data of `libvector.so` into another memory segment
- Relocating any references in `prog21` to symbols defined by `libc.so` and `libvector.so`

Finally, the dynamic linker passes control to the application. From this point on, the locations of the shared libraries are fixed and do not change during execution of the program.

7.11   Loading and Linking Shared Libraries from Applications

Up to this point, we have discussed the scenario in which the dynamic linker loads and links shared libraries when an application is loaded, just before it executes. However, it is also possible for an application to request the dynamic linker to load and link arbitrary shared libraries while the application is running, without having to link in the applications against those libraries at compile time.

Dynamic linking is a powerful and useful technique. Here are some examples in the real world:

- *Distributing software.* Developers of Microsoft Windows applications frequently use shared libraries to distribute software updates. They generate a new copy of a shared library, which users can then download and use as a replacement for the current version. The next time they run their application, it will automatically link and load the new shared library.

- *Building high-performance Web servers.* Many Web servers generate *dynamic content*, such as personalized Web pages, account balances, and banner ads. Early Web servers generated dynamic content by using `fork` and `execve` to create a child process and run a "CGI program" in the context of the child. However, modern high-performance Web servers can generate dynamic content using a more efficient and sophisticated approach based on dynamic linking.

  The idea is to package each function that generates dynamic content in a shared library. When a request arrives from a Web browser, the server dynamically loads and links the appropriate function and then calls it directly, as opposed to using `fork` and `execve` to run the function in the context of a child process. The function remains cached in the server's address space, so subsequent requests can be handled at the cost of a simple function call. This can have a significant impact on the throughput of a busy site. Further, existing functions can be updated and new functions can be added at run time, without stopping the server.

Linux systems provide a simple interface to the dynamic linker that allows application programs to load and link shared libraries at run time.

```
#include <dlfcn.h>

void *dlopen(const char *filename, int flag);
                        Returns: pointer to handle if OK, NULL on error
```

The `dlopen` function loads and links the shared library `filename`. The external symbols in `filename` are resolved using libraries previously opened with the `RTLD_GLOBAL` flag. If the current executable was compiled with the `-rdynamic` flag, then its global symbols are also available for symbol resolution. The `flag` argument must include either `RTLD_NOW`, which tells the linker to resolve references to external symbols immediately, or the `RTLD_LAZY` flag, which instructs the linker to defer symbol resolution until code from the library is executed. Either of these values can be ORed with the `RTLD_GLOBAL` flag.

```
#include <dlfcn.h>

void *dlsym(void *handle, char *symbol);
```
                                    Returns: pointer to symbol if OK, NULL on error

The `dlsym` function takes a `handle` to a previously opened shared library and a `symbol` name and returns the address of the symbol, if it exists, or NULL otherwise.

```
#include <dlfcn.h>

int dlclose (void *handle);
```
                                                Returns: 0 if OK, −1 on error

The `dlclose` function unloads the shared library if no other shared libraries are still using it.

```
#include <dlfcn.h>

const char *dlerror(void);
```
                Returns: error message if previous call to dlopen, dlsym, or dlclose failed;
                                                NULL if previous call was OK

The `dlerror` function returns a string describing the most recent error that occurred as a result of calling `dlopen`, `dlsym`, or `dlclose`, or NULL if no error occurred.

Figure 7.17 shows how we would use this interface to dynamically link our `libvector.so` shared library at run time and then invoke its `addvec` routine. To compile the program, we would invoke GCC in the following way:

```
linux> gcc -rdynamic -o prog2r dll.c -ldl
```

—— *code/link/dll.c*

```c
1    #include <stdio.h>
2    #include <stdlib.h>
3    #include <dlfcn.h>
4
5    int x[2] = {1, 2};
6    int y[2] = {3, 4};
7    int z[2];
8
9    int main()
10   {
11       void *handle;
12       void (*addvec)(int *, int *, int *, int);
13       char *error;
14
15       /* Dynamically load the shared library containing addvec() */
16       handle = dlopen("./libvector.so", RTLD_LAZY);
17       if (!handle) {
18           fprintf(stderr, "%s\n", dlerror());
19           exit(1);
20       }
21
22       /* Get a pointer to the addvec() function we just loaded */
23       addvec = dlsym(handle, "addvec");
24       if ((error = dlerror()) != NULL) {
25           fprintf(stderr, "%s\n", error);
26           exit(1);
27       }
28
29       /* Now we can call addvec() just like any other function */
30       addvec(x, y, z, 2);
31       printf("z = [%d %d]\n", z[0], z[1]);
32
33       /* Unload the shared library */
34       if (dlclose(handle) < 0) {
35           fprintf(stderr, "%s\n", dlerror());
36           exit(1);
37       }
38       return 0;
39   }
```

—— *code/link/dll.c*

Figure 7.17 Example program 3. Dynamically loads and links the shared library
libvector.so at run time.

Aside   Shared libraries and the Java Native Interface

Java defines a standard calling convention called *Java Native Interface (JNI)* that allows "native" C and C++ functions to be called from Java programs. The basic idea of JNI is to compile the native C function, say, `foo`, into a shared library, say, `foo.so`. When a running Java program attempts to invoke function `foo`, the Java interpreter uses the `dlopen` interface (or something like it) to dynamically link and load `foo.so` and then call `foo`.

7.12   Position-Independent Code (PIC)

A key purpose of shared libraries is to allow multiple running processes to share the same library code in memory and thus save precious memory resources. So how can multiple processes share a single copy of a program? One approach would be to assign a priori a dedicated chunk of the address space to each shared library, and then require the loader to always load the shared library at that address. While straightforward, this approach creates some serious problems. It would be an inefficient use of the address space because portions of the space would be allocated even if a process didn't use the library. It would also be difficult to manage. We would have to ensure that none of the chunks overlapped. Each time a library was modified, we would have to make sure that it still fit in its assigned chunk. If not, then we would have to find a new chunk. And if we created a new library, we would have to find room for it. Over time, given the hundreds of libraries and versions of libraries in a system, it would be difficult to keep the address space from fragmenting into lots of small unused but unusable holes. Even worse, the assignment of libraries to memory would be different for each system, thus creating even more management headaches.

To avoid these problems, modern systems compile the code segments of shared modules so that they can be loaded anywhere in memory without having to be modified by the linker. With this approach, a single copy of a shared module's code segment can be shared by an unlimited number of processes. (Of course, each process will still get its own copy of the read/write data segment.)

Code that can be loaded without needing any relocations is known as *position-independent code (PIC)*. Users direct GNU compilation systems to generate PIC code with the `-fpic` option to GCC. Shared libraries must always be compiled with this option.

On x86-64 systems, references to symbols in the same executable object module require no special treatment to be PIC. These references can be compiled using PC-relative addressing and relocated by the static linker when it builds the object file. However, references to external procedures and global variables that are defined by shared modules require some special techniques, which we describe next.

PIC Data References

Compilers generate PIC references to global variables by exploiting the following interesting fact: no matter where we load an object module (including shared

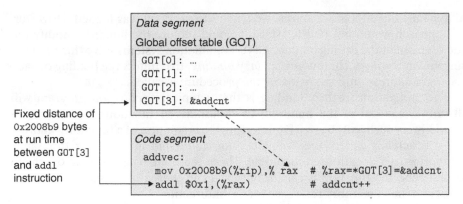

Figure 7.18 Using the GOT to reference a global variable. The addvec routine in libvector.so references addcnt indirectly through the GOT for libvector.so.

object modules) in memory, the data segment is always the same distance from the code segment. Thus, the *distance* between any instruction in the code segment and any variable in the data segment is a run-time constant, independent of the absolute memory locations of the code and data segments.

Compilers that want to generate PIC references to global variables exploit this fact by creating a table called the *global offset table (GOT)* at the beginning of the data segment. The GOT contains an 8-byte entry for each global data object (procedure or global variable) that is referenced by the object module. The compiler also generates a relocation record for each entry in the GOT. At load time, the dynamic linker relocates each GOT entry so that it contains the absolute address of the object. Each object module that references global objects has its own GOT.

Figure 7.18 shows the GOT from our example libvector.so shared module. The addvec routine loads the address of the global variable addcnt indirectly via GOT[3] and then increments addcnt in memory. The key idea here is that the offset in the PC-relative reference to GOT[3] is a run-time constant.

Since addcnt is defined by the libvector.so module, the compiler could have exploited the constant distance between the code and data segments by generating a direct PC-relative reference to addcnt and adding a relocation for the linker to resolve when it builds the shared module. However, if addcnt were defined by another shared module, then the indirect access through the GOT would be necessary. In this case, the compiler has chosen to use the most general solution, the GOT, for all references.

PIC Function Calls

Suppose that a program calls a function that is defined by a shared library. The compiler has no way of predicting the run-time address of the function, since the shared module that defines it could be loaded anywhere at run time. The normal approach would be to generate a relocation record for the reference, which the dynamic linker could then resolve when the program was loaded. However, this approach would not be PIC, since it would require the linker to modify the code segment of the calling module. GNU compilation systems solve this problem using an interesting technique, called *lazy binding*, that defers the binding of each procedure address until the *first time* the procedure is called.

The motivation for lazy binding is that a typical application program will call only a handful of the hundreds or thousands of functions exported by a shared library such as libc.so. By deferring the resolution of a function's address until it is actually called, the dynamic linker can avoid hundreds or thousands of unnecessary relocations at load time. There is a nontrivial run-time overhead the first time the function is called, but each call thereafter costs only a single instruction and a memory reference for the indirection.

Lazy binding is implemented with a compact yet somewhat complex interaction between two data structures: the GOT and the *procedure linkage table (PLT)*. If an object module calls any functions that are defined in shared libraries, then it has its own GOT and PLT. The GOT is part of the data segment. The PLT is part of the code segment.

Figure 7.19 shows how the PLT and GOT work together to resolve the address of a function at run time. First, let's examine the contents of each of these tables.

Procedure linkage table (PLT). The PLT is an array of 16-byte code entries. PLT[0] is a special entry that jumps into the dynamic linker. Each shared library function called by the executable has its own PLT entry. Each of

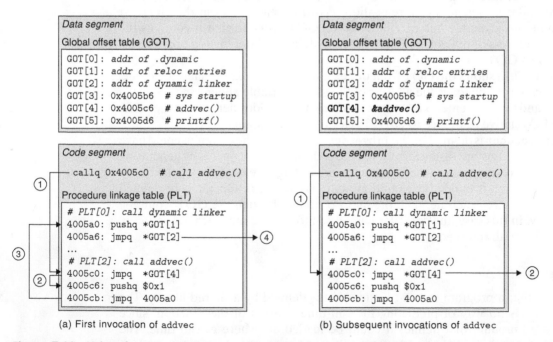

(a) First invocation of addvec

(b) Subsequent invocations of addvec

Figure 7.19   Using the PLT and GOT to call external functions. The dynamic linker resolves the address of addvec the first time it is called.

these entries is responsible for invoking a specific function. PLT[1] (not shown here) invokes the system startup function (__libc_start_main), which initializes the execution environment, calls the main function, and handles its return value. Entries starting at PLT[2] invoke functions called by the user code. In our example, PLT[2] invokes addvec and PLT[3] (not shown) invokes printf.

Global offset table (GOT). As we have seen, the GOT is an array of 8-byte address entries. When used in conjunction with the PLT, GOT[0] and GOT[1] contain information that the dynamic linker uses when it resolves function addresses. GOT[2] is the entry point for the dynamic linker in the ld-linux.so module. Each of the remaining entries corresponds to a called function whose address needs to be resolved at run time. Each has a matching PLT entry. For example, GOT[4] and PLT[2] correspond to addvec. Initially, each GOT entry points to the second instruction in the corresponding PLT entry.

Figure 7.19(a) shows how the GOT and PLT work together to lazily resolve the run-time address of function addvec the first time it is called:

Step 1. Instead of directly calling addvec, the program calls into PLT[2], which is the PLT entry for addvec.

Step 2. The first PLT instruction does an indirect jump through GOT[4]. Since each GOT entry initially points to the second instruction in its corresponding PLT entry, the indirect jump simply transfers control back to the next instruction in PLT[2].

Step 3. After pushing an ID for addvec (0x1) onto the stack, PLT[2] jumps to PLT[0].

Step 4. PLT[0] pushes an argument for the dynamic linker indirectly through GOT[1] and then jumps into the dynamic linker indirectly through GOT[2]. The dynamic linker uses the two stack entries to determine the run-time location of addvec, overwrites GOT[4] with this address, and passes control to addvec.

Figure 7.19(b) shows the control flow for any subsequent invocations of addvec:

Step 1. Control passes to PLT[2] as before.

Step 2. However, this time the indirect jump through GOT[4] transfers control directly to addvec.

7.13 Library Interpositioning

Linux linkers support a powerful technique, called *library interpositioning*, that allows you to intercept calls to shared library functions and execute your own code instead. Using interpositioning, you could trace the number of times a particular library function is called, validate and trace its input and output values, or even replace it with a completely different implementation.

Here's the basic idea: Given some *target function* to be interposed on, you create a *wrapper function* whose prototype is identical to the target function. Using some particular interpositioning mechanism, you then trick the system into calling the wrapper function instead of the target function. The wrapper function typically executes its own logic, then calls the target function and passes its return value back to the caller.

Interpositioning can occur at compile time, link time, or run time as the program is being loaded and executed. To explore these different mechanisms, we will use the example program in Figure 7.20(a) as a running example. It calls the malloc and free functions from the C standard library (libc.so). The call to malloc allocates a block of 32 bytes from the heap and returns a pointer to the block. The call to free gives the block back to the heap, for use by subsequent calls to malloc. Our goal is to use interpositioning to trace the calls to malloc and free as the program runs.

7.13.1 Compile-Time Interpositioning

Figure 7.20 shows how to use the C preprocessor to interpose at compile time. Each wrapper function in mymalloc.c (Figure 7.20(c)) calls the target function, prints a trace, and returns. The local malloc.h header file (Figure 7.20(b)) instructs the preprocessor to replace each call to a target function with a call to its wrapper. Here is how to compile and link the program:

```
linux> gcc -DCOMPILETIME -c mymalloc.c
linux> gcc -I. -o intc int.c mymalloc.o
```

The interpositioning happens because of the -I. argument, which tells the C preprocessor to look for malloc.h in the current directory before looking in the usual system directories. Notice that the wrappers in mymalloc.c are compiled with the standard malloc.h header file.

Running the program gives the following trace:

```
linux> ./intc
malloc(32)=0x9ee010
free(0x9ee010)
```

7.13.2 Link-Time Interpositioning

The Linux static linker supports link-time interpositioning with the --wrap f flag. This flag tells the linker to resolve references to symbol f as __wrap_f (two underscores for the prefix), and to resolve references to symbol __real_f (two underscores for the prefix) as f. Figure 7.21 shows the wrappers for our example program.

Here is how to compile the source files into relocatable object files:

```
linux> gcc -DLINKTIME -c mymalloc.c
linux> gcc -c int.c
```

(a) Example program int.c

code/link/interpose/int.c

```
1   #include <stdio.h>
2   #include <malloc.h>
3
4   int main()
5   {
6       int *p = malloc(32);
7       free(p);
8       return(0);
9   }
```

code/link/interpose/int.c

(b) Local malloc.h file

code/link/interpose/malloc.h

```
1   #define malloc(size) mymalloc(size)
2   #define free(ptr) myfree(ptr)
3
4   void *mymalloc(size_t size);
5   void myfree(void *ptr);
```

code/link/interpose/malloc.h

(c) Wrapper functions in mymalloc.c

code/link/interpose/mymalloc.c

```
1   #ifdef COMPILETIME
2   #include <stdio.h>
3   #include <malloc.h>
4
5   /* malloc wrapper function */
6   void *mymalloc(size_t size)
7   {
8       void *ptr = malloc(size);
9       printf("malloc(%d)=%p\n",
10              (int)size, ptr);
11      return ptr;
12  }
13
14  /* free wrapper function */
15  void myfree(void *ptr)
16  {
17      free(ptr);
18      printf("free(%p)\n", ptr);
19  }
20  #endif
```

code/link/interpose/mymalloc.c

Figure 7.20   Compile-time interpositioning with the C preprocessor.

————————————————————————— code/link/interpose/mymalloc.c

```
1    #ifdef LINKTIME
2    #include <stdio.h>
3
4    void *__real_malloc(size_t size);
5    void __real_free(void *ptr);
6
7    /* malloc wrapper function */
8    void *__wrap_malloc(size_t size)
9    {
10       void *ptr = __real_malloc(size); /* Call libc malloc */
11       printf("malloc(%d) = %p\n", (int)size, ptr);
12       return ptr;
13   }
14
15   /* free wrapper function */
16   void __wrap_free(void *ptr)
17   {
18       __real_free(ptr); /* Call libc free */
19       printf("free(%p)\n", ptr);
20   }
21   #endif
```

————————————————————————— code/link/interpose/mymalloc.c

Figure 7.21 Link-time interpositioning with the `--wrap` flag.

And here is how to link the object files into an executable:

```
linux> gcc -Wl,--wrap,malloc -Wl,--wrap,free -o intl int.o mymalloc.o
```

The `-Wl,option` flag passes `option` to the linker. Each comma in `option` is replaced with a space. So `-Wl,--wrap,malloc` passes `--wrap malloc` to the linker, and similarly for `-Wl,--wrap,free`.

Running the program gives the following trace:

```
linux> ./intl
malloc(32) = 0x18cf010
free(0x18cf010)
```

7.13.3 Run-Time Interpositioning

Compile-time interpositioning requires access to a program's source files. Link-time interpositioning requires access to its relocatable object files. However, there is a mechanism for interpositioning at run time that requires access only to the executable object file. This fascinating mechanism is based on the dynamic linker's `LD_PRELOAD` environment variable.

If the `LD_PRELOAD` environment variable is set to a list of shared library pathnames (separated by spaces or colons), then when you load and execute a program, the dynamic linker (LD-LINUX.SO) will search the `LD_PRELOAD` libraries first, before any other shared libraries, when it resolves undefined references. With this mechanism, you can interpose on any function in any shared library, including `libc.so`, when you load and execute any executable.

Figure 7.22 shows the wrappers for `malloc` and `free`. In each wrapper, the call to `dlsym` returns the pointer to the target `libc` function. The wrapper then calls the target function, prints a trace, and returns.

Here is how to build the shared library that contains the wrapper functions:

```
linux> gcc -DRUNTIME -shared -fpic -o mymalloc.so mymalloc.c -ldl
```

Here is how to compile the main program:

```
linux> gcc -o intr int.c
```

Here is how to run the program from the bash shell:[3]

```
linux> LD_PRELOAD="./mymalloc.so" ./intr
malloc(32) = 0x1bf7010
free(0x1bf7010)
```

And here is how to run it from the csh or tcsh shells:

```
linux> (setenv LD_PRELOAD "./mymalloc.so"; ./intr; unsetenv LD_PRELOAD)
malloc(32) = 0x2157010
free(0x2157010)
```

Notice that you can use `LD_PRELOAD` to interpose on the library calls of *any* executable program!

```
linux> LD_PRELOAD="./mymalloc.so" /usr/bin/uptime
malloc(568) = 0x21bb010
free(0x21bb010)
malloc(15) = 0x21bb010
malloc(568) = 0x21bb030
malloc(2255) = 0x21bb270
free(0x21bb030)
malloc(20) = 0x21bb030
malloc(20) = 0x21bb050
malloc(20) = 0x21bb070
malloc(20) = 0x21bb090
malloc(20) = 0x21bb0b0
malloc(384) = 0x21bb0d0
 20:47:36 up 85 days,  6:04,  1 user,  load average: 0.10, 0.04, 0.05
```

---

3. If you don't know what shell you are running, type `printenv SHELL` at the command line.

————————————————————————————— code/link/interpose/mymalloc.c

```
1    #ifdef RUNTIME
2    #define _GNU_SOURCE
3    #include <stdio.h>
4    #include <stdlib.h>
5    #include <dlfcn.h>
6
7    /* malloc wrapper function */
8    void *malloc(size_t size)
9    {
10       void *(*mallocp)(size_t size);
11       char *error;
12
13       mallocp = dlsym(RTLD_NEXT, "malloc"); /* Get address of libc malloc */
14       if ((error = dlerror()) != NULL) {
15           fputs(error, stderr);
16           exit(1);
17       }
18       char *ptr = mallocp(size); /* Call libc malloc */
19       printf("malloc(%d) = %p\n", (int)size, ptr);
20       return ptr;
21   }
22
23   /* free wrapper function */
24   void free(void *ptr)
25   {
26       void (*freep)(void *) = NULL;
27       char *error;
28
29       if (!ptr)
30           return;
31
32       freep = dlsym(RTLD_NEXT, "free"); /* Get address of libc free */
33       if ((error = dlerror()) != NULL) {
34           fputs(error, stderr);
35           exit(1);
36       }
37       freep(ptr); /* Call libc free */
38       printf("free(%p)\n", ptr);
39   }
40   #endif
```

————————————————————————————— code/link/interpose/mymalloc.c

Figure 7.22   Run-time interpositioning with `LD_PRELOAD`.

7.14   Tools for Manipulating Object Files

There are a number of tools available on Linux systems to help you understand and manipulate object files. In particular, the GNU *binutils* package is especially helpful and runs on every Linux platform.

AR. Creates static libraries, and inserts, deletes, lists, and extracts members.

STRINGS. Lists all of the printable strings contained in an object file.

STRIP. Deletes symbol table information from an object file.

NM. Lists the symbols defined in the symbol table of an object file.

SIZE. Lists the names and sizes of the sections in an object file.

READELF. Displays the complete structure of an object file, including all of the information encoded in the ELF header. Subsumes the functionality of SIZE and NM.

OBJDUMP. The mother of all binary tools. Can display all of the information in an object file. Its most useful function is disassembling the binary instructions in the .text section.

Linux systems also provide the LDD program for manipulating shared libraries:

LDD: Lists the shared libraries that an executable needs at run time.

7.15   Summary

Linking can be performed at compile time by static linkers and at load time and run time by dynamic linkers. Linkers manipulate binary files called object files, which come in three different forms: relocatable, executable, and shared. Relocatable object files are combined by static linkers into an executable object file that can be loaded into memory and executed. Shared object files (shared libraries) are linked and loaded by dynamic linkers at run time, either implicitly when the calling program is loaded and begins executing, or on demand, when the program calls functions from the dlopen library.

The two main tasks of linkers are symbol resolution, where each global symbol in an object file is bound to a unique definition, and relocation, where the ultimate memory address for each symbol is determined and where references to those objects are modified.

Static linkers are invoked by compiler drivers such as GCC. They combine multiple relocatable object files into a single executable object file. Multiple object files can define the same symbol, and the rules that linkers use for silently resolving these multiple definitions can introduce subtle bugs in user programs.

Multiple object files can be concatenated in a single static library. Linkers use libraries to resolve symbol references in other object modules. The left-to-right sequential scan that many linkers use to resolve symbol references is another source of confusing link-time errors.

Loaders map the contents of executable files into memory and run the program. Linkers can also produce partially linked executable object files with unresolved references to the routines and data defined in a shared library. At load time, the loader maps the partially linked executable into memory and then calls a dynamic linker, which completes the linking task by loading the shared library and relocating the references in the program.

Shared libraries that are compiled as position-independent code can be loaded anywhere and shared at run time by multiple processes. Applications can also use the dynamic linker at run time in order to load, link, and access the functions and data in shared libraries.

Bibliographic Notes

Linking is poorly documented in the computer systems literature. Since it lies at the intersection of compilers, computer architecture, and operating systems, linking requires an understanding of code generation, machine-language programming, program instantiation, and virtual memory. It does not fit neatly into any of the usual computer systems specialties and thus is not well covered by the classic texts in these areas. However, Levine's monograph provides a good general reference on the subject [69]. The original IA32 specifications for ELF and DWARF (a specification for the contents of the .debug and .line sections) are described in [54]. The x86-64 extensions to the ELF file format are described in [36]. The x86-64 application binary interface (ABI) describes the conventions for compiling, linking, and running x86-64 programs, including the rules for relocation and position-independent code [77].

Homework Problems

7.6 ◆

This problem concerns the m.o module from Figure 7.5 and the following version of the swap.c function that counts the number of times it has been called:

```
1    extern int buf[];
2
3    int *bufp0 = &buf[0];
4    static int *bufp1;
5
6    static void incr()
7    {
8        static int count=0;
9
10       count++;
11   }
12
13   void swap()
14   {
```

```
15        int temp;
16
17        incr();
18        bufp1 = &buf[1];
19        temp = *bufp0;
20        *bufp0 = *bufp1;
21        *bufp1 = temp;
22    }
```

For each symbol that is defined and referenced in swap.o, indicate if it will have a symbol table entry in the .symtab section in module swap.o. If so, indicate the module that defines the symbol (swap.o or m.o), the symbol type (local, global, or extern), and the section (.text, .data, or .bss) it occupies in that module.

Symbol	swap.o .symtab entry?	Symbol type	Module where defined	Section
buf	_____	_____	_____	_____
bufp0	_____	_____	_____	_____
bufp1	_____	_____	_____	_____
swap	_____	_____	_____	_____
temp	_____	_____	_____	_____
incr	_____	_____	_____	_____
count	_____	_____	_____	_____

7.7 ◆

Without changing any variable names, modify bar5.c on page 683 so that foo5.c prints the correct values of x and y (i.e., the hex representations of integers 15213 and 15212).

7.8 ◆

In this problem, let REF(x.i) → DEF(x.k) denote that the linker will associate an arbitrary reference to symbol x in module i to the definition of x in module k. For each example below, use this notation to indicate how the linker would resolve references to the multiply-defined symbol in each module. If there is a link-time error (rule 1), write "ERROR". If the linker arbitrarily chooses one of the definitions (rule 3), write "UNKNOWN".

```
A. /* Module 1 */         /* Module 2 */
   int main()             static int main=1[
   {                      int p2()
   }                      {
                          }
```

    (a) REF(main.1) → DEF(_____._____)

    (b) REF(main.2) → DEF(_____._____)

B.
```
/* Module 1 */        /* Module 2 */
int x;                double x;
void main()           int p2()
{                     {
}                     }
```

    (a) REF(x.1) → DEF(_____._____)

    (b) REF(x.2) → DEF(_____._____)

C.
```
/* Module 1 */        /* Module 2 */
int x=1;              double x=1.0;
void main()           int p2()
{                     {
}                     }
```

    (a) REF(x.1) → DEF(_____._____)

    (b) REF(x.2) → DEF(_____._____)

7.9 ◆

Consider the following program, which consists of two object modules:

```
1   /* foo6.c */
2   void p2(void);
3
4   int main()
5   {
6       p2();
7       return 0;
8   }
```

```
1   /* bar6.c */
2   #include <stdio.h>
3
4   char main;
5
6   void p2()
7   {
8       printf("0x%x\n", main);
9   }
```

When this program is compiled and executed on an x86-64 Linux system, it prints the string 0x48\n and terminates normally, even though function p2 never initializes variable main. Can you explain this?

7.10 ◆◆

Let a and b denote object modules or static libraries in the current directory, and let a→b denote that a depends on b, in the sense that b defines a symbol that is referenced by a. For each of the following scenarios, show the minimal command line (i.e., one with the least number of object file and library arguments) that will allow the static linker to resolve all symbol references:

A. p.o → libx.a → p.o

B. p.o → libx.a → liby.a *and* liby.a → libx.a

C. p.o → libx.a → liby.a → libz.a *and* liby.a → libx.a → libz.a

7.11 ◆◆

The program header in Figure 7.14 indicates that the data segment occupies 0x230 bytes in memory. However, only the first 0x228 bytes of these come from the sections of the executable file. What causes this discrepancy?

7.12 ◆◆

Consider the call to function swap in object file m.o (Problem 7.6).

```
9:    e8 00 00 00 00          callq  e <main+0xe>      swap()
```

with the following relocation entry:

```
r.offset = 0xa
r.symbol = swap
r.type   = R_X86_64_PC32
r.addend = -4
```

A. Suppose that the linker relocates .text in m.o to address 0x4004e0 and swap to address 0x4004f8. Then what is the value of the relocated reference to swap in the callq instruction?

B. Suppose that the linker relocates .text in m.o to address 0x4004d0 and swap to address 0x400500. Then what is the value of the relocated reference to swap in the callq instruction?

7.13 ◆◆

Performing the following tasks will help you become more familiar with the various tools for manipulating object files.

A. How many object files are contained in the versions of libc.a and libm.a on your system?

B. Does gcc -Og produce different executable code than gcc -Og -g?

C. What shared libraries does the GCC driver on your system use?

Solutions to Practice Problems

Solution to Problem 7.1 (page 678)

The purpose of this problem is to help you understand the relationship between linker symbols and C variables and functions. Notice that the C local variable temp does *not* have a symbol table entry.

Symbol	.symtab entry?	Symbol type	Module where defined	Section
buf	Yes	extern	m.o	.data
bufp0	Yes	global	swap.o	.data
bufp1	Yes	global	swap.o	COMMON
swap	Yes	global	swap.o	.text
temp	No	—	—	—

Solution to Problem 7.2 (page 684)

This is a simple drill that checks your understanding of the rules that a Unix linker uses when it resolves global symbols that are defined in more than one module. Understanding these rules can help you avoid some nasty programming bugs.

A. The linker chooses the strong symbol defined in module 1 over the weak symbol defined in module 2 (rule 2):

(a) REF(main.1) → DEF(main.1)

(b) REF(main.2) → DEF(main.1)

B. This is an ERROR, because each module defines a strong symbol main (rule 1).

C. The linker chooses the strong symbol defined in module 2 over the weak symbol defined in module 1 (rule 2):

(a) REF(x.1) → DEF(x.2)

(b) REF(x.2) → DEF(x.2)

Solution to Problem 7.3 (page 689)

Placing static libraries in the wrong order on the command line is a common source of linker errors that confuses many programmers. However, once you understand how linkers use static libraries to resolve references, it's pretty straightforward. This little drill checks your understanding of this idea:

A. `linux> gcc p.o libx.a`

B. `linux> gcc p.o libx.a liby.a`

C. `linux> gcc p.o libx.a liby.a libx.a`

Solution to Problem 7.4 (page 694)

This problem concerns the disassembly listing in Figure 7.12(a). Our purpose here is to give you some practice reading disassembly listings and to check your understanding of PC-relative addressing.

A. The hex address of the relocated reference in line 5 is 0x4004df.

B. The hex value of the relocated reference in line 5 is 0x5. Remember that the disassembly listing shows the value of the reference in little-endian byte order.

Solution to Problem 7.5 (page 695)

This problem tests your understanding of how the linker relocates PC-relative references. You were given that

```
ADDR(s) = ADDR(.text) = 0x4004d0
```

and

```
ADDR(r.symbol) = ADDR(swap) = 0x4004e8
```

Using the algorithm in Figure 7.10, the linker first computes the run-time address of the reference:

```
refaddr = ADDR(s)  + r.offset
        = 0x4004d0 + 0xa
        = 0x4004da
```

It then updates the reference:

```
*refptr = (unsigned) (ADDR(r.symbol) + r.addend - refaddr)
        = (unsigned) (0x4004e8      + (-4)     - 0x4004da)
        = (unsigned) (0xa)
```

Thus, in the resulting executable object file, the PC-relative reference to swap has a value of 0xa:

```
4004d9:   e8 0a 00 00 00            callq  4004e8 <swap>
```

CHAPTER 9

Virtual Memory

Processes in a system share the CPU and main memory with other processes. However, sharing the main memory poses some special challenges. As demand on the CPU increases, processes slow down in some reasonably smooth way. But if too many processes need too much memory, then some of them will simply not be able to run. When a program is out of space, it is out of luck. Memory is also vulnerable to corruption. If some process inadvertently writes to the memory used by another process, that process might fail in some bewildering fashion totally unrelated to the program logic.

In order to manage memory more efficiently and with fewer errors, modern systems provide an abstraction of main memory known as *virtual memory (VM)*. Virtual memory is an elegant interaction of hardware exceptions, hardware address translation, main memory, disk files, and kernel software that provides each process with a large, uniform, and private address space. With one clean mechanism, virtual memory provides three important capabilities: (1) It uses main memory efficiently by treating it as a cache for an address space stored on disk, keeping only the active areas in main memory and transferring data back and forth between disk and memory as needed. (2) It simplifies memory management by providing each process with a uniform address space. (3) It protects the address space of each process from corruption by other processes.

Virtual memory is one of the great ideas in computer systems. A major reason for its success is that it works silently and automatically, without any intervention from the application programmer. Since virtual memory works so well behind the scenes, why would a programmer need to understand it? There are several reasons.

- *Virtual memory is central.* Virtual memory pervades all levels of computer systems, playing key roles in the design of hardware exceptions, assemblers, linkers, loaders, shared objects, files, and processes. Understanding virtual memory will help you better understand how systems work in general.

- *Virtual memory is powerful.* Virtual memory gives applications powerful capabilities to create and destroy chunks of memory, map chunks of memory to portions of disk files, and share memory with other processes. For example, did you know that you can read or modify the contents of a disk file by reading and writing memory locations? Or that you can load the contents of a file into memory without doing any explicit copying? Understanding virtual memory will help you harness its powerful capabilities in your applications.

- *Virtual memory is dangerous.* Applications interact with virtual memory every time they reference a variable, dereference a pointer, or make a call to a dynamic allocation package such as `malloc`. If virtual memory is used improperly, applications can suffer from perplexing and insidious memory-related bugs. For example, a program with a bad pointer can crash immediately with a "segmentation fault" or a "protection fault," run silently for hours before crashing, or scariest of all, run to completion with incorrect results. Understanding virtual memory, and the allocation packages such as `malloc` that manage it, can help you avoid these errors.

This chapter looks at virtual memory from two angles. The first half of the chapter describes how virtual memory works. The second half describes how virtual memory is used and managed by applications. There is no avoiding the fact that VM is complicated, and the discussion reflects this in places. The good news is that if you work through the details, you will be able to simulate the virtual memory mechanism of a small system by hand, and the virtual memory idea will be forever demystified.

The second half builds on this understanding, showing you how to use and manage virtual memory in your programs. You will learn how to manage virtual memory via explicit memory mapping and calls to dynamic storage allocators such as the `malloc` package. You will also learn about a host of common memory-related errors in C programs and how to avoid them.

9.1 Physical and Virtual Addressing

The main memory of a computer system is organized as an array of M contiguous byte-size cells. Each byte has a unique *physical address (PA)*. The first byte has an address of 0, the next byte an address of 1, the next byte an address of 2, and so on. Given this simple organization, the most natural way for a CPU to access memory would be to use physical addresses. We call this approach *physical addressing*. Figure 9.1 shows an example of physical addressing in the context of a load instruction that reads the 4-byte word starting at physical address 4. When the CPU executes the load instruction, it generates an effective physical address and passes it to main memory over the memory bus. The main memory fetches the 4-byte word starting at physical address 4 and returns it to the CPU, which stores it in a register.

Early PCs used physical addressing, and systems such as digital signal processors, embedded microcontrollers, and Cray supercomputers continue to do so. However, modern processors use a form of addressing known as *virtual addressing*, as shown in Figure 9.2.

Figure 9.1

A system that uses physical addressing.

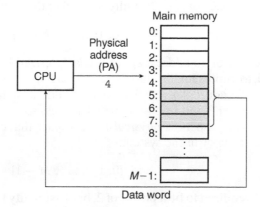

Data word

Figure 9.2
A system that uses virtual addressing.

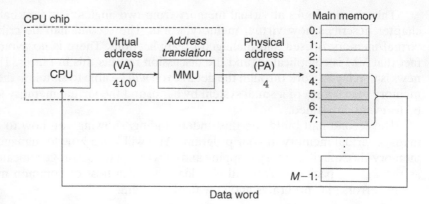

With virtual addressing, the CPU accesses main memory by generating a *virtual address (VA)*, which is converted to the appropriate physical address before being sent to main memory. The task of converting a virtual address to a physical one is known as *address translation*. Like exception handling, address translation requires close cooperation between the CPU hardware and the operating system. Dedicated hardware on the CPU chip called the *memory management unit (MMU)* translates virtual addresses on the fly, using a lookup table stored in main memory whose contents are managed by the operating system.

9.2 Address Spaces

An *address space* is an ordered set of nonnegative integer addresses

$$\{0, 1, 2, \ldots\}$$

If the integers in the address space are consecutive, then we say that it is a *linear address space*. To simplify our discussion, we will always assume linear address spaces. In a system with virtual memory, the CPU generates virtual addresses from an address space of $N = 2^n$ addresses called the *virtual address space*:

$$\{0, 1, 2, \ldots, N - 1\}$$

The size of an address space is characterized by the number of bits that are needed to represent the largest address. For example, a virtual address space with $N = 2^n$ addresses is called an *n*-bit address space. Modern systems typically support either 32-bit or 64-bit virtual address spaces.

A system also has a *physical address space* that corresponds to the M bytes of physical memory in the system:

$$\{0, 1, 2, \ldots, M - 1\}$$

M is not required to be a power of 2, but to simplify the discussion, we will assume that $M = 2^m$.

The concept of an address space is important because it makes a clean distinction between data objects (bytes) and their attributes (addresses). Once we recognize this distinction, then we can generalize and allow each data object to have multiple independent addresses, each chosen from a different address space. This is the basic idea of virtual memory. Each byte of main memory has a virtual address chosen from the virtual address space, and a physical address chosen from the physical address space.

Practice Problem 9.1 (solution page 880)

Complete the following table, filling in the missing entries and replacing each question mark with the appropriate integer. Use the following units: $K = 2^{10}$ (kilo), $M = 2^{20}$ (mega), $G = 2^{30}$ (giga), $T = 2^{40}$ (tera), $P = 2^{50}$ (peta), or $E = 2^{60}$ (exa).

Number of virtual address bits (n)	Number of virtual addresses (N)	Largest possible virtual address
8	_____	_____
_____	$2^? = 64\,K$	_____
_____	_____	$2^{32} - 1 = ?\,G - 1$
_____	$2^? = 256\,T$	_____
64	_____	_____

9.3 VM as a Tool for Caching

Conceptually, a virtual memory is organized as an array of N contiguous byte-size cells stored on disk. Each byte has a unique virtual address that serves as an index into the array. The contents of the array on disk are cached in main memory. As with any other cache in the memory hierarchy, the data on disk (the lower level) is partitioned into blocks that serve as the transfer units between the disk and the main memory (the upper level). VM systems handle this by partitioning the virtual memory into fixed-size blocks called *virtual pages (VPs)*. Each virtual page is $P = 2^p$ bytes in size. Similarly, physical memory is partitioned into *physical pages (PPs)*, also P bytes in size. (Physical pages are also referred to as *page frames*.)

At any point in time, the set of virtual pages is partitioned into three disjoint subsets:

Unallocated. Pages that have not yet been allocated (or created) by the VM system. Unallocated blocks do not have any data associated with them, and thus do not occupy any space on disk.

Cached. Allocated pages that are currently cached in physical memory.

Uncached. Allocated pages that are not cached in physical memory.

The example in Figure 9.3 shows a small virtual memory with eight virtual pages. Virtual pages 0 and 3 have not been allocated yet, and thus do not yet exist

Figure 9.3
How a VM system uses
main memory as a cache.

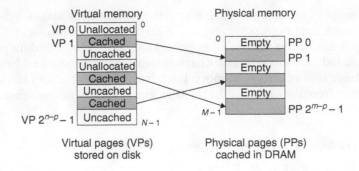

on disk. Virtual pages 1, 4, and 6 are cached in physical memory. Pages 2, 5, and 7 are allocated but are not currently cached in physical memory.

9.3.1 DRAM Cache Organization

To help us keep the different caches in the memory hierarchy straight, we will use the term *SRAM cache* to denote the L1, L2, and L3 cache memories between the CPU and main memory, and the term *DRAM cache* to denote the VM system's cache that caches virtual pages in main memory.

The position of the DRAM cache in the memory hierarchy has a big impact on the way that it is organized. Recall that a DRAM is at least 10 times slower than an SRAM and that disk is about 100,000 times slower than a DRAM. Thus, misses in DRAM caches are very expensive compared to misses in SRAM caches because DRAM cache misses are served from disk, while SRAM cache misses are usually served from DRAM-based main memory. Further, the cost of reading the first byte from a disk sector is about 100,000 times slower than reading successive bytes in the sector. The bottom line is that the organization of the DRAM cache is driven entirely by the enormous cost of misses.

Because of the large miss penalty and the expense of accessing the first byte, virtual pages tend to be large—typically 4 KB to 2 MB. Due to the large miss penalty, DRAM caches are fully associative; that is, any virtual page can be placed in any physical page. The replacement policy on misses also assumes greater importance, because the penalty associated with replacing the wrong virtual page is so high. Thus, operating systems use much more sophisticated replacement algorithms for DRAM caches than the hardware does for SRAM caches. (These replacement algorithms are beyond our scope here.) Finally, because of the large access time of disk, DRAM caches always use write-back instead of write-through.

9.3.2 Page Tables

As with any cache, the VM system must have some way to determine if a virtual page is cached somewhere in DRAM. If so, the system must determine which physical page it is cached in. If there is a miss, the system must determine

Figure 9.4
Page table.

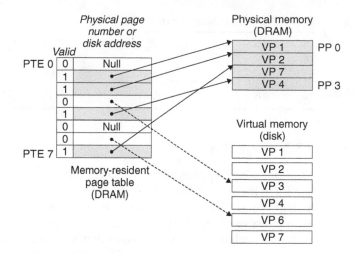

where the virtual page is stored on disk, select a victim page in physical memory, and copy the virtual page from disk to DRAM, replacing the victim page.

These capabilities are provided by a combination of operating system software, address translation hardware in the MMU (memory management unit), and a data structure stored in physical memory known as a *page table* that maps virtual pages to physical pages. The address translation hardware reads the page table each time it converts a virtual address to a physical address. The operating system is responsible for maintaining the contents of the page table and transferring pages back and forth between disk and DRAM.

Figure 9.4 shows the basic organization of a page table. A page table is an array of *page table entries (PTEs)*. Each page in the virtual address space has a PTE at a fixed offset in the page table. For our purposes, we will assume that each PTE consists of a *valid bit* and an n-bit address field. The valid bit indicates whether the virtual page is currently cached in DRAM. If the valid bit is set, the address field indicates the start of the corresponding physical page in DRAM where the virtual page is cached. If the valid bit is not set, then a null address indicates that the virtual page has not yet been allocated. Otherwise, the address points to the start of the virtual page on disk.

The example in Figure 9.4 shows a page table for a system with eight virtual pages and four physical pages. Four virtual pages (VP 1, VP 2, VP 4, and VP 7) are currently cached in DRAM. Two pages (VP 0 and VP 5) have not yet been allocated, and the rest (VP 3 and VP 6) have been allocated but are not currently cached. An important point to notice about Figure 9.4 is that because the DRAM cache is fully associative, any physical page can contain any virtual page.

Practice Problem 9.2 (solution page 881)

Determine the number of page table entries (PTEs) that are needed for the following combinations of virtual address size (n) and page size (P):

n	$P = 2^p$	Number of PTEs
16	4K	_____
16	8K	_____
32	4K	_____
32	8K	_____

9.3.3 Page Hits

Consider what happens when the CPU reads a word of virtual memory contained in VP 2, which is cached in DRAM (Figure 9.5). Using a technique we will describe in detail in Section 9.6, the address translation hardware uses the virtual address as an index to locate PTE 2 and read it from memory. Since the valid bit is set, the address translation hardware knows that VP 2 is cached in memory. So it uses the physical memory address in the PTE (which points to the start of the cached page in PP 1) to construct the physical address of the word.

9.3.4 Page Faults

In virtual memory parlance, a DRAM cache miss is known as a *page fault*. Figure 9.6 shows the state of our example page table before the fault. The CPU has referenced a word in VP 3, which is not cached in DRAM. The address translation hardware reads PTE 3 from memory, infers from the valid bit that VP 3 is not cached, and triggers a page fault exception. The page fault exception invokes a page fault exception handler in the kernel, which selects a victim page—in this case, VP 4 stored in PP 3. If VP 4 has been modified, then the kernel copies it back to disk. In either case, the kernel modifies the page table entry for VP 4 to reflect the fact that VP 4 is no longer cached in main memory.

Figure 9.5
VM page hit. The reference to a word in VP 2 is a hit.

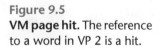
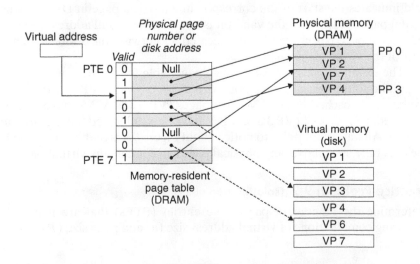

Figure 9.6

VM page fault (before).
The reference to a word in
VP 3 is a miss and triggers
a page fault.

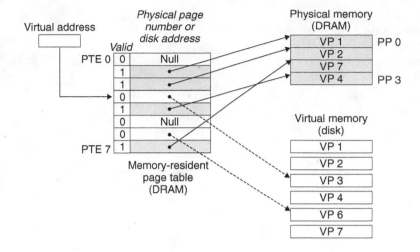

Figure 9.7

VM page fault (after).
The page fault handler
selects VP 4 as the victim
and replaces it with a copy
of VP 3 from disk. After the
page fault handler restarts
the faulting instruction, it
will read the word from
memory normally, without
generating an exception.

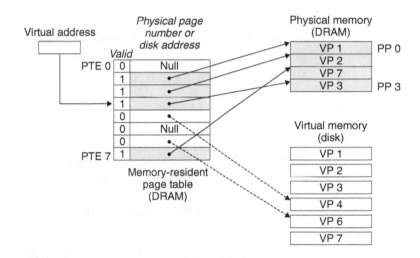

Next, the kernel copies VP 3 from disk to PP 3 in memory, updates PTE 3, and then returns. When the handler returns, it restarts the faulting instruction, which resends the faulting virtual address to the address translation hardware. But now, VP 3 is cached in main memory, and the page hit is handled normally by the address translation hardware. Figure 9.7 shows the state of our example page table after the page fault.

Virtual memory was invented in the early 1960s, long before the widening CPU-memory gap spawned SRAM caches. As a result, virtual memory systems use a different terminology from SRAM caches, even though many of the ideas are similar. In virtual memory parlance, blocks are known as *pages*. The activity of transferring a page between disk and memory is known as *swapping* or *paging*. Pages are *swapped in* (*paged in*) from disk to DRAM, and *swapped out* (*paged out*) from DRAM to disk. The strategy of waiting until the last moment to swap

Figure 9.8
Allocating a new virtual page. The kernel allocates VP 5 on disk and points PTE 5 to this new location.

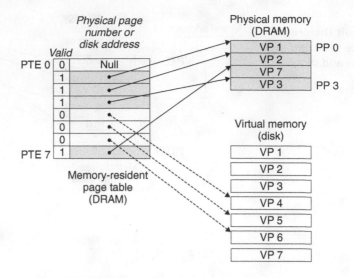

in a page, when a miss occurs, is known as *demand paging*. Other approaches, such as trying to predict misses and swap pages in before they are actually referenced, are possible. However, all modern systems use demand paging.

9.3.5 Allocating Pages

Figure 9.8 shows the effect on our example page table when the operating system allocates a new page of virtual memory—for example, as a result of calling `malloc`. In the example, VP 5 is allocated by creating room on disk and updating PTE 5 to point to the newly created page on disk.

9.3.6 Locality to the Rescue Again

When many of us learn about the idea of virtual memory, our first impression is often that it must be terribly inefficient. Given the large miss penalties, we worry that paging will destroy program performance. In practice, virtual memory works well, mainly because of our old friend *locality*.

Although the total number of distinct pages that programs reference during an entire run might exceed the total size of physical memory, the principle of locality promises that at any point in time they will tend to work on a smaller set of *active pages* known as the *working set* or *resident set*. After an initial overhead where the working set is paged into memory, subsequent references to the working set result in hits, with no additional disk traffic.

As long as our programs have good temporal locality, virtual memory systems work quite well. But of course, not all programs exhibit good temporal locality. If the working set size exceeds the size of physical memory, then the program can produce an unfortunate situation known as *thrashing*, where pages are swapped in and out continuously. Although virtual memory is usually efficient, if a program's performance slows to a crawl, the wise programmer will consider the possibility that it is thrashing.

Figure 9.9

How VM provides processes with separate address spaces. The operating system maintains a separate page table for each process in the system.

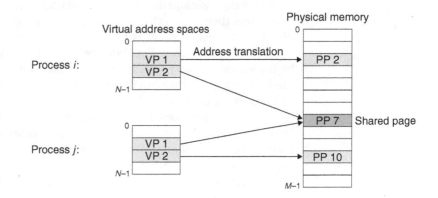

9.4 VM as a Tool for Memory Management

In the last section, we saw how virtual memory provides a mechanism for using the DRAM to cache pages from a typically larger virtual address space. Interestingly, some early systems such as the DEC PDP-11/70 supported a virtual address space that was *smaller* than the available physical memory. Yet virtual memory was still a useful mechanism because it greatly simplified memory management and provided a natural way to protect memory.

Thus far, we have assumed a single page table that maps a single virtual address space to the physical address space. In fact, operating systems provide a separate page table, and thus a separate virtual address space, for each process. Figure 9.9 shows the basic idea. In the example, the page table for process i maps VP 1 to PP 2 and VP 2 to PP 7. Similarly, the page table for process j maps VP 1 to PP 7 and VP 2 to PP 10. Notice that multiple virtual pages can be mapped to the same shared physical page.

The combination of demand paging and separate virtual address spaces has a profound impact on the way that memory is used and managed in a system. In particular, VM simplifies linking and loading, the sharing of code and data, and allocating memory to applications.

- *Simplifying linking.* A separate address space allows each process to use the same basic format for its memory image, regardless of where the code and data actually reside in physical memory. For example, as we saw in Figure 8.13, every process on a given Linux system has a similar memory format. For 64-bit address spaces, the code segment *always* starts at virtual address 0x400000. The data segment follows the code segment after a suitable alignment gap. The stack occupies the highest portion of the user process address space and grows downward. Such uniformity greatly simplifies the design and implementation of linkers, allowing them to produce fully linked executables that are independent of the ultimate location of the code and data in physical memory.

- *Simplifying loading.* Virtual memory also makes it easy to load executable and shared object files into memory. To load the .text and .data sections of an object file into a newly created process, the Linux loader allocates virtual pages for the code and data segments, marks them as invalid (i.e., not cached), and points their page table entries to the appropriate locations in the object file. The interesting point is that the loader never actually copies any data from disk into memory. The data are paged in automatically and on demand by the virtual memory system the first time each page is referenced, either by the CPU when it fetches an instruction or by an executing instruction when it references a memory location.

  This notion of mapping a set of contiguous virtual pages to an arbitrary location in an arbitrary file is known as *memory mapping.* Linux provides a system call called mmap that allows application programs to do their own memory mapping. We will describe application-level memory mapping in more detail in Section 9.8.

- *Simplifying sharing.* Separate address spaces provide the operating system with a consistent mechanism for managing sharing between user processes and the operating system itself. In general, each process has its own private code, data, heap, and stack areas that are not shared with any other process. In this case, the operating system creates page tables that map the corresponding virtual pages to disjoint physical pages.

  However, in some instances it is desirable for processes to share code and data. For example, every process must call the same operating system kernel code, and every C program makes calls to routines in the standard C library such as printf. Rather than including separate copies of the kernel and standard C library in each process, the operating system can arrange for multiple processes to share a single copy of this code by mapping the appropriate virtual pages in different processes to the same physical pages, as we saw in Figure 9.9.

- *Simplifying memory allocation.* Virtual memory provides a simple mechanism for allocating additional memory to user processes. When a program running in a user process requests additional heap space (e.g., as a result of calling malloc), the operating system allocates an appropriate number, say, k, of contiguous virtual memory pages, and maps them to k arbitrary physical pages located anywhere in physical memory. Because of the way page tables work, there is no need for the operating system to locate k contiguous pages of physical memory. The pages can be scattered randomly in physical memory.

9.5   VM as a Tool for Memory Protection

Any modern computer system must provide the means for the operating system to control access to the memory system. A user process should not be allowed

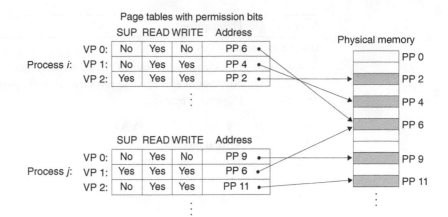

Figure 9.10

Using VM to provide page-level memory protection.

to modify its read-only code section. Nor should it be allowed to read or modify any of the code and data structures in the kernel. It should not be allowed to read or write the private memory of other processes, and it should not be allowed to modify any virtual pages that are shared with other processes, unless all parties explicitly allow it (via calls to explicit interprocess communication system calls).

As we have seen, providing separate virtual address spaces makes it easy to isolate the private memories of different processes. But the address translation mechanism can be extended in a natural way to provide even finer access control. Since the address translation hardware reads a PTE each time the CPU generates an address, it is straightforward to control access to the contents of a virtual page by adding some additional permission bits to the PTE. Figure 9.10 shows the general idea.

In this example, we have added three permission bits to each PTE. The SUP bit indicates whether processes must be running in kernel (supervisor) mode to access the page. Processes running in kernel mode can access any page, but processes running in user mode are only allowed to access pages for which SUP is 0. The READ and WRITE bits control read and write access to the page. For example, if process *i* is running in user mode, then it has permission to read VP 0 and to read or write VP 1. However, it is not allowed to access VP 2.

If an instruction violates these permissions, then the CPU triggers a general protection fault that transfers control to an exception handler in the kernel, which sends a SIGSEGV signal to the offending process. Linux shells typically report this exception as a "segmentation fault."

9.6 Address Translation

This section covers the basics of address translation. Our aim is to give you an appreciation of the hardware's role in supporting virtual memory, with enough detail so that you can work through some concrete examples by hand. However, keep in mind that we are omitting a number of details, especially related to timing,

Symbol	Description
Basic parameters	
$N = 2^n$	Number of addresses in virtual address space
$M = 2^m$	Number of addresses in physical address space
$P = 2^p$	Page size (bytes)
Components of a virtual address (VA)	
VPO	Virtual page offset (bytes)
VPN	Virtual page number
TLBI	TLB index
TLBT	TLB tag
Components of a physical address (PA)	
PPO	Physical page offset (bytes)
PPN	Physical page number
CO	Byte offset within cache block
CI	Cache index
CT	Cache tag

Figure 9.11 Summary of address translation symbols.

that are important to hardware designers but are beyond our scope. For your reference, Figure 9.11 summarizes the symbols that we will be using throughout this section.

Formally, address translation is a mapping between the elements of an N-element virtual address space (VAS) and an M-element physical address space (PAS),

$$\text{MAP: VAS} \rightarrow \text{PAS} \cup \emptyset$$

where

$$\text{MAP}(A) = \begin{cases} A' & \text{if data at virtual addr. } A \text{ are present at physical addr. } A' \text{ in PAS} \\ \emptyset & \text{if data at virtual addr. } A \text{ are not present in physical memory} \end{cases}$$

Figure 9.12 shows how the MMU uses the page table to perform this mapping. A control register in the CPU, the *page table base register (PTBR)* points to the current page table. The n-bit virtual address has two components: a p-bit *virtual page offset (VPO)* and an $(n - p)$-bit *virtual page number (VPN)*. The MMU uses the VPN to select the appropriate PTE. For example, VPN 0 selects PTE 0, VPN 1 selects PTE 1, and so on. The corresponding physical address is the concatenation of the *physical page number (PPN)* from the page table entry and the VPO from the virtual address. Notice that since the physical and virtual pages are both P bytes, the *physical page offset (PPO)* is identical to the VPO.

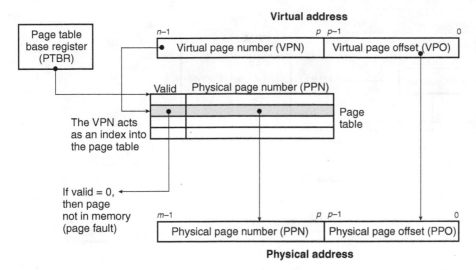

Figure 9.12 Address translation with a page table.

Figure 9.13(a) shows the steps that the CPU hardware performs when there is a page hit.

Step 1. The processor generates a virtual address and sends it to the MMU.

Step 2. The MMU generates the PTE address and requests it from the cache/ main memory.

Step 3. The cache/main memory returns the PTE to the MMU.

Step 4. The MMU constructs the physical address and sends it to the cache/main memory.

Step 5. The cache/main memory returns the requested data word to the processor.

Unlike a page hit, which is handled entirely by hardware, handling a page fault requires cooperation between hardware and the operating system kernel (Figure 9.13(b)).

Steps 1 to 3. The same as steps 1 to 3 in Figure 9.13(a).

Step 4. The valid bit in the PTE is zero, so the MMU triggers an exception, which transfers control in the CPU to a page fault exception handler in the operating system kernel.

Step 5. The fault handler identifies a victim page in physical memory, and if that page has been modified, pages it out to disk.

Step 6. The fault handler pages in the new page and updates the PTE in memory.

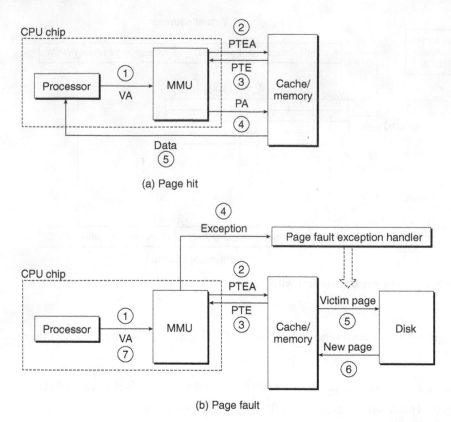

Figure 9.13 Operational view of page hits and page faults. VA: virtual address. PTEA: page table entry address. PTE: page table entry. PA: physical address.

Step 7. The fault handler returns to the original process, causing the faulting instruction to be restarted. The CPU resends the offending virtual address to the MMU. Because the virtual page is now cached in physical memory, there is a hit, and after the MMU performs the steps in Figure 9.13(a), the main memory returns the requested word to the processor.

Practice Problem 9.3 (solution page 881)

Given a 32-bit virtual address space and a 24-bit physical address, determine the number of bits in the VPN, VPO, PPN, and PPO for the following page sizes P:

	Number of			
P	VPN bits	VPO bits	PPN bits	PPO bits
1 KB	_____	_____	_____	_____
2 KB	_____	_____	_____	_____
4 KB	_____	_____	_____	_____
8 KB	_____	_____	_____	_____

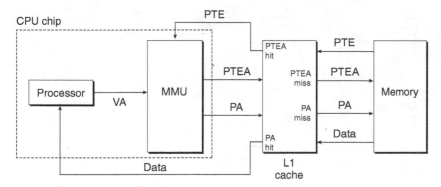

Figure 9.14 Integrating VM with a physically addressed cache. VA: virtual address. PTEA: page table entry address. PTE: page table entry. PA: physical address.

9.6.1 Integrating Caches and VM

In any system that uses both virtual memory and SRAM caches, there is the issue of whether to use virtual or physical addresses to access the SRAM cache. Although a detailed discussion of the trade-offs is beyond our scope here, most systems opt for physical addressing. With physical addressing, it is straightforward for multiple processes to have blocks in the cache at the same time and to share blocks from the same virtual pages. Further, the cache does not have to deal with protection issues, because access rights are checked as part of the address translation process.

Figure 9.14 shows how a physically addressed cache might be integrated with virtual memory. The main idea is that the address translation occurs before the cache lookup. Notice that page table entries can be cached, just like any other data words.

9.6.2 Speeding Up Address Translation with a TLB

As we have seen, every time the CPU generates a virtual address, the MMU must refer to a PTE in order to translate the virtual address into a physical address. In the worst case, this requires an additional fetch from memory, at a cost of tens to hundreds of cycles. If the PTE happens to be cached in L1, then the cost goes down to a handful of cycles. However, many systems try to eliminate even this cost by including a small cache of PTEs in the MMU called a *translation lookaside buffer (TLB)*.

A TLB is a small, virtually addressed cache where each line holds a block consisting of a single PTE. A TLB usually has a high degree of associativity. As shown in Figure 9.15, the index and tag fields that are used for set selection and line matching are extracted from the virtual page number in the virtual address. If the TLB has $T = 2^t$ sets, then the *TLB index (TLBI)* consists of the t least significant bits of the VPN, and the *TLB tag (TLBT)* consists of the remaining bits in the VPN.

Figure 9.15
Components of a virtual address that are used to access the TLB.

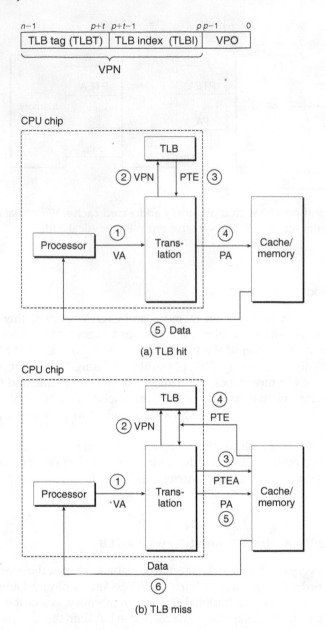

Figure 9.16
Operational view of a TLB hit and miss.

Figure 9.16(a) shows the steps involved when there is a TLB hit (the usual case). The key point here is that all of the address translation steps are performed inside the on-chip MMU and thus are fast.

Step 1. The CPU generates a virtual address.

Steps 2 and 3. The MMU fetches the appropriate PTE from the TLB.

Step 4. The MMU translates the virtual address to a physical address and sends it to the cache/main memory.

Step 5. The cache/main memory returns the requested data word to the CPU.

When there is a TLB miss, then the MMU must fetch the PTE from the L1 cache, as shown in Figure 9.16(b). The newly fetched PTE is stored in the TLB, possibly overwriting an existing entry.

9.6.3 Multi-Level Page Tables

Thus far, we have assumed that the system uses a single page table to do address translation. But if we had a 32-bit address space, 4 KB pages, and a 4-byte PTE, then we would need a 4 MB page table resident in memory at all times, even if the application referenced only a small chunk of the virtual address space. The problem is compounded for systems with 64-bit address spaces.

The common approach for compacting the page table is to use a hierarchy of page tables instead. The idea is easiest to understand with a concrete example. Consider a 32-bit virtual address space partitioned into 4 KB pages, with page table entries that are 4 bytes each. Suppose also that at this point in time the virtual address space has the following form: The first 2 K pages of memory are allocated for code and data, the next 6 K pages are unallocated, the next 1,023 pages are also unallocated, and the next page is allocated for the user stack. Figure 9.17 shows how we might construct a two-level page table hierarchy for this virtual address space.

Each PTE in the level 1 table is responsible for mapping a 4 MB chunk of the virtual address space, where each chunk consists of 1,024 contiguous pages. For example, PTE 0 maps the first chunk, PTE 1 the next chunk, and so on. Given that the address space is 4 GB, 1,024 PTEs are sufficient to cover the entire space.

If every page in chunk i is unallocated, then level 1 PTE i is null. For example, in Figure 9.17, chunks 2–7 are unallocated. However, if at least one page in chunk i is allocated, then level 1 PTE i points to the base of a level 2 page table. For example, in Figure 9.17, all or portions of chunks 0, 1, and 8 are allocated, so their level 1 PTEs point to level 2 page tables.

Each PTE in a level 2 page table is responsible for mapping a 4-KB page of virtual memory, just as before when we looked at single-level page tables. Notice that with 4-byte PTEs, each level 1 and level 2 page table is 4 kilobytes, which conveniently is the same size as a page.

This scheme reduces memory requirements in two ways. First, if a PTE in the level 1 table is null, then the corresponding level 2 page table does not even have to exist. This represents a significant potential savings, since most of the 4 GB virtual address space for a typical program is unallocated. Second, only the level 1 table needs to be in main memory at all times. The level 2 page tables can be created and paged in and out by the VM system as they are needed, which reduces pressure on main memory. Only the most heavily used level 2 page tables need to be cached in main memory.

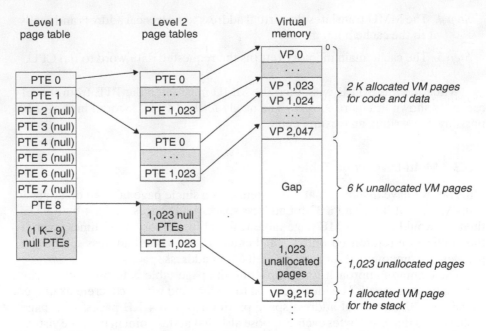

Figure 9.17 A two-level page table hierarchy. Notice that addresses increase from top to bottom.

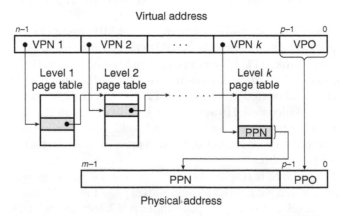

Figure 9.18 Address translation with a k-level page table.

Figure 9.18 summarizes address translation with a k-level page table hierarchy. The virtual address is partitioned into k VPNs and a VPO. Each VPN i, $1 \leq i \leq k$, is an index into a page table at level i. Each PTE in a level j table, $1 \leq j \leq k - 1$, points to the base of some page table at level $j + 1$. Each PTE in a level k table contains either the PPN of some physical page or the address of a disk block. To construct the physical address, the MMU must access k PTEs before it can determine the PPN. As with a single-level hierarchy, the PPO is identical to the VPO.

Accessing k PTEs may seem expensive and impractical at first glance. However, the TLB comes to the rescue here by caching PTEs from the page tables at the different levels. In practice, address translation with multi-level page tables is not significantly slower than with single-level page tables.

9.6.4 Putting It Together: End-to-End Address Translation

In this section, we put it all together with a concrete example of end-to-end address translation on a small system with a TLB and L1 d-cache. To keep things manageable, we make the following assumptions:

- The memory is byte addressable.
- Memory accesses are to *1-byte words* (not 4-byte words).
- Virtual addresses are 14 bits wide ($n = 14$).
- Physical addresses are 12 bits wide ($m = 12$).
- The page size is 64 bytes ($P = 64$).
- The TLB is 4-way set associative with 16 total entries.
- The L1 d-cache is physically addressed and direct mapped, with a 4-byte line size and 16 total sets.

Figure 9.19 shows the formats of the virtual and physical addresses. Since each page is $2^6 = 64$ bytes, the low-order 6 bits of the virtual and physical addresses serve as the VPO and PPO, respectively. The high-order 8 bits of the virtual address serve as the VPN. The high-order 6 bits of the physical address serve as the PPN.

Figure 9.20 shows a snapshot of our little memory system, including the TLB (Figure 9.20(a)), a portion of the page table (Figure 9.20(b)), and the L1 cache (Figure 9.20(c)). Above the figures of the TLB and cache, we have also shown how the bits of the virtual and physical addresses are partitioned by the hardware as it accesses these devices.

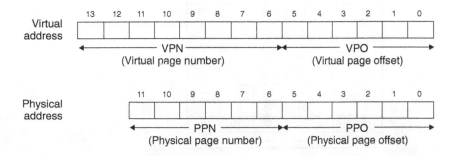

Figure 9.19 Addressing for small memory system. Assume 14-bit virtual addresses ($n = 14$), 12-bit physical addresses ($m = 12$), and 64-byte pages ($P = 64$).

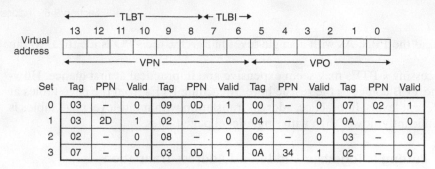

	TLBT						TLBI	
	13 12 11 10 9 8 7			6 5 4 3 2 1 0				

Virtual address

VPN ◄———► VPO

Set	Tag	PPN	Valid	Tag	PPN	Valid	Tag	PPN	Valid	Tag	PPN	Valid
0	03	–	0	09	0D	1	00	–	0	07	02	1
1	03	2D	1	02	–	0	04	–	0	0A	–	0
2	02	–	0	08	–	0	06	–	0	03	–	0
3	07	–	0	03	0D	1	0A	34	1	02	–	0

(a) TLB: 4 sets, 16 entries, 4-way set associative

VPN	PPN	Valid		VPN	PPN	Valid
00	28	1		08	13	1
01	—	0		09	17	1
02	33	1		0A	09	1
03	02	1		0B	—	0
04	—	0		0C	—	0
05	16	1		0D	2D	1
06	—	0		0E	11	1
07	—	0		0F	0D	1

(b) Page table: Only the first 16 PTEs are shown

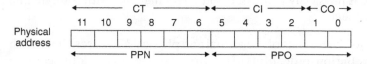

	CT			CI		CO
	11 10 9 8 7		6 5 4 3 2		1 0

Physical address

PPN ◄———► PPO

Idx	Tag	Valid	Blk 0	Blk 1	Blk 2	Blk 3
0	19	1	99	11	23	11
1	15	0	—	—	—	—
2	1B	1	00	02	04	08
3	36	0	—	—	—	—
4	32	1	43	6D	8F	09
5	0D	1	36	72	F0	1D
6	31	0	—	—	—	—
7	16	1	11	C2	DF	03
8	24	1	3A	00	51	89
9	2D	0	—	—	—	—
A	2D	1	93	15	DA	3B
B	0B	0	—	—	—	—
C	12	0	—	—	—	—
D	16	1	04	96	34	15
E	13	1	83	77	1B	D3
F	14	0	—	—	—	—

(c) Cache: 16 sets, 4-byte blocks, direct mapped

Figure 9.20 TLB, page table, and cache for small memory system. All values in the TLB, page table, and cache are in hexadecimal notation.

TLB. The TLB is virtually addressed using the bits of the VPN. Since the TLB has four sets, the 2 low-order bits of the VPN serve as the set index (TLBI). The remaining 6 high-order bits serve as the tag (TLBT) that distinguishes the different VPNs that might map to the same TLB set.

Page table. The page table is a single-level design with a total of $2^8 = 256$ page table entries (PTEs). However, we are only interested in the first 16 of these. For convenience, we have labeled each PTE with the VPN that indexes it; but keep in mind that these VPNs are not part of the page table and not stored in memory. Also, notice that the PPN of each invalid PTE is denoted with a dash to reinforce the idea that whatever bit values might happen to be stored there are not meaningful.

Cache. The direct-mapped cache is addressed by the fields in the physical address. Since each block is 4 bytes, the low-order 2 bits of the physical address serve as the block offset (CO). Since there are 16 sets, the next 4 bits serve as the set index (CI). The remaining 6 bits serve as the tag (CT).

Given this initial setup, let's see what happens when the CPU executes a load instruction that reads the byte at address 0x03d4. (Recall that our hypothetical CPU reads 1-byte words rather than 4-byte words.) To begin this kind of manual simulation, we find it helpful to write down the bits in the virtual address, identify the various fields we will need, and determine their hex values. The hardware performs a similar task when it decodes the address.

			TLBT				TLBI							
			0x03				0x03							
Bit position	13	12	11	10	9	8	7	6	5	4	3	2	1	0
VA = 0x03d4	0	0	0	0	1	1	1	1	0	1	0	1	0	0
				VPN							VPO			
				0x0f							0x14			

To begin, the MMU extracts the VPN (0x0F) from the virtual address and checks with the TLB to see if it has cached a copy of PTE 0x0F from some previous memory reference. The TLB extracts the TLB index (0x03) and the TLB tag (0x3) from the VPN, hits on a valid match in the second entry of set 0x3, and returns the cached PPN (0x0D) to the MMU.

If the TLB had missed, then the MMU would need to fetch the PTE from main memory. However, in this case, we got lucky and had a TLB hit. The MMU now has everything it needs to form the physical address. It does this by concatenating the PPN (0x0D) from the PTE with the VPO (0x14) from the virtual address, which forms the physical address (0x354).

Next, the MMU sends the physical address to the cache, which extracts the cache offset CO (0x0), the cache set index CI (0x5), and the cache tag CT (0x0D) from the physical address.

	CT						CI			CO	
			0x0d					0x05		0x0	
Bit position	11	10	9	8	7	6	5	4	3	2	1	0
PA = 0x354	0	0	1	1	0	1	0	1	0	1	0	0
			PPN					PPO			
			0x0d					0x14			

Since the tag in set 0x5 matches CT, the cache detects a hit, reads out the data byte (0x36) at offset CO, and returns it to the MMU, which then passes it back to the CPU.

Other paths through the translation process are also possible. For example, if the TLB misses, then the MMU must fetch the PPN from a PTE in the page table. If the resulting PTE is invalid, then there is a page fault and the kernel must page in the appropriate page and rerun the load instruction. Another possibility is that the PTE is valid, but the necessary memory block misses in the cache.

Practice Problem 9.4 (solution page 881)

Show how the example memory system in Section 9.6.4 translates a virtual address into a physical address and accesses the cache. For the given virtual address, indicate the TLB entry accessed, physical address, and cache byte value returned. Indicate whether the TLB misses, whether a page fault occurs, and whether a cache miss occurs. If there is a cache miss, enter "—" for "Cache byte returned." If there is a page fault, enter "—" for "PPN" and leave parts C and D blank.

Virtual address: 0x03d7

A. Virtual address format

13	12	11	10	9	8	7	6	5	4	3	2	1	0

B. Address translation

Parameter	Value
VPN	_____
TLB index	_____
TLB tag	_____
TLB hit? (Y/N)	_____
Page fault? (Y/N)	_____
PPN	_____

C. Physical address format

11	10	9	8	7	6	5	4	3	2	1	0

D. Physical memory reference

Parameter	Value
Byte offset	_____
Cache index	_____
Cache tag	_____
Cache hit? (Y/N)	_____
Cache byte returned	_____

9.7   Case Study: The Intel Core i7/Linux Memory System

We conclude our discussion of virtual memory mechanisms with a case study of a real system: an Intel Core i7 running Linux. Although the underlying Haswell microarchitecture allows for full 64-bit virtual and physical address spaces, the current Core i7 implementations (and those for the foreseeable future) support a 48-bit (256 TB) virtual address space and a 52-bit (4 PB) physical address space, along with a compatibility mode that supports 32-bit (4 GB) virtual and physical address spaces.

Figure 9.21 gives the highlights of the Core i7 memory system. The *processor package* (chip) includes four cores, a large L3 cache shared by all of the cores, and

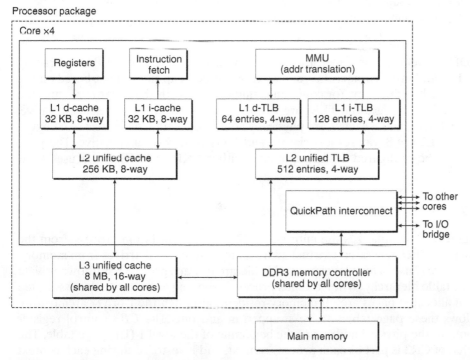

Figure 9.21   The Core i7 memory system.

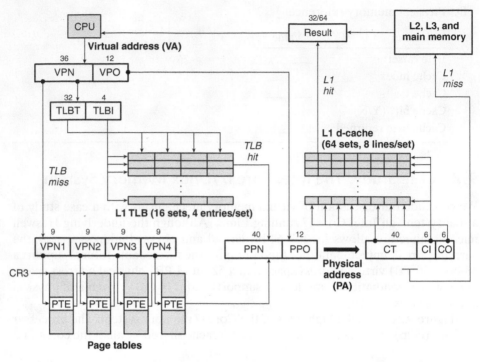

Figure 9.22 Summary of Core i7 address translation. For simplicity, the i-caches, i-TLB, and L2 unified TLB are not shown.

a DDR3 memory controller. Each core contains a hierarchy of TLBs, a hierarchy of data and instruction caches, and a set of fast point-to-point links, based on the QuickPath technology, for communicating directly with the other cores and the external I/O bridge. The TLBs are virtually addressed, and 4-way set associative. The L1, L2, and L3 caches are physically addressed, with a block size of 64 bytes. L1 and L2 are 8-way set associative, and L3 is 16-way set associative. The page size can be configured at start-up time as either 4 KB or 4 MB. Linux uses 4 KB pages.

9.7.1 Core i7 Address Translation

Figure 9.22 summarizes the entire Core i7 address translation process, from the time the CPU generates a virtual address until a data word arrives from memory. The Core i7 uses a four-level page table hierarchy. Each process has its own private page table hierarchy. When a Linux process is running, the page tables associated with allocated pages are all memory-resident, although the Core i7 architecture allows these page tables to be swapped in and out. The *CR3* control register contains the physical address of the beginning of the level 1 (L1) page table. The value of CR3 is part of each process context, and is restored during each context switch.

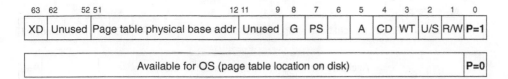

Field	Description
P	Child page table present in physical memory (1) or not (0).
R/W	Read-only or read-write access permission for all reachable pages.
U/S	User or supervisor (kernel) mode access permission for all reachable pages.
WT	Write-through or write-back cache policy for the child page table.
CD	Caching disabled or enabled for the child page table.
A	Reference bit (set by MMU on reads and writes, cleared by software).
PS	Page size either 4 KB or 4 MB (defined for level 1 PTEs only).
Base addr	40 most significant bits of physical base address of child page table.
XD	Disable or enable instruction fetches from all pages reachable from this PTE.

Figure 9.23 Format of level 1, level 2, and level 3 page table entries. Each entry references a 4 KB child page table.

Figure 9.23 shows the format of an entry in a level 1, level 2, or level 3 page table. When $P = 1$ (which is always the case with Linux), the address field contains a 40-bit physical page number (PPN) that points to the beginning of the appropriate page table. Notice that this imposes a 4 KB alignment requirement on page tables.

Figure 9.24 shows the format of an entry in a level 4 page table. When $P = 1$, the address field contains a 40-bit PPN that points to the base of some page in physical memory. Again, this imposes a 4 KB alignment requirement on physical pages.

The PTE has three permission bits that control access to the page. The R/W bit determines whether the contents of a page are read/write or read-only. The U/S bit, which determines whether the page can be accessed in user mode, protects code and data in the operating system kernel from user programs. The XD (execute disable) bit, which was introduced in 64-bit systems, can be used to disable instruction fetches from individual memory pages. This is an important new feature that allows the operating system kernel to reduce the risk of buffer overflow attacks by restricting execution to the read-only code segment.

As the MMU translates each virtual address, it also updates two other bits that can be used by the kernel's page fault handler. The MMU sets the A bit, which is known as a *reference bit*, each time a page is accessed. The kernel can use the reference bit to implement its page replacement algorithm. The MMU sets the D bit, or *dirty bit*, each time the page is written to. A page that has been modified is sometimes called a *dirty page*. The dirty bit tells the kernel whether or not it must

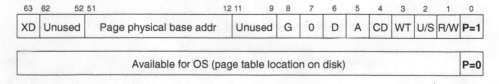

Field	Description
P	Child page present in physical memory (1) or not (0).
R/W	Read-only or read/write access permission for child page.
U/S	User or supervisor mode (kernel mode) access permission for child page.
WT	Write-through or write-back cache policy for the child page.
CD	Cache disabled or enabled.
A	Reference bit (set by MMU on reads and writes, cleared by software).
D	Dirty bit (set by MMU on writes, cleared by software).
G	Global page (don't evict from TLB on task switch).
Base addr	40 most significant bits of physical base address of child page.
XD	Disable or enable instruction fetches from the child page.

Figure 9.24 Format of level 4 page table entries. Each entry references a 4 KB child page.

write back a victim page before it copies in a replacement page. The kernel can call a special kernel-mode instruction to clear the reference or dirty bits.

Figure 9.25 shows how the Core i7 MMU uses the four levels of page tables to translate a virtual address to a physical address. The 36-bit VPN is partitioned into four 9-bit chunks, each of which is used as an offset into a page table. The CR3 register contains the physical address of the L1 page table. VPN 1 provides an offset to an L1 PTE, which contains the base address of the L2 page table. VPN 2 provides an offset to an L2 PTE, and so on.

9.7.2 Linux Virtual Memory System

A virtual memory system requires close cooperation between the hardware and the kernel. Details vary from version to version, and a complete description is beyond our scope. Nonetheless, our aim in this section is to describe enough of the Linux virtual memory system to give you a sense of how a real operating system organizes virtual memory and how it handles page faults.

Linux maintains a separate virtual address space for each process of the form shown in Figure 9.26. We have seen this picture a number of times already, with its familiar code, data, heap, shared library, and stack segments. Now that we understand address translation, we can fill in some more details about the kernel virtual memory that lies above the user stack.

The kernel virtual memory contains the code and data structures in the kernel. Some regions of the kernel virtual memory are mapped to physical pages that

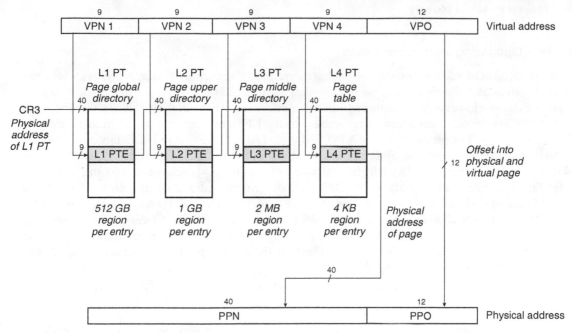

Figure 9.25 Core i7 page table translation. PT: page table; PTE: page table entry; VPN: virtual page number; VPO: virtual page offset; PPN: physical page number; PPO: physical page offset. The Linux names for the four levels of page tables are also shown.

Figure 9.26
The virtual memory of a Linux process.

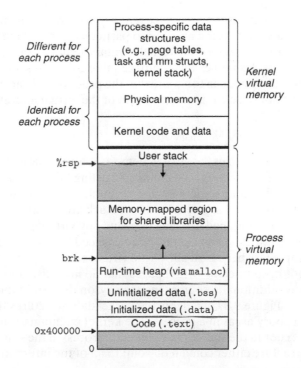

Aside Optimizing address translation

In our discussion of address translation, we have described a sequential two-step process where the MMU (1) translates the virtual address to a physical address and then (2) passes the physical address to the L1 cache. However, real hardware implementations use a neat trick that allows these steps to be partially overlapped, thus speeding up accesses to the L1 cache. For example, a virtual address on a Core i7 with 4 KB pages has 12 bits of VPO, and these bits are identical to the 12 bits of PPO in the corresponding physical address. Since the 8-way set associative physically addressed L1 caches have 64 sets and 64-byte cache blocks, each physical address has 6 ($\log_2 64$) cache offset bits and 6 ($\log_2 64$) index bits. These 12 bits fit exactly in the 12-bit VPO of a virtual address, which is no accident! When the CPU needs a virtual address translated, it sends the VPN to the MMU and the VPO to the L1 cache. While the MMU is requesting a page table entry from the TLB, the L1 cache is busy using the VPO bits to find the appropriate set and read out the eight tags and corresponding data words in that set. When the MMU gets the PPN back from the TLB, the cache is ready to try to match the PPN to one of these eight tags.

are shared by all processes. For example, each process shares the kernel's code and global data structures. Interestingly, Linux also maps a set of contiguous virtual pages (equal in size to the total amount of DRAM in the system) to the corresponding set of contiguous physical pages. This provides the kernel with a convenient way to access any specific location in physical memory—for example, when it needs to access page tables or to perform memory-mapped I/O operations on devices that are mapped to particular physical memory locations.

Other regions of kernel virtual memory contain data that differ for each process. Examples include page tables, the stack that the kernel uses when it is executing code in the context of the process, and various data structures that keep track of the current organization of the virtual address space.

Linux Virtual Memory Areas

Linux organizes the virtual memory as a collection of *areas* (also called *segments*). An area is a contiguous chunk of existing (allocated) virtual memory whose pages are related in some way. For example, the code segment, data segment, heap, shared library segment, and user stack are all distinct areas. Each existing virtual page is contained in some area, and any virtual page that is not part of some area does not exist and cannot be referenced by the process. The notion of an area is important because it allows the virtual address space to have gaps. The kernel does not keep track of virtual pages that do not exist, and such pages do not consume any additional resources in memory, on disk, or in the kernel itself.

Figure 9.27 highlights the kernel data structures that keep track of the virtual memory areas in a process. The kernel maintains a distinct task structure (task_ struct in the source code) for each process in the system. The elements of the task structure either contain or point to all of the information that the kernel needs to

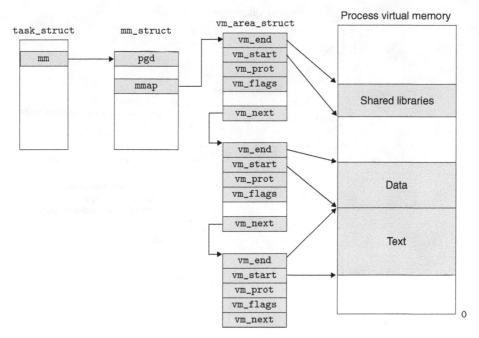

Figure 9.27   How Linux organizes virtual memory.

run the process (e.g., the PID, pointer to the user stack, name of the executable object file, and program counter).

One of the entries in the task structure points to an `mm_struct` that characterizes the current state of the virtual memory. The two fields of interest to us are `pgd`, which points to the base of the level 1 table (the page global directory), and `mmap`, which points to a list of `vm_area_structs` (area structs), each of which characterizes an area of the current virtual address space. When the kernel runs this process, it stores `pgd` in the CR3 control register.

For our purposes, the area struct for a particular area contains the following fields:

`fvm_start`. Points to the beginning of the area.

`vm_end`. Points to the end of the area.

`vm_prot`. Describes the read/write permissions for all of the pages contained in the area.

`vm_flags`. Describes (among other things) whether the pages in the area are shared with other processes or private to this process.

`vm_next`. Points to the next area struct in the list.

Figure 9.28
Linux page fault handling.

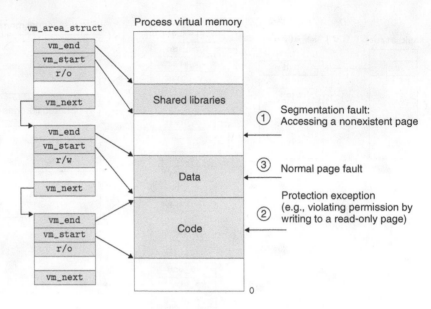

Linux Page Fault Exception Handling

Suppose the MMU triggers a page fault while trying to translate some virtual address A. The exception results in a transfer of control to the kernel's page fault handler, which then performs the following steps:

1. Is virtual address A legal? In other words, does A lie within an area defined by some area struct? To answer this question, the fault handler searches the list of area structs, comparing A with the `vm_start` and `vm_end` in each area struct. If the instruction is not legal, then the fault handler triggers a segmentation fault, which terminates the process. This situation is labeled "1" in Figure 9.28.

   Because a process can create an arbitrary number of new virtual memory areas (using the `mmap` function described in the next section), a sequential search of the list of area structs might be very costly. So in practice, Linux superimposes a tree on the list, using some fields that we have not shown, and performs the search on this tree.

2. Is the attempted memory access legal? In other words, does the process have permission to read, write, or execute the pages in this area? For example, was the page fault the result of a store instruction trying to write to a read-only page in the code segment? Is the page fault the result of a process running in user mode that is attempting to read a word from kernel virtual memory? If the attempted access is not legal, then the fault handler triggers a protection exception, which terminates the process. This situation is labeled "2" in Figure 9.28.

3. At this point, the kernel knows that the page fault resulted from a legal operation on a legal virtual address. It handles the fault by selecting a victim page, swapping out the victim page if it is dirty, swapping in the new page,

and updating the page table. When the page fault handler returns, the CPU restarts the faulting instruction, which sends A to the MMU again. This time, the MMU translates A normally, without generating a page fault.

9.8   Memory Mapping

Linux initializes the contents of a virtual memory area by associating it with an *object* on disk, a process known as *memory mapping*. Areas can be mapped to one of two types of objects:

1. *Regular file in the Linux file system:* An area can be mapped to a contiguous section of a regular disk file, such as an executable object file. The file section is divided into page-size pieces, with each piece containing the initial contents of a virtual page. Because of demand paging, none of these virtual pages is actually swapped into physical memory until the CPU first *touches* the page (i.e., issues a virtual address that falls within that page's region of the address space). If the area is larger than the file section, then the area is padded with zeros.

2. *Anonymous file:* An area can also be mapped to an anonymous file, created by the kernel, that contains all binary zeros. The first time the CPU touches a virtual page in such an area, the kernel finds an appropriate victim page in physical memory, swaps out the victim page if it is dirty, overwrites the victim page with binary zeros, and updates the page table to mark the page as resident. Notice that no data are actually transferred between disk and memory. For this reason, pages in areas that are mapped to anonymous files are sometimes called *demand-zero pages*.

In either case, once a virtual page is initialized, it is swapped back and forth between a special *swap file* maintained by the kernel. The swap file is also known as the *swap space* or the *swap area*. An important point to realize is that at any point in time, the swap space bounds the total amount of virtual pages that can be allocated by the currently running processes.

9.8.1   Shared Objects Revisited

The idea of memory mapping resulted from a clever insight that if the virtual memory system could be integrated into the conventional file system, then it could provide a simple and efficient way to load programs and data into memory.

As we have seen, the process abstraction promises to provide each process with its own private virtual address space that is protected from errant writes or reads by other processes. However, many processes have identical read-only code areas. For example, each process that runs the Linux shell program bash has the same code area. Further, many programs need to access identical copies of read-only run-time library code. For example, every C program requires functions from the standard C library such as printf. It would be extremely wasteful for each process to keep duplicate copies of these commonly used codes in physical memory. Fortunately, memory mapping provides us with a clean mechanism for controlling how objects are shared by multiple processes.

An object can be mapped into an area of virtual memory as either a *shared object* or a *private object*. If a process maps a shared object into an area of its virtual address space, then any writes that the process makes to that area are visible to any other processes that have also mapped the shared object into their virtual memory. Further, the changes are also reflected in the original object on disk.

Changes made to an area mapped to a private object, on the other hand, are not visible to other processes, and any writes that the process makes to the area are *not* reflected back to the object on disk. A virtual memory area into which a shared object is mapped is often called a *shared area*. Similarly for a *private area*.

Suppose that process 1 maps a shared object into an area of its virtual memory, as shown in Figure 9.29(a). Now suppose that process 2 maps the same shared ob-

Figure 9.29

A shared object. (a) After process 1 maps the shared object. (b) After process 2 maps the same shared object. (Note that the physical pages are not necessarily contiguous.)

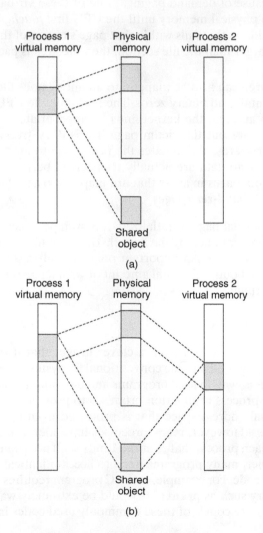

Figure 9.30

A private copy-on-write object. (a) After both processes have mapped the private copy-on-write object. (b) After process 2 writes to a page in the private area.

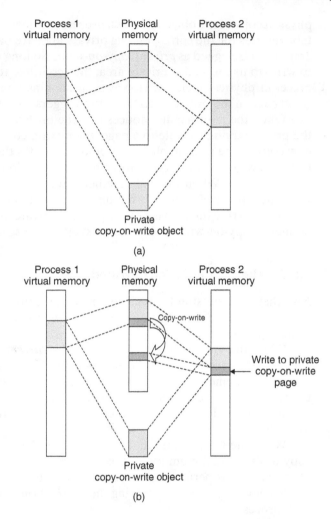

ject into its address space (not necessarily at the same virtual address as process 1), as shown in Figure 9.29(b).

Since each object has a unique filename, the kernel can quickly determine that process 1 has already mapped this object and can point the page table entries in process 2 to the appropriate physical pages. The key point is that only a single copy of the shared object needs to be stored in physical memory, even though the object is mapped into multiple shared areas. For convenience, we have shown the physical pages as being contiguous, but of course this is not true in general.

Private objects are mapped into virtual memory using a clever technique known as *copy-on-write*. A private object begins life in exactly the same way as a shared object, with only one copy of the private object stored in physical memory. For example, Figure 9.30(a) shows a case where two processes have mapped a private object into different areas of their virtual memories but share the same physical copy of the object. For each process that maps the private object, the page table entries for the corresponding private area are flagged as read-only, and the area struct is flagged as *private copy-on-write*. So long as neither process attempts to write to its respective private area, they continue to share a single copy of the object in physical memory. However, as soon as a process attempts to write to some page in the private area, the write triggers a protection fault.

When the fault handler notices that the protection exception was caused by the process trying to write to a page in a private copy-on-write area, it creates a new copy of the page in physical memory, updates the page table entry to point to the new copy, and then restores write permissions to the page, as shown in Figure 9.30(b). When the fault handler returns, the CPU re-executes the write, which now proceeds normally on the newly created page.

By deferring the copying of the pages in private objects until the last possible moment, copy-on-write makes the most efficient use of scarce physical memory.

9.8.2   The `fork` Function Revisited

Now that we understand virtual memory and memory mapping, we can get a clear idea of how the `fork` function creates a new process with its own independent virtual address space.

When the `fork` function is called by the *current process*, the kernel creates various data structures for the *new process* and assigns it a unique PID. To create the virtual memory for the new process, it creates exact copies of the current process's `mm_struct`, area structs, and page tables. It flags each page in both processes as read-only, and flags each area struct in both processes as private copy-on-write.

When the `fork` returns in the new process, the new process now has an exact copy of the virtual memory as it existed when the fork was called. When either of the processes performs any subsequent writes, the copy-on-write mechanism creates new pages, thus preserving the abstraction of a private address space for each process.

9.8.3   The `execve` Function Revisited

Virtual memory and memory mapping also play key roles in the process of loading programs into memory. Now that we understand these concepts, we can understand how the `execve` function really loads and executes programs. Suppose that the program running in the current process makes the following call:

```
execve("a.out", NULL, NULL);
```

As you learned in Chapter 8, the `execve` function loads and runs the program contained in the executable object file `a.out` within the current process, effectively replacing the current program with the `a.out` program. Loading and running `a.out` requires the following steps:

Figure 9.31
How the loader maps the areas of the user address space.

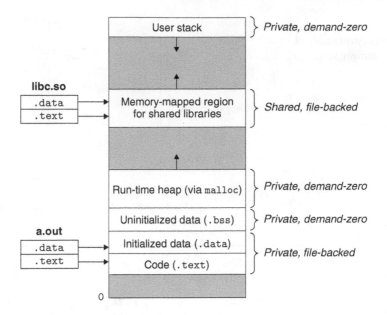

1. *Delete existing user areas.* Delete the existing area structs in the user portion of the current process's virtual address.

2. *Map private areas.* Create new area structs for the code, data, bss, and stack areas of the new program. All of these new areas are private copy-on-write. The code and data areas are mapped to the .text and .data sections of the a.out file. The bss area is demand-zero, mapped to an anonymous file whose size is contained in a.out. The stack and heap area are also demand-zero, initially of zero length. Figure 9.31 summarizes the different mappings of the private areas.

3. *Map shared areas.* If the a.out program was linked with shared objects, such as the standard C library libc.so, then these objects are dynamically linked into the program, and then mapped into the shared region of the user's virtual address space.

4. *Set the program counter (PC).* The last thing that execve does is to set the program counter in the current process's context to point to the entry point in the code area.

The next time this process is scheduled, it will begin execution from the entry point. Linux will swap in code and data pages as needed.

9.8.4   User-Level Memory Mapping with the mmap Function

Linux processes can use the mmap function to create new areas of virtual memory and to map objects into these areas.

Figure 9.32
Visual interpretation of mmap arguments.

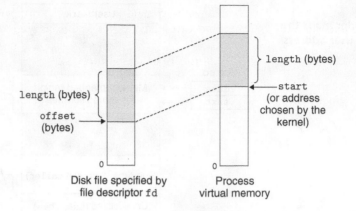

```
#include <unistd.h>
#include <sys/mman.h>

void   *mmap(void *start, size_t length, int prot, int flags,
             int fd, off_t offset);
                Returns: pointer to mapped area if OK, MAP_FAILED (−1) on error
```

The mmap function asks the kernel to create a new virtual memory area, preferably one that starts at address start, and to map a contiguous chunk of the object specified by file descriptor fd to the new area. The contiguous object chunk has a size of length bytes and starts at an offset of offset bytes from the beginning of the file. The start address is merely a hint, and is usually specified as NULL. For our purposes, we will always assume a NULL start address. Figure 9.32 depicts the meaning of these arguments.

The prot argument contains bits that describe the access permissions of the newly mapped virtual memory area (i.e., the vm_prot bits in the corresponding area struct).

PROT_EXEC. Pages in the area consist of instructions that may be executed by the CPU.

PROT_READ. Pages in the area may be read.

PROT_WRITE. Pages in the area may be written.

PROT_NONE. Pages in the area cannot be accessed.

The flags argument consists of bits that describe the type of the mapped object. If the MAP_ANON flag bit is set, then the backing store is an anonymous object and the corresponding virtual pages are demand-zero. MAP_PRIVATE indicates a private copy-on-write object, and MAP_SHARED indicates a shared object. For example,

```
bufp = Mmap(NULL, size, PROT_READ, MAP_PRIVATE|MAP_ANON, 0, 0);
```

asks the kernel to create a new read-only, private, demand-zero area of virtual memory containing `size` bytes. If the call is successful, then `bufp` contains the address of the new area.

The `munmap` function deletes regions of virtual memory:

```
#include <unistd.h>
#include <sys/mman.h>

int munmap(void *start, size_t length);
                                        Returns: 0 if OK, −1 on error
```

The `munmap` function deletes the area starting at virtual address `start` and consisting of the next `length` bytes. Subsequent references to the deleted region result in segmentation faults.

Practice Problem 9.5 (solution page 882)

Write a C program `mmapcopy.c` that uses `mmap` to copy an arbitrary-size disk file to `stdout`. The name of the input file should be passed as a command-line argument.

9.9 Dynamic Memory Allocation

While it is certainly possible to use the low-level `mmap` and `munmap` functions to create and delete areas of virtual memory, C programmers typically find it more convenient and more portable to use a *dynamic memory allocator* when they need to acquire additional virtual memory at run time.

A dynamic memory allocator maintains an area of a process's virtual memory known as the *heap* (Figure 9.33). Details vary from system to system, but without loss of generality, we will assume that the heap is an area of demand-zero memory that begins immediately after the uninitialized data area and grows upward (toward higher addresses). For each process, the kernel maintains a variable `brk` (pronounced "break") that points to the top of the heap.

An allocator maintains the heap as a collection of various-size *blocks*. Each block is a contiguous chunk of virtual memory that is either *allocated* or *free*. An allocated block has been explicitly reserved for use by the application. A free block is available to be allocated. A free block remains free until it is explicitly allocated by the application. An allocated block remains allocated until it is freed, either explicitly by the application or implicitly by the memory allocator itself.

Allocators come in two basic styles. Both styles require the application to explicitly allocate blocks. They differ about which entity is responsible for freeing allocated blocks.

- *Explicit allocators* require the application to explicitly free any allocated blocks. For example, the C standard library provides an explicit allocator called the `malloc` package. C programs allocate a block by calling the `malloc`

Figure 9.33
The heap.

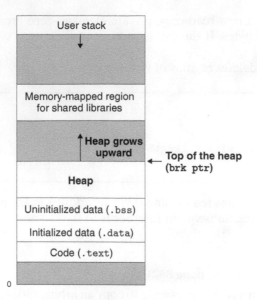

function, and free a block by calling the free function. The new and delete calls in C++ are comparable.

- *Implicit allocators*, on the other hand, require the allocator to detect when an allocated block is no longer being used by the program and then free the block. Implicit allocators are also known as *garbage collectors*, and the process of automatically freeing unused allocated blocks is known as *garbage collection*. For example, higher-level languages such as Lisp, ML, and Java rely on garbage collection to free allocated blocks.

The remainder of this section discusses the design and implementation of explicit allocators. We will discuss implicit allocators in Section 9.10. For concreteness, our discussion focuses on allocators that manage heap memory. However, you should be aware that memory allocation is a general idea that arises in a variety of contexts. For example, applications that do intensive manipulation of graphs will often use the standard allocator to acquire a large block of virtual memory and then use an application-specific allocator to manage the memory within that block as the nodes of the graph are created and destroyed.

9.9.1 The malloc and free Functions

The C standard library provides an explicit allocator known as the malloc package. Programs allocate blocks from the heap by calling the malloc function.

```
#include <stdlib.h>

void *malloc(size_t size);
```
                    Returns: pointer to allocated block if OK, NULL on error

---

Aside   How big is a word?

Recall from our discussion of machine code in Chapter 3 that Intel refers to 4-byte objects as *double words*. However, throughout this section, we will assume that *words* are 4-byte objects and that *double words* are 8-byte objects, which is consistent with conventional terminology.

The malloc function returns a pointer to a block of memory of at least size bytes that is suitably aligned for any kind of data object that might be contained in the block. In practice, the alignment depends on whether the code is compiled to run in 32-bit mode (gcc –m32) or 64-bit mode (the default). In 32-bit mode, malloc returns a block whose address is always a multiple of 8. In 64-bit mode, the address is always a multiple of 16.

If malloc encounters a problem (e.g., the program requests a block of memory that is larger than the available virtual memory), then it returns NULL and sets errno. Malloc does not initialize the memory it returns. Applications that want initialized dynamic memory can use calloc, a thin wrapper around the malloc function that initializes the allocated memory to zero. Applications that want to change the size of a previously allocated block can use the realloc function.

Dynamic memory allocators such as malloc can allocate or deallocate heap memory explicitly by using the mmap and munmap functions, or they can use the sbrk function:

```
#include <unistd.h>

void *sbrk(intptr_t incr);
                                 Returns: old brk pointer on success, −1 on error
```

The sbrk function grows or shrinks the heap by adding incr to the kernel's brk pointer. If successful, it returns the old value of brk, otherwise it returns −1 and sets errno to ENOMEM. If incr is zero, then sbrk returns the current value of brk. Calling sbrk with a negative incr is legal but tricky because the return value (the old value of brk) points to abs(incr) bytes past the new top of the heap.

Programs free allocated heap blocks by calling the free function.

```
#include <stdlib.h>

void free(void *ptr);
                                                            Returns: nothing
```

The ptr argument must point to the beginning of an allocated block that was obtained from malloc, calloc, or realloc. If not, then the behavior of free is undefined. Even worse, since it returns nothing, free gives no indication to the application that something is wrong. As we shall see in Section 9.11, this can produce some baffling run-time errors.

Figure 9.34

Allocating and freeing blocks with `malloc` **and** `free`. Each square corresponds to a word. Each heavy rectangle corresponds to a block. Allocated blocks are shaded. Padded regions of allocated blocks are shaded with a darker blue. Free blocks are unshaded. Heap addresses increase from left to right.

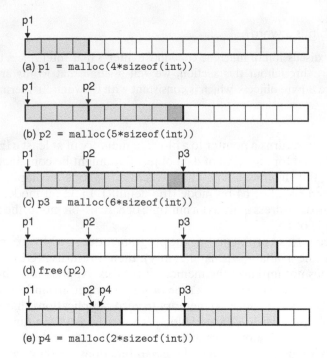

(a) `p1 = malloc(4*sizeof(int))`

(b) `p2 = malloc(5*sizeof(int))`

(c) `p3 = malloc(6*sizeof(int))`

(d) `free(p2)`

(e) `p4 = malloc(2*sizeof(int))`

Figure 9.34 shows how an implementation of `malloc` and `free` might manage a (very) small heap of 16 words for a C program. Each box represents a 4-byte word. The heavy-lined rectangles correspond to allocated blocks (shaded) and free blocks (unshaded). Initially, the heap consists of a single 16-word double-word-aligned free block.[1]

Figure 9.34(a). The program asks for a four-word block. `Malloc` responds by carving out a four-word block from the front of the free block and returning a pointer to the first word of the block.

Figure 9.34(b). The program requests a five-word block. `Malloc` responds by allocating a six-word block from the front of the free block. In this example, `malloc` pads the block with an extra word in order to keep the free block aligned on a double-word boundary.

Figure 9.34(c). The program requests a six-word block and `malloc` responds by carving out a six-word block from the free block.

Figure 9.34(d). The program frees the six-word block that was allocated in Figure 9.34(b). Notice that after the call to `free` returns, the pointer p2

---

1. Throughout this section, we will assume that the allocator returns blocks aligned to 8-byte double-word boundaries.

still points to the freed block. It is the responsibility of the application not to use p2 again until it is reinitialized by a new call to `malloc`.

Figure 9.34(e).   The program requests a two-word block. In this case, `malloc` allocates a portion of the block that was freed in the previous step and returns a pointer to this new block.

9.9.2   Why Dynamic Memory Allocation?

The most important reason that programs use dynamic memory allocation is that often they do not know the sizes of certain data structures until the program actually runs. For example, suppose we are asked to write a C program that reads a list of n ASCII integers, one integer per line, from `stdin` into a C array. The input consists of the integer n, followed by the n integers to be read and stored into the array. The simplest approach is to define the array statically with some hard-coded maximum array size:

```
1    #include "csapp.h"
2    #define MAXN 15213
3
4    int array[MAXN];
5
6    int main()
7    {
8        int i, n;
9
10       scanf("%d", &n);
11       if (n > MAXN)
12           app_error("Input file too big");
13       for (i = 0; i < n; i++)
14           scanf("%d", &array[i]);
15       exit(0);
16   }
```

Allocating arrays with hard-coded sizes like this is often a bad idea. The value of MAXN is arbitrary and has no relation to the actual amount of available virtual memory on the machine. Further, if the user of this program wanted to read a file that was larger than MAXN, the only recourse would be to recompile the program with a larger value of MAXN. While not a problem for this simple example, the presence of hard-coded array bounds can become a maintenance nightmare for large software products with millions of lines of code and numerous users.

A better approach is to allocate the array dynamically, at run time, after the value of n becomes known. With this approach, the maximum size of the array is limited only by the amount of available virtual memory.

```
1    #include "csapp.h"
2
3    int main()
4    {
5        int *array, i, n;
6
7        scanf("%d", &n);
8        array = (int *)Malloc(n * sizeof(int));
9        for (i = 0; i < n; i++)
10           scanf("%d", &array[i]);
11       free(array);
12       exit(0);
13   }
```

Dynamic memory allocation is a useful and important programming technique. However, in order to use allocators correctly and efficiently, programmers need to have an understanding of how they work. We will discuss some of the gruesome errors that can result from the improper use of allocators in Section 9.11.

9.9.3 Allocator Requirements and Goals

Explicit allocators must operate within some rather stringent constraints:

Handling arbitrary request sequences. An application can make an arbitrary sequence of allocate and free requests, subject to the constraint that each free request must correspond to a currently allocated block obtained from a previous allocate request. Thus, the allocator cannot make any assumptions about the ordering of allocate and free requests. For example, the allocator cannot assume that all allocate requests are accompanied by a matching free request, or that matching allocate and free requests are nested.

Making immediate responses to requests. The allocator must respond immediately to allocate requests. Thus, the allocator is not allowed to reorder or buffer requests in order to improve performance.

Using only the heap. In order for the allocator to be scalable, any nonscalar data structures used by the allocator must be stored in the heap itself.

Aligning blocks (alignment requirement). The allocator must align blocks in such a way that they can hold any type of data object.

Not modifying allocated blocks. Allocators can only manipulate or change free blocks. In particular, they are not allowed to modify or move blocks once they are allocated. Thus, techniques such as compaction of allocated blocks are not permitted.

Working within these constraints, the author of an allocator attempts to meet the often conflicting performance goals of maximizing throughput and memory utilization.

Goal 1: Maximizing throughput. Given some sequence of n allocate and free requests

$$R_0, R_1, \ldots, R_k, \ldots, R_{n-1}$$

we would like to maximize an allocator's *throughput*, which is defined as the number of requests that it completes per unit time. For example, if an allocator completes 500 allocate requests and 500 free requests in 1 second, then its throughput is 1,000 operations per second. In general, we can maximize throughput by minimizing the average time to satisfy allocate and free requests. As we'll see, it is not too difficult to develop allocators with reasonably good performance where the worst-case running time of an allocate request is linear in the number of free blocks and the running time of a free request is constant.

Goal 2: Maximizing memory utilization. Naive programmers often incorrectly assume that virtual memory is an unlimited resource. In fact, the total amount of virtual memory allocated by all of the processes in a system is limited by the amount of swap space on disk. Good programmers know that virtual memory is a finite resource that must be used efficiently. This is especially true for a dynamic memory allocator that might be asked to allocate and free large blocks of memory.

There are a number of ways to characterize how efficiently an allocator uses the heap. In our experience, the most useful metric is *peak utilization*. As before, we are given some sequence of n allocate and free requests

$$R_0, R_1, \ldots, R_k, \ldots, R_{n-1}$$

If an application requests a block of p bytes, then the resulting allocated block has a *payload* of p bytes. After request R_k has completed, let the *aggregate payload*, denoted P_k, be the sum of the payloads of the currently allocated blocks, and let H_k denote the current (monotonically nondecreasing) size of the heap.

Then the peak utilization over the first $k + 1$ requests, denoted by U_k, is given by

$$U_k = \frac{\max_{i \leq k} P_i}{H_k}$$

The objective of the allocator, then, is to maximize the peak utilization U_{n-1} over the entire sequence. As we will see, there is a tension between maximizing throughput and utilization. In particular, it is easy to write an allocator that maximizes throughput at the expense of heap utilization. One of the interesting challenges in any allocator design is finding an appropriate balance between the two goals.

Aside   Relaxing the monotonicity assumption

We could relax the monotonically nondecreasing assumption in our definition of U_k and allow the heap to grow up and down by letting H_k be the high-water mark over the first $k + 1$ requests.

9.9.4   Fragmentation

The primary cause of poor heap utilization is a phenomenon known as *fragmentation*, which occurs when otherwise unused memory is not available to satisfy allocate requests. There are two forms of fragmentation: *internal fragmentation* and *external fragmentation*.

Internal fragmentation occurs when an allocated block is larger than the payload. This might happen for a number of reasons. For example, the implementation of an allocator might impose a minimum size on allocated blocks that is greater than some requested payload. Or, as we saw in Figure 9.34(b), the allocator might increase the block size in order to satisfy alignment constraints.

Internal fragmentation is straightforward to quantify. It is simply the sum of the differences between the sizes of the allocated blocks and their payloads. Thus, at any point in time, the amount of internal fragmentation depends only on the pattern of previous requests and the allocator implementation.

External fragmentation occurs when there *is* enough aggregate free memory to satisfy an allocate request, but no single free block is large enough to handle the request. For example, if the request in Figure 9.34(e) were for eight words rather than two words, then the request could not be satisfied without requesting additional virtual memory from the kernel, even though there are eight free words remaining in the heap. The problem arises because these eight words are spread over two free blocks.

External fragmentation is much more difficult to quantify than internal fragmentation because it depends not only on the pattern of previous requests and the allocator implementation but also on the pattern of *future* requests. For example, suppose that after k requests all of the free blocks are exactly four words in size. Does this heap suffer from external fragmentation? The answer depends on the pattern of future requests. If all of the future allocate requests are for blocks that are smaller than or equal to four words, then there is no external fragmentation. On the other hand, if one or more requests ask for blocks larger than four words, then the heap does suffer from external fragmentation.

Since external fragmentation is difficult to quantify and impossible to predict, allocators typically employ heuristics that attempt to maintain small numbers of larger free blocks rather than large numbers of smaller free blocks.

9.9.5   Implementation Issues

The simplest imaginable allocator would organize the heap as a large array of bytes and a pointer p that initially points to the first byte of the array. To allocate size bytes, `malloc` would save the current value of p on the stack, increment p by size, and return the old value of p to the caller. `Free` would simply return to the caller without doing anything.

This naive allocator is an extreme point in the design space. Since each `malloc` and `free` execute only a handful of instructions, throughput would be extremely good. However, since the allocator never reuses any blocks, memory utilization would be extremely bad. A practical allocator that strikes a better balance between throughput and utilization must consider the following issues:

Free block organization. How do we keep track of free blocks?

Placement. How do we choose an appropriate free block in which to place a newly allocated block?

Splitting. After we place a newly allocated block in some free block, what do we do with the remainder of the free block?

Coalescing. What do we do with a block that has just been freed?

The rest of this section looks at these issues in more detail. Since the basic techniques of placement, splitting, and coalescing cut across many different free block organizations, we will introduce them in the context of a simple free block organization known as an implicit free list.

9.9.6 Implicit Free Lists

Any practical allocator needs some data structure that allows it to distinguish block boundaries and to distinguish between allocated and free blocks. Most allocators embed this information in the blocks themselves. One simple approach is shown in Figure 9.35.

In this case, a block consists of a one-word *header*, the payload, and possibly some additional *padding*. The header encodes the block size (including the header and any padding) as well as whether the block is allocated or free. If we impose a double-word alignment constraint, then the block size is always a multiple of 8 and the 3 low-order bits of the block size are always zero. Thus, we need to store only the 29 high-order bits of the block size, freeing the remaining 3 bits to encode other information. In this case, we are using the least significant of these bits

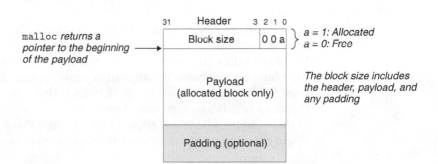

Figure 9.35
Format of a simple heap block.

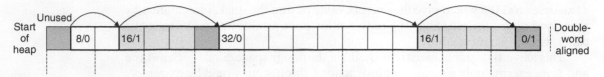

Figure 9.36 Organizing the heap with an implicit free list. Allocated blocks are shaded. Free blocks are unshaded. Headers are labeled with (size (bytes)/allocated bit).

(the *allocated bit*) to indicate whether the block is allocated or free. For example, suppose we have an allocated block with a block size of 24 (0x18) bytes. Then its header would be

```
0x00000018 | 0x1 = 0x00000019
```

Similarly, a free block with a block size of 40 (0x28) bytes would have a header of

```
0x00000028 | 0x0 = 0x00000028
```

The header is followed by the payload that the application requested when it called `malloc`. The payload is followed by a chunk of unused padding that can be any size. There are a number of reasons for the padding. For example, the padding might be part of an allocator's strategy for combating external fragmentation. Or it might be needed to satisfy the alignment requirement.

Given the block format in Figure 9.35, we can organize the heap as a sequence of contiguous allocated and free blocks, as shown in Figure 9.36.

We call this organization an *implicit free list* because the free blocks are linked implicitly by the size fields in the headers. The allocator can indirectly traverse the entire set of free blocks by traversing *all* of the blocks in the heap. Notice that we need some kind of specially marked end block—in this example, a terminating header with the allocated bit set and a size of zero. (As we will see in Section 9.9.12, setting the allocated bit simplifies the coalescing of free blocks.)

The advantage of an implicit free list is simplicity. A significant disadvantage is that the cost of any operation that requires a search of the free list, such as placing allocated blocks, will be linear in the *total* number of allocated and free blocks in the heap.

It is important to realize that the system's alignment requirement and the allocator's choice of block format impose a *minimum block size* on the allocator. No allocated or free block may be smaller than this minimum. For example, if we assume a double-word alignment requirement, then the size of each block must be a multiple of two words (8 bytes). Thus, the block format in Figure 9.35 induces a minimum block size of two words: one word for the header and another to maintain the alignment requirement. Even if the application were to request a single byte, the allocator would still create a two-word block.

Practice Problem 9.6 (solution page 883)

Determine the block sizes and header values that would result from the following sequence of malloc requests. Assumptions: (1) The allocator maintains double-word alignment and uses an implicit free list with the block format from Figure 9.35. (2) Block sizes are rounded up to the nearest multiple of 8 bytes.

Request	Block size (decimal bytes)	Block header (hex)
malloc(1)	_____	_____
malloc(5)	_____	_____
malloc(12)	_____	_____
malloc(13)	_____	_____

9.9.7 Placing Allocated Blocks

When an application requests a block of k bytes, the allocator searches the free list for a free block that is large enough to hold the requested block. The manner in which the allocator performs this search is determined by the *placement policy*. Some common policies are first fit, next fit, and best fit.

First fit searches the free list from the beginning and chooses the first free block that fits. *Next fit* is similar to first fit, but instead of starting each search at the beginning of the list, it starts each search where the previous search left off. *Best fit* examines every free block and chooses the free block with the smallest size that fits.

An advantage of first fit is that it tends to retain large free blocks at the end of the list. A disadvantage is that it tends to leave "splinters" of small free blocks toward the beginning of the list, which will increase the search time for larger blocks. Next fit was first proposed by Donald Knuth as an alternative to first fit, motivated by the idea that if we found a fit in some free block the last time, there is a good chance that we will find a fit the next time in the remainder of the block. Next fit can run significantly faster than first fit, especially if the front of the list becomes littered with many small splinters. However, some studies suggest that next fit suffers from worse memory utilization than first fit. Studies have found that best fit generally enjoys better memory utilization than either first fit or next fit. However, the disadvantage of using best fit with simple free list organizations such as the implicit free list is that it requires an exhaustive search of the heap. Later, we will look at more sophisticated segregated free list organizations that approximate a best-fit policy without an exhaustive search of the heap.

9.9.8 Splitting Free Blocks

Once the allocator has located a free block that fits, it must make another policy decision about how much of the free block to allocate. One option is to use the entire free block. Although simple and fast, the main disadvantage is that it

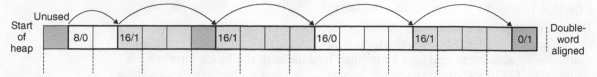

Figure 9.37 Splitting a free block to satisfy a three-word allocation request. Allocated blocks are shaded. Free blocks are unshaded. Headers are labeled with (size (bytes)/allocated bit).

introduces internal fragmentation. If the placement policy tends to produce good fits, then some additional internal fragmentation might be acceptable.

However, if the fit is not good, then the allocator will usually opt to *split* the free block into two parts. The first part becomes the allocated block, and the remainder becomes a new free block. Figure 9.37 shows how the allocator might split the eight-word free block in Figure 9.36 to satisfy an application's request for three words of heap memory.

9.9.9 Getting Additional Heap Memory

What happens if the allocator is unable to find a fit for the requested block? One option is to try to create some larger free blocks by merging (coalescing) free blocks that are physically adjacent in memory (next section). However, if this does not yield a sufficiently large block, or if the free blocks are already maximally coalesced, then the allocator asks the kernel for additional heap memory by calling the sbrk function. The allocator transforms the additional memory into one large free block, inserts the block into the free list, and then places the requested block in this new free block.

9.9.10 Coalescing Free Blocks

When the allocator frees an allocated block, there might be other free blocks that are adjacent to the newly freed block. Such adjacent free blocks can cause a phenomenon known as *false fragmentation*, where there is a lot of available free memory chopped up into small, unusable free blocks. For example, Figure 9.38 shows the result of freeing the block that was allocated in Figure 9.37. The result is two adjacent free blocks with payloads of three words each. As a result, a subsequent request for a payload of four words would fail, even though the aggregate size of the two free blocks is large enough to satisfy the request.

To combat false fragmentation, any practical allocator must merge adjacent free blocks in a process known as *coalescing*. This raises an important policy decision about when to perform coalescing. The allocator can opt for *immediate coalescing* by merging any adjacent blocks each time a block is freed. Or it can opt for *deferred coalescing* by waiting to coalesce free blocks at some later time. For example, the allocator might defer coalescing until some allocation request fails, and then scan the entire heap, coalescing all free blocks.

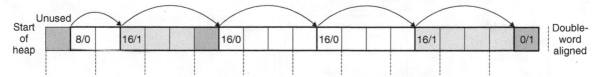

Figure 9.38   An example of false fragmentation. Allocated blocks are shaded. Free blocks are unshaded. Headers are labeled with (size (bytes)/allocated bit).

Immediate coalescing is straightforward and can be performed in constant time, but with some request patterns it can introduce a form of thrashing where a block is repeatedly coalesced and then split soon thereafter. For example, in Figure 9.38, a repeated pattern of allocating and freeing a three-word block would introduce a lot of unnecessary splitting and coalescing. In our discussion of allocators, we will assume immediate coalescing, but you should be aware that fast allocators often opt for some form of deferred coalescing.

9.9.11   Coalescing with Boundary Tags

How does an allocator implement coalescing? Let us refer to the block we want to free as the *current block*. Then coalescing the next free block (in memory) is straightforward and efficient. The header of the current block points to the header of the next block, which can be checked to determine if the next block is free. If so, its size is simply added to the size of the current header and the blocks are coalesced in constant time.

But how would we coalesce the previous block? Given an implicit free list of blocks with headers, the only option would be to search the entire list, remembering the location of the previous block, until we reached the current block. With an implicit free list, this means that each call to `free` would require time linear in the size of the heap. Even with more sophisticated free list organizations, the search time would not be constant.

Knuth developed a clever and general technique, known as *boundary tags*, that allows for constant-time coalescing of the previous block. The idea, which is shown in Figure 9.39, is to add a *footer* (the boundary tag) at the end of each block, where the footer is a replica of the header. If each block includes such a footer, then the allocator can determine the starting location and status of the previous block by inspecting its footer, which is always one word away from the start of the current block.

Consider all the cases that can exist when the allocator frees the current block:

1. The previous and next blocks are both allocated.
2. The previous block is allocated and the next block is free.
3. The previous block is free and the next block is allocated.
4. The previous and next blocks are both free.

Figure 9.39
Format of heap block that uses a boundary tag.

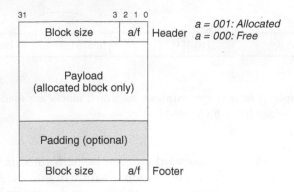

a = 001: Allocated
a = 000: Free

Figure 9.40 shows how we would coalesce each of the four cases.

In case 1, both adjacent blocks are allocated and thus no coalescing is possible. So the status of the current block is simply changed from allocated to free. In case 2, the current block is merged with the next block. The header of the current block and the footer of the next block are updated with the combined sizes of the current and next blocks. In case 3, the previous block is merged with the current block. The header of the previous block and the footer of the current block are updated with the combined sizes of the two blocks. In case 4, all three blocks are merged to form a single free block, with the header of the previous block and the footer of the next block updated with the combined sizes of the three blocks. In each case, the coalescing is performed in constant time.

The idea of boundary tags is a simple and elegant one that generalizes to many different types of allocators and free list organizations. However, there is a potential disadvantage. Requiring each block to contain both a header and a footer can introduce significant memory overhead if an application manipulates many small blocks. For example, if a graph application dynamically creates and destroys graph nodes by making repeated calls to `malloc` and `free`, and each graph node requires only a couple of words of memory, then the header and the footer will consume half of each allocated block.

Fortunately, there is a clever optimization of boundary tags that eliminates the need for a footer in allocated blocks. Recall that when we attempt to coalesce the current block with the previous and next blocks in memory, the size field in the footer of the previous block is only needed if the previous block is *free*. If we were to store the allocated/free bit of the previous block in one of the excess low-order bits of the current block, then allocated blocks would not need footers, and we could use that extra space for payload. Note, however, that free blocks would still need footers.

Practice Problem 9.7 (solution page 883)

Determine the minimum block size for each of the following combinations of alignment requirements and block formats. Assumptions: Implicit free list, zero-size payloads are not allowed, and headers and footers are stored in 4-byte words.

Figure 9.40
Coalescing with boundary tags. Case 1: prev and next allocated. Case 2: prev allocated, next free. Case 3: prev free, next allocated. Case 4: next and prev free.

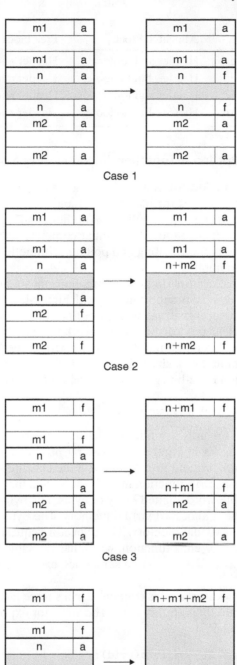

Alignment	Allocated block	Free block	Minimum block size (bytes)
Single word	Header and footer	Header and footer	_____
Single word	Header, but no footer	Header and footer	_____
Double word	Header and footer	Header and footer	_____
Double word	Header, but no footer	Header and footer	_____

9.9.12   Putting It Together: Implementing a Simple Allocator

Building an allocator is a challenging task. The design space is large, with numerous alternatives for block format and free list format, as well as placement, splitting, and coalescing policies. Another challenge is that you are often forced to program outside the safe, familiar confines of the type system, relying on the error-prone pointer casting and pointer arithmetic that is typical of low-level systems programming.

While allocators do not require enormous amounts of code, they are subtle and unforgiving. Students familiar with higher-level languages such as C++ or Java often hit a conceptual wall when they first encounter this style of programming. To help you clear this hurdle, we will work through the implementation of a simple allocator based on an implicit free list with immediate boundary-tag coalescing. The maximum block size is $2^{32} = 4$ GB. The code is 64-bit clean, running without modification in 32-bit (gcc −m32) or 64-bit (gcc −m64) processes.

General Allocator Design

Our allocator uses a model of the memory system provided by the memlib.c package shown in Figure 9.41. The purpose of the model is to allow us to run our allocator without interfering with the existing system-level malloc package.

The mem_init function models the virtual memory available to the heap as a large double-word aligned array of bytes. The bytes between mem_heap and mem_brk represent allocated virtual memory. The bytes following mem_brk represent unallocated virtual memory. The allocator requests additional heap memory by calling the mem_sbrk function, which has the same interface as the system's sbrk function, as well as the same semantics, except that it rejects requests to shrink the heap.

The allocator itself is contained in a source file (mm.c) that users can compile and link into their applications. The allocator exports three functions to application programs:

```
1    extern int mm_init(void);
2    extern void *mm_malloc (size_t size);
3    extern void mm_free (void *ptr);
```

The mm_init function initializes the allocator, returning 0 if successful and −1 otherwise. The mm_malloc and mm_free functions have the same interfaces and semantics as their system counterparts. The allocator uses the block format

—————————————————————————————————— code/vm/malloc/memlib.c

```
1   /* Private global variables */
2   static char *mem_heap;      /* Points to first byte of heap */
3   static char *mem_brk;       /* Points to last byte of heap plus 1 */
4   static char *mem_max_addr;  /* Max legal heap addr plus 1*/
5
6   /*
7    * mem_init - Initialize the memory system model
8    */
9   void mem_init(void)
10  {
11      mem_heap = (char *)Malloc(MAX_HEAP);
12      mem_brk = (char *)mem_heap;
13      mem_max_addr = (char *)(mem_heap + MAX_HEAP);
14  }
15
16  /*
17   * mem_sbrk - Simple model of the sbrk function. Extends the heap
18   *     by incr bytes and returns the start address of the new area. In
19   *     this model, the heap cannot be shrunk.
20   */
21  void *mem_sbrk(int incr)
22  {
23      char *old_brk = mem_brk;
24
25      if ( (incr < 0) || ((mem_brk + incr) > mem_max_addr)) {
26          errno = ENOMEM;
27          fprintf(stderr, "ERROR: mem_sbrk failed. Ran out of memory...\n");
28          return (void *)-1;
29      }
30      mem_brk += incr;
31      return (void *)old_brk;
32  }
```

—————————————————————————————————— code/vm/malloc/memlib.c

Figure 9.41 `memlib.c`: **Memory system model.**

shown in Figure 9.39. The minimum block size is 16 bytes. The free list is organized
as an implicit free list, with the invariant form shown in Figure 9.42.

The first word is an unused padding word aligned to a double-word boundary.
The padding is followed by a special *prologue block*, which is an 8-byte allocated
block consisting of only a header and a footer. The prologue block is created
during initialization and is never freed. Following the prologue block are zero
or more regular blocks that are created by calls to malloc or free. The heap
always ends with a special *epilogue block*, which is a zero-size allocated block

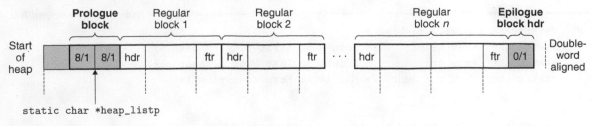

Figure 9.42 Invariant form of the implicit free list.

that consists of only a header. The prologue and epilogue blocks are tricks that eliminate the edge conditions during coalescing. The allocator uses a single private (static) global variable (heap_listp) that always points to the prologue block. (As a minor optimization, we could make it point to the next block instead of the prologue block.)

Basic Constants and Macros for Manipulating the Free List

Figure 9.43 shows some basic constants and macros that we will use throughout the allocator code. Lines 2–4 define some basic size constants: the sizes of words (WSIZE) and double words (DSIZE), and the size of the initial free block and the default size for expanding the heap (CHUNKSIZE).

Manipulating the headers and footers in the free list can be troublesome because it demands extensive use of casting and pointer arithmetic. Thus, we find it helpful to define a small set of macros for accessing and traversing the free list (lines 9–25). The PACK macro (line 9) combines a size and an allocate bit and returns a value that can be stored in a header or footer.

The GET macro (line 12) reads and returns the word referenced by argument p. The casting here is crucial. The argument p is typically a (void *) pointer, which cannot be dereferenced directly. Similarly, the PUT macro (line 13) stores val in the word pointed at by argument p.

The GET_SIZE and GET_ALLOC macros (lines 16–17) return the size and allocated bit, respectively, from a header or footer at address p. The remaining macros operate on *block pointers* (denoted bp) that point to the first payload byte. Given a block pointer bp, the HDRP and FTRP macros (lines 20–21) return pointers to the block header and footer, respectively. The NEXT_BLKP and PREV_BLKP macros (lines 24–25) return the block pointers of the next and previous blocks, respectively.

The macros can be composed in various ways to manipulate the free list. For example, given a pointer bp to the current block, we could use the following line of code to determine the size of the next block in memory:

```
size_t size = GET_SIZE(HDRP(NEXT_BLKP(bp)));
```

————————————————————————— code/vm/malloc/mm.c

```c
1   /* Basic constants and macros */
2   #define WSIZE       4       /* Word and header/footer size (bytes) */
3   #define DSIZE       8       /* Double word size (bytes) */
4   #define CHUNKSIZE   (1<<12) /* Extend heap by this amount (bytes) */
5
6   #define MAX(x, y) ((x) > (y)? (x) : (y))
7
8   /* Pack a size and allocated bit into a word */
9   #define PACK(size, alloc)  ((size) | (alloc))
10
11  /* Read and write a word at address p */
12  #define GET(p)       (*(unsigned int *)(p))
13  #define PUT(p, val)  (*(unsigned int *)(p) = (val))
14
15  /* Read the size and allocated fields from address p */
16  #define GET_SIZE(p)  (GET(p) & ~0x7)
17  #define GET_ALLOC(p) (GET(p) & 0x1)
18
19  /* Given block ptr bp, compute address of its header and footer */
20  #define HDRP(bp)        ((char *)(bp) - WSIZE)
21  #define FTRP(bp)        ((char *)(bp) + GET_SIZE(HDRP(bp)) - DSIZE)
22
23  /* Given block ptr bp, compute address of next and previous blocks */
24  #define NEXT_BLKP(bp)   ((char *)(bp) + GET_SIZE(((char *)(bp) - WSIZE)))
25  #define PREV_BLKP(bp)   ((char *)(bp) - GET_SIZE(((char *)(bp) - DSIZE)))
```

————————————————————————— code/vm/malloc/mm.c

Figure 9.43   Basic constants and macros for manipulating the free list.

Creating the Initial Free List

Before calling mm_malloc or mm_free, the application must initialize the heap by
calling the mm_init function (Figure 9.44).

The mm_init function gets four words from the memory system and initializes
them to create the empty free list (lines 4–10). It then calls the extend_heap
function (Figure 9.45), which extends the heap by CHUNKSIZE bytes and creates
the initial free block. At this point, the allocator is initialized and ready to accept
allocate and free requests from the application.

The extend_heap function is invoked in two different circumstances: (1) when
the heap is initialized and (2) when mm_malloc is unable to find a suitable fit. To
maintain alignment, extend_heap rounds up the requested size to the nearest

code/vm/malloc/mm.c

```
1   int mm_init(void)
2   {
3       /* Create the initial empty heap */
4       if ((heap_listp = mem_sbrk(4*WSIZE)) == (void *)-1)
5           return -1;
6       PUT(heap_listp, 0);                          /* Alignment padding */
7       PUT(heap_listp + (1*WSIZE), PACK(DSIZE, 1)); /* Prologue header */
8       PUT(heap_listp + (2*WSIZE), PACK(DSIZE, 1)); /* Prologue footer */
9       PUT(heap_listp + (3*WSIZE), PACK(0, 1));     /* Epilogue header */
10      heap_listp += (2*WSIZE);
11
12      /* Extend the empty heap with a free block of CHUNKSIZE bytes */
13      if (extend_heap(CHUNKSIZE/WSIZE) == NULL)
14          return -1;
15      return 0;
16  }
```

code/vm/malloc/mm.c

Figure 9.44 mm_init **creates a heap with an initial free block.**

code/vm/malloc/mm.c

```
1   static void *extend_heap(size_t words)
2   {
3       char *bp;
4       size_t size;
5
6       /* Allocate an even number of words to maintain alignment */
7       size = (words % 2) ? (words+1) * WSIZE : words * WSIZE;
8       if ((long)(bp = mem_sbrk(size)) == -1)
9           return NULL;
10
11      /* Initialize free block header/footer and the epilogue header */
12      PUT(HDRP(bp), PACK(size, 0));         /* Free block header */
13      PUT(FTRP(bp), PACK(size, 0));         /* Free block footer */
14      PUT(HDRP(NEXT_BLKP(bp)), PACK(0, 1)); /* New epilogue header */
15
16      /* Coalesce if the previous block was free */
17      return coalesce(bp);
18  }
```

code/vm/malloc/mm.c

Figure 9.45 extend_heap **extends the heap with a new free block.**

multiple of 2 words (8 bytes) and then requests the additional heap space from the memory system (lines 7–9).

The remainder of the extend_heap function (lines 12–17) is somewhat subtle. The heap begins on a double-word aligned boundary, and every call to extend_ heap returns a block whose size is an integral number of double words. Thus, every call to mem_sbrk returns a double-word aligned chunk of memory immediately following the header of the epilogue block. This header becomes the header of the new free block (line 12), and the last word of the chunk becomes the new epilogue block header (line 14). Finally, in the likely case that the previous heap was terminated by a free block, we call the coalesce function to merge the two free blocks and return the block pointer of the merged blocks (line 17).

Freeing and Coalescing Blocks

An application frees a previously allocated block by calling the mm_free function (Figure 9.46), which frees the requested block (bp) and then merges adjacent free blocks using the boundary-tags coalescing technique described in Section 9.9.11.

The code in the coalesce helper function is a straightforward implementation of the four cases outlined in Figure 9.40. There is one somewhat subtle aspect. The free list format we have chosen—with its prologue and epilogue blocks that are always marked as allocated—allows us to ignore the potentially troublesome edge conditions where the requested block bp is at the beginning or end of the heap. Without these special blocks, the code would be messier, more error prone, and slower because we would have to check for these rare edge conditions on each and every free request.

Allocating Blocks

An application requests a block of size bytes of memory by calling the mm_malloc function (Figure 9.47). After checking for spurious requests, the allocator must adjust the requested block size to allow room for the header and the footer, and to satisfy the double-word alignment requirement. Lines 12–13 enforce the minimum block size of 16 bytes: 8 bytes to satisfy the alignment requirement and 8 more bytes for the overhead of the header and footer. For requests over 8 bytes (line 15), the general rule is to add in the overhead bytes and then round up to the nearest multiple of 8.

Once the allocator has adjusted the requested size, it searches the free list for a suitable free block (line 18). If there is a fit, then the allocator places the requested block and optionally splits the excess (line 19) and then returns the address of the newly allocated block.

If the allocator cannot find a fit, it extends the heap with a new free block (lines 24–26), places the requested block in the new free block, optionally splitting the block (line 27), and then returns a pointer to the newly allocated block.

———————————————————— code/vm/malloc/mm.c

```
1   void mm_free(void *bp)
2   {
3       size_t size = GET_SIZE(HDRP(bp));
4
5       PUT(HDRP(bp), PACK(size, 0));
6       PUT(FTRP(bp), PACK(size, 0));
7       coalesce(bp);
8   }
9
10  static void *coalesce(void *bp)
11  {
12      size_t prev_alloc = GET_ALLOC(FTRP(PREV_BLKP(bp)));
13      size_t next_alloc = GET_ALLOC(HDRP(NEXT_BLKP(bp)));
14      size_t size = GET_SIZE(HDRP(bp));
15
16      if (prev_alloc && next_alloc) {            /* Case 1 */
17          return bp;
18      }
19
20      else if (prev_alloc && !next_alloc) {      /* Case 2 */
21          size += GET_SIZE(HDRP(NEXT_BLKP(bp)));
22          PUT(HDRP(bp), PACK(size, 0));
23          PUT(FTRP(bp), PACK(size,0));
24      }
25
26      else if (!prev_alloc && next_alloc) {      /* Case 3 */
27          size += GET_SIZE(HDRP(PREV_BLKP(bp)));
28          PUT(FTRP(bp), PACK(size, 0));
29          PUT(HDRP(PREV_BLKP(bp)), PACK(size, 0));
30          bp = PREV_BLKP(bp);
31      }
32
33      else {                                     /* Case 4 */
34          size += GET_SIZE(HDRP(PREV_BLKP(bp))) +
35              GET_SIZE(FTRP(NEXT_BLKP(bp)));
36          PUT(HDRP(PREV_BLKP(bp)), PACK(size, 0));
37          PUT(FTRP(NEXT_BLKP(bp)), PACK(size, 0));
38          bp = PREV_BLKP(bp);
39      }
40      return bp;
41  }
```

———————————————————— code/vm/malloc/mm.c

Figure 9.46 `mm_free` **frees a block and uses boundary-tag coalescing to merge it with any adjacent free blocks in constant time.**

code/vm/malloc/mm.c

```
1   void *mm_malloc(size_t size)
2   {
3       size_t asize;      /* Adjusted block size */
4       size_t extendsize; /* Amount to extend heap if no fit */
5       char *bp;
6
7       /* Ignore spurious requests */
8       if (size == 0)
9           return NULL;
10
11      /* Adjust block size to include overhead and alignment reqs. */
12      if (size <= DSIZE)
13          asize = 2*DSIZE;
14      else
15          asize = DSIZE * ((size + (DSIZE) + (DSIZE-1)) / DSIZE);
16
17      /* Search the free list for a fit */
18      if ((bp = find_fit(asize)) != NULL) {
19          place(bp, asize);
20          return bp;
21      }
22
23      /* No fit found. Get more memory and place the block */
24      extendsize = MAX(asize,CHUNKSIZE);
25      if ((bp = extend_heap(extendsize/WSIZE)) == NULL)
26          return NULL;
27      place(bp, asize);
28      return bp;
29  }
```

code/vm/malloc/mm.c

Figure 9.47 mm_malloc **allocates a block from the free list.**

Practice Problem 9.8 (solution page 884)

Implement a find_fit function for the simple allocator described in Section 9.9.12.

```
static void *find_fit(size_t asize)
```

Your solution should perform a first-fit search of the implicit free list.

Practice Problem 9.9 (solution page 884)

Implement a place function for the example allocator.

```
static void place(void *bp, size_t asize)
```

Your solution should place the requested block at the beginning of the free block, splitting only if the size of the remainder would equal or exceed the minimum block size.

9.9.13 Explicit Free Lists

The implicit free list provides us with a simple way to introduce some basic allocator concepts. However, because block allocation time is linear in the total number of heap blocks, the implicit free list is not appropriate for a general-purpose allocator (although it might be fine for a special-purpose allocator where the number of heap blocks is known beforehand to be small).

A better approach is to organize the free blocks into some form of explicit data structure. Since by definition the body of a free block is not needed by the program, the pointers that implement the data structure can be stored within the bodies of the free blocks. For example, the heap can be organized as a doubly linked free list by including a `pred` (predecessor) and `succ` (successor) pointer in each free block, as shown in Figure 9.48.

Using a doubly linked list instead of an implicit free list reduces the first-fit allocation time from linear in the total number of blocks to linear in the number of *free* blocks. However, the time to free a block can be either linear or constant, depending on the policy we choose for ordering the blocks in the free list.

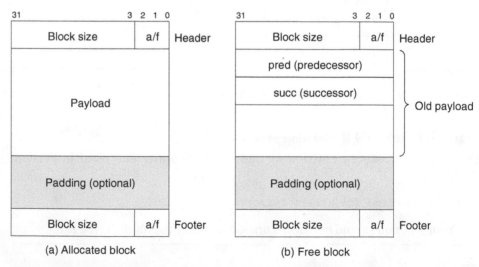

(a) Allocated block   (b) Free block

Figure 9.48 Format of heap blocks that use doubly linked free lists.

One approach is to maintain the list in *last-in first-out* (LIFO) order by in-serting newly freed blocks at the beginning of the list. With a LIFO ordering and a first-fit placement policy, the allocator inspects the most recently used blocks first. In this case, freeing a block can be performed in constant time. If boundary tags are used, then coalescing can also be performed in constant time.

Another approach is to maintain the list in *address order*, where the address of each block in the list is less than the address of its successor. In this case, freeing a block requires a linear-time search to locate the appropriate predecessor. The trade-off is that address-ordered first fit enjoys better memory utilization than LIFO-ordered first fit, approaching the utilization of best fit.

A disadvantage of explicit lists in general is that free blocks must be large enough to contain all of the necessary pointers, as well as the header and possibly a footer. This results in a larger minimum block size and increases the potential for internal fragmentation.

9.9.14 Segregated Free Lists

As we have seen, an allocator that uses a single linked list of free blocks requires time linear in the number of free blocks to allocate a block. A popular approach for reducing the allocation time, known generally as *segregated storage*, is to maintain multiple free lists, where each list holds blocks that are roughly the same size. The general idea is to partition the set of all possible block sizes into equivalence classes called *size classes*. There are many ways to define the size classes. For example, we might partition the block sizes by powers of 2:

$$\{1\}, \{2\}, \{3, 4\}, \{5–8\}, \cdots, \{1,025–2,048\}, \{2,049–4,096\}, \{4,097–\infty\}$$

Or we might assign small blocks to their own size classes and partition large blocks by powers of 2:

$$\{1\}, \{2\}, \{3\}, \cdots, \{1,023\}, \{1,024\}, \{1,025–2,048\}, \{2,049–4,096\}, \{4,097–\infty\}$$

The allocator maintains an array of free lists, with one free list per size class, ordered by increasing size. When the allocator needs a block of size n, it searches the appropriate free list. If it cannot find a block that fits, it searches the next list, and so on.

The dynamic storage allocation literature describes dozens of variants of seg-regated storage that differ in how they define size classes, when they perform coalescing, when they request additional heap memory from the operating sys-tem, whether they allow splitting, and so forth. To give you a sense of what is possible, we will describe two of the basic approaches: *simple segregated storage* and *segregated fits*.

Simple Segregated Storage

With simple segregated storage, the free list for each size class contains same-size blocks, each the size of the largest element of the size class. For example, if some size class is defined as {17–32}, then the free list for that class consists entirely of blocks of size 32.

To allocate a block of some given size, we check the appropriate free list. If the list is not empty, we simply allocate the first block in its entirety. Free blocks are never split to satisfy allocation requests. If the list is empty, the allocator requests a fixed-size chunk of additional memory from the operating system (typically a multiple of the page size), divides the chunk into equal-size blocks, and links the blocks together to form the new free list. To free a block, the allocator simply inserts the block at the front of the appropriate free list.

There are a number of advantages to this simple scheme. Allocating and freeing blocks are both fast constant-time operations. Further, the combination of the same-size blocks in each chunk, no splitting, and no coalescing means that there is very little per-block memory overhead. Since each chunk has only same-size blocks, the size of an allocated block can be inferred from its address. Since there is no coalescing, allocated blocks do not need an allocated/free flag in the header. Thus, allocated blocks require no headers, and since there is no coalescing, they do not require any footers either. Since allocate and free operations insert and delete blocks at the beginning of the free list, the list need only be singly linked instead of doubly linked. The bottom line is that the only required field in any block is a one-word succ pointer in each free block, and thus the minimum block size is only one word.

A significant disadvantage is that simple segregated storage is susceptible to internal and external fragmentation. Internal fragmentation is possible because free blocks are never split. Worse, certain reference patterns can cause extreme external fragmentation because free blocks are never coalesced (Practice Problem 9.10).

Practice Problem 9.10 (solution page 885)

Describe a reference pattern that results in severe external fragmentation in an allocator based on simple segregated storage.

Segregated Fits

With this approach, the allocator maintains an array of free lists. Each free list is associated with a size class and is organized as some kind of explicit or implicit list. Each list contains potentially different-size blocks whose sizes are members of the size class. There are many variants of segregated fits allocators. Here we describe a simple version.

To allocate a block, we determine the size class of the request and do a first-fit search of the appropriate free list for a block that fits. If we find one, then we (optionally) split it and insert the fragment in the appropriate free list. If we cannot find a block that fits, then we search the free list for the next larger size class. We repeat until we find a block that fits. If none of the free lists yields a block that fits, then we request additional heap memory from the operating system, allocate the block out of this new heap memory, and place the remainder in the appropriate size class. To free a block, we coalesce and place the result on the appropriate free list.

The segregated fits approach is a popular choice with production-quality allocators such as the GNU `malloc` package provided in the C standard library because it is both fast and memory efficient. Search times are reduced because searches are limited to particular parts of the heap instead of the entire heap. Memory utilization can improve because of the interesting fact that a simple first-fit search of a segregated free list approximates a best-fit search of the entire heap.

Buddy Systems

A *buddy system* is a special case of segregated fits where each size class is a power of 2. The basic idea is that, given a heap of 2^m words, we maintain a separate free list for each block size 2^k, where $0 \leq k \leq m$. Requested block sizes are rounded up to the nearest power of 2. Originally, there is one free block of size 2^m words.

To allocate a block of size 2^k, we find the first available block of size 2^j, such that $k \leq j \leq m$. If $j = k$, then we are done. Otherwise, we recursively split the block in half until $j = k$. As we perform this splitting, each remaining half (known as a *buddy*) is placed on the appropriate free list. To free a block of size 2^k, we continue coalescing with the free buddies. When we encounter an allocated buddy, we stop the coalescing.

A key fact about buddy systems is that, given the address and size of a block, it is easy to compute the address of its buddy. For example, a block of size 32 bytes with address

$$xxx \ldots x00000$$

has its buddy at address

$$xxx \ldots x10000$$

In other words, the addresses of a block and its buddy differ in exactly one bit position.

The major advantage of a buddy system allocator is its fast searching and coalescing. The major disadvantage is that the power-of-2 requirement on the block size can cause significant internal fragmentation. For this reason, buddy system allocators are not appropriate for general-purpose workloads. However, for certain application-specific workloads, where the block sizes are known in advance to be powers of 2, buddy system allocators have a certain appeal.

9.10 Garbage Collection

With an explicit allocator such as the C `malloc` package, an application allocates and frees heap blocks by making calls to `malloc` and `free`. It is the application's responsibility to free any allocated blocks that it no longer needs.

Failing to free allocated blocks is a common programming error. For example, consider the following C function that allocates a block of temporary storage as part of its processing:

```
1    void garbage()
2    {
3        int *p = (int *)Malloc(15213);
4
5        return; /* Array p is garbage at this point */
6    }
```

Since p is no longer needed by the program, it should have been freed before garbage returned. Unfortunately, the programmer has forgotten to free the block. It remains allocated for the lifetime of the program, needlessly occupying heap space that could be used to satisfy subsequent allocation requests.

A *garbage collector* is a dynamic storage allocator that automatically frees allocated blocks that are no longer needed by the program. Such blocks are known as *garbage* (hence the term "garbage collector"). The process of automatically reclaiming heap storage is known as *garbage collection*. In a system that supports garbage collection, applications explicitly allocate heap blocks but never explicitly free them. In the context of a C program, the application calls malloc but never calls free. Instead, the garbage collector periodically identifies the garbage blocks and makes the appropriate calls to free to place those blocks back on the free list.

Garbage collection dates back to Lisp systems developed by John McCarthy at MIT in the early 1960s. It is an important part of modern language systems such as Java, ML, Perl, and Mathematica, and it remains an active and important area of research. The literature describes an amazing number of approaches for garbage collection. We will limit our discussion to McCarthy's original *Mark&Sweep* algorithm, which is interesting because it can be built on top of an existing malloc package to provide garbage collection for C and C++ programs.

9.10.1   Garbage Collector Basics

A garbage collector views memory as a directed *reachability graph* of the form shown in Figure 9.49. The nodes of the graph are partitioned into a set of *root nodes* and a set of *heap nodes*. Each heap node corresponds to an allocated block in the heap. A directed edge $p \rightarrow q$ means that some location in block p points to some location in block q. Root nodes correspond to locations not in the heap that contain pointers into the heap. These locations can be registers, variables on the stack, or global variables in the read/write data area of virtual memory.

We say that a node p is *reachable* if there exists a directed path from any root node to p. At any point in time, the unreachable nodes correspond to garbage that can never be used again by the application. The role of a garbage collector is to maintain some representation of the reachability graph and periodically reclaim the unreachable nodes by freeing them and returning them to the free list.

Figure 9.49
A garbage collector's view of memory as a directed graph.

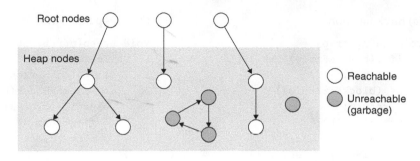

Figure 9.50
Integrating a conserva-tive garbage collector and a C malloc package.

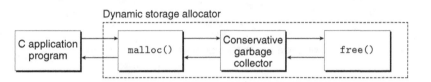

Garbage collectors for languages like ML and Java, which exert tight control over how applications create and use pointers, can maintain an exact representa-tion of the reachability graph and thus can reclaim all garbage. However, collectors for languages like C and C++ cannot in general maintain exact representations of the reachability graph. Such collectors are known as *conservative garbage col-lectors*. They are conservative in the sense that each reachable block is correctly identified as reachable, while some unreachable nodes might be incorrectly iden-tified as reachable.

Collectors can provide their service on demand, or they can run as separate threads in parallel with the application, continuously updating the reachability graph and reclaiming garbage. For example, consider how we might incorporate a conservative collector for C programs into an existing malloc package, as shown in Figure 9.50.

The application calls malloc in the usual manner whenever it needs heap space. If malloc is unable to find a free block that fits, then it calls the garbage col-lector in hopes of reclaiming some garbage to the free list. The collector identifies the garbage blocks and returns them to the heap by calling the free function. The key idea is that the collector calls free instead of the application. When the call to the collector returns, malloc tries again to find a free block that fits. If that fails, then it can ask the operating system for additional memory. Eventually, malloc returns a pointer to the requested block (if successful) or the NULL pointer (if unsuccessful).

9.10.2 Mark&Sweep Garbage Collectors

A Mark&Sweep garbage collector consists of a *mark phase*, which marks all reachable and allocated descendants of the root nodes, followed by a *sweep phase*, which frees each unmarked allocated block. Typically, one of the spare low-order bits in the block header is used to indicate whether a block is marked or not.

(a) mark function

```
void mark(ptr p) {
    if ((b = isPtr(p)) == NULL)
      return;
    if (blockMarked(b))
      return;
    markBlock(b);
    len = length(b);
    for (i=0; i < len; i++)
      mark(b[i]);
    return;
}
```

(b) sweep function

```
void sweep(ptr b, ptr end) {
    while (b < end) {
        if (blockMarked(b))
            unmarkBlock(b);
        else if (blockAllocated(b))
            free(b);
        b = nextBlock(b);
    }
    return;
}
```

Figure 9.51 Pseudocode for the mark and sweep functions.

Our description of Mark&Sweep will assume the following functions, where ptr is defined as typedef void *ptr:

ptr isPtr(ptr p). If p points to some word in an allocated block, it returns a pointer b to the beginning of that block. Returns NULL otherwise.

int blockMarked(ptr b). Returns true if block b is already marked.

int blockAllocated(ptr b). Returns true if block b is allocated.

void markBlock(ptr b). Marks block b.

int length(ptr b). Returns the length in words (excluding the header) of block b.

void unmarkBlock(ptr b). Changes the status of block b from marked to un-marked.

ptr nextBlock(ptr b). Returns the successor of block *b* in the heap.

The mark phase calls the mark function shown in Figure 9.51(a) once for each root node. The mark function returns immediately if p does not point to an allocated and unmarked heap block. Otherwise, it marks the block and calls itself recursively on each word in block. Each call to the mark function marks any unmarked and reachable descendants of some root node. At the end of the mark phase, any allocated block that is not marked is guaranteed to be unreachable and, hence, garbage that can be reclaimed in the sweep phase.

The sweep phase is a single call to the sweep function shown in Figure 9.51(b). The sweep function iterates over each block in the heap, freeing any unmarked allocated blocks (i.e., garbage) that it encounters.

Figure 9.52 shows a graphical interpretation of Mark&Sweep for a small heap. Block boundaries are indicated by heavy lines. Each square corresponds to a word of memory. Each block has a one-word header, which is either marked or unmarked.

Figure 9.52

Mark&Sweep example.
Note that the arrows in this example denote memory references, not free list pointers.

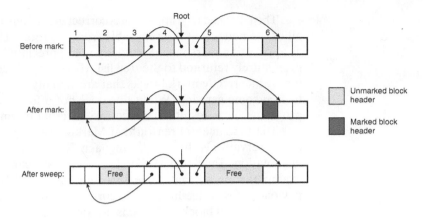

Figure 9.53

Left and right pointers in a balanced tree of allocated blocks.

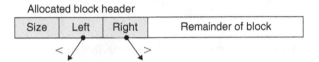

Initially, the heap in Figure 9.52 consists of six allocated blocks, each of which is unmarked. Block 3 contains a pointer to block 1. Block 4 contains pointers to blocks 3 and 6. The root points to block 4. After the mark phase, blocks 1, 3, 4, and 6 are marked because they are reachable from the root. Blocks 2 and 5 are unmarked because they are unreachable. After the sweep phase, the two unreachable blocks are reclaimed to the free list.

9.10.3 Conservative Mark&Sweep for C Programs

Mark&Sweep is an appropriate approach for garbage collecting C programs because it works in place without moving any blocks. However, the C language poses some interesting challenges for the implementation of the isPtr function.

First, C does not tag memory locations with any type information. Thus, there is no obvious way for isPtr to determine if its input parameter p is a pointer or not. Second, even if we were to know that p was a pointer, there would be no obvious way for isPtr to determine whether p points to some location in the payload of an allocated block.

One solution to the latter problem is to maintain the set of allocated blocks as a balanced binary tree that maintains the invariant that all blocks in the left subtree are located at smaller addresses and all blocks in the right subtree are located in larger addresses. As shown in Figure 9.53, this requires two additional fields (left and right) in the header of each allocated block. Each field points to the header of some allocated block. The isPtr(ptr p) function uses the tree to perform a binary search of the allocated blocks. At each step, it relies on the size field in the block header to determine if p falls within the extent of the block.

The balanced tree approach is correct in the sense that it is guaranteed to mark all of the nodes that are reachable from the roots. This is a necessary guarantee, as application users would certainly not appreciate having their allocated blocks prematurely returned to the free list. However, it is conservative in the sense that it may incorrectly mark blocks that are actually unreachable, and thus it may fail to free some garbage. While this does not affect the correctness of application programs, it can result in unnecessary external fragmentation.

The fundamental reason that Mark&Sweep collectors for C programs must be conservative is that the C language does not tag memory locations with type information. Thus, scalars like ints or floats can masquerade as pointers. For example, suppose that some reachable allocated block contains an int in its payload whose value happens to correspond to an address in the payload of some other allocated block b. There is no way for the collector to infer that the data is really an int and not a pointer. Therefore, the allocator must conservatively mark block b as reachable, when in fact it might not be.

9.11 Common Memory-Related Bugs in C Programs

Managing and using virtual memory can be a difficult and error-prone task for C programmers. Memory-related bugs are among the most frightening because they often manifest themselves at a distance, in both time and space, from the source of the bug. Write the wrong data to the wrong location, and your program can run for hours before it finally fails in some distant part of the program. We conclude our discussion of virtual memory with a look at of some of the common memory-related bugs.

9.11.1 Dereferencing Bad Pointers

As we learned in Section 9.7.2, there are large holes in the virtual address space of a process that are not mapped to any meaningful data. If we attempt to dereference a pointer into one of these holes, the operating system will terminate our program with a segmentation exception. Also, some areas of virtual memory are read-only. Attempting to write to one of these areas terminates the program with a protection exception.

A common example of dereferencing a bad pointer is the classic scanf bug. Suppose we want to use scanf to read an integer from stdin into a variable. The correct way to do this is to pass scanf a format string and the *address* of the variable:

```
scanf("%d", &val)
```

However, it is easy for new C programmers (and experienced ones too!) to pass the *contents* of val instead of its address:

```
scanf("%d", val)
```

In this case, scanf will interpret the contents of val as an address and attempt to write a word to that location. In the best case, the program terminates immediately with an exception. In the worst case, the contents of val correspond to some valid read/write area of virtual memory, and we overwrite memory, usually with disastrous and baffling consequences much later.

9.11.2   Reading Uninitialized Memory

While bss memory locations (such as uninitialized global C variables) are always initialized to zeros by the loader, this is not true for heap memory. A common error is to assume that heap memory is initialized to zero:

```
1    /* Return y = Ax */
2    int *matvec(int **A, int *x, int n)
3    {
4        int i, j;
5
6        int *y = (int *)Malloc(n * sizeof(int));
7
8        for (i = 0; i < n; i++)
9            for (j = 0; j < n; j++)
10               y[i] += A[i][j] * x[j];
11       return y;
12   }
```

In this example, the programmer has incorrectly assumed that vector y has been initialized to zero. A correct implementation would explicitly zero y[i] or use calloc.

9.11.3   Allowing Stack Buffer Overflows

As we saw in Section 3.10.3, a program has a *buffer overflow bug* if it writes to a target buffer on the stack without examining the size of the input string. For example, the following function has a buffer overflow bug because the gets function copies an arbitrary-length string to the buffer. To fix this, we would need to use the fgets function, which limits the size of the input string.

```
1    void bufoverflow()
2    {
3        char buf[64];
4
5        gets(buf); /* Here is the stack buffer overflow bug */
6        return;
7    }
```

9.11.4 Assuming That Pointers and the Objects They Point to Are the Same Size

One common mistake is to assume that pointers to objects are the same size as the objects they point to:

```
1   /* Create an nxm array */
2   int **makeArray1(int n, int m)
3   {
4       int i;
5       int **A = (int **)Malloc(n * sizeof(int));
6
7       for (i = 0; i < n; i++)
8           A[i] = (int *)Malloc(m * sizeof(int));
9       return A;
10  }
```

The intent here is to create an array of n pointers, each of which points to an array of m ints. However, because the programmer has written sizeof(int) instead of sizeof(int *) in line 5, the code actually creates an array of ints.

This code will run fine on machines where ints and pointers to ints are the same size. But if we run this code on a machine like the Core i7, where a pointer is larger than an int, then the loop in lines 7–8 will write past the end of the A array. Since one of these words will likely be the boundary-tag footer of the allocated block, we may not discover the error until we free the block much later in the program, at which point the coalescing code in the allocator will fail dramatically and for no apparent reason. This is an insidious example of the kind of "action at a distance" that is so typical of memory-related programming bugs.

9.11.5 Making Off-by-One Errors

Off-by-one errors are another common source of overwriting bugs:

```
1   /* Create an nxm array */
2   int **makeArray2(int n, int m)
3   {
4       int i;
5       int **A = (int **)Malloc(n * sizeof(int *));
6
7       for (i = 0; i <= n; i++)
8           A[i] = (int *)Malloc(m * sizeof(int));
9       return A;
10  }
```

This is another version of the program in the previous section. Here we have created an n-element array of pointers in line 5 but then tried to initialize $n + 1$ of its elements in lines 7 and 8, in the process overwriting some memory that follows the A array.

9.11.6   Referencing a Pointer Instead of the Object It Points To

If we are not careful about the precedence and associativity of C operators, then we incorrectly manipulate a pointer instead of the object it points to. For example, consider the following function, whose purpose is to remove the first item in a binary heap of *size items and then reheapify the remaining *size − 1 items:

```
1    int *binheapDelete(int **binheap, int *size)
2    {
3        int *packet = binheap[0];
4
5        binheap[0] = binheap[*size - 1];
6        *size--; /* This should be (*size)-- */
7        heapify(binheap, *size, 0);
8        return(packet);
9    }
```

In line 6, the intent is to decrement the integer value pointed to by the size pointer. However, because the unary −− and ∗ operators have the same precedence and associate from right to left, the code in line 6 actually decrements the pointer itself instead of the integer value that it points to. If we are lucky, the program will crash immediately. But more likely we will be left scratching our heads when the program produces an incorrect answer much later in its execution. The moral here is to use parentheses whenever in doubt about precedence and associativity. For example, in line 6, we should have clearly stated our intent by using the expression (*size)--.

9.11.7   Misunderstanding Pointer Arithmetic

Another common mistake is to forget that arithmetic operations on pointers are performed in units that are the size of the objects they point to, which are not necessarily bytes. For example, the intent of the following function is to scan an array of ints and return a pointer to the first occurrence of val:

```
1    int *search(int *p, int val)
2    {
3        while (*p && *p != val)
4            p += sizeof(int); /* Should be p++ */
5        return p;
6    }
```

However, because line 4 increments the pointer by 4 (the number of bytes in an integer) each time through the loop, the function incorrectly scans every fourth integer in the array.

9.11.8 Referencing Nonexistent Variables

Naive C programmers who do not understand the stack discipline will sometimes reference local variables that are no longer valid, as in the following example:

```
1   int *stackref ()
2   {
3       int val;
4
5       return &val;
6   }
```

This function returns a pointer (say, p) to a local variable on the stack and then pops its stack frame. Although p still points to a valid memory address, it no longer points to a valid variable. When other functions are called later in the program, the memory will be reused for their stack frames. Later, if the program assigns some value to *p, then it might actually be modifying an entry in another function's stack frame, with potentially disastrous and baffling consequences.

9.11.9 Referencing Data in Free Heap Blocks

A similar error is to reference data in heap blocks that have already been freed. Consider the following example, which allocates an integer array x in line 6, prematurely frees block x in line 10, and then later references it in line 14:

```
1   int *heapref(int n, int m)
2   {
3       int i;
4       int *x, *y;
5
6       x = (int *)Malloc(n * sizeof(int));
7
8          // Other calls to malloc and free go here
9
10      free(x);
11
12      y = (int *)Malloc(m * sizeof(int));
13      for (i = 0; i < m; i++)
14          y[i] = x[i]++; /* Oops! x[i] is a word in a free block */
15
16      return y;
17  }
```

Depending on the pattern of `malloc` and `free` calls that occur between lines 6 and 10, when the program references x[i] in line 14, the array x might be part of some other allocated heap block and may have been overwritten. As with many memory-related bugs, the error will only become evident later in the program when we notice that the values in y are corrupted.

9.11.10   Introducing Memory Leaks

Memory leaks are slow, silent killers that occur when programmers inadvertently create garbage in the heap by forgetting to free allocated blocks. For example, the following function allocates a heap block x and then returns without freeing it:

```
1    void leak(int n)
2    {
3        int *x = (int *)Malloc(n * sizeof(int));
4
5        return;  /* x is garbage at this point */
6    }
```

If leak is called frequently, then the heap will gradually fill up with garbage, in the worst case consuming the entire virtual address space. Memory leaks are particularly serious for programs such as daemons and servers, which by definition never terminate.

9.12   Summary

Virtual memory is an abstraction of main memory. Processors that support virtual memory reference main memory using a form of indirection known as virtual addressing. The processor generates a virtual address, which is translated into a physical address before being sent to the main memory. The translation of addresses from a virtual address space to a physical address space requires close cooperation between hardware and software. Dedicated hardware translates virtual addresses using page tables whose contents are supplied by the operating system.

Virtual memory provides three important capabilities. First, it automatically caches recently used contents of the virtual address space stored on disk in main memory. The block in a virtual memory cache is known as a page. A reference to a page on disk triggers a page fault that transfers control to a fault handler in the operating system. The fault handler copies the page from disk to the main memory cache, writing back the evicted page if necessary. Second, virtual memory simplifies memory management, which in turn simplifies linking, sharing data between processes, the allocation of memory for processes, and program loading. Finally, virtual memory simplifies memory protection by incorporating protection bits into every page table entry.

The process of address translation must be integrated with the operation of any hardware caches in the system. Most page table entries are located in the L1 cache, but the cost of accessing page table entries from L1 is usually eliminated by an on-chip cache of page table entries called a TLB.

Modern systems initialize chunks of virtual memory by associating them with chunks of files on disk, a process known as memory mapping. Memory mapping provides an efficient mechanism for sharing data, creating new processes, and loading programs. Applications can manually create and delete areas of the virtual address space using the mmap function. However, most programs rely on a dynamic memory allocator such as malloc, which manages memory in an area of the virtual address space called the heap. Dynamic memory allocators are application-level programs with a system-level feel, directly manipulating memory without much help from the type system. Allocators come in two flavors. Explicit allocators require applications to explicitly free their memory blocks. Implicit allocators (garbage collectors) free any unused and unreachable blocks automatically.

Managing and using memory is a difficult and error-prone task for C programmers. Examples of common errors include dereferencing bad pointers, reading uninitialized memory, allowing stack buffer overflows, assuming that pointers and the objects they point to are the same size, referencing a pointer instead of the object it points to, misunderstanding pointer arithmetic, referencing nonexistent variables, and introducing memory leaks.

Bibliographic Notes

Kilburn and his colleagues published the first description of virtual memory [63]. Architecture texts contain additional details about the hardware's role in virtual memory [46]. Operating systems texts contain additional information about the operating system's role [102, 106, 113]. Bovet and Cesati [11] give a detailed description of the Linux virtual memory system. Intel Corporation provides detailed documentation on 32-bit and 64-bit address translation on IA processors [52].

Knuth wrote the classic work on storage allocation in 1968 [64]. Since that time, there has been a tremendous amount of work in the area. Wilson, Johnstone, Neely, and Boles have written a beautiful survey and performance evaluation of explicit allocators [118]. The general comments in this book about the throughput and utilization of different allocator strategies are paraphrased from their survey. Jones and Lins provide a comprehensive survey of garbage collection [56]. Kernighan and Ritchie [61] show the complete code for a simple allocator based on an explicit free list with a block size and successor pointer in each free block. The code is interesting in that it uses unions to eliminate a lot of the complicated pointer arithmetic, but at the expense of a linear-time (rather than constant-time) free operation. Doug Lea developed a widely used open-source malloc package called dlmalloc [67].

Homework Problems

9.11 ◆
In the following series of problems, you are to show how the example memory system in Section 9.6.4 translates a virtual address into a physical address and accesses the cache. For the given virtual address, indicate the TLB entry accessed,

the physical address, and the cache byte value returned. Indicate whether the TLB misses, whether a page fault occurs, and whether a cache miss occurs. If there is a cache miss, enter "—" for "Cache byte returned." If there is a page fault, enter "—" for "PPN" and leave parts C and D blank.

Virtual address: 0x027c

A. Virtual address format

13	12	11	10	9	8	7	6	5	4	3	2	1	0

B. Address translation

Parameter	Value
VPN	_____
TLB index	_____
TLB tag	_____
TLB hit? (Y/N)	_____
Page fault? (Y/N)	_____
PPN	_____

C. Physical address format

11	10	9	8	7	6	5	4	3	2	1	0

D. Physical memory reference

Parameter	Value
Byte offset	_____
Cache index	_____
Cache tag	_____
Cache hit? (Y/N)	_____
Cache byte returned	_____

9.12 ◆
Repeat Problem 9.11 for the following address.

Virtual address: 0x03a9

A. Virtual address format

13	12	11	10	9	8	7	6	5	4	3	2	1	0

B. Address translation

Parameter	Value
VPN	_____
TLB index	_____
TLB tag	_____
TLB hit? (Y/N)	_____
Page fault? (Y/N)	_____
PPN	_____

C. Physical address format

11	10	9	8	7	6	5	4	3	2	1	0

D. Physical memory reference

Parameter	Value
Byte offset	_____
Cache index	_____
Cache tag	_____
Cache hit? (Y/N)	_____
Cache byte returned	_____

9.13 ◆

Repeat Problem 9.11 for the following address.

Virtual address: 0x0040

13	12	11	10	9	8	7	6	5	4	3	2	1	0

A. Address translation

Parameter	Value
VPN	_____
TLB index	_____
TLB tag	_____
TLB hit? (Y/N)	_____
Page fault? (Y/N)	_____
PPN	_____

B. Physical address format

11	10	9	8	7	6	5	4	3	2	1	0

C. Physical memory reference

Parameter	Value
Byte offset	_____
Cache index	_____
Cache tag	_____
Cache hit? (Y/N)	_____
Cache byte returned	_____

9.14 ◆◆

Given an input file `hello.txt` that consists of the string `Hello, world!\n`, write a C program that uses `mmap` to change the contents of `hello.txt` to `Jello, world!\n`.

9.15 ◆

Determine the block sizes and header values that would result from the following sequence of `malloc` requests. Assumptions: (1) The allocator maintains double-word alignment and uses an implicit free list with the block format from Figure 9.35. (2) Block sizes are rounded up to the nearest multiple of 8 bytes.

Request	Block size (decimal bytes)	Block header (hex)
`malloc(3)`	_____	_____
`malloc(11)`	_____	_____
`malloc(20)`	_____	_____
`malloc(21)`	_____	_____

9.16 ◆

Determine the minimum block size for each of the following combinations of alignment requirements and block formats. Assumptions: Explicit free list, 4-byte `pred` and `succ` pointers in each free block, zero-size payloads are not allowed, and headers and footers are stored in 4-byte words.

Alignment	Allocated block	Free block	Minimum block size (bytes)
Single word	Header and footer	Header and footer	_____
Single word	Header, but no footer	Header and footer	_____
Double word	Header and footer	Header and footer	_____
Double word	Header, but no footer	Header and footer	_____

9.17 ◆◆◆

Develop a version of the allocator in Section 9.9.12 that performs a next-fit search instead of a first-fit search.

9.18 ◆◆◆

The allocator in Section 9.9.12 requires both a header and a footer for each block in order to perform constant-time coalescing. Modify the allocator so that free blocks require a header and a footer, but allocated blocks require only a header.

9.19 ◆

You are given three groups of statements relating to memory management and garbage collection below. In each group, only one statement is true. Your task is to indicate which statement is true.

1. (a) In a buddy system, up to 50% of the space can be wasted due to internal fragmentation.
   (b) The first-fit memory allocation algorithm is slower than the best-fit algorithm (on average).
   (c) Deallocation using boundary tags is fast only when the list of free blocks is ordered according to increasing memory addresses.
   (d) The buddy system suffers from internal fragmentation, but not from external fragmentation.

2. (a) Using the first-fit algorithm on a free list that is ordered according to decreasing block sizes results in low performance for allocations, but avoids external fragmentation.
   (b) For the best-fit method, the list of free blocks should be ordered according to increasing memory addresses.
   (c) The best-fit method chooses the largest free block into which the requested segment fits.
   (d) Using the first-fit algorithm on a free list that is ordered according to increasing block sizes is equivalent to using the best-fit algorithm.

3. Mark&Sweep garbage collectors are called conservative if
   (a) They coalesce freed memory only when a memory request cannot be satisfied.
   (b) They treat everything that looks like a pointer as a pointer.
   (c) They perform garbage collection only when they run out of memory.
   (d) They do not free memory blocks forming a cyclic list.

9.20 ◆◆◆◆

Write your own version of malloc and free, and compare its running time and space utilization to the version of malloc provided in the standard C library.

Solutions to Practice Problems

Solution to Problem 9.1 (page 805)

This problem gives you some appreciation for the sizes of different address spaces. At one point in time, a 32-bit address space seemed impossibly large. But now there are database and scientific applications that need more, and you can expect this trend to continue. At some point in your lifetime, expect to find yourself complaining about the cramped 64-bit address space on your personal computer!

Number of address bits (n)	Number of virtual addresses (N)	Largest possible virtual address
8	$2^8 = 256$	$2^8 - 1 = 255$
16	$2^{16} = 64 \text{ K}$	$2^{16} - 1 = 64 \text{ K} - 1$
32	$2^{32} = 4 \text{ G}$	$2^{32} - 1 = 4 \text{ G} - 1$
48	$2^{48} = 256 \text{ T}$	$2^{48} - 1 = 256 \text{ T} - 1$
64	$2^{64} = 16{,}384 \text{ P}$	$2^{64} - 1 = 16{,}384 \text{ P} - 1$

Solution to Problem 9.2 (page 807)

Since each virtual page is $P = 2^p$ bytes, there are a total of $2^n/2^p = 2^{n-p}$ possible pages in the system, each of which needs a page table entry (PTE).

n	$P = 2^p$	Number of PTEs
16	4 K	16
16	8 K	8
32	4 K	1 M
32	8 K	512 K

Solution to Problem 9.3 (page 816)

You need to understand this kind of problem well in order to fully grasp address translation. Here is how to solve the first subproblem: We are given $n = 32$ virtual address bits and $m = 24$ physical address bits. A page size of $P = 1$ KB means we need $\log_2(1 \text{ K}) = 10$ bits for both the VPO and PPO. (Recall that the VPO and PPO are identical.) The remaining address bits are the VPN and PPN, respectively.

P	Number of			
	VPN bits	VPO bits	PPN bits	PPO bits
1 KB	22	10	14	10
2 KB	21	11	13	11
4 KB	20	12	12	12
8 KB	19	13	11	13

Solution to Problem 9.4 (page 824)

Doing a few of these manual simulations is a great way to firm up your understanding of address translation. You might find it helpful to write out all the bits in the addresses and then draw boxes around the different bit fields, such as VPN, TLBI, and so on. In this particular problem, there are no misses of any kind: the TLB has a copy of the PTE and the cache has a copy of the requested data words. See Problems 9.11, 9.12, and 9.13 for some different combinations of hits and misses.

A. 00 0011 1101 0111

B.

Parameter	Value
VPN	0xf
TLB index	0x3
TLB tag	0x3
TLB hit? (Y/N)	Y
Page fault? (Y/N)	N
PPN	0xd

C. 0011 0101 0111

D.

Parameter	Value
Byte offset	0x3
Cache index	0x5
Cache tag	0xd
Cache hit? (Y/N)	Y
Cache byte returned	0x1d

Solution to Problem 9.5 (page 839)

Solving this problem will give you a good feel for the idea of memory mapping. Try it yourself. We haven't discussed the open, fstat, or write functions, so you'll need to read their man pages to see how they work.

——————————————————————————————— *code/vm/mmapcopy.c*

```
1    #include "csapp.h"
2
3    /*
4     * mmapcopy - uses mmap to copy file fd to stdout
5     */
6    void mmapcopy(int fd, int size)
7    {
8        char *bufp; /* ptr to memory-mapped VM area */
9
10       bufp = Mmap(NULL, size, PROT_READ, MAP_PRIVATE, fd, 0);
11       Write(1, bufp, size);
12       return;
13   }
14
15   /* mmapcopy driver */
16   int main(int argc, char **argv)
17   {
18       struct stat stat;
19       int fd;
20
```

```
21          /* Check for required command-line argument */
22          if (argc != 2) {
23              printf("usage: %s <filename>\n", argv[0]);
24              exit(0);
25          }
26
27          /* Copy the input argument to stdout */
28          fd = Open(argv[1], O_RDONLY, 0);
29          fstat(fd, &stat);
30          mmapcopy(fd, stat.st_size);
31          exit(0);
32      }
```
———————————————————————————————————— *code/vm/mmapcopy.c*

Solution to Problem 9.6 (page 849)

This problem touches on some core ideas such as alignment requirements, minimum block sizes, and header encodings. The general approach for determining the block size is to round the sum of the requested payload and the header size to the nearest multiple of the alignment requirement (in this case, 8 bytes). For example, the block size for the malloc(1) request is $4 + 1 = 5$ rounded up to 8. The block size for the malloc(13) request is $13 + 4 = 17$ rounded up to 24.

Request	Block size (decimal bytes)	Block header (hex)
malloc(1)	8	0x9
malloc(5)	16	0x11
malloc(12)	16	0x11
malloc(13)	24	0x19

Solution to Problem 9.7 (page 852)

The minimum block size can have a significant effect on internal fragmentation. Thus, it is good to understand the minimum block sizes associated with different allocator designs and alignment requirements. The tricky part is to realize that the same block can be allocated or free at different points in time. Thus, the minimum block size is the maximum of the minimum allocated block size and the minimum free block size. For example, in the last subproblem, the minimum allocated block size is a 4-byte header and a 1-byte payload rounded up to 8 bytes. The minimum free block size is a 4-byte header and 4-byte footer, which is already a multiple of 8 and doesn't need to be rounded. So the minimum block size for this allocator is 8 bytes.

Alignment	Allocated block	Free block	Minimum block size (bytes)
Single word	Header and footer	Header and footer	12
Single word	Header, but no footer	Header and footer	8
Double word	Header and footer	Header and footer	16
Double word	Header, but no footer	Header and footer	8

Solution to Problem 9.8 (page 861)

There is nothing very tricky here. But the solution requires you to understand how the rest of our simple implicit-list allocator works and how to manipulate and traverse blocks.

——————————————————————————————————— *code/vm/malloc/mm.c*

```
1   static void *find_fit(size_t asize)
2   {
3       /* First-fit search */
4       void *bp;
5
6       for (bp = heap_listp; GET_SIZE(HDRP(bp)) > 0; bp = NEXT_BLKP(bp)) {
7           if (!GET_ALLOC(HDRP(bp)) && (asize <= GET_SIZE(HDRP(bp)))) {
8               return bp;
9           }
10      }
11      return NULL; /* No fit */
12  #endif
13  }
```

——————————————————————————————————— *code/vm/malloc/mm.c*

Solution to Problem 9.9 (page 861)

This is another warm-up exercise to help you become familiar with allocators. Notice that for this allocator the minimum block size is 16 bytes. If the remainder of the block after splitting would be greater than or equal to the minimum block size, then we go ahead and split the block (lines 6–10). The only tricky part here is to realize that you need to place the new allocated block (lines 6 and 7) before moving to the next block (line 8).

——————————————————————————————————— *code/vm/malloc/mm.c*

```
1   static void place(void *bp, size_t asize)
2   {
3       size_t csize = GET_SIZE(HDRP(bp));
4
5       if ((csize - asize) >= (2*DSIZE)) {
6           PUT(HDRP(bp), PACK(asize, 1));
7           PUT(FTRP(bp), PACK(asize, 1));
8           bp = NEXT_BLKP(bp);
9           PUT(HDRP(bp), PACK(csize-asize, 0));
10          PUT(FTRP(bp), PACK(csize-asize, 0));
11      }
12      else {
13          PUT(HDRP(bp), PACK(csize, 1));
14          PUT(FTRP(bp), PACK(csize, 1));
15      }
16  }
```

——————————————————————————————————— *code/vm/malloc/mm.c*

Solution to Problem 9.10 (page 864)

Here is one pattern that will cause external fragmentation: The application makes numerous allocation and free requests to the first size class, followed by numerous allocation and free requests to the second size class, followed by numerous allocation and free requests to the third size class, and so on. For each size class, the allocator creates a lot of memory that is never reclaimed because the allocator doesn't coalesce, and because the application never requests blocks from that size class again.

APPENDIX **A**

Error Handling

Programmers should *always* check the error codes returned by system-level functions. There are many subtle ways that things can go wrong, and it only makes sense to use the status information that the kernel is able to provide us. Unfortunately, programmers are often reluctant to do error checking because it clutters their code, turning a single line of code into a multi-line conditional statement. Error checking is also confusing because different functions indicate errors in different ways.

We were faced with a similar problem when writing this text. On the one hand, we would like our code examples to be concise and simple to read. On the other hand, we do not want to give students the wrong impression that it is OK to skip error checking. To resolve these issues, we have adopted an approach based on *error-handling wrappers* that was pioneered by W. Richard Stevens in his network programming text [110].

The idea is that given some base system-level function foo, we define a wrapper function Foo with identical arguments, but with the first letter capitalized. The wrapper calls the base function and checks for errors. If it detects an error, the wrapper prints an informative message and terminates the process. Otherwise, it returns to the caller. Notice that if there are no errors, the wrapper behaves exactly like the base function. Put another way, if a program runs correctly with wrappers, it will run correctly if we render the first letter of each wrapper in lowercase and recompile.

The wrappers are packaged in a single source file (csapp.c) that is compiled and linked into each program. A separate header file (csapp.h) contains the function prototypes for the wrappers.

This appendix gives a tutorial on the different kinds of error handling in Unix systems and gives examples of the different styles of error-handling wrappers. Copies of the csapp.h and csapp.c files are available at the CS:APP Web site.

A.1   Error Handling in Unix Systems

The systems-level function calls that we will encounter in this book use three different styles for returning errors: *Unix-style*, *Posix-style*, and *GAI-style*.

Unix-Style Error Handling

Functions such as `fork` and `wait` that were developed in the early days of Unix (as well as some older Posix functions) overload the function return value with both error codes *and* useful results. For example, when the Unix-style `wait` function encounters an error (e.g., there is no child process to reap), it returns −1 and sets the global variable `errno` to an error code that indicates the cause of the error. If `wait` completes successfully, then it returns the useful result, which is the PID of the reaped child. Unix-style error-handling code is typically of the following form:

```
1    if ((pid = wait(NULL)) < 0) {
2        fprintf(stderr, "wait error: %s\n", strerror(errno));
3        exit(0);
4    }
```

The `strerror` function returns a text description for a particular value of `errno`.

Posix-Style Error Handling

Many of the newer Posix functions such as Pthreads use the return value only to indicate success (zero) or failure (nonzero). Any useful results are returned in function arguments that are passed by reference. We refer to this approach as *Posix-style error handling*. For example, the Posix-style `pthread_create` function indicates success or failure with its return value and returns the ID of the newly created thread (the useful result) by reference in its first argument. Posix-style error-handling code is typically of the following form:

```
1    if ((retcode = pthread_create(&tid, NULL, thread, NULL)) != 0) {
2        fprintf(stderr, "pthread_create error: %s\n", strerror(retcode));
3        exit(0);
4    }
```

The `strerror` function returns a text description for a particular value of `retcode`.

GAI-Style Error Handling

The `getaddrinfo` (GAI) and `getnameinfo` functions return zero on success and a nonzero value on failure. GAI error-handling code is typically of the following form:

```
1    if ((retcode = getaddrinfo(host, service, &hints, &result)) != 0) {
2        fprintf(stderr, "getaddrinfo error: %s\n", gai_strerror(retcode));
3        exit(0);
4    }
```

The `gai_strerror` function returns a text description for a particular value of `retcode`.

Summary of Error-Reporting Functions

Thoughout this book, we use the following error-reporting functions to accommodate different error-handling styles.

```
#include "csapp.h"

void unix_error(char *msg);
void posix_error(int code, char *msg);
void gai_error(int code, char *msg);
void app_error(char *msg);
                                                    Returns: nothing
```

As their names suggest, the `unix_error`, `posix_error`, and `gai_error` functions report Unix-style, Posix-style, and GAI-style errors and then terminate. The `app_error` function is included as a convenience for application errors. It simply prints its input and then terminates. Figure A.1 shows the code for the error-reporting functions.

A.2   Error-Handling Wrappers

Here are some examples of the different error-handling wrappers.

Unix-style error-handling wrappers. Figure A.2 shows the wrapper for the Unix-style `wait` function. If the `wait` returns with an error, the wrapper prints an informative message and then exits. Otherwise, it returns a PID to the caller. Figure A.3 shows the wrapper for the Unix-style `kill` function. Notice that this function, unlike `wait`, returns `void` on success.

Posix-style error-handling wrappers. Figure A.4 shows the wrapper for the Posix-style `pthread_detach` function. Like most Posix-style functions, it does not overload useful results with error-return codes, so the wrapper returns `void` on success.

GAI-style error-handling wrappers. Figure A.5 shows the error-handling wrapper for the GAI-style `getaddrinfo` function.

code/src/csapp.c

```
1   void unix_error(char *msg) /* Unix-style error */
2   {
3       fprintf(stderr, "%s: %s\n", msg, strerror(errno));
4       exit(0);
5   }
6
7   void posix_error(int code, char *msg) /* Posix-style error */
8   {
9       fprintf(stderr, "%s: %s\n", msg, strerror(code));
10      exit(0);
11  }
12
13  void gai_error(int code, char *msg) /* Getaddrinfo-style error */
14  {
15      fprintf(stderr, "%s: %s\n", msg, gai_strerror(code));
16      exit(0);
17  }
18
19  void app_error(char *msg) /* Application error */
20  {
21      fprintf(stderr, "%s\n", msg);
22      exit(0);
23  }
```

code/src/csapp.c

Figure A.1 Error-reporting functions.

code/src/csapp.c

```
1   pid_t Wait(int *status)
2   {
3       pid_t pid;
4
5       if ((pid  = wait(status)) < 0)
6           unix_error("Wait error");
7       return pid;
8   }
```

code/src/csapp.c

Figure A.2 Wrapper for Unix-style wait function.

code/src/csapp.c

```
1   void Kill(pid_t pid, int signum)
2   {
3       int rc;
4
5       if ((rc = kill(pid, signum)) < 0)
6           unix_error("Kill error");
7   }
```

code/src/csapp.c

Figure A.3   Wrapper for Unix-style kill **function.**

code/src/csapp.c

```
1   void Pthread_detach(pthread_t tid) {
2       int rc;
3
4       if ((rc = pthread_detach(tid)) != 0)
5           posix_error(rc, "Pthread_detach error");
6   }
```

code/src/csapp.c

Figure A.4   Wrapper for Posix-style pthread_detach **function.**

code/src/csapp.c

```
1   void Getaddrinfo(const char *node, const char *service,
2                   const struct addrinfo *hints, struct addrinfo **res)
3   {
4       int rc;
5
6       if ((rc = getaddrinfo(node, service, hints, res)) != 0)
7           gai_error(rc, "Getaddrinfo error");
8   }
```

code/src/csapp.c

Figure A.5   Wrapper for GAI-style getaddrinfo **function.**

References

[1] Advanced Micro Devices, Inc. *Software Optimization Guide for AMD64 Processors*, 2005. Publication Number 25112.

[2] Advanced Micro Devices, Inc. *AMD64 Architecture Programmer's Manual, Volume 1: Application Programming*, 2013. Publication Number 24592.

[3] Advanced Micro Devices, Inc. *AMD64 Architecture Programmer's Manual, Volume 3: General-Purpose and System Instructions*, 2013. Publication Number 24594.

[4] Advanced Micro Devices, Inc. *AMD64 Architecture Programmer's Manual, Volume 4: 128-Bit and 256-Bit Media Instructions*, 2013. Publication Number 26568.

[5] K. Arnold, J. Gosling, and D. Holmes. *The Java Programming Language, Fourth Edition*. Prentice Hall, 2005.

[6] T. Berners-Lee, R. Fielding, and H. Frystyk. Hypertext transfer protocol - HTTP/1.0. RFC 1945, 1996.

[7] A. Birrell. An introduction to programming with threads. Technical Report 35, Digital Systems Research Center, 1989.

[8] A. Birrell, M. Isard, C. Thacker, and T. Wobber. A design for high-performance flash disks. *SIGOPS Operating Systems Review* 41(2):88–93, 2007.

[9] G. E. Blelloch, J. T. Fineman, P. B. Gibbons, and H. V. Simhadri. Scheduling irregular parallel computations on hierarchical caches. In *Proceedings of the 23rd Symposium on Parallelism in Algorithms and Architectures (SPAA)*, pages 355–366. ACM, June 2011.

[10] S. Borkar. Thousand core chips: A technology perspective. In *Proceedings of the 44th Design Automation Conference*, pages 746–749. ACM, 2007.

[11] D. Bovet and M. Cesati. *Understanding the Linux Kernel, Third Edition*. O'Reilly Media, Inc., 2005.

[12] A. Demke Brown and T. Mowry. Taming the memory hogs: Using compiler-inserted releases to manage physical memory intelligently. In *Proceedings of the 4th Symposium on Operating Systems Design and Implementation (OSDI)*, pages 31–44. Usenix, October 2000.

[13] R. E. Bryant. Term-level verification of a pipelined CISC microprocessor. Technical Report CMU-CS-05-195, Carnegie Mellon University, School of Computer Science, 2005.

[14] R. E. Bryant and D. R. O'Hallaron. Introducing computer systems from a programmer's perspective. In *Proceedings of the Technical Symposium on Computer Science Education (SIGCSE)*, pages 90–94. ACM, February 2001.

[15] D. Butenhof. *Programming with Posix Threads*. Addison-Wesley, 1997.

[16] S. Carson and P. Reynolds. The geometry of semaphore programs. *ACM Transactions on Programming Languages and Systems* 9(1):25–53, 1987.

[17] J. B. Carter, W. C. Hsieh, L. B. Stoller, M. R. Swanson, L. Zhang, E. L. Brunvand, A. Davis, C.-C. Kuo, R. Kuramkote, M. A. Parker, L. Schaelicke, and T. Tateyama. Impulse: Building a smarter memory controller. In *Proceedings of the 5th International Symposium on High Performance Computer Architecture (HPCA)*, pages 70–79. ACM, January 1999.

[18] K. Chang, D. Lee, Z. Chishti, A. Alameldeen, C. Wilkerson, Y. Kim, and O. Mutlu. Improving DRAM performance by parallelizing refreshes with accesses. In *Proceedings of the 20th International Symposium on High-Performance Computer Architecture (HPCA)*. ACM, February 2014.

[19] S. Chellappa, F. Franchetti, and M. Püschel. How to write fast numerical code: A small introduction. In *Generative and Transformational Techniques in Software Engineering II*, volume 5235 of *Lecture Notes in Computer Science*, pages 196–259. Springer-Verlag, 2008.

[20] P. Chen, E. Lee, G. Gibson, R. Katz, and D. Patterson. RAID: High-performance, reliable secondary storage. *ACM Computing Surveys* 26(2):145–185, June 1994.

[21] S. Chen, P. Gibbons, and T. Mowry. Improving index performance through prefetching. In *Proceedings of the 2001 ACM SIGMOD International Conference on Management of Data*, pages 235–246. ACM, May 2001.

[22] T. Chilimbi, M. Hill, and J. Larus. Cache-conscious structure layout. In *Proceedings of the 1999 ACM Conference on Programming Language Design and Implementation (PLDI)*, pages 1–12. ACM, May 1999.

[23] E. Coffman, M. Elphick, and A. Shoshani. System deadlocks. *ACM Computing Surveys* 3(2):67–78, June 1971.

[24] D. Cohen. On holy wars and a plea for peace. *IEEE Computer* 14(10):48–54, October 1981.

[25] P. J. Courtois, F. Heymans, and D. L. Parnas. Concurrent control with "readers" and "writers." *Communications of the ACM* 14(10):667–668, 1971.

[26] C. Cowan, P. Wagle, C. Pu, S. Beattie, and J. Walpole. Buffer overflows: Attacks and defenses for the vulnerability of the decade. In *DARPA Information Survivability Conference and Expo (DISCEX)*, volume 2, pages 119–129, March 2000.

[27] J. H. Crawford. The i486 CPU: Executing instructions in one clock cycle. *IEEE Micro* 10(1):27–36, February 1990.

[28] V. Cuppu, B. Jacob, B. Davis, and T. Mudge. A performance comparison of contemporary DRAM architectures. In *Proceedings of the 26th International Symposium on Computer Architecture (ISCA)*, pages 222–233, ACM, 1999.

[29] B. Davis, B. Jacob, and T. Mudge. The new DRAM interfaces: SDRAM, RDRAM, and variants. In *Proceedings of the 3rd International Symposium on High Performance Computing (ISHPC)*, volume 1940 of *Lecture Notes in Computer Science*, pages 26–31. Springer-Verlag, October 2000.

[30] E. Demaine. Cache-oblivious algorithms and data structures. In *Lecture Notes from the EEF Summer School on Massive Data Sets*. BRICS, University of Aarhus, Denmark, 2002.

[31] E. W. Dijkstra. Cooperating sequential processes. Technical Report EWD-123, Technological University, Eindhoven, the Netherlands, 1965.

[32] C. Ding and K. Kennedy. Improving cache performance of dynamic applications through data and computation reorganizations at run time. In *Proceedings of the 1999 ACM Conference on Programming Language Design and Implementation (PLDI)*, pages 229–241. ACM, May 1999.

[33] M. Dowson. The Ariane 5 software failure. *SIGSOFT Software Engineering Notes* 22(2):84, 1997.

[34] U. Drepper. User-level IPv6 programming introduction. Available at http://www.akkadia.org/drepper/userapi-ipv6.html, 2008.

[35] M. W. Eichen and J. A. Rochlis. With microscope and tweezers: An analysis of the Internet virus of November, 1988. In *Proceedings of the IEEE Symposium on Research in Security and Privacy*, pages 326–343. IEEE, 1989.

[36] *ELF-64 Object File Format, Version 1.5 Draft 2*, 1998. Available at http://www.uclibc.org/docs/elf-64-gen.pdf.

[37] R. Fielding, J. Gettys, J. Mogul, H. Frystyk, L. Masinter, P. Leach, and T. Berners-Lee. Hypertext transfer protocol - HTTP/1.1. RFC 2616, 1999.

[38] M. Frigo, C. E. Leiserson, H. Prokop, and S. Ramachandran. Cache-oblivious algorithms. In *Proceedings of the 40th IEEE Symposium on Foundations of Computer Science (FOCS)*, pages 285–297. IEEE, August 1999.

[39] M. Frigo and V. Strumpen. The cache complexity of multithreaded cache oblivious algorithms. In *Proceedings of the 18th Symposium on Paral-*

lelism in Algorithms and Architectures (SPAA), pages 271–280. ACM, 2006.

[40] G. Gibson, D. Nagle, K. Amiri, J. Butler, F. Chang, H. Gobioff, C. Hardin, E. Riedel, D. Rochberg, and J. Zelenka. A cost-effective, high-bandwidth storage architecture. In *Proceedings of the 8th International Conference on Architectural Support for Programming Languages and Operating Systems (ASPLOS)*, pages 92–103. ACM, October 1998.

[41] G. Gibson and R. Van Meter. Network attached storage architecture. *Communications of the ACM* 43(11):37–45, November 2000.

[42] Google. IPv6 Adoption. Available at http://www.google.com/intl/en/ipv6/statistics.html.

[43] J. Gustafson. Reevaluating Amdahl's law. *Communications of the ACM* 31(5):532–533, August 1988.

[44] L. Gwennap. New algorithm improves branch prediction. *Microprocessor Report* 9(4), March 1995.

[45] S. P. Harbison and G. L. Steele, Jr. *C, A Reference Manual, Fifth Edition*. Prentice Hall, 2002.

[46] J. L. Hennessy and D. A. Patterson. *Computer Architecture: A Quantitative Approach, Fifth Edition*. Morgan Kaufmann, 2011.

[47] M. Herlihy and N. Shavit. *The Art of Multiprocessor Programming*. Morgan Kaufmann, 2008.

[48] C. A. R. Hoare. Monitors: An operating system structuring concept. *Communications of the ACM* 17(10):549–557, October 1974.

[49] Intel Corporation. *Intel 64 and IA-32 Architectures Optimization Reference Manual*. Available at http://www.intel.com/content/www/us/en/processors/architectures-software-developer-manuals.html.

[50] Intel Corporation. *Intel 64 and IA-32 Architectures Software Developer's Manual, Volume 1: Basic Architecture*. Available at http://www.intel.com/content/www/us/en/processors/architectures-software-developer-manuals.html.

[51] Intel Corporation. *Intel 64 and IA-32 Architectures Software Developer's Manual, Volume 2: Instruction Set Reference*. Available at http://www.intel.com/content/www/us/en/processors/architectures-software-developer-manuals.html.

[52] Intel Corporation. *Intel 64 and IA-32 Architectures Software Developer's Manual, Volume 3a: System Programming Guide, Part 1*. Available at http://www.intel.com/content/www/us/en/processors/architectures-software-developer-manuals.html.

[53] Intel Corporation. *Intel Solid-State Drive 730 Series: Product Specification*. Available at http://www.intel.com/content/www/us/en/solid-state-drives/ssd-730-series-spec.html.

[54] Intel Corporation. *Tool Interface Standards Portable Formats Specification, Version 1.1*, 1993. Order number 241597.

[55] F. Jones, B. Prince, R. Norwood, J. Hartigan, W. Vogley, C. Hart, and D. Bondurant. Memory—a new era of fast dynamic RAMs (for video applications). *IEEE Spectrum*, pages 43–45, October 1992.

[56] R. Jones and R. Lins. *Garbage Collection: Algorithms for Automatic Dynamic Memory Management*. Wiley, 1996.

[57] M. Kaashoek, D. Engler, G. Ganger, H. Briceo, R. Hunt, D. Maziers, T. Pinckney, R. Grimm, J. Jannotti, and K. MacKenzie. Application performance and flexibility on Exokernel systems. In *Proceedings of the 16th ACM Symposium on Operating System Principles (SOSP)*, pages 52–65. ACM, October 1997.

[58] R. Katz and G. Borriello. *Contemporary Logic Design, Second Edition*. Prentice Hall, 2005.

[59] B. W. Kernighan and R. Pike. *The Practice of Programming*. Addison-Wesley, 1999.

[60] B. Kernighan and D. Ritchie. *The C Programming Language, First Edition*. Prentice Hall, 1978.

[61] B. Kernighan and D. Ritchie. *The C Programming Language, Second Edition*. Prentice Hall, 1988.

[62] Michael Kerrisk. *The Linux Programming Interface*. No Starch Press, 2010.

[63] T. Kilburn, B. Edwards, M. Lanigan, and F. Sumner. One-level storage system. *IRE*

Transactions on Electronic Computers EC-11:223–235, April 1962.

[64] D. Knuth. *The Art of Computer Programming, Volume 1: Fundamental Algorithms, Third Edition.* Addison-Wesley, 1997.

[65] J. Kurose and K. Ross. *Computer Networking: A Top-Down Approach, Sixth Edition.* Addison-Wesley, 2012.

[66] M. Lam, E. Rothberg, and M. Wolf. The cache performance and optimizations of blocked algorithms. In *Proceedings of the 4th International Conference on Architectural Support for Programming Languages and Operating Systems (ASPLOS)*, pages 63–74. ACM, April 1991.

[67] D. Lea. A memory allocator. Available at http://gee.cs.oswego.edu/dl/html/malloc.html, 1996.

[68] C. E. Leiserson and J. B. Saxe. Retiming synchronous circuitry. *Algorithmica* 6(1–6), June 1991.

[69] J. R. Levine. *Linkers and Loaders.* Morgan Kaufmann, 1999.

[70] David Levinthal. *Performance Analysis Guide for Intel Core i7 Processor and Intel Xeon 5500 Processors.* Available at https://software.intel.com/sites/products/collateral/hpc/vtune/performance_analysis_guide.pdf.

[71] C. Lin and L. Snyder. *Principles of Parallel Programming.* Addison Wesley, 2008.

[72] Y. Lin and D. Padua. Compiler analysis of irregular memory accesses. In *Proceedings of the 2000 ACM Conference on Programming Language Design and Implementation (PLDI)*, pages 157–168. ACM, June 2000.

[73] J. L. Lions. Ariane 5 Flight 501 failure. Technical Report, European Space Agency, July 1996.

[74] S. Macguire. *Writing Solid Code.* Microsoft Press, 1993.

[75] S. A. Mahlke, W. Y. Chen, J. C. Gyllenhal, and W. W. Hwu. Compiler code transformations for superscalar-based high-performance systems. In *Proceedings of the 1992 ACM/IEEE Conference on Supercomputing*, pages 808–817. ACM, 1992.

[76] E. Marshall. Fatal error: How Patriot overlooked a Scud. *Science*, page 1347, March 13, 1992.

[77] M. Matz, J. Hubička, A. Jaeger, and M. Mitchell. System V application binary interface AMD64 architecture processor supplement. Technical Report, x86-64.org, 2013. Available at http://www.x86-64.org/documentation_folder/abi-0.99.pdf.

[78] J. Morris, M. Satyanarayanan, M. Conner, J. Howard, D. Rosenthal, and F. Smith. Andrew: A distributed personal computing environment. *Communications of the ACM*, pages 184–201, March 1986.

[79] T. Mowry, M. Lam, and A. Gupta. Design and evaluation of a compiler algorithm for prefetching. In *Proceedings of the 5th International Conference on Architectural Support for Programming Languages and Operating Systems (ASPLOS)*, pages 62–73. ACM, October 1992.

[80] S. S. Muchnick. *Advanced Compiler Design and Implementation.* Morgan Kaufmann, 1997.

[81] S. Nath and P. Gibbons. Online maintenance of very large random samples on flash storage. In *Proceedings of VLDB*, pages 970–983. VLDB Endowment, August 2008.

[82] M. Overton. *Numerical Computing with IEEE Floating Point Arithmetic.* SIAM, 2001.

[83] D. Patterson, G. Gibson, and R. Katz. A case for redundant arrays of inexpensive disks (RAID). In *Proceedings of the 1998 ACM SIGMOD International Conference on Management of Data*, pages 109–116. ACM, June 1988.

[84] L. Peterson and B. Davie. *Computer Networks: A Systems Approach, Fifth Edition.* Morgan Kaufmann, 2011.

[85] J. Pincus and B. Baker. Beyond stack smashing: Recent advances in exploiting buffer overruns. *IEEE Security and Privacy* 2(4):20–27, 2004.

[86] S. Przybylski. *Cache and Memory Hierarchy Design: A Performance-Directed Approach.* Morgan Kaufmann, 1990.

[87] W. Pugh. The Omega test: A fast and practical integer programming algorithm for depen-

dence analysis. *Communications of the ACM* 35(8):102–114, August 1992.

[88] W. Pugh. Fixing the Java memory model. In *Proceedings of the ACM Conference on Java Grande*, pages 89–98. ACM, June 1999.

[89] J. Rabaey, A. Chandrakasan, and B. Nikolic. *Digital Integrated Circuits: A Design Perspective, Second Edition.* Prentice Hall, 2003.

[90] J. Reinders. *Intel Threading Building Blocks.* O'Reilly, 2007.

[91] D. Ritchie. The evolution of the Unix time-sharing system. *AT&T Bell Laboratories Technical Journal* 63(6 Part 2):1577–1593, October 1984.

[92] D. Ritchie. The development of the C language. In *Proceedings of the 2nd ACM SIGPLAN Conference on History of Programming Languages*, pages 201–208. ACM, April 1993.

[93] D. Ritchie and K. Thompson. The Unix time-sharing system. *Communications of the ACM* 17(7):365–367, July 1974.

[94] M. Satyanarayanan, J. Kistler, P. Kumar, M. Okasaki, E. Siegel, and D. Steere. Coda: A highly available file system for a distributed workstation environment. *IEEE Transactions on Computers* 39(4):447–459, April 1990.

[95] J. Schindler and G. Ganger. Automated disk drive characterization. Technical Report CMU-CS-99-176, School of Computer Science, Carnegie Mellon University, 1999.

[96] F. B. Schneider and K. P. Birman. The monoculture risk put into context. *IEEE Security and Privacy* 7(1):14–17, January 2009.

[97] R. C. Seacord. *Secure Coding in C and C++, Second Edition.* Addison-Wesley, 2013.

[98] R. Sedgewick and K. Wayne. *Algorithms, Fourth Edition.* Addison-Wesley, 2011.

[99] H. Shacham, M. Page, B. Pfaff, E.-J. Goh, N. Modadugu, and D. Boneh. On the effectiveness of address-space randomization. In *Proceedings of the 11th ACM Conference on Computer and Communications Security (CCS)*, pages 298–307. ACM, 2004.

[100] J. P. Shen and M. Lipasti. *Modern Processor Design: Fundamentals of Superscalar Processors.* McGraw Hill, 2005.

[101] B. Shriver and B. Smith. *The Anatomy of a High-Performance Microprocessor: A Systems Perspective.* IEEE Computer Society, 1998.

[102] A. Silberschatz, P. Galvin, and G. Gagne. *Operating Systems Concepts, Ninth Edition.* Wiley, 2014.

[103] R. Skeel. Roundoff error and the Patriot missile. *SIAM News* 25(4):11, July 1992.

[104] A. Smith. Cache memories. *ACM Computing Surveys* 14(3), September 1982.

[105] E. H. Spafford. The Internet worm program: An analysis. Technical Report CSD-TR-823, Department of Computer Science, Purdue University, 1988.

[106] W. Stallings. *Operating Systems: Internals and Design Principles, Eighth Edition.* Prentice Hall, 2014.

[107] W. R. Stevens. *TCP/IP Illustrated, Volume 3: TCP for Transactions, HTTP, NNTP and the Unix Domain Protocols.* Addison-Wesley, 1996.

[108] W. R. Stevens. *Unix Network Programming: Interprocess Communications, Second Edition,* volume 2. Prentice Hall, 1998.

[109] W. R. Stevens and K. R. Fall. *TCP/IP Illustrated, Volume 1: The Protocols, Second Edition.* Addison-Wesley, 2011.

[110] W. R. Stevens, B. Fenner, and A. M. Rudoff. *Unix Network Programming: The Sockets Networking API, Third Edition,* volume 1. Prentice Hall, 2003.

[111] W. R. Stevens and S. A. Rago. *Advanced Programming in the Unix Environment, Third Edition.* Addison-Wesley, 2013.

[112] T. Stricker and T. Gross. Global address space, non-uniform bandwidth: A memory system performance characterization of parallel systems. In *Proceedings of the 3rd International Symposium on High Performance Computer Architecture (HPCA)*, pages 168–179. IEEE, February 1997.

[113] A. S. Tanenbaum and H. Bos. *Modern Operating Systems, Fourth Edition.* Prentice Hall, 2015.

[114] A. S. Tanenbaum and D. Wetherall. *Computer Networks, Fifth Edition.* Prentice Hall, 2010.

[115] K. P. Wadleigh and I. L. Crawford. *Software Optimization for High-Performance Computing: Creating Faster Applications.* Prentice Hall, 2000.

[116] J. F. Wakerly. *Digital Design Principles and Practices, Fourth Edition.* Prentice Hall, 2005.

[117] M. V. Wilkes. Slave memories and dynamic storage allocation. *IEEE Transactions on Electronic Computers*, EC-14(2), April 1965.

[118] P. Wilson, M. Johnstone, M. Neely, and D. Boles. Dynamic storage allocation: A survey and critical review. In *International Workshop on Memory Management*, volume 986 of *Lecture Notes in Computer Science*, pages 1–116. Springer-Verlag, 1995.

[119] M. Wolf and M. Lam. A data locality algorithm. In *Proceedings of the 1991 ACM Conference on Programming Language Design and Implementation (PLDI)*, pages 30–44, June 1991.

[120] G. R. Wright and W. R. Stevens. *TCP/IP Illustrated, Volume 2: The Implementation.* Addison-Wesley, 1995.

[121] J. Wylie, M. Bigrigg, J. Strunk, G. Ganger, H. Kiliccote, and P. Khosla. Survivable information storage systems. *IEEE Computer* 33:61–68, August 2000.

[122] T.-Y. Yeh and Y. N. Patt. Alternative implementation of two-level adaptive branch prediction. In *Proceedings of the 19th Annual International Symposium on Computer Architecture (ISCA)*, pages 451–461. ACM, 1998.

Index

Page numbers of defining references are *italicized*. Entries that belong to a hardware or software system are followed by a tag in brackets that identifies the system, along with a brief description to jog your memory. Here is the list of tags and their meanings.

[C]	C language construct
[C Stdlib]	C standard library function
[CS:APP]	Program or function developed in this text
[HCL]	HCL language construct
[Unix]	Unix program, function, variable, or constant
[x86-64]	x86-64 machine-language instruction
[Y86-64]	Y86-64 machine-language instruction